introduction to

ELECTROMAGNETIC FIELDS AND WAVES

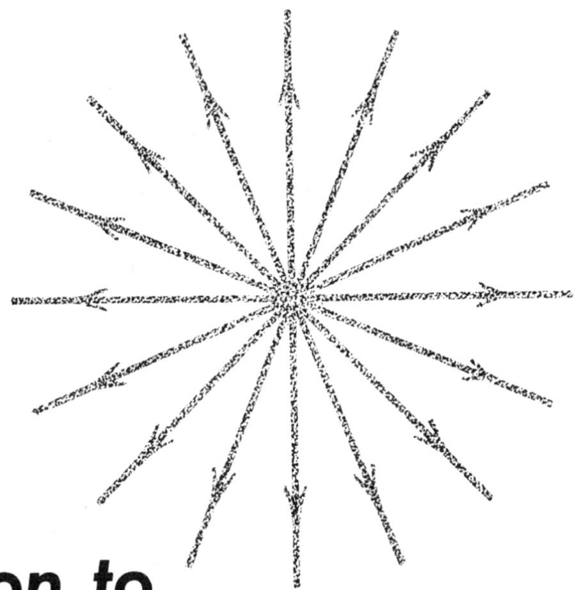

introduction to ELECTROMAGNETIC FIELDS AND WAVES

CHARLES A. HOLT, *Department of Electrical Engineering*
Virginia Polytechnic Institute

JOHN WILEY & SONS, INC., NEW YORK • LONDON

Library of Congress Catalog Card Number: 63-11435

Printed in the United States of America

Preface

In 1873 James Clerk Maxwell published his treatise, *Electricity and Magnetism*, and electromagnetism was placed on firm mathematical ground. Just as Newton's laws are the basis of classical mechanics, Maxwell's equations are the basis of classical electromagnetism, which provides the scientific foundation of the art of electrical engineering. This book is an introduction to the fundamental ideas of electromagnetic field theory.

Traditionally, introductory texts on field theory begin with and emphasize the study of the special case of statics. In this book I have chosen to begin with and emphasize the study of *dynamic, time-changing electromagnetism*. This approach offers a great many advantages, and I shall now enumerate several of them.

1. The electric and magnetic fields are defined side by side in terms of the forces acting on stationary and moving charges. From the Lorentz force equation it is easily shown that two observers with relative motion observe different electric and magnetic forces on the same charge even though both measure the same total force. Shortly thereafter the student learns that time-changing electric and magnetic fields always exist together, one producing the other. Thus the close interrelationship between the electric and magnetic fields is established early.

2. The general field equations, presented early in the text, do not have to be modified or generalized as the student progresses. On the contrary, the student works with the same fundamental equations throughout the text. He applies the integral, differential, and potential forms of Maxwell's equations to many situations. The full significance of the field equations becomes apparent only after repeated applications of their various forms.

3. There are two entirely different concepts measured in volts. One of these is electromotive force, or voltage. The other is electric potential. For the special case of static fields, voltage and potential difference are

equivalent. If the student is to appreciate the real meaning of these basic concepts, and if he is to understand the important distinction between them, the nonconservative nature of the dynamic fields must be emphasized.

4. Electrostatics and magnetostatics, along with circuit concepts, wave propagation, and radiation, can be treated logically as applications. They thus serve to *strengthen* the student's knowledge of the fundamental electromagnetic laws.

5. The general approach is, I believe, easier for the student. Certainly it is far more interesting. From almost the beginning, applications of the theory can be made to machines, transmission lines, waveguides, antennas, resonant cavities, transistors, vacuum tubes, and other devices familiar to the student.

The book begins with a historical sketch of electrical science from the times of the ancients to our modern day. A glimpse of the personalities and thought processes of the early electrical experimenters serves to stimulate the student's interest and to prepare the way for acceptance of the mathematical equations of later chapters.

The material is organized to enable the student to observe electromagnetism developed as a logical and unified science. Several postulates are emphasized, and deduced from these are equations basic to the study of electrostatics, magnetostatics, electric and magnetic circuits, transmission lines, waveguides, and antennas. These derivations and deductions reveal a clear and unmistakable *unity* among the many equations utilized in the various areas of electromagnetism, and this unity should greatly aid the student's understanding of electrical science.

Some topics receiving rather unusual emphasis for an introductory text are potential theory, wave propagation, and circuit concepts. I believe that potential theory requires heavy emphasis if the student is to understand the meaning, use, and value of the potential functions. The subject of wave propagation is far too important to defer to a later course, as is often done. Field theory without wave propagation is *pre-Maxwellian* electromagnetism. The unusual emphasis on circuit concepts is largely due to the full treatment given to skin effect. Circuit theory is developed initially for alternating currents, with skin effect present, and the low-frequency expressions for the circuit parameters are found by letting the frequency approach zero.

The subject of statics, investigated in Chapters 16, 17, and 18, is not neglected. The static field equations are simply the general field equations with the time derivatives set equal to zero. For example, Poisson's equation is the wave equation for the electric scalar potential with the time-varying terms eliminated. The usual topics are discussed, including the calculation of the inductance and the capacitance of long parallel cylinders, the method of virtual work, the method of images, the fields and potentials of vacuum diodes and PN junctions, the magnetic circuit, and the electric and magnetic theory of materials.

The text is neither descriptive nor superficial. I have carefully and precisely defined all quantities introduced. From the field equations selected as postulates, all additional equations are derived. The student should examine these derivations, for they help him to understand better the results. However, I have diligently endeavored to make them as simple as possible. Although mathematical rigor may sometimes be lacking, precision is not compromised.

The mathematical background required for a study of this book consists of a working knowledge of elementary calculus. This must be supplemented with a reasonable amount of mathematical courage. For example, the student must be willing to work with wave equations even though he may never have seen one before. The mathematics of vector analysis, because it promotes understanding, is discussed and utilized. Normally, the mathematics of complex exponentials is employed when dealing with wave propagation, retarded potentials, and the fields of an alternating current element. However, to students not thoroughly familiar with complex exponentials, their use tends to obscure the meaning of the equations, and furthermore, there is no real need for such mathematics in the development of the basic theory. Therefore, complex exponentials are used only in the later chapters that treat lines, waveguides, and antennas. Those who wish to do so, of course, can easily convert the equations with sinusoidal time functions into complex-exponential form, and many students may well find this parallel development interesting and beneficial.

The level of presentation is not too difficult for the average undergraduate student, provided he is serious-minded and willing to work hard. A large number of problems are included, and these have been prepared to help clarify and illustrate the theory. It is strongly recommended that the student work many of these problems. Sustained study and effort will, I believe, yield in return a solid and well-founded knowledge of electromagnetism.

The material of the first eighteen chapters requires about six semester-hours and is recommended as a first course in electrical engineering. It certainly provides an excellent foundation for later work in circuits, electronics, materials, and energy conversion. To help the student who is studying circuit theory concurrently, the variables voltage and current, the concepts of resistance, inductance, and capacitance, and Kirchhoff's laws are introduced as early as possible, well ahead of the chapters devoted exclusively to circuit concepts. The analysis of electric circuits might well accompany the second half of the course. In most circumstances the study of electromagnetism, as presented in this text, can be begun at the sophomore level. A prior physics course on electricity and magnetism is desirable, but not essential. The last five chapters treat energy transmission and radiation at a level suitable for juniors or seniors.

Although this book is intended primarily for engineering students, it is believed that the approach and coverage will appeal to other students of science, especially those desiring a single course in electrical theory that will provide sufficient background for advanced work in electrical engineering.

To those reviewers who contributed critical and helpful comments, to my colleagues and students for their many suggestions, and to Virginia Polytechnic Institute for providing the opportunity for me to do this work, I am indeed grateful.

CHARLES A. HOLT

Blacksburg, Va.
December 1962

Contents

List of Symbols

Symbol	Quantity	Symbol	Quality
$\mathbf{A}$	magnetic vector potential	S	a surface; area
	vector point function	$\mathbf{T}$	torque
$\mathbf{B}$	magnetic flux density	T	time (dimension); torque
	vector point function	V	volume
C	a path; capacitance; constant		d-c voltage; rms voltage
$\mathbf{D}$	electric flux density	W	work (energy); width
D	diffusion constant	X	a function of x
$\mathbf{E}$	electric field intensity	Y	a function of y
$\mathbf{F}$	force	Z	a function of z; impedance
$\mathbf{H}$	magnetic field intensity	$\mathbf{a}$	unit vector; acceleration
I	direct current; rms current	c	velocity of light
I_m	maximum current		3×10^8 m/sec
$\mathbf{J}$	convection current density $\rho\mathbf{v}$	$d\mathbf{l}$	differential vector length
$\mathbf{J}_d$	displacement current density $\dot{\mathbf{D}}$	dl	magnitude of $d\mathbf{l}$
$\mathbf{J}_t$	total current density $(\mathbf{J} + \mathbf{J}_d)$	$d\mathbf{S}$	differential vector surface
$\mathbf{J}_s$	surface current density	dS	magnitude of $d\mathbf{S}$
$[\mathbf{J}]$	current density at time $t - r/v$	e	electronic charge
K	kinetic energy		1.602×10^{-19} coulomb
L	length (dimension); inductance	f	frequency
L_i	internal inductance	h	Planck's constant
L_e	external inductance		6.625×10^{-34} joule-sec
$\mathbf{M}$	magnetization	$\mathbf{i}$	unit vector along x-axis
M	mass; mutual inductance	i	convection current
N	number of turns	i_d	displacement current
N_a	density of acceptor atoms	i_t	total current $(i + i_d)$
N_d	density of donor atoms	$[i]$	current at time $t - r/v$
$\mathbf{P}$	polarization	$\mathbf{j}$	unit vector along y-axis
P	time-average power	$\mathbf{k}$	unit vector along z-axis
Q	charge (dimension)	k	a constant
R	resistance	l	length
R_s	surface resistivity	$\mathbf{m}$	magnetic dipole moment
$\mathbf{S}$	Poynting vector $\mathbf{E} \times \mathbf{H}$	m	mass

Symbol	Quantity	Symbol	Quantity
m_0	rest mass of electron 9.11×10^{-31} kg	λ	wavelength
$\mathbf{n}$	unit vector normal to a surface	μ	permeability; mobility
n	free-electron density	μ_r	relative permeability
$\mathbf{p}$	electric dipole moment momentum	μ_0	permeability of free space $4\pi \times 10^{-7}$ henry/m
p	power; hole density	ρ	charge density; resistivity
q	charge	ρ_l	linear charge density
r	cylindrical coordinate spherical coordinate	ρ_s	surface charge density
t	time	$[\rho]$	charge density at time $t - r/v$
$\mathbf{v}$	velocity	σ	conductivity
v	voltage	τ_p	hole lifetime; phase delay
w	energy density	Φ	magnetic flux (flux linkages)
α	angle; attenuation constant	φ	magnetic flux cylindrical coordinate spherical coordinate
β	angle; phase constant	ϕ	electric scalar potential scalar point function
γ	angle; propagation constant	χ	susceptibility
Δ	a small quantity	Ψ	displacement
δ	skin depth	ψ	electric flux
ϵ	permittivity	ω	angular frequency angular velocity
ϵ_r	dielectric constant	$\mathscr{P}$	permeance
ϵ_0	permittivity of free space 8.854×10^{-12} farad/m	$\mathscr{R}$	reluctance
η	intrinsic impedance	$\boldsymbol{\nabla}$	del (nabla) operator
Θ	phase angle	∇^2	scalar Laplacian operator
θ	spherical coordinate; angle	$\boldsymbol{\nabla}^2$	vector Laplacian operator

Special Symbols for Lines, Waveguides, and Antennas

Symbol	Quantity	Symbol	Quantity
R	resistance per unit length	α_c	attenuation constant (due to copper losses)
L	inductance per unit length	α_d	attenuation constant (due to dielectric losses)
G	conductance per unit length	f_c	cut-off frequency
C	capacitance per unit length	k_c	$\sqrt{\gamma^2 + \omega^2\mu\epsilon - j\omega\mu\sigma} = \sqrt{k_x^2 + k_y^2}$
Y	admittance per unit length	k_x	$m\pi/a$ with m an integer
Z	impedance per unit length	k_y	$n\pi/b$ with n an integer
Z_i	input impedance	K	radiation intensity
Z_t	transfer impedance	g	antenna gain
Z_0	characteristic impedance		
R_0	characteristic resistance		
S	standing-wave ratio		
ρ	reflection coefficient		

Vectors are in boldface.

A dot over a scalar or vector indicates a partial time derivative.

A bar over a scalar or vector indicates a phasor quantity.

Crosses are used in illustrations to indicate arrows directed into the paper.

Dots are used in illustrations to indicate arrows directed out of the paper.

Historical Sketch of Electromagnetism

CHAPTER 1

The history of electromagnetism is an interesting and fascinating story. The student who is to grasp and appreciate fully the important electrical concepts should have at least some knowledge of their historical background. The electrical equations do not seem quite so mysterious if we understand the original reasoning that led to their development. In a limited space this chapter attempts to present the logic employed by the founding fathers of electromagnetism in deducing the important electromagnetic laws. Many fundamental concepts are introduced. It is believed that this introduction will help the student to understand the mathematical development presented in later chapters. Furthermore, it is hoped that the student's interest in electromagnetism will be stimulated.

1-1. EARLY HISTORY

William Gilbert (1544–1603)

The history of electrical science is often considered to have begun with the publication of the book *De Magnete* by Dr. William Gilbert in the year 1600. Prior to Gilbert, very little had been accomplished in electrical science. The Greek philosopher Thales in 600 B.C., and probably men before his time, knew that the minerals amber and jet, when rubbed, attracted light bodies. The Greek name for amber is *electron*, from which the word *electricity* was derived. The shock-giving properties of the torpedo fish had been observed. Mariners used the magnetic properties of the lodestone to guide their ships, and had observed compass dip and the variation of the compass in different positions on the earth's surface. The fact that the lodestone retained its magnetic properties even when broken was known. Thus the knowledge of electricity and magnetism was indeed meager when Gilbert began his investigations.

Dr. William Gilbert was an Englishman who lived in an era of great expansion in England's history. He was a prosperous physician who served Queen Elizabeth I. Gilbert's curiosity about the peculiar properties of amber, jet, and the lodestone led him into extensive experimentation. He worked many years and spent his fortune on his experiments. His study was the first step forward since Thales, who lived more than 2000 years before Gilbert.

Dr. Gilbert determined that a wide variety of materials, in addition to amber and jet, would attract light bodies after being rubbed. These materials—such as glass, sulphur, crystals, gems, and wax—he called *electrics*. Substances which would not exhibit the attractive power when rubbed were called *anelectrics*. Some of Gilbert's accomplishments are:

(1) He classified materials as electric or nonelectric.
(2) He observed that electrified bodies attract every kind of substance, but only iron responds magnetically.
(3) He devised the pivoted metallic needle to measure electrification.
(4) He discovered that heating electrics tends to destroy their attractive power, and that electric attraction does not penetrate a flame although magnetic attraction does.
(5) He found that electric action can be screened by paper, fabric, and metal, while magnetic action penetrates thick materials, except iron.
(6) He deduced that the earth is a magnet, like the lodestone, and he referred to the ends of a magnetic needle as *north* and *south poles*.

In his book Gilbert presented detailed descriptions of his experiments. By doing so, he established a pattern of scientific investigation. His book was widely read, and many minds were stimulated.

The Next 150 Years—1600 to 1750

In 1625 an experimenter, Cabeo, observed that electricity can be conducted from one body to another. He also reported electrical repulsion for the first time.

A crude, electrostatic, frictional generator was invented in 1660 by a

German, Otto von Guericke. It consisted of a sulphur globe about six inches in diameter, mounted on an iron shaft which rested on wooden supports. The shaft was rotated, and the ball was rubbed by hand. Friction produced a charge on the sulphur ball. In experiments performed with the charged globe von Guericke made the following observations:

(1) Light objects were attracted to the globe; after contact, however, they were repelled. If these objects were then touched by hand, they were once again attracted.
(2) Light objects were attracted to a long linen thread attached to the charged globe. Threads over three feet in length were used.
(3) If the ball was rubbed in a dark room, light was observed.
(4) When the charged globe was placed on the hand held next to the ear, "roarings and crashings" were heard. This noise was due to the very minute sparks occurring during the discharge through the hand.

Guericke's generator created much interest, and more efficient machines followed. In about 1709 Francis Hauksbee developed a machine with a glass globe which was rotated rapidly by means of a hand crank and rubbed with wool. He observed electrical sparks when the ball was being rubbed. Improved machines used a chain on the side opposite the rubbed side to collect the electricity and transfer it to insulated conductors, which could be strongly charged. These conductors produced sparks when held near a grounded conductor. Additional improvements resulted in frictional machines capable of producing long sparks.

About 1733 duFay of France observed that electrified bodies either attract or repel one another. He noted that, when two bodies are electrified by contact with the same electrified body, they then repel one another. He concluded that there are two kinds of electricity, and that bodies with like kinds of electricity repel each other whereas bodies with unlike kinds of electricity attract one another. DuFay called the electricity associated with glass, after being rubbed with silk, *vitreous* electricity, and the electricity associated with resin, after being rubbed with fur, was called *resinous* electricity. The names vitreous and resinous were later changed to *positive* and *negative*, respectively, by Franklin.

In 1736 bodies that would transmit static electricity from one part to all other parts were called conductors. Nonconductors were called insulators.

An important discovery occurred in 1745. Two experimenters, believing that electricity was a fluid, attempted to fill a glass jar with electricity by means of a frictional machine. A wire from the machine was placed in the jar. When no results were obtained, they filled the jar with water and tried again, but still without success. In dismantling the apparatus one experimenter picked up the jar with water while the wire from the machine was still immersed in the water. His other hand touched the wire, and to his surprise he received a strong jolt in the arms and chest. It was almost unbelievable that electricity, which could attract only light objects such as feathers, contained such power. The experiment became the subject of everyday conversation. A number of people throughout Europe made a living repeating the experiment before the curious, demonstrating electrical shock.

Soon it was learned that a dry bottle, coated inside and out with tinfoil, was an improvement on the water bottle. Such a bottle was called a *Leyden jar*, which was the first capacitor. In 1746 Watson of London suggested that the discharge of the Leyden jar through the arms and chest of a man caused something to pass through the body. Watson also suggested that all bodies contain electricity, which he described as an electric fluid. He reasoned that uncharged bodies contain only a normal amount of this fluid and, therefore, exhibit no effects. The two kinds of electricity, he proposed, were due to an excess or a deficiency of electric fluid.

1-2. THE DEVELOPMENT OF ELECTROSTATICS

Benjamin Franklin (1706–1790)

Benjamin Franklin's interest in electrical science began in 1746. He attended a lecture on electricity in Boston and was so fascinated that he bought the lecturer's equipment and had it shipped to Philadelphia. His experiments greatly interested him, as well as many of his friends. Franklin retired from his printing work in 1748 at the age of forty-two in order to concentrate on his electrical experiments.

Using a frictional electrostatic generator, Franklin investigated the discharge of electricity from sharp points. He observed that the "stream of fire" at the end of a wire connected to the glass globe of a frictional machine was "long, large, and much diverging, and makes a snapping noise." As the wire seemed to be "throwing the fire out," he called the vitreous electricity *positive*. The fire from the end of a wire connected to a sulphur globe "is short, small, and makes a hissing noise." In this case the wire seemed to be "drinking in" the fire, so Franklin called the electric charge on the globe *negative*. He stated, however, that he did not really know which kind of electricity corresponded to an excess of electrical fluid.

Franklin experimented with the Leyden jar and discovered that it had positive electricity on one metallic coating and an equal amount of negative electricity on the other metallic coating. He proved this by suspending a pith ball between two wires connected to the two coatings. The pith ball moved back and forth between the wires, transporting charge from one coating to the other, until finally the charges had equalized. The coatings were then determined to be uncharged. Franklin developed a parallel-plate capacitor with glass dielectric, and he demonstrated that energy was stored in the glass. He also discovered that a charged hollow conductor has charge only on its outer surface.

Franklin's greatest contribution was his single-fluid theory of electricity, which had been suggested by Watson and others. In accordance with this theory, electricity is neither created nor destroyed. When two bodies are rubbed, one acquires an excess of electricity and the other has a deficiency, but the total amount of electricity is constant. Franklin's experiments verified this. Indeed, no exceptions to the principle of the conservation of electric charge have ever been observed. Franklin's theory differed in one important respect from that of his predecessors. He rejected the idea that forces between charged bodies were due to a physical fluid that existed in the space surrounding the bodies. He believed that the forces were actions at a distance. The one-fluid action-at-a-distance theory was generally accepted. It is accepted today with the understanding that forces are communicated through a medium by means of an electric field that surrounds all charged bodies.

Franklin noted the similarity between lightning and the electric spark, as others had also done, and his experiments confirmed the identity. His celebrated kite experiment was performed in 1752. His kite, flown during a thunderstorm, contained a pointed wire at the top. At the bottom of the twine, which became conductive when wet, a silk ribbon was used as an insulator, and Franklin stood indoors to keep the ribbon dry. A key, connected to the bottom of the twine, was used to charge a Leyden jar. Franklin succeeded in drawing electricity from thunderclouds with his pointed wire on the kite, and some of this electricity was transferred by the twine to his Leyden jar. He performed this experiment many times, determining that most thunderclouds are charged with negative electricity. An important result of these endeavors was his invention of the lightning rod, adding to his world-wide popularity. Franklin's kite experiment was repeated by other experimenters, one of whom was killed by a lightning bolt in 1753, the first recorded casualty of electrical science.

Developments in Electrostatics Following Franklin

After Franklin's investigations the science of electrostatics advanced fairly rapidly. In 1759 Aepinus, a German physics professor, published the results of his experiments. He discovered that parallel metal plates, separated by air, behave like a Leyden jar. Aepinus investigated electrification by induction. He found that a charged body, when brought near an insulated conductor, induces equal and unlike charges on the opposite sides of the conductor. He explained that the charged body attracts the opposite kind of charge toward it, leaving a deficiency on the far side. Aepinus found that touching the conductor momentarily to a ground connection caused a flow of charge to or from ground. In this manner he was able to charge a conductor by induction, and this could be repeated again and again.

Charles Coulomb (1736–1806), a French physicist, investigated the law of force between charges. Priestly had earlier suggested that this was an inverse-square law, similar to the law of gravitational attraction. Coulomb constructed a sensitive torsion balance to measure the force directly. It consisted of two small conducting spheres, one fixed in position, the other mounted on a horizontal rod suspended by a vertical wire which was free to twist. When charges were placed on the conducting spheres, the wire twisted through an angle proportional to the force. Within the limits of experimental error, Coulomb established that the force is directly proportional to the product of the charges and inversely proportional to the distance squared.

Coulomb performed many experiments on the distribution of charge on conductors. His experiments revealed that electric charge is confined to the surface of a conductor, with the surface charge density greater where the surface is more convex and less where it is concave. The fact that the charge density is large at sharp points was known to Franklin. Coulomb also showed that the force on a small metal ball held near the surface of a charged conductor is proportional to the surface charge density. In addition, he investigated the law of force between magnetic poles. This investigation established the inverse-square law of attraction (or *repulsion*) of unlike (or *like*) magnetic poles.

Henry Cavendish (1731–1810), an English chemist and physicist, made many important discoveries but did not publish his work. His notes were edited by Maxwell in 1879. Cavendish discussed and explained electrical theory very clearly. He verified the inverse-square law of force between charges. Many of the results of the research work of Coulomb, Faraday, Ohm, and others had been anticipated by Cavendish. He discovered and measured the dielectric constant, or permittivity, of a medium, and he introduced the idea of electric potential.

The mathematical theory of electrostatics was greatly advanced by Poisson, whose paper on this subject was published in 1812. Poisson recognized that static charges on conductors must be distributed in such a manner that no force acts on the charges in the interior regions, for otherwise the charges would move. Poisson proved mathematically that the surface charge density of a conductor is greater where the surface is more convex. He applied the mathematical theory of gravitation to electrostatics, introducing an electrical potential function corresponding to gravitational potential, and he formulated a differential equation involving his electrostatic potential function and space coordinates. The solution of this equation, subject to appropriate boundary conditions, determines the potential distribution in space, from which the charge distribution on the surfaces of conductors can be determined.

1-3. CURRENT ELECTRICITY—GALVANI AND VOLTA

Prior to 1780 electrical experiments dealt with static electricity. In 1780 an Italian professor of anatomy, Galvani, discovered an important new electrical phenomenon. By accident he observed that the legs of a dissected frog would twitch violently when a nearby electrostatic generator produced a spark, provided a scalpel was in contact with the nerves of the frog. For twenty years he investigated this phenomenon, publishing his observations and his theory of *animal electricity* in 1791.

During his investigations Galvani found that lightning flashes also caused the muscles in a frog's leg to contract. This discovery was made by attaching long wires to the leg tissues during a thunderstorm. Each time the lightning flashed the muscles contracted. Galvani and his contemporaries could not understand the results of these experiments. Actually his frog leg was a sensitive detector of electric current. The scalpel, or the wire, served as an antenna which received electromagnetic radiation from the electric spark or from lightning. Galvani had observed electromagnetic induction but failed to recognize it. A second great discovery was made during these experiments. Galvani observed that, when two wires of different metals were connected to different parts of the frog leg, the muscles twitched momentarily at the instant the wires were joined together. This effect was produced by a small voltage that is developed across a junction of two dissimilar metals; this junction voltage is called *contact potential.*

Galvani erroneously believed that the source of his electricity was the animal tissue of the frog's leg. He proposed a theory of animal electricity which created much interest and led to considerable controversy.

Volta, an Italian physics professor, repeated Galvani's experiments. He soon became convinced that the source of electricity was at the metallic contact and that the frog's muscles served only as a detector. Volta scorned the theory of animal electricity, which Galvani vigorously defended. Volta arranged a number of metallic pairs in series. Instead of using animal tissue as the connecting links between the metallic pairs, he substituted solutions of salts or acids, and powerful electrical effects were obtained.

One arrangement used a number of cups containing a salt solution. A strip of zinc and a strip of copper were placed in each cup with short wires connecting the copper of one cup to the zinc of the next. Another arrangement, called the *voltaic pile*, consisted of dozens of little round plates about one inch in diameter. Half of the plates were made of one metal and half were made of another metal, such as silver and zinc. A vertical column of silver-zinc pairs was formed, with each pair separated from the next by a paper card that had been soaked in a salt solution.

Volta's pile could produce a feeble electrical shock. It caused sparks when the wires at each end of the pile were touched and separated. Most important of all, it provided a continuous source of electricity. The voltaic pile, or battery, replaced the electrostatic generators and Leyden jars used for so many years to produce and store electricity. Larger and improved batteries were soon developed, and the new source of constant-flow electricity led to many new discoveries.

Volta's theory of contact potential was accepted and the theory of animal electricity was discarded. However, Volta was wrong regarding the theory of his voltaic pile. He still believed that the source of electricity was at the metallic contacts. Other experimenters proved, at a later date, that the generation of electric current by his pile was the result of chemical action.

1-4. THE BEGINNING OF ELECTROMAGNETISM

Hans Christian Oersted

The fact that electricity and magnetism are related had been suspected by scientists for many years prior to Oersted's discovery. Benjamin Franklin had observed that electrical discharges produce a magnetic effect on iron. Lightning occasionally magnetized objects made of iron. The magnetic compass of a ship was known to be unreliable after a lightning strike. In 1802 an Italian jurist, Romagnosi, discovered that an electric current causes a magnetic needle to deflect. Communication was poor in those days, and his report, consisting only of a letter to a local newspaper, was unnoticed.

The Danish experimenter, H. C. Oersted, began investigating electromagnetism in 1807. He announced that the purpose of his investigations was to determine a relationship between electricity and magnetism. After thirteen years of frustrating efforts, Oersted succeeded. His brilliant discovery, which was properly announced to the scientific world, was that a wire carrying a current exerts a force on a magnet placed near the wire. Thus Oersted showed that an electric current produces a magnetic field, a discovery of fundamental importance. The year 1820 marks the beginning of electromagnetism as a science.

In his experiments Oersted found that the direction of the force on one end of a magnetic needle near a current-carrying wire is along a circular path around the wire. He also determined that the magnet exerts a force on the wire, in accordance with Newton's law of action and reaction.

Andre Marie Ampère (1775–1836)

Professor Ampère, a French mathematician and physicist, was very much impressed with Oersted's discovery. Ampère knew that magnetic poles produce magnetic fields and that two poles either attract or repel one another. He reasoned that electric currents, which produce magnetic fields, should also exert forces on one another. Only one week after Ampère heard the news of Oersted's discovery, he presented a paper before the French Academy of Sciences describing an important experiment on electromagnetism. Ampère had determined that two parallel wires carrying currents in the same direction attract each other, but repel if the currents are opposite. He called the new science of electromagnetism *electrodynamics*. For the next several years he enthusiastically investigated electromagnetism, mathematically and experimentally, with important results.

Ampère classified *electromotive action* into two subdivisions, which he called *electric tension* and *electric current*. Electric tension referred to the attraction and repulsion effects of electrified bodies not electrically connected. Electric current referred to the effects of electromotive action applied to a completed circuit. He noted that "the ordinary electrometer indicates when there is tension," and he stated that a magnetic compass could be used as a current meter, for which he proposed the name *galvanometer*.

Ampère determined that each elemental length of a circuit with an electric current exerts a force on every other elemental length. The concept of a *current element*, which is the product of the current i and the differential length dl, is due to Ampère. He developed the mathematical expression for the force between current elements, and this force law is often called *Ampère's law*.

It is interesting to note that Ampère suggested that the magnetic field of a permanent magnet is probably due to electric currents produced by the action of the iron particles on one another. The physicists of today accept the theory that magnetism in iron is caused by the interactions of certain electrons of the atoms of the ferromagnetic solid, resulting in a spontaneous alignment of the *spin magnetic moments.*

1-5. GEORG SIMON OHM (1789-1854) AND CIRCUIT THEORY

Ohm was a German mathematician who began experimenting with electricity about 1824. Using a voltaic pile, or battery, he studied current electricity in wires of various sizes and wires of different materials. Ohm compared the flow of electricity along a wire with the flow of heat along a rod. He knew, of course, that the quantity of heat flowing per second was proportional to the temperature difference, and this led him to believe that the electric current was proportional to some kind of a driving force. Because he used an electroscope to measure this driving force, he called it the *electroscopic force.* Ohm's electroscopic force was actally the same as Poisson's electrostatic potential difference.

Ohm thought that it should be possible to predict the current in a circuit when the electroscopic force was known. He regarded current as the flow of electric charge, and he measured both current and electroscopic force, or voltage. His discoveries led to the development of electric circuit theory. Some of his more important deductions are:

(1) He determined that the current in a metallic circuit is directly proportional to the applied voltage. Today we call the constant of proportionality R, in the equation $v = iR$, the circuit resistance, and the relationship is known as *Ohm's law.*
(2) He found that the current through a cross section of a series circuit is the same as the current through any other cross section of the circuit, regardless of the shape or material of the conductors forming the circuit.
(3) He showed that the resistance of a series circuit is the sum of the resistances of the various parts of the circuit.
(4) He measured the division of current between branches.
(5) He noted that the conductivity of his metallic circuits decreased when the temperature increased.

The results of Ohm's experimental work were published in 1827. His book was somewhat vague and ambiguous, and as a result it was probably misunderstood. The publication met bitter criticism and was rejected as being foolish. Ohm was disappointed and discouraged, and his teaching career was ruined. However, the vast importance of his work gradually came to be recognized and finally, after many years, Ohm was honored for his many contributions to electrical science.

1-6. ADVANCES IN ELECTROMAGNETISM

Gauss (1777–1855) and Weber (1804–1891)

Karl Gauss was a great German mathematician whose contributions to electrical science were primarily in the field of terrestrial magnetism. Wilhelm Weber was a physicist who worked closely with Gauss. Together they published much information on the earth's magnetic declination, the location and shift of the earth's magnetic poles, and the strength of the earth's magnetic field. Gauss did important mathematical work in potential theory. He and Weber designed a nonmagnetic observatory and, utilizing Faraday's discovery, they developed an electric telegraph in 1834. Weber made an important contribution to magnetic theory in 1852. He proposed that each molecule is a permanent magnet, which tends to stay in its established orientation because of a frictional force. Although this idea is not wholly accepted today, Weber's theory advanced the understanding of magnetism.

Michael Faraday (1791–1867)

Volta's battery and Oersted's discovery led to the development of electromagnets, consisting of many turns of wire coiled about an iron core. Many scientists believed that, because electric currents produce magnetism, somehow it should be possible to cause magnetism to produce electric currents. Many unsuccessful attempts were made before Faraday succeeded.

Michael Faraday, an English physicist and chemist, became an assistant of the Royal Institution in 1813. In 1825 he was made director of the laboratory. His contributions to chemistry are substantial, but he is famous primarily because of his outstanding contributions to electrical science.

In 1821 Faraday devised an experiment in which a magnetic pole rotated continuously around a wire carrying an electric current. He also caused a wire carrying an electric current to rotate about a stationary magnet. In this experiment a short bar magnet was placed upright in the bottom of a cup of mercury. A wire, hanging from a pivot above, dipped into the mercury. The end of the wire in the mercury cup was free to move. Faraday passed a current through the wire, causing it to revolve around the magnetic pole. In another of his early experiments Faraday succeeded in causing a balanced wire, carrying an electric current, to move as a result of the earth's magnetic field.

Faraday's greatest discovery was made in 1831, and recognition by the scientific world was immediate. In this experiment Faraday wound two coils of insulated wire on an iron ring about six inches in diameter. The two ends of one coil were connected together with a copper wire which passed just over a magnetic needle three feet from the iron ring. The ends of the other coil were connected to a battery. At the instant the battery connection was made, the magnetic needle moved; after a few oscillations it settled in its original position. On breaking the battery connection, the needle was momentarily disturbed again. When Faraday substituted a copper ring for the iron ring, the needle deflections were very feeble. This experiment showed that a *changing magnetism* in the iron ring produced an electric current in the shorted coil. After ten years of experimenting with electromagnetism, Faraday had succeeded in converting magnetic force into electric force, and electrical science moved a great step forward.

The fact that an electric current produces magnetism was shown by Oersted in 1820. The discovery that changing magnetism produces an electric force occurred in 1831. These principles are utilized in most of today's electric generators. A number of ways of producing an electric current are known by man. Some examples are the battery, the thermocouple, the photoelectric cell, and the frictional machines. However, the generation of electric current by changing magnetism, discovered by Faraday, is by far the most important method. Also, efficient transmission of electrical energy is made possible by the transformer, a device similar to Faraday's iron ring wound with two coils.

Faraday continued his experiments. In one experiment in 1831 he constructed a solenoid consisting of 220 feet of coiled wire, and he connected the wire ends to a galvanometer. When a cylindrical bar magnet was plunged into the coil, the galvanometer deflected; when the magnet was withdrawn, the needle deflected the opposite way. Also in 1831, Faraday constructed the first electric generator. This machine consisted of a copper disk one foot in diameter, with an edge of the disk passing between two poles of a large permanent magnet. Faraday cranked the disk by hand, producing rotation. Two sliding contacts, one at the center of the disk, the other on the rim, were connected to a galvanometer, which deflected while the disk was rotating. When the direction of rotation of the disk was reversed, the galvanometer needle deflected the opposite way. This generator produced a steady electric current through the galvanometer.

Faraday made many other important contributions to electrical science. In 1833 he published the important results of his research work on electrolysis, or chemical decomposition due to an electric current. The words *electrode*, *anode*, *cathode*, *electrolyte* and *ion* are some of the many terms introduced by Faraday. He explained electrochemical decomposition, electrochemical conduction, and the operation of the voltaic pile. In 1845 Faraday investigated the propagation of light in a magnetic field. One of his experiments showed that the plane of polarization of a light beam can be rotated by the action of a magnet. Thus he established a relationship between electromagnetism and light, and he suggested that light waves might be transverse vibrations traveling along his lines of electric and magnetic force. He found that all substances have some magnetic properties. Materials that tend to move toward the stronger regions of a magnetic field were called *paramagnetic*; those that tend to move into weaker parts of the field were called *diamagnetic*.

Faraday's contributions to the science of electrostatics are substantial. In 1837 he discovered that the force between charged particles is decreased when the surrounding space is filled with an insulator instead of air. This property of an insulator was given the name *specific inductive capacity*; today it is called *permittivity*. Faraday found that different insulators, or dielectrics, have different permittivities.

A famous experiment performed by Faraday is the *ice-pail* experiment. A metal can, actually an ice-pail, and a gold-leaf electroscope were used. The gold-leaf electroscope consists essentially of two thin, delicate gold leaves hanging limply from a metal rod. When a small charge of positive or negative electricity is deposited on the rod, the leaves spread apart, or diverge, because the leaves have like charges that repel one another. This instrument is a sensitive detector of electric charge. In the ice-pail experiment the outer surface of the can is connected to the electroscope. Faraday performed and explained the experiments which will now be described.

Suppose a metal ball with a positive charge is lowered into the can without touching it. An equal negative charge is induced on the inside of the can, leaving an equal positive charge on the outside, causing the gold leaves to diverge. This divergence is independent of the position of the ball in the can. When the charged conductor is withdrawn, the leaves collapse. Next, suppose the charged conductor is inserted into the can, causing the leaves to diverge, and then is touched to the inside of the can. The positive charge on the ball and the negative charge on the inside of the can neutralize each other, leaving the positive charge on the outside unaffected. The divergence of the leaves is also unaffected. The uncharged ball can be removed with no effect on the divergence of the leaves.

With the electroscope discharged and with the ball charged, suppose the ball is placed inside the can again, causing the leaves to diverge. If the can is touched with the hand, the leaves collapse, because the charge on the outer surface is neutralized while the negative charge on the inner surface is held by the charged ball. Removing the ball causes the leaves to diverge exactly the same as before, because the can has a net negative charge equal to the positive charge on the ball. If the ball is now touched to the can, both are completely discharged. These experiments illustrate concepts of fundamental importance, such as the conservation of electric charge and charging by induction.

Another interesting experiment performed by Faraday illustrates the conservation of charge and electrical shielding. Faraday constructed a large box, insulated from ground and covered with tin foil connected to an electroscope. Inside the box he charged conductors with frictional machines and also by induction. The leaves of an external electroscope did not move, indicating that the net charge inside the box was always zero. Next the electroscope was placed inside the box and insulated from the tin foil. The box was then strongly charged, even giving off long sparks, but the sensitive electroscope inside the box was unaffected. The electrical effects outside the box were completely shielded by the tin foil.

Faraday's concept of *lines of force* is of considerable importance. In the electric field Faraday visualized lines of electric force, a line being everywhere in the direction of the force that would act on a small charged particle. In the magnetic field he visualized lines of magnetic force being everywhere in the direction of the force that would act on one end of a magnetic needle. According to Faraday's concept, a permanent magnet always has lines of magnetic force from one pole to the other, and an electric current always has lines of magnetic force encircling it. Faraday regarded the induction of current by magnetism as due to a change in the lines of magnetic force.

Joseph Henry (1797–1878)

Joseph Henry was born in Albany, N.Y., of Scottish ancestry. He left school when thirteen to become the apprentice of a watchmaker. However, a popular book on natural history impressed him so much that he returned to school at sixteen, attending Albany Academy. After completing the prescribed course, he continued his studies, and in 1826 he became professor of mathematics and natural philosophy at the Albany Academy. At this time he started experimenting with electromagnetism.

Henry's experiments began with a study of electromagnets. His improvements greatly increased the magnetic power of these devices. He constructed electromagnets with many coils in series and electromagnets with many coils in parallel. He determined that the best arrangement of coils depends on the nature of the electric battery used. In 1831 he built an electromagnet which could lift more than a ton.

Also in 1831, Henry constructed an electric motor. It consisted of a bar of iron, pivoted at the middle, with a coil of wire about it. Below the ends of the pivoted bar were the north poles of two magnets. A current through the coil made the bar an electromagnet and caused it to tip. When the bar tipped, an ingenious arrangement reversed the current, and hence the magnetic poles of the bar, causing the bar to tip the other way. Each time it tipped, the current reversed. Seventy-five vibrations per minute were obtained. Henry suggested that the principle, or a modification of it, might be applied to some useful purpose. This electric motor was certainly the forerunner of the electric motor of today.

An outstanding contribution was Henry's invention of the first practical electromagnetic telegraph in 1831. This was several years before Gauss and Weber developed a similar telegraph. Henry used a high-voltage low-current battery, connected to a wire more than a mile long. At the distant end he used an electromagnet with many turns of wire, and a signal from the sending end energized the electromagnet, causing a bell to ring. In 1844 the first commercial telegraph line was completed, from Baltimore to Washington.

Henry announced his important discovery of self-induction in 1832. In his experiments he observed that sparks occur when a circuit is broken, although there are no sparks when the circuit is connected. He noted that the effect is increased when the wire is coiled or when the current in the wire is increased. Henry reasoned that the interruption of current in each part of the wire induces a current in each neighboring part of the same wire, the induced current producing the spark. Thus the phenomenon of self-induction was discovered by Joseph Henry, and the unit of self-inductance is called the *henry* in his honor.

In addition to self-induction, Joseph Henry also observed mutual induction at about the same time as Faraday. Because Faraday published first, he receives the credit. However, Henry is recognized as the discoverer of electromagnetic self-induction.

In 1835 Henry used a weak electromagnet to control the circuit of a more powerful magnet. This was the first *relay*, and this invention is used extensively in electrical control circuits. Henry developed noninductive windings. He built the first transformers capable of changing the voltage level, and he explained the principles involved in transformer construction. He found that a current induced in a circuit by electromagnetic induction can induce a current in another circuit. He transmitted electric force through the walls of buildings by means of electromagnetic induction.

Henry also investigated spark discharges of a Leyden jar. By observing the magnetic effect of these discharges on steel needles, he determined that they are oscillatory, with electric charges moving rapidly back and forth between the conductors.

1-7. JAMES CLERK MAXWELL (1831-1879)

In 1873 Maxwell's great treatise, *Electricity and Magnetism*, was published. "This work was one of the most splendid monuments ever raised by the genius of a single individual," according to the *Encyclopaedia Britannica*.* H. H. Skilling, in his book *Exploring Electricity*,† says, "The work was so excellent that it is one of the milestones of the science of electricity. Nothing of comparable importance had occurred since Faraday discovered electrical induction, more than forty years earlier."

James Clerk Maxwell was a Scottish physicist, mathematician, and electrical experimenter. He attended the universities at Edinburgh and Cambridge. As a student he began contributing valuable papers to the physical sciences. He was a teacher by profession. His contributions to the kinetic theory of gases and to optics are outstanding, but his greatest work was with electricity. In 1871 he became the first holder of the professorship of experimental physics at Cambridge, and he directed the plans of the newly founded Cavendish laboratory. He died at the early age of forty-eight.

Shortly after Maxwell graduated from Cambridge he wrote a paper, *On Faraday's Lines of Force*, and sent a copy of it to Faraday, who was then sixty-five years of age. This paper attempted to express Faraday's ideas in mathematical form, and Faraday was impressed. The concept of lines of electric and magnetic force had a powerful appeal to Maxwell. The physicists of Maxwell's day regarded the forces between charges and currents as being action-at-a-distance, with nothing occurring in the intervening space. Furthermore, it was commonly believed that electric and magnetic effects were transmitted instantly. Maxwell rejected these ideas, as did Faraday. Maxwell regarded the surrounding medium as being thrown into a state of constraint by the lines of force which carried the attractive power with them. He devoted much of his life to developing this theory. The results of his brilliant work appeared in fully developed form in *Electricity and Magnetism*.

In this classic work Maxwell treated electric and magnetic fields in dynamic vector terms. He gathered up the ideas of his predecessors and presented them in clear mathematical form. His resulting equations are properly called *Maxwell's equations*.

Maxwell introduced the concept of *displacement current*, which is the current through an insulator due to a time-changing electric field. When a capacitor is being charged, there is a current in the wires leading to the plates. Maxwell considered that there is also a current in the dielectric

* Vol. 15, p. 120, 1956.

† The Ronald Press Co., New York, 1948.

between the plates due to the time rate of increase of the electric lines of force in the dielectric. The introduction of displacement current into his equations resolved inconsistencies that would otherwise be present. For example, the electromagnetic laws indicated that the net current over any closed surface should be zero. Without the concept of displacement current a violation would occur for a surface constructed around only one plate of a capacitor being charged. Another inconsistency occurs when the equations are transformed to a coordinate system moving at constant velocity, for the equations change their form if displacement current is not included. Observers on a platform or body moving at a constant velocity would certainly not be expected to have different electromagnetic laws.

Maxwell deduced his first fundamental equation, often called the *Maxwell-Faraday law*, somewhat as indicated by the following steps:

(1) Faraday had shown that the current induced in a metallic circuit is proportional to the time rate of change of the lines of magnetic force linking the circuit.
(2) Ohm and Kirchhoff had found that the current in a circuit is proportional to the electromotive force acting around the circuit.
(3) From these facts Maxwell reasoned that there is an induced electromotive force proportional to the rate of change of the magnetic lines of force passing through the circuit.
(4) An electromotive force implies that work is required to move a unit charge around the circuit. Consequently, an electric field, which exerts a force on electric charges, must be present. Thus Maxwell deduced that there is an electric field produced by the changing magnetism.
(5) Maxwell extended his reasoning to include any circuits in space, regardless of whether or not they followed metallic paths. He concluded that a time-varying magnetic field induces an electric field and that the lines of force of the electric field are closed curves around the lines of force of the magnetic field.
(6) By reducing the circuit to infinitesimal size Maxwell obtained the relation between the induced electric field at a point in space and the time-changing magnetic field at the same point. His resulting equation in vector notation is $\mathbf{curl\ E} = -\dot{\mathbf{B}}$, with $\mathbf{E}$ denoting the electric field intensity and $\mathbf{B}$ denoting the changing magnetic flux density. The precise meaning of this equation will be discussed later.

Oersted and Ampère had determined that an electric current in a wire produces a magnetic field directed around the wire and having a strength proportional to the current. From this it is clear that the work required to move a magnetic pole around a path that encircles the wire is proportional to the current. Maxwell's second fundamental relation, often called the *Maxwell-Ampère law*, is a mathematical statement of this magnetic effect. However, Maxwell regarded current as consisting of displacement current as well as the flow of electric charge, and he introduced displacement current into his equation. As in the case of his first equation, he reduced the path to infinitesimal size, thus obtaining a relationship between the induced magnetic field and the total current density at a point. The total current density includes, of course, the displacement current density. His resulting equation in vector notation is $\mathbf{curl\ H} = \mathbf{J}_t$, with $\mathbf{H}$ denoting the magnetic field intensity and $\mathbf{J}_t$ denoting the total current density.

From Maxwell's first equation it follows that *a time-changing magnetic field induces an electric field.* From Maxwell's second equation, an electric current, including displacement current, induces a magnetic field. As a time-changing electric field results in displacement current, it follows that *a time-changing electric field induces a magnetic field.* Therefore, time-changing electric and magnetic fields exist together, one producing the other. Maxwell deduced mathematically that this relationship would result in electromagnetic waves being propagated from any electrical disturbance, traveling with a velocity equal to $1/\sqrt{\mu\epsilon}$, where μ and ϵ are constants of the medium called *permeability* and *permittivity*, respectively. For free space the velocity becomes 3×10^8 meters/second. Maxwell knew that the velocity of light was approximately this same value. This led him to speculate that light was wave motion of electric and magnetic lines of force, and the electromagnetic wave theory of light was thus established on firm mathematical ground.

The *classical theory* of electromagnetism is based on Maxwell's equations, just as the classical theory of mechanics is based on Newton's laws. Because of the increasing complexity of electrical equipment and the many new developments occurring in electrical engineering, it is more important today than ever before for the scientist and engineer to be well-grounded in the basic fundamentals, and Maxwell's equations are the fundamental equations of electromagnetism. We shall see later that all the important relations in electricity and magnetism, except the electrodynamics of rapidly moving systems and some phenomena on the atomic scale, can be deduced as logical consequences of Maxwell's equations.

There are two additional relationships often included in the set of equations known as Maxwell's equations. One of these is the mathematical statement that the magnetic lines of force have no beginning and no end. The other states mathematically that the electric lines of force are either also endless or they start and terminate only on electric charges. These two equations can, however, be deduced from the two fundamental relations and the conservation of charge. Therefore, they contain no additional basic information.

Maxwell's theory created much interest. It was not wholly accepted until Hertz demonstrated experimentally, fifteen years later, that electromagnetic waves do exist when electrical disturbances occur. However, we must regard classical electromagnetism not as physical reality but as a useful mathematical abstraction, for exceptions are encountered in the electrodynamics of systems moving with large velocities and in phenomena associated with the intimate electrical structure of matter.

1-8. ELECTROMAGNETIC WAVES AND HEINRICH HERTZ (1857–1894)

Heinrich Hertz studied physics under Helmholtz at the University of Berlin. Helmholtz was interested in Maxwell's ideas, and he encouraged Hertz to study this new electromagnetic theory. The German physicists had long accepted Weber's theory that electric and magnetic forces are

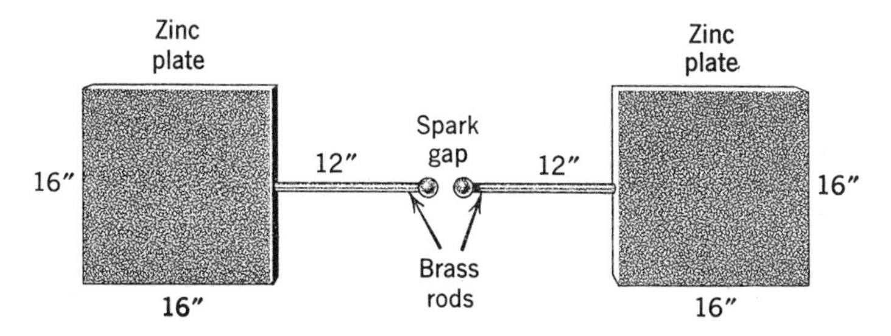

FIG. 1-1. Hertz's electric-wave generator.

transmitted instantly. Hertz decided to ascertain which theory, Weber's or Maxwell's, was correct.

Hertz worked on his electrical experiments for a number of years, trying to prove that an electrical disturbance radiated electromagnetic waves in accordance with Maxwell's theory. He knew that the discharge of a capacitor through a spark gap was oscillatory. He utilized this principle in the design of his electric-wave generator, illustrated in Fig. 1-1.

Hertz connected the two poles of an induction coil to the two brass rods of his spark-gap generator. When the current in the induction coil was interrupted, the high induced voltage produced a spark across the gap. For a brief instant electric charge oscillated between the zinc plates, and across the spark gap, at a frequency of some millions of times per second. According to Maxwell, this spark should produce electromagnetic waves, and Hertz's big problem was to devise a method for detecting these waves, assuming that they exist.

For a detector Hertz used a piece of wire bent into a circular shape with a tiny spark gap between the ends. Hertz reasoned that electromagnetic waves should induce a voltage in this loop, causing a spark to appear across the tiny gap. He sat in a darkened room with his detector about ten meters away from his oscillator, and he observed very minute sparks across the gap of his detector. Hertz's crude detector was the first radio receiver. At the far end of the room Hertz covered the wall with a sheet of zinc in order to reflect the waves. The incident and the reflected waves produced standing waves, which Hertz verified by placing his detector at different distances from the oscillator. Hertz determined the frequency of his oscillator, and he used his detector to measure the wavelength of the standing waves. The product of the frequency and the wavelength yielded the velocity of propagation of the waves. Just as Maxwell had predicted, *the wave velocity was the same as the known velocity of light*. Thus in 1888 Heinrich Hertz succeeded in his experiments, and Maxwell's theory scored a brilliant victory.

During his experiments Hertz demonstrated that electromagnetic waves can be reflected, refracted, and polarized like light and heat waves. He showed that the waves from his oscillator were plane polarized, with the electric field being parallel to the wires of the oscillator, with the magnetic field being perpendicular to the electric field, and with both fields perpendicular to the direction of propagation. Many of his experiments were conducted at microwave frequencies, around 1000 megacycles. At the age of thirty-two, in 1889, he delivered his famous lecture on the relations between light and electricity. His evidence was conclusive that light is an electromagnetic phenomenon. Unfortunately, Hertz died at the early age of thirty-six. In his honor electromagnetic waves are often called *Hertzian waves*.

The use of electric waves to transmit information began in 1896, by Marconi in Italy. In 1901, before the development of the vacuum tube, Marconi succeeded in transmitting a signal across the Atlantic Ocean. Radio communication developed with considerable rapidity.

1-9. ENERGY, MOMENTUM, AND MASS OF THE ELECTROMAGNETIC WAVE

From Maxwell's equations it can be deduced that an electromagnetic wave contains energy which flows in the direction of propagation. This result was published in 1884 by J. H. Poynting. Poynting showed that the flow of energy per unit area per unit time equals $EH \sin \theta$, where E and H are the magnitudes of the electric and magnetic field intensities and θ is the angle between the vectors $\mathbf{E}$ and $\mathbf{H}$. Poynting also showed that, when power is transmitted by a pair of wires from a source to a load, the energy can be regarded as flowing in the space around the wires, not in the wires themselves. The wires serve to guide the energy of the electromagnetic waves, and any energy in the wires is dissipated as heat. Our telephone lines of today employ amplifiers at frequent intervals to replace the energy dissipated in the wires. On the other hand, it is possible to communicate over long distances without intermediate amplifiers, provided energy-consuming conductors are not present.

In 1893 J. J. Thomson showed that an electromagnetic wave possesses momentum which is proportional to Poynting's flow of energy. When an electromagnetic wave strikes an absorbing plate, the law of conservation of momentum prescribes that the plate must acquire momentum, and if the plate is free to move, it should do so. This has been verified experimentally. Momentum is a property of mass, equaling mass times velocity. As electromagnetic waves have momentum, it follows that there is mass associated with these waves. Hence electromagnetic waves have energy, momentum, and mass, and they move through space by means of wave motion. Material particles also have energy, momentum, and mass, and it is believed that particles move through space by means of some sort of wave motion, this motion being governed by the laws of wave mechanics. We conclude that electromagnetic waves and material particles are, in many respects, quite similar.

1-10. PHYSICAL MEDIA AND CHARGE IN ELECTROMAGNETIC THEORY

In electromagnetic field theory, the electrical properties of a material body are taken into account by regarding the body as a continuous medium having a conductivity σ, a permittivity ϵ, and a permeability μ. It is believed that bodies are actually composed of discrete particles separated by space. However, material substances can be treated as continuous media by utilizing the concepts of conductivity, permittivity, and permeability. The theory that has developed to explain the electrical properties of solids is often called *solid-state electronics*, and the basis of this theory is *quantum mechanics*.

In field theory electric charge is usually considered to be continuous, although we know it actually exists in discrete quantities. The concept of a continuous charge distribution is valid when the charge being considered is large compared with the charge of an electron. Certainly when billions of electrons are in a small volume, the discrete nature of the electrical charge loses its significance. In copper there are about 10^{23} free electrons per cubic centimeter.

1-11. DEVELOPMENT OF THE ELECTRON THEORY

Electrical Discharges in Gases at Low Pressure

The first investigation of discharges in gases at reduced pressure was made by Watson in 1752. He used a glass tube about three feet long. Watson observed that the reduced pressure made it easier to obtain an electrical discharge and that the sparks were spread out somewhat like a flame.

Faraday continued the studies in 1838, using lower pressures. He observed a glow at the negative electrode, followed by a dark space called the *Faraday dark space*, followed in turn by a luminous region which extended to the positive electrode.

Around 1850 improved pumps made investigations at greatly reduced pressure possible. It was found that a dark space exists between the negative electrode and the first glow region. This dark space is called the *Crookes dark space*. As the pressure is reduced, the Crookes dark space expands and causes the walls of the glass tube to glow. In 1869 Hittorf placed a solid object in the Crookes dark space between the cathode and the glass. It produced a shadow in the light emitted by the glass. This led him to believe that the cathode emitted rays, and these rays were called *cathode rays*. In 1871 it was suggested that these cathode rays consist of small particles containing negative charges.

William Crookes performed his famous experiments with cathode rays around 1879. He used a pressure so low that the Crookes dark space extended from the negative to the positive electrode. Crookes demonstrated that the cathode rays cause many substances to glow. By means of a slit he obtained a narrow beam of rays, and he showed that this beam can be deflected by a magnetic field. His experiments convinced him, as well as many others, that the cathode rays consist of high-velocity negatively charged particles.

In 1887 Heinrich Hertz discovered the *photoelectric effect*. Hertz observed that ultraviolet light aids the passage of sparks across a spark gap. Shortly afterwards, it was determined that the ultraviolet light on the negative electrode caused negative electricity to escape.

Several experimenters independently measured the ratio of charge to mass for the cathode rays. This ratio agreed closely with the charge-mass ratio of the negative particles emitted by the photoelectric effect. These experiments established beyond doubt the fact that the cathode rays are negative particles. As cathode rays were readily obtained from different substances, it appeared that these negative particles were a basic constituent of matter. Lorentz had formulated his electron theory in 1892, and in accordance with his theory, the negative particles of the cathode rays were regarded as electrons. This was later verified by many experiments.

Lorentz's Electron Theory

H. A. Lorentz introduced the modern electron theory in 1892. Only a few of the important concepts of his theory will be presented here. Lorentz proposed that matter contains small spherical particles, each with a negative charge. He called these particles *electrons*. Conductors were regarded as containing free electrons, which would drift when an electric field was applied, thus producing an electric current. In insulators the electrons were not free, according to Lorentz, and therefore an insulator could not carry a current of moving charges. He suggested that the displacement current in an insulator is the sum of the displacement current in a vacuum and the current due to a slight displacement of the bound electrons. Lorentz believed that all magnetic fields are produced by electric currents, and he proposed that the electric and magnetic properties of a body are due to its electrons.

The theory developed by Lorentz was based on the experimental work of many of his contemporaries. In 1876 Rowland had demonstrated that a moving electrostatic charge produces a magnetic field. He did this by rotating a charged plate, which caused a magnetic needle to deflect. This experiment indicated that a moving charge is equivalent to an electric current. The many experiments with cathode rays and the photoelectric effect, as well as the work done by Maxwell, helped Lorentz to develop his ideas. The Lorentz electron theory might well be considered as the beginning of modern electrical science.

X Rays

A new kind of radiation, referred to as *X rays*, was discovered in 1895 by W. K. Röntgen, who determined that radiation results when high-energy electrons strike a solid. The X rays travel in straight lines, are very penetrating, affect a photographic plate, and produce fluorescence in certain substances. It was soon determined that these X rays are very short light waves. It was also determined that they can make an insulator conducting. Experiments with this new radiation led to the development of the ionic theory of gaseous conduction, and X rays became an important tool in the study of the solid state.

The Atom Theory

J. J. Thomson designed an atom theory about 1898. It was already known that matter has negative electrons. From their penetrating power Thomson deduced that these electrons are very much smaller than atoms. Because matter is normally electrically neutral, Thomson suggested that an atom contains positive electricity equal to the negative electricity of the electrons. He viewed the electrons as being arranged in layers, with the chemical properties determined by those in the outermost layer. The positive electricity was regarded as distributed throughout the atom. Thomson believed that the chemically inert atoms have stable arrangements of their electrons. With this theory, Thomson successfully explained many of the properties of atoms.

In 1901 a study of black-body radiation by the German physicist, Max Planck, indicated that electromagnetic energy is radiated not as a continuous wave but in the form of discrete bundles, or *quanta*, of energy, called *photons*. The energy W of each photon is proportional to the frequency f of oscillation of the electrons, and the constant of proportionality h in the expression $W = hf$ is called *Planck's constant*. Planck's ideas were deduced from the photoelectric effect and other phenomena, and his quantum theory was rapidly developed by Bohr and others.

The atom theory of Thomson, which was further developed by Rutherford, and the radiation theory of Planck led the Danish physicist, Niels Bohr, to develop his atom theory in 1913. Bohr's atom can be compared to a small solar system, with negative electrons orbiting about the positive nucleus. Bohr made some rather arbitrary assumptions which were later supported by quantum mechanics. The Bohr theory had many successes, but it soon became apparent that it was inadequate. A new theory was needed in order to explain atomic phenomena.

Quantum (Wave) Mechanics

Planck's quantum theory, that radiation consists of discrete bundles of energy, plus evidence that photons possess momentum and mass, showed that light can be regarded as corpuscular, acting like a wave only when large numbers of photons are observed. It became evident that classical mechanics, based on Newton's laws, and classical electromagnetism, based on Maxwell's equations, were inadequate to deal with atomic behavior.

The fact that light has some properties of both particles and waves led to the belief that particles may also exhibit a dual nature, having some of the properties of waves as well as the properties commonly attributed to material particles. In 1925 de Broglie proposed that a free particle has a wavelength associated with it, with the wavelength equal to h/p, where h is Planck's constant and p is the momentum of the particle. This was investigated by Davisson and Germer in 1926. In their experiments they established that electrons could be diffracted like waves, and they determined that the electron's wavelength is the same as predicted by de Broglie. Many experiments have since been performed to support de Broglie's theory. Thus we know that both light and material particles have both corpuscular and wave properties.

The theory that evolved from Planck's quantum theory and de Broglie's theory is called *quantum mechanics*, or *wave mechanics*. In 1926 Schrödinger incorporated the de Broglie wavelength into a wave equation, and Schrödinger's wave equation is the foundation of quantum mechanics. Quantum mechanics is the basis of *modern* electrical science. In fact, molecules, solids, liquids, gases, electricity, magnetism, light, as well as chemistry, metallurgy, and other sciences can be explained by quantum mechanics. It does not, however, describe completely what takes place inside the nucleus of the atom.

The classical theories of electromagnetism and mechanics are still valid, and they are as useful as they ever have been. Quantum mechanics develops into classical electromagnetism and classical mechanics for large-scale phenomena. Inside the atom, however, quantum mechanics must be used. The fact that the classical theories are logical consequences of the quantum-mechanical theory applied to large-scale phenomena is known as the *Correspondence Principle*.

The question will probably arise in the student's mind as to what an electron really is. At times we find it is treated as though it is a particle. At other times we find it treated as though it is a wave. Actually the electron is neither a particle nor a wave. It is a fundamental entity of matter, and it cannot be described by saying it is something else more familiar. We must define and describe it in terms of its properties, the principal properties being its charge, mass, wavelength, and spin. The motion of an electron is governed by the laws of quantum mechanics. A similar argument applies to the other fundamental entities, such as protons and neutrons.

Likewise, the photon is neither a particle nor a wave. It also is a fundamental entity, characterized by certain properties. The photon is believed to consist of electric and magnetic fields. It has a certain amount of energy proportional to its frequency, a definite momentum, and the velocity of light. As the photon has momentum, it must have mass. However, its *rest mass* must be zero, for otherwise its mass at the velocity of light would be infinite in accordance with relativity theory.

REFERENCES

Attwood, S. S., *Electric and Magnetic Fields*, John Wiley and Sons, New York, 3rd ed., 1949, Appendix III.

Dibner, B., *Ten Founding Fathers of the Electrical Science*, Burndy Library, Inc., Norwalk, Conn., 1954.

Faraday, M., *Experimental Researches in Electricity*, B. Quaritch, London, 1839, 1955.

Heaviside, O., *Electromagnetic Theory*, 3 vols., Dover Publications, New York, 1950.

Hertz, H. R., *Electric Waves*, Macmillan and Co., Ltd., London, 1900.

Maxwell, J. C., *A Treatise on Electricity and Magnetism*, 2 vols., Dover Publications, New York, 3rd ed., 1954.

Skilling, H. H., *Exploring Electricity*, The Ronald Press Co., New York, 1948.

Sommerfield, A., *Electrodynamics*, Academic Press, New York, 1952, Sec. 1 of Part 1.

Whittaker, E., *A History of the Theories of Aether and Electricity*, Vol. 1, *Classical Theories*, Philosophical Library, New York, 1951.

PROBLEMS

Section 1-2

1-1. Explain how Aepinus was able to charge a body by induction. Utilize a suitable sketch.

1-2. Express Coulomb's inverse-square law of force between electric charges as a mathematical equation.

Section 1-6

1-3. Sketch Faraday's experimental apparatus that demonstrated that a changing magnetism can produce an electric current.

1-4. Sketch Faraday's first electric generator.

1-5. Describe and explain Faraday's ice-pail experiments. Utilize suitable sketches.

Section 1-7

1-6. Explain how Maxwell deduced that light was probably an electromagnetic wave.

Section 1-11

1-7. Occasionally we read in the literature that an electron is at times a particle but that at other times it is a wave. Explain why this statement about the electron is incorrect.

1-8. Given below are twenty-three names with associated numbers and twenty-three phrases with associated letters. Match the names and phrases suitably, and indicate your selections by associating a letter with each number.

1 Gilbert, **2** von Gucricke, **3** Franklin, **4** Coulomb, **5** Poisson, **6** Galvani, **7** Volta, **8** Oersted, **9** Ampère, **10** Ohm, **11** Gauss and Weber, **12** Faraday, **13** Henry, **14** Maxwell, **15** Hertz, **16** Poynting, **17** Crookes, **18** Lorentz, **19** Röntgen, **20** Thomson, **21** Planck, **22** de Broglie, **23** Schrödinger.

a electron theory, *b* inverse-square law, *c* terrestrial magnetism, *d* wave equation of quantum mechanics, *e* cathode rays, *f* self-induction, *g* established a pattern of scientific investigation, *h* changing magnetism produces an electric current, *i* X rays, *j* animal electricity, *k* classical electromagnetic theory, *l* energy flow in electromagnetic waves, *m* electrostatic frictional generator, *n* battery, *o* electric currents exert forces on one another, *p* wavelength of a particle, *q* atom theory *r* current in a metallic circuit is proportional to the applied voltage, *s* single-fluid theory of electricity, *t* experimental verification of Maxwell's theory, *u* electric current exerts a force on a magnetic pole, *v* mathematical theory of electrostatics, *w* quantum theory and photon.

Introduction to Vectors

CHAPTER 2

The mathematical development of electromagnetic theory utilizes both scalars and vectors. A *scalar* is a quantity with magnitude only, whereas a *vector* has both magnitude and direction.

In this chapter we shall consider some of the elementary properties of vectors, with special emphasis given to derivatives and integrals of vectors. It is very important that the vector notation and principles are thoroughly understood, for much of the material to be presented later is based on the mathematics discussed here. At the end of the chapter are numerous problems, designed to help the student obtain the necessary familiarity with elementary vector concepts.

2-1. SCALARS AND VECTORS

A scalar quantity, having magnitude only, can be represented by a single number. Temperature, energy, and power are examples. When a scalar is associated with each point of a region, a *scalar function*, or *field*, is said to exist. As an example of a scalar field let us consider the temperature field of an object. Each point has a certain temperature. Of course, the temperature may vary from point to point, and at each point it may vary with time. However, at a given point at a particular time the temperature is completely specified by a single number.

On the other hand, a vector cannot be completely specified by a single number. Three numbers are required. These may be the rectangular components of the vector, or they may be the spatial components in some other coordinate system. Force, velocity, and acceleration are common examples of vectors.

A *vector function*, or *field*, exists in a region that has a vector quantity associated with each of its points. For example, a moving fluid has a certain velocity at each point. Of course, the velocity may vary from point to point, and at each point it may vary with time. However, at a given point at a particular time the velocity is completely specified by three

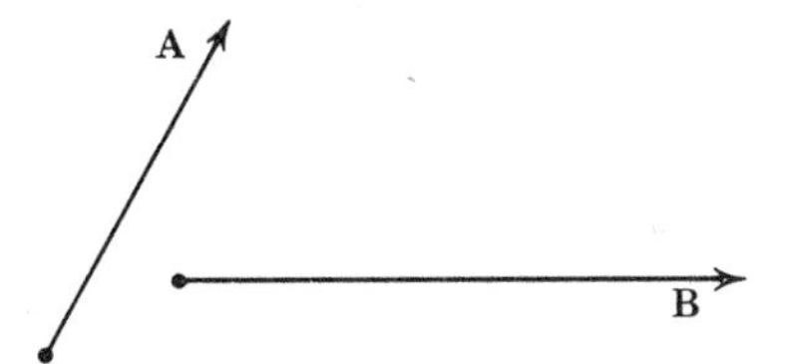

FIG. 2-1*a*. Vectors **A** and **B**.

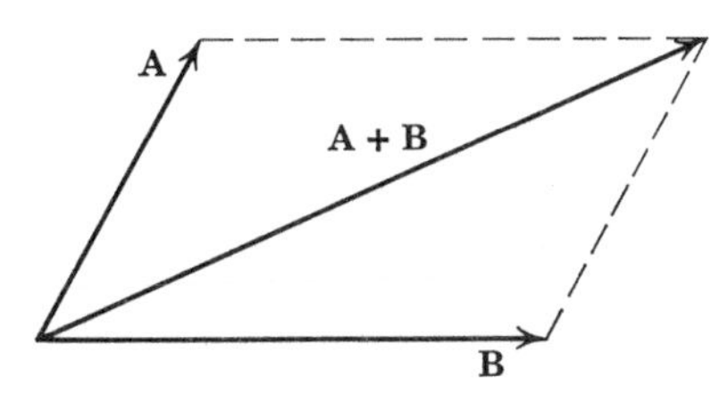

FIG. 2-1*b*. Addition of **A** and **B**.

ordered numbers. These may be v_x, v_y, and v_z, or they may be the velocity components in some other coordinate system.

Vectors are added according to the parallelogram law. Two vectors **A** and **B** are shown in Fig. 2-1*a*, and their addition according to the parallelogram law is shown in Fig. 2-1*b*. Note that the two vectors do not need to be located at the same point. A vector can be moved from one point to another without changing its value, provided its magnitude and direction remain unchanged. Also note that the vectors **A**, **B**, and $\mathbf{A} + \mathbf{B}$ can be drawn to form a triangle. The use of boldface type for symbols denoting vector quantities is conventional.

We have learned that a vector can be represented by a set of three ordered numbers, such as its rectangular components, and that vectors combine according to the parallelogram law. It is evident that the addition of two vectors can be accomplished by adding their respective rectangular components to obtain the components of the resulting vector. It follows that a vector **A** can be defined mathematically, with reference to rectangular coordinates, by the relations

$$\mathbf{A} = (A_x, A_y, A_z) \tag{2-1}$$

$$\mathbf{A} + \mathbf{B} = (A_x + B_x, A_y + B_y, A_z + B_z) \tag{2-2}$$

with **B** also denoting a vector. Note that A_x, A_y, and A_z are scalars, representing the rectangular components of the vector. Each component is specified by a single number.

The magnitude of a vector **A** is a scalar, represented by A or $|\mathbf{A}|$. The symbol A will, in some circumstances, be allowed to have a negative sign,

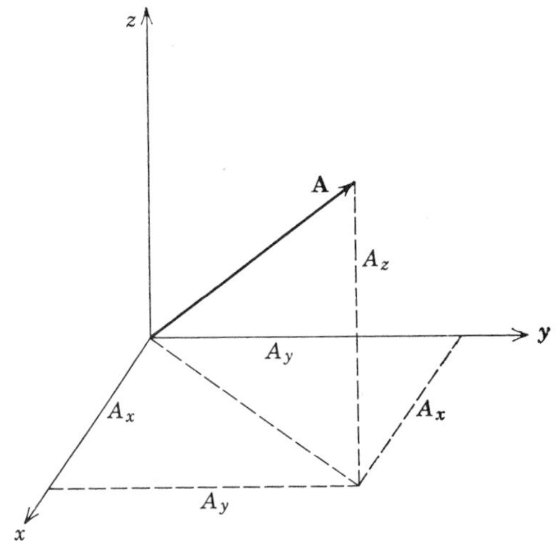

FIG. 2-2. Rectangular components of **A**.

whereas the symbol $|\mathbf{A}|$ is always understood to denote the positive magnitude. In terms of the rectangular components the magnitude of **A** is $(A_x^2 + A_y^2 + A_z^2)^{1/2}$. For verification refer to Fig. 2-2. Note that A_x and A_y form the legs of a right triangle whose hypotenuse and A_z form the legs of a second right triangle of hypotenuse A.

From our addition rule, $\mathbf{A} + \mathbf{A} = (2A_x, 2A_y, 2A_z)$. As multiplication of a vector by a scalar is merely repeated addition, it follows that $a\mathbf{A} = (aA_x, aA_y, aA_z)$. If a is -1, then $-\mathbf{A} = (-A_x, -A_y, -A_z)$. The vector $-\mathbf{A}$ has the same magnitude as **A**, but its direction is opposite that of **A**.

2-2. THE RECTANGULAR FORM OF A VECTOR

It is customary and convenient to express vectors in terms of unit vectors directed along the axes of the coordinate system. Let **i**, **j**, and **k** denote unit vectors in the directions of the x, y, and z axes, respectively. Then $\mathbf{i} = (1, 0, 0)$, $\mathbf{j} = (0, 1, 0)$, and $\mathbf{k} = (0, 0, 1)$. Clearly

$$A_x\mathbf{i} = (A_x, 0, 0)$$
$$A_y\mathbf{j} = (0, A_y, 0)$$
$$A_z\mathbf{k} = (0, 0, A_z)$$

Addition yields $A_x\mathbf{i} + A_y\mathbf{j} + A_z\mathbf{k} = (A_x, A_y, A_z)$. We conclude that the vector $\mathbf{A}$ can be expanded as the sum of the vectors $A_x\mathbf{i}$, $A_y\mathbf{j}$, and $A_z\mathbf{k}$, or

$$\mathbf{A} = A_x\mathbf{i} + A_y\mathbf{j} + A_z\mathbf{k} \tag{2-3}$$

This is the rectangular form of the vector $\mathbf{A}$. Note that $A_x\mathbf{i}$ is a *vector* parallel with the x axis and that A_x is the *scalar magnitude* of this vector. Similar statements apply to the terms containing A_y and A_z.

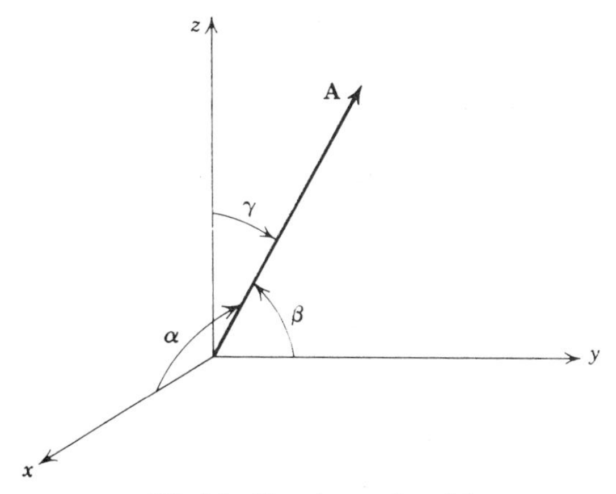

FIG. 2-3. Direction angles of **A**.

From the addition rule the sum of two vectors is

$$\mathbf{A} + \mathbf{B} = (A_x + B_x)\mathbf{i} + (A_y + B_y)\mathbf{j} + (A_z + B_z)\mathbf{k}$$

Obviously, the *commutative law* applies to vector addition; that is, $\mathbf{A} + \mathbf{B} = \mathbf{B} + \mathbf{A}$. Vector addition is also *associative*, for $(\mathbf{A} + \mathbf{B}) + \mathbf{C} = \mathbf{A} + (\mathbf{B} + \mathbf{C})$. The vector $a\mathbf{A}$ is $aA_x\mathbf{i} + aA_y\mathbf{j} + aA_z\mathbf{k}$.

The *direction angles* α, β, and γ are the angles formed by a vector $\mathbf{A}$ and the positive x, y, and z coordinate axes, respectively, as shown in Fig. 2-3. The cosines of these angles are called the *direction cosines* and are usually designated l, m, and n. It is evident that

$$l = \cos\alpha = A_x/A$$
$$m = \cos\beta = A_y/A$$
$$n = \cos\gamma = A_z/A$$

The direction angles have values between zero and 180°. A direction angle between 90° and 180° has a *negative* direction cosine.

2-3. THE SCALAR PRODUCT OF TWO VECTORS

We are familiar with the multiplication of scalars, and we have considered the multiplication of a scalar and a vector. We shall now examine the product of two vectors, with attention in this section given to the *scalar*, or *dot*, *product*. The scalar product of **A** and **B**, written $\mathbf{A} \cdot \mathbf{B}$ and

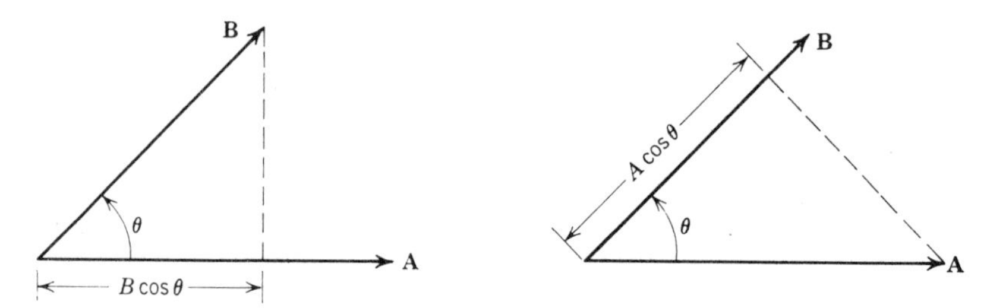

FIG. 2-4. Projections of vectors on one another.

read "**A** dot **B**," is defined as the product of the magnitude A, the magnitude B, and the cosine of the smaller angle θ between the vectors **A** and **B**, giving

$$\mathbf{A} \cdot \mathbf{B} = AB \cos \theta \tag{2-4}$$

We note that the scalar product yields, by definition, a scalar quantity. This quantity is positive if the angle θ between the vectors is less than 90°, but the product is negative if θ is between 90° and 180°. The angle θ is, of course, always between zero and 180°. The scalar product of **A** and **B** can be written $A(B \cos \theta)$. As $B \cos \theta$ denotes the component of **B** in the direction of **A**, we can regard the scalar product as representing *the magnitude A multiplied by the projection of* **B** *upon* **A**. Also, if we wish, we can express $\mathbf{A} \cdot \mathbf{B}$ by $(A \cos \theta)B$, which is *the magnitude B multiplied by the component of* **A** *in the direction of* **B**. The projections of the vectors on one another are shown in Fig. 2-4. Both viewpoints are equally valid, and both are useful.

Clearly, the dot product is commutative; that is, $\mathbf{A} \cdot \mathbf{B} = \mathbf{B} \cdot \mathbf{A}$. It is also distributive, with $\mathbf{A} \cdot (\mathbf{B} + \mathbf{C}) = \mathbf{A} \cdot \mathbf{B} + \mathbf{A} \cdot \mathbf{C}$. To show this, refer to Fig. 2-5. The vector **C** is drawn from the tip of **B**. The distance ab along **A** is the projection of **B** on **A**, the distance bc along **A** is the projection of **C** on **A**, and the distance ac is the projection of the vector $\mathbf{B} + \mathbf{C}$ on **A**. It follows that $\mathbf{A} \cdot (\mathbf{B} + \mathbf{C}) = A(ac)$ and the sum of $\mathbf{A} \cdot \mathbf{B}$ and $\mathbf{A} \cdot \mathbf{C}$ is $A(ab) + A(bc)$. As $ac = ab + bc$, the distributive rule is verified.

In rectangular coordinates we have

$$\mathbf{A} \cdot \mathbf{B} = (A_x\mathbf{i} + A_y\mathbf{j} + A_z\mathbf{k}) \cdot (B_x\mathbf{i} + B_y\mathbf{j} + B_z\mathbf{k})$$

The distributive rule justifies treating this term by term. Noting that $\mathbf{i} \cdot \mathbf{i} = \mathbf{j} \cdot \mathbf{j} = \mathbf{k} \cdot \mathbf{k} = 1$ and $\mathbf{i} \cdot \mathbf{j} = \mathbf{j} \cdot \mathbf{k} = \mathbf{k} \cdot \mathbf{i} = 0$, the preceding expression becomes

$$\mathbf{A} \cdot \mathbf{B} = A_xB_x + A_yB_y + A_zB_z \tag{2-5}$$

Thus the scalar product of two vectors can be found by adding together the products of their x components, their y components, and their z components.

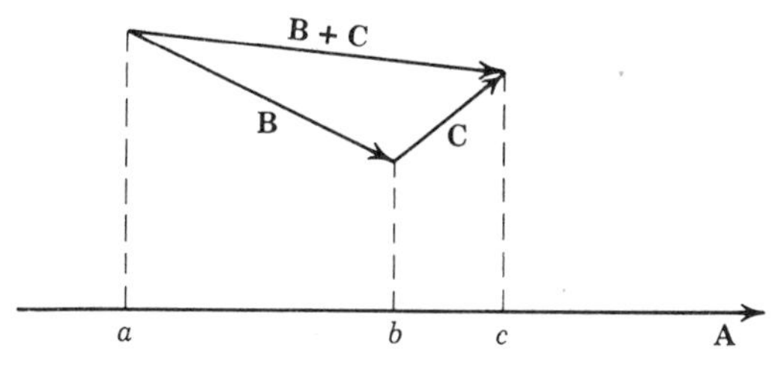

FIG. 2-5. Projections of vectors upon **A**.

We note that $\mathbf{A} \cdot \mathbf{A} = A_x^2 + A_y^2 + A_z^2 = A^2$. The scalar product $\mathbf{A} \cdot \mathbf{A}$ is often expressed as $\mathbf{A}^2$. Consequently

$$\mathbf{A}^2 = \mathbf{A} \cdot \mathbf{A} = A^2 \tag{2-6}$$

2-4. THE VECTOR PRODUCT OF TWO VECTORS

Another important product of vectors is the *vector*, or *cross*, *product*. The vector product of **A** and **B**, written $\mathbf{A} \times \mathbf{B}$ and usually read "**A** cross **B**," is defined as the vector $AB \sin\theta\, \mathbf{n}$, with **n** denoting a unit vector normal to the plane of **A** and **B**, with sense determined by the *right-hand rule*. By this rule the extended thumb of the right hand gives the direction of **n** provided the closed fingers point through the angle θ *from* **A** *toward* **B**. These relations are shown in Fig. 2-6. As before, the angle θ is the smaller angle between the two vectors, with possible values from zero to 180°. In mathematical form

$$\mathbf{A} \times \mathbf{B} = AB \sin\theta\, \mathbf{n} \tag{2-7}$$

By definition, the vector product yields a vector. Its magnitude is $AB \sin\theta$, which obviously equals AB_n and also A_nB, with B_n denoting the component of **B** normal to **A** and with A_n denoting the component of **A** normal to **B**. The direction of the vector $\mathbf{A} \times \mathbf{B}$ is normal to the plane formed by the vectors **A** and **B** drawn from a common point, with sense determined by the right-hand rule.

The commutative law does not apply to the cross product. The magnitudes of the vectors $\mathbf{A} \times \mathbf{B}$ and $\mathbf{B} \times \mathbf{A}$ are equal, but their directions are opposite. Therefore, $\mathbf{A} \times \mathbf{B} = -\mathbf{B} \times \mathbf{A}$. However, it can be shown* that the vector product is distributive, with $\mathbf{A} \times (\mathbf{B} + \mathbf{C}) = \mathbf{A} \times \mathbf{B} + \mathbf{A} \times \mathbf{C}$.

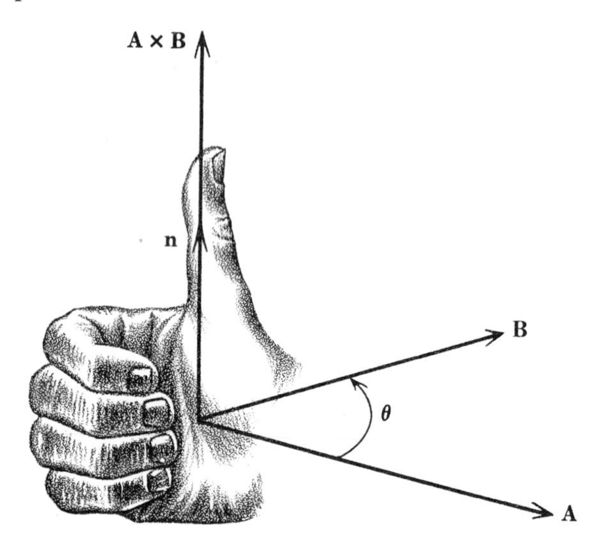

FIG. 2-6. The vector product and the right-hand rule.

Let us now determine the vector product in rectangular form. We have

$$\mathbf{A} \times \mathbf{B} = (A_x\mathbf{i} + A_y\mathbf{j} + A_z\mathbf{k}) \times (B_x\mathbf{i} + B_y\mathbf{j} + B_z\mathbf{k})$$

By the distributive rule we can expand this term by term. As $\mathbf{i} \times \mathbf{i} = \mathbf{j} \times \mathbf{j} = \mathbf{k} \times \mathbf{k} = 0$ and $\mathbf{i} \times \mathbf{j} = \mathbf{k}$, $\mathbf{j} \times \mathbf{k} = \mathbf{i}$, and $\mathbf{k} \times \mathbf{i} = \mathbf{j}$, the result is

$$\mathbf{A} \times \mathbf{B} = (A_yB_z - A_zB_y)\mathbf{i} + (A_zB_x - A_xB_z)\mathbf{j} + (A_xB_y - A_yB_x)\mathbf{k}$$

This can be expressed as

$$\mathbf{A} \times \mathbf{B} = \begin{vmatrix} \mathbf{i} & \mathbf{j} & \mathbf{k} \\ A_x & A_y & A_z \\ B_x & B_y & B_z \end{vmatrix} \qquad (2\text{-}8)$$

This form is convenient to write and easy to remember. Note that the x, y, and z components of the first vector in the cross product are above those of the second vector. Equation (2-8) is used to evaluate the vector product when the rectangular components of $\mathbf{A}$ and $\mathbf{B}$ are known.

The associative rule does not apply to the vector product; $\mathbf{A} \times (\mathbf{B} \times \mathbf{C})$ is not necessarily equal to $(\mathbf{A} \times \mathbf{B}) \times \mathbf{C}$.

* M. R. Spiegel, *Vector Analysis*, Schaum Publishing Co., New York, 1950, p. 23.

2-5. SOME MULTIPLE PRODUCTS OF VECTORS

The vector $\mathbf{A} \times \mathbf{B}$ is normal to both **A** and **B**. Therefore

$$(\mathbf{A} \times \mathbf{B}) \cdot \mathbf{A} = (\mathbf{A} \times \mathbf{B}) \cdot \mathbf{B} = 0 \tag{2-9}$$

The following identities are readily verified by substituting the rectangular forms of the vectors and performing the indicated operations:

$$\mathbf{A} \times (\mathbf{B} \times \mathbf{C}) = (\mathbf{A} \cdot \mathbf{C})\mathbf{B} - (\mathbf{A} \cdot \mathbf{B})\mathbf{C} \tag{2-10}$$

$$(\mathbf{A} \times \mathbf{B}) \cdot (\mathbf{C} \times \mathbf{D}) = (\mathbf{A} \cdot \mathbf{C})(\mathbf{B} \cdot \mathbf{D}) - (\mathbf{A} \cdot \mathbf{D})(\mathbf{B} \cdot \mathbf{C}) \tag{2-11}$$

$$\mathbf{A} \cdot (\mathbf{B} \times \mathbf{C}) = \mathbf{B} \cdot (\mathbf{C} \times \mathbf{A}) = \mathbf{C} \cdot (\mathbf{A} \times \mathbf{B}) \tag{2-12}$$

The area of a parallelogram formed by the vectors **A** and **B** drawn from a common point is the magnitude of $\mathbf{A} \times \mathbf{B}$. It follows that each term of Eq. (2-12) gives the volume of a parallelepiped formed by the vectors **A**, **B**, and **C** drawn from a common point.

Some products of vectors have no meaning. For example, **AB** is undefined. The expression $(\mathbf{A} \cdot \mathbf{B}) \times \mathbf{C}$ has no meaning, for $\mathbf{A} \cdot \mathbf{B}$ is a scalar. Division of vectors is undefined.

2-6. DIFFERENTIATION OF A VECTOR

The derivative of a vector **A** is a vector whose magnitude and direction may be quite different from those of **A**. To illustrate this let us consider a particle moving with velocity **v**. The time derivative of **v** is the acceleration **a** of the particle. Suppose the particle is moving along a straight path with decreasing velocity. The acceleration **a** has direction opposite that of the velocity vector **v**. If the particle is moving along a circular path with constant speed, its acceleration, which equals $d\mathbf{v}/dt$, is directed toward the center of the circle, and **a** and **v** are normal to one another. These are, of course, special cases. We shall now examine the precise meaning of the derivative of a vector with respect to a scalar.

Let $\mathbf{A}(t)$ be a function of the scalar variable t. As t varies, both the magnitude and direction of **A** may vary, with a change Δt producing a change $\Delta\mathbf{A}$ in **A**. This change $\Delta\mathbf{A} = \mathbf{A}(t + \Delta t) - \mathbf{A}(t)$, and $\Delta\mathbf{A}$ is obviously a vector. The derivative of **A** with respect to t is defined as the limit of the ratio $\Delta\mathbf{A}/\Delta t$ as Δt approaches zero. Thus

$$\frac{d\mathbf{A}}{dt} = \lim_{\Delta t \to 0} \frac{\Delta\mathbf{A}}{\Delta t} \tag{2-13}$$

provided the limit exists.

The vector $\Delta\mathbf{A} = \mathbf{A}(t + \Delta t) - \mathbf{A}(t)$. In rectangular form this becomes $\Delta\mathbf{A} = \Delta A_x\,\mathbf{i} + \Delta A_y\,\mathbf{j} + \Delta A_z\,\mathbf{k}$, with $\Delta A_x = A_x(t + \Delta t) - A_x(t)$ and with ΔA_y and ΔA_z similarly defined. Upon substitution of the rectangular form of $\Delta\mathbf{A}$ into Eq. (2-13), it becomes evident that

$$\frac{d\mathbf{A}}{dt} = \frac{dA_x}{dt}\,\mathbf{i} + \frac{dA_y}{dt}\,\mathbf{j} + \frac{dA_z}{dt}\,\mathbf{k} \tag{2-14}$$

This important result shows that a vector can be differentiated by taking derivatives of its scalar components.

Presented next are a few vector identities involving derivatives of vectors. They are readily verified by expressing the vectors in terms of their rectangular components and performing the indicated operations.

$$\frac{d}{dt}(\mathbf{A} + \mathbf{B}) = \frac{d\mathbf{A}}{dt} + \frac{d\mathbf{B}}{dt} \tag{2-15}$$

$$\frac{d}{dt}(\mathbf{A} \cdot \mathbf{B}) = \frac{d\mathbf{A}}{dt} \cdot \mathbf{B} + \mathbf{A} \cdot \frac{d\mathbf{B}}{dt} \tag{2-16}$$

$$\frac{d}{dt}(\mathbf{A} \times \mathbf{B}) = \frac{d\mathbf{A}}{dt} \times \mathbf{B} + \mathbf{A} \times \frac{d\mathbf{B}}{dt} \tag{2-17}$$

$$\frac{d}{dt}(u\mathbf{A}) = u\,\frac{d\mathbf{A}}{dt} + \mathbf{A}\,\frac{du}{dt} \tag{2-18}$$

$$\mathbf{A} \cdot \frac{d\mathbf{A}}{dt} = A\,\frac{dA}{dt} \tag{2-19}$$

In verifying Eq. (2-19) keep in mind that, in general, $\mathbf{A}$ and $d\mathbf{A}/dt$ are *not* in the same direction and dA/dt is *not* the magnitude of $d\mathbf{A}/dt$.

Usually, a vector $\mathbf{A}$ is a function of several variables. The derivative of $\mathbf{A}$ with respect to one of these variables, with the others treated as constants, is called a *partial derivative*. For example, the partial derivative of $\mathbf{A}(x, y, z, t)$ with respect to x is

$$\frac{\partial\mathbf{A}}{\partial x} = \frac{\partial A_x}{\partial x}\,\mathbf{i} + \frac{\partial A_y}{\partial x}\,\mathbf{j} + \frac{\partial A_z}{\partial x}\,\mathbf{k}$$

When evaluating the partial derivatives, we regard the variables y, z, and time t as constants. The result gives the rate at which $\mathbf{A}$ changes with respect to x, as x alone varies, at a point in space at a particular instant of time. If the rate at which $\mathbf{A}$ changes with respect to time is desired at a fixed point in space, we must evaluate the partial time derivative of $\mathbf{A}$ at the point.

The partial derivative of **A** with respect to time is frequently denoted by the symbol $\dot{\mathbf{A}}$, and this notation is used in this book. Henceforth, we shall understand that a dot placed above either a vector or a scalar symbol denotes a partial time derivative. Additional dots denote additional partial time derivatives. Thus

$$\dot{\mathbf{A}} = \frac{\partial \mathbf{A}}{\partial t} \qquad \ddot{\mathbf{A}} = \frac{\partial^2 \mathbf{A}}{\partial t^2}$$

2-7. THE LINE INTEGRAL OF A VECTOR

One of the most important mathematical concepts which we shall utilize in our study of electromagnetism is the line integral of a vector.

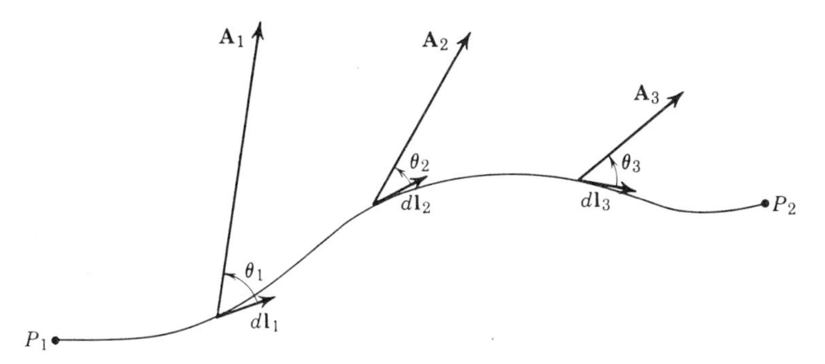

FIG. 2-7. A path in a vector field.

As this is an integration along a path in space, let us consider a path C in a region containing a vector field **A**. The path C, extending from point P_1 to P_2, is shown in Fig. 2-7. The vector **A** varies from point to point along the path, with possible values of **A** indicated at three points.

The path C can be approximated by a large number of straight elemental segments, each of length Δl. At an arbitrary point along the path let A_l denote the component of **A** in the direction of the elemental path length at that point. Then $A_l = A \cos \theta$, with both A and θ varying from point to point. Let us form the product $A_l \, \Delta l$ and add together all such products so that all the elemental lengths of the path are included. The limit of the resulting summation of the terms $A_l \, \Delta l$, as Δl approaches zero, is the *line integral* of **A** along the path C. This is the summation of the differentials $A_l \, dl$ over the entire length of the path. We can express the line integral in vector notation. Each differential path length can be regarded as a vector $d\mathbf{l}$, with magnitude dl and with direction along the path as shown in

Fig. 2-7. Then $A_l\,dl = \mathbf{A}\cdot d\mathbf{l}$. Alternate forms for denoting the line integral of **A** along the path C are

$$\int_C A_l\,dl = \int_C A\cos\theta\,dl = \int_C \mathbf{A}\cdot d\mathbf{l} \tag{2-20}$$

The line integral is especially important in electromagnetic theory. The fundamental laws of electromagnetism involve line integrals, and if the student is to understand these basic laws, he must understand the meaning of the line integral.

The vector $d\mathbf{l}$ can be expressed in rectangular form. Its rectangular components are the projections of the differential length onto the x, y, and z axes. Clearly, $d\mathbf{l} = dx\,\mathbf{i} + dy\,\mathbf{j} + dz\,\mathbf{k}$. As $\mathbf{A} = A_x\mathbf{i} + A_y\mathbf{j} + A_z\mathbf{k}$, it follows that

$$\int_C \mathbf{A}\cdot d\mathbf{l} = \int_C (A_x\,dx + A_y\,dy + A_z\,dz) \tag{2-21}$$

The line integral around a *closed* path C is called the *circulation* of the vector **A**. Hence

$$\text{Circulation of } \mathbf{A} = \oint_C \mathbf{A}\cdot d\mathbf{l} \tag{2-22}$$

The small circle on the integral sign signifies that the path C is closed. The circulation of a vector field **A** about a path in a region may be positive, negative, or zero. In certain special cases the vector field **A** is such that its circulation is zero for every closed path C in a region. If this is the case, the field is said to be a *conservative field*, and the vector **A** is a *conservative vector*. Thus by definition a vector field **A** is conservative, provided the circulation of **A** is zero around every closed path in the region. If a vector field is not conservative, it is said to be *nonconservative*, and the vector is a nonconservative vector.

A conservative field is often called an *irrotational field*, or a *lamellar field*. Usually the term *conservative* is used with reference to fields of force, and the term *irrotational* is used with reference to physical fluids. Examples of conservative fields are the gravitational force field and the electrostatic field. An example of a nonconservative field is the velocity field of the particles on the rim of a rotating wheel, for the line integral of the velocity vector around the rim of the wheel is obviously not zero. Time-changing electric and magnetic fields are nonconservative.

The line integral of a nonconservative vector along a path between two points depends on the actual path of integration. However, if the field is

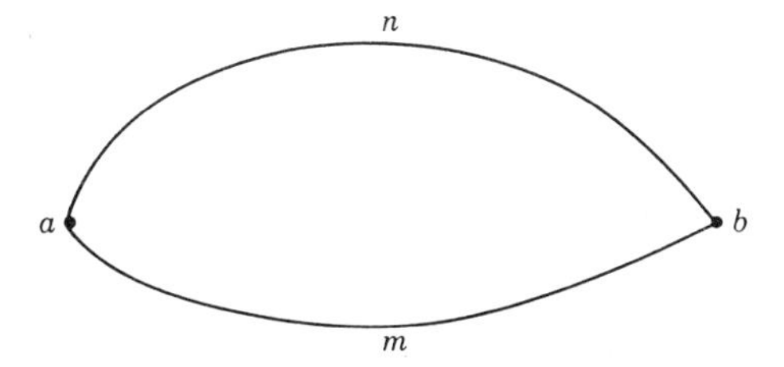

FIG. 2-8. Two arbitrary paths between a and b.

conservative, the value of the line integral is independent of the path of integration, depending only on the end points. To verify this statement, let us refer to the closed path C of Fig. 2-8, assumed to be located in a conservative field $\mathbf{A}$. The line integral of $\mathbf{A}$ along the path *amb* added to the line integral along the path *bna* is zero, for $\mathbf{A}$ has zero circulation. It follows that the line integral along *amb* equals the negative of the line integral along *bna*. Reversing the direction of integration along a path simply changes the sign of the integral. Therefore, the line integrals along the paths *amb* and *anb* are equal. As these paths are arbitrary selections, we deduce that the line integral of $\mathbf{A}$ between the points a and b is the same along all paths connecting the points, provided the field is conservative. *In a conservative field the line integral depends only on the end points of the path and is independent of the actual path of integration.* This is an important deduction that will be utilized frequently.

We shall now consider two examples to help us understand the meaning of the line integral.

EXAMPLE 1. Find the line integral of $\mathbf{A}$ along each side of the square path of Fig. 2-9, in the counterclockwise direction, for $\mathbf{A} = (2 + y)\mathbf{i}$. Also, determine the circulation of $\mathbf{A}$. The length of each side is unity.

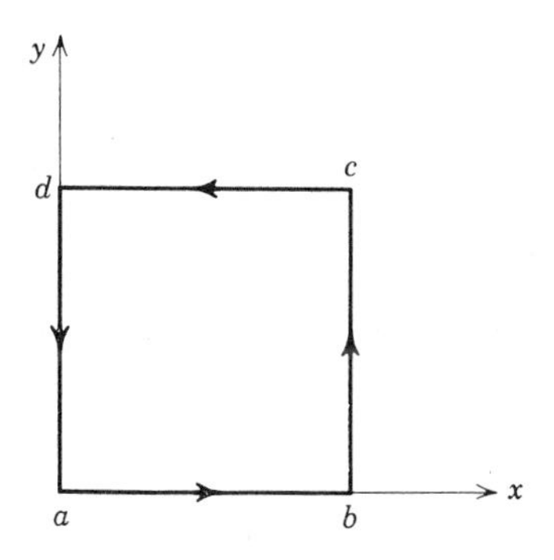

FIG. 2-9. Square path in xy-plane.

Solution.

$$\int_{ab} \mathbf{A} \cdot d\mathbf{l} = \int_0^1 2\, dx = 2$$

$$\int_{bc} \mathbf{A} \cdot d\mathbf{l} = \int_0^1 0\, dy = 0$$

$$\int_{cd} \mathbf{A} \cdot d\mathbf{l} = \int_1^0 3\, dx = -3$$

$$\int_{da} \mathbf{A} \cdot d\mathbf{l} = \int_1^0 0\, dy = 0$$

$$\oint_C \mathbf{A} \cdot d\mathbf{l} = 2 + 0 - 3 + 0 = -1$$

EXAMPLE 2. Evaluate the line integral of $\mathbf{A}$ along the path $x = y^2$ from (0, 0) to (1, 1), for $\mathbf{A} = (x + y^2)\mathbf{i} + (x^2 + y)\mathbf{j}$.

Solution. As $A_x = x + y^2$ and $A_y = x^2 + y$, it follows from Eq. (2-21) that

$$\int_C \mathbf{A} \cdot d\mathbf{l} = \int [(x + y^2)\, dx + (x^2 + y)\, dy]$$

But $x = y^2$ and $dx = 2y\, dy$. Substituting for x and dx and combining terms, we obtain

$$\int_C \mathbf{A} \cdot d\mathbf{l} = \int (y^4 + 4y^3 + y)\, dy$$

The y limits are 0 and 1. Evaluating the integral, we find the value of the line integral to be 1.70.

2-8. SOME SPECIAL INTEGRALS

In rectangular form the differential vector path length $d\mathbf{l}$ is

$$d\mathbf{l} = dx\, \mathbf{i} + dy\, \mathbf{j} + dz\, \mathbf{k}$$

The magnitude dl of the vector $d\mathbf{l}$ is

$$dl = +\sqrt{(dx)^2 + (dy)^2 + (dz)^2}$$

The integral of dl along a path C is simply the summation of the differential path lengths and, therefore, the value of the integral is the length of the path. It should be noted that, by definition, dl is always positive.

Next, let us consider the integral of $d\mathbf{l}$ along a path C. This integral is a summation of differential vectors, and the result is a vector. Obviously, the x component of the result is the integral of dx, and this may be positive, negative, or zero, depending on the x limits. Thus the integral of $d\mathbf{l}$ is a vector, and each component of the vector may be positive, negative, or zero. Occasionally, the integral of $d\mathbf{l}$ around a closed path is encountered. Clearly, each component of the resulting vector is zero, for the limits of integration are identical. The path begins and ends at the same point, and the integrals of dx, dy, and dz are zero. For comparison, the integrals of $d\mathbf{l}$ and dl around a closed path C are given below.

$$\oint_C d\mathbf{l} = 0 \qquad \oint_C dl = \text{length of closed path}$$

Although the differential dl, defined as the positive magnitude of $d\mathbf{l}$, is always positive, the differentials dx, dy, and dz can be positive or negative. For example, dx denotes a differential *increase* in x. When x is increasing, dx is positive, but when x is decreasing, the differential increase dx is negative. When the integral of dx is evaluated around a closed path, the positive and negative differentials cancel, giving zero as the result. A simple example illustrating that dx has negative values is the integral of dx from 1 to 0, which equals -1. This integral is the summation of the differentials dx as x decreases from one to zero, and the result is a negative number. The vector $dx\,\mathbf{i}$ is directed along the positive x-axis if the limits of x are such that x is increasing. On the other hand, *the vector $dx\,\mathbf{i}$ has a direction opposite that of $\mathbf{i}$ if the limits are chosen so that x is decreasing.* It is important that this be clearly understood.

We shall encounter integrals of the form $\int \mathbf{A}\, dl$ along a path C in space. Such an integral is a summation of vectors, and hence the result is a vector. The following examples will help us understand the meaning of integrals of this type.

EXAMPLE 1. If $\mathbf{A} = x^3\mathbf{i} + xy\mathbf{j} + xyz\mathbf{k}$, evaluate $\int \mathbf{A}\, dl$ along the x-axis between the origin and $x = -1$.

Solution. Clearly, $dl = |dx|$. If the limits of x are taken from 0 to -1, dx is negative, and $dl = -dx$. At points on the path of integration, y and z are zero, and $\mathbf{A} = x^3\mathbf{i}$. Therefore,

$$\int_C \mathbf{A}\, dl = -\int_0^{-1} x^3\mathbf{i}\, dx$$

The unit vector $\mathbf{i}$ is a constant that can be taken outside the integral. The result is $-0.25\mathbf{i}$.

EXAMPLE 2. If $\mathbf{A} = x^2\mathbf{i} + xyz\mathbf{j} + 2\mathbf{k}$, evaluate $\oint \mathbf{A}\, dl$ around the circle $x^2 + y^2 = 1$ in the plane $z = 1$.

Solution. As $z = 1$, $\mathbf{A} = x^2\mathbf{i} + xy\mathbf{j} + 2\mathbf{k}$. Also, $dz = 0$, and $dl = [(dx)^2 + (dy)^2]^{1/2}$. From $x^2 + y^2 = 1$, it follows that $dx = -(y/x)\, dy$. Therefore, the differential length dl is

$$dl = \sqrt{(y/x)^2(dy)^2 + (dy)^2} = \sqrt{(x^2 + y^2)(dy/x)^2}$$

As $x^2 + y^2 = 1$, the differential dl is $|dy/x|$, recalling that dl is always positive. The integral becomes

$$\oint_C \mathbf{A}\,dl = \oint_C (x^2\mathbf{i} + xy\mathbf{j} + 2\mathbf{k})\,|dy/x|$$

It is convenient to divide the circle into halves, with one semicircle having x positive and the other semicircle having x negative. First, we shall evaluate the integral along the semicircle with x positive. If we integrate from $y = -1$ to $y = 1$, both dy and x are positive, and $|dy/x| = dy/x$. Also, $x = +\sqrt{1 - y^2}$ at points on this path. Substituting for x and simplifying the result, we obtain

$$\int_{-1}^{1} [(1 - y^2)^{1/2}\mathbf{i} + y\mathbf{j} + 2(1 - y^2)^{-1/2}\mathbf{k}]\,dy$$

Each component can now be integrated, and the result is $0.5\pi\mathbf{i} + 2\pi\mathbf{k}$.

We shall now consider the semicircle with x negative. If we integrate from $y = 1$ to $y = -1$, both dy and x are negative, and $|dy/x| = dy/x$. Also, $x = -\sqrt{1 - y^2}$. Substituting for x and simplifying the result, we obtain

$$\int_{1}^{-1} [-(1 - y^2)^{1/2}\mathbf{i} + y\mathbf{j} - 2(1 - y^2)^{-1/2}\mathbf{k}]\,dy$$

The result of the integration is $0.5\pi\mathbf{i} + 2\pi\mathbf{k}$, as before. It follows that the integral around the closed path of the circle is the vector $\pi\mathbf{i} + 4\pi\mathbf{k}$. An easier method for solving this problem is indicated in Prob. 2-57.

2-9. THE SURFACE INTEGRAL OF A VECTOR

Another important integral which we shall utilize frequently in our study of electromagnetism is the surface integral of a vector. As this involves an integration over a surface in space, let us consider a two-sided surface S in a region containing a vector field $\mathbf{A}$. One side is arbitrarily selected as the positive side. Let ΔS denote a very small planar area tangent to S at a point P. Suppose a unit vector $\mathbf{n}$ is constructed at P normal to ΔS and directed out of the positive side, as shown in Fig. 2-10. If A_n denotes the component of $\mathbf{A}$ in the direction of $\mathbf{n}$ at P, then $A_n\,\Delta S$ is called the *flux* of $\mathbf{A}$ through the elemental area ΔS. The total flux of $\mathbf{A}$ over the entire surface S is found by adding the fluxes of $\mathbf{A}$ over all elemental areas, with each ΔS approaching the limit zero. The limit of the summation, taken over S, is the integral $\int A_n\,dS$, and this integral is called the *surface integral* of the vector $\mathbf{A}$ over S. It is also referred to as the *flux* of the vector $\mathbf{A}$ through the surface S.

The surface integral of $\mathbf{A}$ over S is the summation of the differentials $A_n\,dS$ over the surface. A_n is the component of $\mathbf{A}$ normal to dS, and it is referred to as the normal component of $\mathbf{A}$. In general, A_n varies from point to point over S. At each point A_n is the component of $\mathbf{A}$ in the direction of the unit vector $\mathbf{n}$, which is normal to dS directed out of the positive side. Clearly, A_n at a point may be positive, negative, or zero.

We can express a surface integral in vector notation. A_n is the projection of **A** onto the unit vector **n**. Consequently, $A_n = \mathbf{A} \cdot \mathbf{n}$. It is convenient to treat a differential surface area as a vector quantity $d\mathbf{S}$ of magnitude dS and direction corresponding to that of **n**. Thus $d\mathbf{S} = dS\,\mathbf{n}$, and the concept of a differential vector surface is utilized throughout this text. Several forms of the surface integral of **A** over S are

$$\int_S A_n\,dS = \int_S \mathbf{A} \cdot \mathbf{n}\,dS = \int_S \mathbf{A} \cdot d\mathbf{S} \tag{2-23}$$

The differential vector surface $d\mathbf{S}$ can be resolved into rectangular components. Its x component is the projection of dS upon the yz-plane.

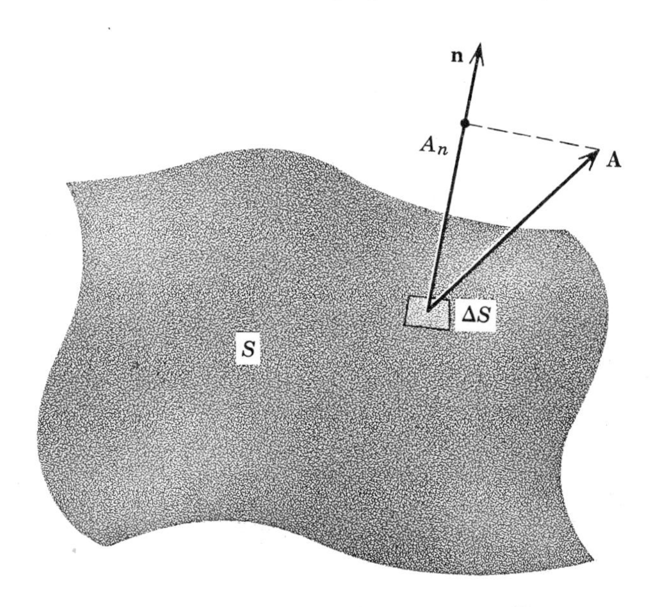

FIG. 2-10. **n** is normal to the element ΔS of S.

Consequently, $dS_x = dy\,dz$. The y and z components of $d\mathbf{S}$ are the projections of dS upon the zx and xy planes, respectively. In rectangular form the vector $d\mathbf{S}$ is

$$d\mathbf{S} = dy\,dz\,\mathbf{i} + dz\,dx\,\mathbf{j} + dx\,dy\,\mathbf{k} \tag{2-24}$$

It follows that

$$\int_S \mathbf{A} \cdot d\mathbf{S} = \iint (A_x\,dy\,dz + A_y\,dz\,dx + A_z\,dx\,dy) \tag{2-25}$$

The surface integral of **A** over a *closed* surface S is denoted by $\oint \mathbf{A} \cdot d\mathbf{S}$. Before a surface integral can be evaluated, one side must be designated as the positive side. However, for a closed surface the outer side is always understood to be the positive side, unless otherwise stated. Therefore, the net outward flux of **A** over the closed surface S is

$$\text{Net outward flux} = \oint_S \mathbf{A} \cdot d\mathbf{S} \tag{2-26}$$

If the integral of Eq. (2-26) is positive, there are *sources* of **A** within the volume bounded by the closed surface S, and these sources produce the field **A**. If the integral of Eq. (2-26) is negative, there are *sinks*, or *negative sources*, of **A** within the volume, and these sinks absorb and destroy **A**. When both sources and sinks are present within the volume, the integral of Eq. (2-26) gives a measure of their algebraically combined strength.

A vector field **A** in a region having no sources or sinks is said to be a *solenoidal field*, and the vector **A** is a *solenoidal vector*. The name comes from the similarity of such fields to the magnetic field about an electric solenoid. As a solenoidal field contains no sources or sinks, the integral of Eq. (2-26) is zero over every closed surface S in the region. For each closed surface the flux that enters equals the flux that leaves, and the net flux is zero. An example of a solenoidal field is the velocity field of an incompressible fluid. The magnetic field is always solenoidal, and the electric field is solenoidal in any region free of charge. However, the electric field in a region containing electric charge is *nonsolenoidal*, for the charges act as sources of the field.

The importance of the concept of a surface integral cannot be overemphasized. To help the student understand the meaning of the surface integral, two illustrative examples are presented below. Additional problems are given at the end of this chapter.

EXAMPLE 1. An electric charge q produces a vector field **D** in the region surrounding the charge. At an arbitrary point P a distance r from the charge q it can be shown that $\mathbf{D} = q/(4\pi r^2)\,\mathbf{a}_r$, with $\mathbf{a}_r$ denoting a unit vector at P directed away from q. Find the flux of **D** over a spherical surface of radius a.

Solution. The outward flux of **D** is

$$\oint_S \mathbf{D} \cdot d\mathbf{S} = \oint_S \frac{q}{4\pi r^2}\,\mathbf{a}_r \cdot \mathbf{n}\,dS$$

But $\mathbf{a}_r \cdot \mathbf{n} = 1$, and $r = a$. Therefore, the flux becomes $q/(4\pi a^2)$ multiplied by the surface integral of dS over the spherical surface. This integral is the area $4\pi a^2$ of the sphere. It follows that the outward flux of **D** is equal to q. This result shows that an electric charge q is a source of electric flux, with the flux leaving q equal to q. If q is negative, the outward flux is, of course, also negative, and the charge is a negative source, or sink.

EXAMPLE 2. If $\mathbf{A} = xyz\mathbf{i} - y\mathbf{j} - x\mathbf{k}$, find the flux of **A** over the surface of the cube of Fig. 2-11. The length of each side of the cube is unity.

Solution. As the surface of the cube is a closed surface, its outer side is the positive side. Each side of the cube will be treated separately, and the results will be added.

At points on the back side *oafe*, the normal component of **A** is $-A_x$, or $-xyz$. As $x = 0$, $A_x = 0$, and the outward flux over this side is zero.

At points on the front surface *cbgd*, $A_x = xyz = yz$, for $x = 1$. The outward flux is

$$\int_0^1 \int_0^1 A_x \, dy \, dz = \int_0^1 y \, dy \int_0^1 z \, dz = 0.25$$

At the surface *oedc* on the left side of the cube, $A_y = -y = 0$, and the flux of **A** is zero.

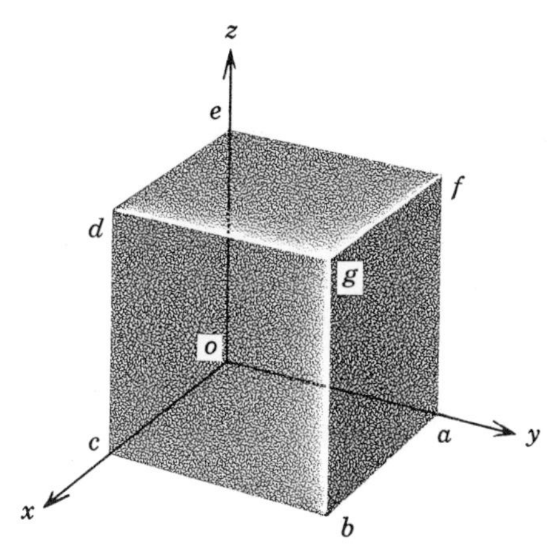

FIG. 2-11. Unit cube.

At the surface *afgb* on the right side, $A_y = -y = -1$. The outward flux is

$$\int_0^1 \int_0^1 -1 \, dz \, dx = -1.00$$

At points on the bottom surface, a differential vector surface $d\mathbf{S}$ is $-dx\,dy\,\mathbf{k}$, with the limits of integration selected so that the product $dx\,dy$ is positive. Clearly, $\mathbf{A} \cdot d\mathbf{S} = x\,dx\,dy$, and the outward flux is

$$\int_0^1 \int_0^1 x \, dx \, dy = 0.50$$

For the top surface, a differential vector surface $d\mathbf{S}$ is $dx\,dy\,\mathbf{k}$, with $dx\,dy$ positive. The scalar product $\mathbf{A} \cdot d\mathbf{S}$ is $-x\,dx\,dy$, and the outward flux is the negative of the flux over the bottom surface, or -0.50.

The net outward flux of **A** over the closed surface of the cube is $0.25 - 1.00 + 0.50 - 0.50$, or -0.75. As the outward flux is negative, there are negative sources, or sinks, of **A** within the volume of the cube. The net *inward* flux is $+0.75$, and the sink strength is also 0.75.

2-10. THE RIGHT-HAND INTEGRATION RULE

The fundamental electromagnetic laws, which will be studied later, equate line and surface integrals. The closed path C around the edge of a surface S is the *boundary path*, or *contour*, of the surface. The basic electromagnetic equations have the general form

$$\oint_C \mathbf{A} \cdot d\mathbf{l} = \int_S \mathbf{B} \cdot d\mathbf{S} \tag{2-27}$$

with C denoting the contour of the surface S.

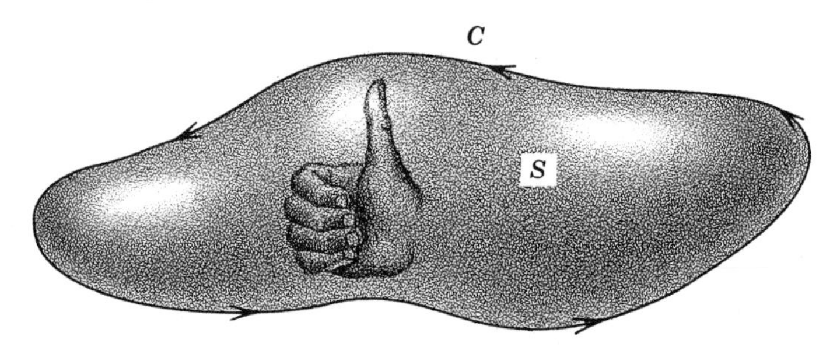

FIG. 2-12. The right-hand integration rule.

In evaluating a surface integral, one side of the surface is arbitrarily designated as positive. The question then arises as to the way the line integral around C is to be evaluated. There are two ways to traverse the path. The circulation of **A** around C in one direction is, of course, the negative of the circulation of **A** around C in the other direction. Consequently, we need a rule regarding the direction to be selected. This rule will now be given.

First, we arbitrarily designate one side of the surface S as positive. Next, we imagine an observer standing on the positive side of S at the boundary C. Now suppose the observer moves around the contour C so as to keep the surface area on his left. This is the direction of integration for the line integral. The rule can be stated in a single sentence. The direction of integration for the line integral is always taken as that direction in which an observer, on the designated positive side of the surface S, must move around C so as to keep the surface area on his left. Whenever a line and a surface integral are equated, as in Eq. (2-27), this rule must be carefully observed.

It is quite helpful to associate the integration rule with one's right hand. We note that, if the right hand is oriented with its extended thumb pointing out of the positive side of the surface, the curled fingers indicate the direction of integration around C, as shown in Fig. 2-12. Consequently, this rule shall henceforth be referred to as the *right-hand integration rule.*

As an example, suppose the surface S is the surface of this page. The contour C is the closed path around the outside edges of this page. Selecting the side facing the reader as the positive side of S, the line integral must be taken in a counterclockwise direction. If the under side of the page is selected as the positive side, the line integral is taken in the opposite direction. In this latter case the signs of both the line and surface integrals differ from the signs of the corresponding integrals in the former case. Regardless of the selection of the positive side, Eq. (2-27) is unchanged.

The student who has mastered the mathematics of this chapter is well prepared for the study of the material of the next seven chapters. The branch of mathematics known as *vector analysis* is discussed in Chapter 10, and the mathematics of *complex exponentials* is discussed in Chapter 19.

REFERENCES

Hayt, W. H. Jr., *Engineering Electromagnetics*, McGraw-Hill Book Co., New York, 1958, Chap. 1.

Heaviside, O., *Electromagnetic Theory*, Dover Publications, New York, 1950, Chap. III of Vol. I. Contains an interesting discussion of the historical introduction of vector methods.

Hildebrand, F. B., *Advanced Calculus for Engineers*, Prentice-Hall, Englewood Cliffs, N.J., 1949, Chap. 6.

Newell, H. E. Jr., *Vector Analysis*, McGraw-Hill Book Co., New York, 1955, Chaps. 1, 2, 3.

Rogers, W. E., *Introduction to Electric Fields*, McGraw-Hill Book Co., New York, 1954, Chap. 1.

Spiegel, M. R., *Vector Analysis*, Schaum Publishing Co., New York, 1959, Chaps. 1, 2, 3.

PROBLEMS

Sections 2-1 *and* 2-2

2-1. If $\mathbf{A} = (3, -4, -2)$ and $\mathbf{B} = (-4, -1, 6)$, determine A, B, $\mathbf{A} + \mathbf{B}$, $-\mathbf{B}$, $\mathbf{A} - \mathbf{B}$, $|\mathbf{A} - \mathbf{B}|$, and $10\mathbf{A} - 4\mathbf{B}$.

2-2. Repeat Prob. 2-1 for $\mathbf{A} = (5, 2, -7)$ and $\mathbf{B} = (-5, 3, 4)$.

2-3. Repeat Prob. 2-1 for $\mathbf{A} = 2\mathbf{i} + 6\mathbf{j} - 4\mathbf{k}$ and $\mathbf{B} = 3\mathbf{i} + 6\mathbf{j} + \mathbf{k}$.

2-4. $\mathbf{A} = 3\mathbf{i} + 5\mathbf{j}$ and $\mathbf{B} = -3\mathbf{i} - 5\mathbf{j}$. (*a*) On a set of xy coordinates, sketch $\mathbf{A}$ and $\mathbf{B}$ to scale, with both vectors drawn from the origin. (*b*) What is the relationship between $\mathbf{A}$ and $\mathbf{B}$? (*c*) Determine the smaller angle between $\mathbf{A}$ and $\mathbf{i}$ and also between $\mathbf{B}$ and $\mathbf{i}$.

2-5. $\mathbf{A} = 2\mathbf{i} - 3\mathbf{j}$ and $\mathbf{B} = 3\mathbf{i} + 4\mathbf{j}$. Sketch the vectors and determine the smaller angle between $\mathbf{A}$ and $\mathbf{B}$.

2-6. Sketch any two vectors $\mathbf{A}$ and $\mathbf{B}$. Draw $\mathbf{A}$, $\mathbf{B}$, and $\mathbf{A} + \mathbf{B}$ so as to form a triangle, and repeat for $\mathbf{A}$, $-\mathbf{B}$, and $\mathbf{A} - \mathbf{B}$.

2-7. Verify that the vectors $\mathbf{A}$, $\mathbf{B}$, and $\mathbf{C}$ can be drawn to form a triangle, if $\mathbf{A} = 2\mathbf{i} + 6\mathbf{j} - 3\mathbf{k}$, $\mathbf{B} = -2\mathbf{i} - 2\mathbf{j} - 2\mathbf{k}$, and $\mathbf{C} = 4\mathbf{j} - 5\mathbf{k}$.

2-8. A vector **r** at the point $P(x, y, z)$, with magnitude equal to the distance from the origin to the point, is directed radially outward from the origin. Sketch the vector **r** at P, and show that $\mathbf{r} = x\mathbf{i} + y\mathbf{j} + z\mathbf{k}$. Also, at the point P find the rectangular form of the unit vector $\mathbf{a}_r$ in the direction of **r**.

2-9. The tail of a vector **A** is at the point (0, 1, 2), and its tip is at the point (1, 2, −3). Find **A** in terms of the unit vectors **i**, **j**, and **k**.

2-10. Find the direction cosines and the direction angles α, β, γ of the vector $\mathbf{A} = 2\mathbf{i} + 4\mathbf{j} - 3\mathbf{k}$.

2-11. Repeat Prob. 2-10 for $\mathbf{A} = -5\mathbf{i} + 6\mathbf{k}$.

2-12. A vector **A** has $A = 10$, and **A** makes angles of 30° and 110° with the unit vectors **i** and **j** respectively. Find **A**, assuming that A_z is negative.

2-13. Prove that $l^2 + m^2 + n^2 = 1$, where l, m, and n are the direction cosines of a vector.

2-14. Determine the unit vector **a** in the direction of the vector $\mathbf{A} = 5\mathbf{i} - 5\mathbf{j} + 10\mathbf{k}$. Express **a** in terms of **i**, **j**, and **k**.

Section 2-3

2-15. $\mathbf{A} = 3\mathbf{i} - 4\mathbf{j} - 2\mathbf{k}$ and $\mathbf{B} = 5\mathbf{i} - 3\mathbf{j} + 4\mathbf{k}$. (*a*) Determine $\mathbf{A} \cdot \mathbf{B}$ and $\mathbf{B} \cdot \mathbf{A}$. (*b*) Find the smaller angle between **A** and **B**, using Eq. (2-4). (*c*) What is the component of **A** in the direction of **B**? (*d*) What is the component of **B** in the direction of **A**?

2-16. Repeat Prob. 2-15 if $\mathbf{A} = 6\mathbf{i} + 10\mathbf{j} - 5\mathbf{k}$ and $\mathbf{B} = -3\mathbf{i} - 2\mathbf{j} + 4\mathbf{k}$.

2-17. Prove that $\mathbf{A} \cdot \mathbf{B}$ equals AB if **A** and **B** are parallel vectors, and prove that $\mathbf{A} \cdot \mathbf{B}$ is zero if **A** and **B** are perpendicular vectors.

2-18. If $\mathbf{A} = -4\mathbf{i} + 2\mathbf{j} - 7\mathbf{k}$, determine $\mathbf{A} \cdot \mathbf{A}$.

2-19. If $\mathbf{A} = -4\mathbf{i} + 5\mathbf{j} + 10\mathbf{k}$, determine $\mathbf{A}^2$.

2-20. $\mathbf{A} = 3\mathbf{i} - 2\mathbf{j} + 5\mathbf{k}$ and $\mathbf{B} = 2\mathbf{i} + 8\mathbf{j} + 2\mathbf{k}$. Show that **A** and **B** are perpendicular to each other.

2-21. If $\mathbf{A} \cdot \mathbf{C} = \mathbf{B} \cdot \mathbf{C}$, discuss the relationship between **A** and **B**.

2-22. $\mathbf{A} \cdot \mathbf{i} = 10$, $\mathbf{A} \cdot \mathbf{j} = -5$, and $\mathbf{A} \cdot \mathbf{k} = 2$. Find **A**.

2-23. $\mathbf{A} = 5\mathbf{i} + 4\mathbf{j} - 6\mathbf{k}$. Find a vector **B** parallel to the xy-plane, having a magnitude of 8, such that $\mathbf{A} \cdot \mathbf{B} = 0$. There are two possible answers.

2-24. The direction cosines (l, m, n) of two vectors **A** and **B** are (0.6, 0.8, 0) and $(\frac{2}{3}, -\frac{2}{3}, \frac{1}{3})$, respectively. Determine the smaller angle between the vectors.

Sections 2-4 *and* 2-5

2-25. $\mathbf{A} = 5\mathbf{i} - 3\mathbf{j} - 2\mathbf{k}$ and $\mathbf{B} = 2\mathbf{i} - 4\mathbf{j} + 4\mathbf{k}$. Determine $\mathbf{A} \times \mathbf{B}$, $\mathbf{B} \times \mathbf{A}$, $|\mathbf{A} \times \mathbf{B}|$, $\sin\theta$, θ, and the unit vector **n** in the direction of $\mathbf{A} \times \mathbf{B}$. The angle θ is the smaller angle between the two vectors.

2-26. Repeat Prob. 2-25 for $\mathbf{A} = -3\mathbf{i} + 6\mathbf{j} - 4\mathbf{k}$ and $\mathbf{B} = \mathbf{i} - 5\mathbf{j} - 2\mathbf{k}$.

2-27. If $\mathbf{A} = 4\mathbf{i} - 3\mathbf{j} - 4\mathbf{k}$ and $\mathbf{B} = -2\mathbf{i} - 5\mathbf{j} - 2\mathbf{k}$, evaluate $\mathbf{A} \times \mathbf{B}$, $(\mathbf{A} \times \mathbf{B}) \cdot \mathbf{B}$, and $(\mathbf{A} \times \mathbf{B}) \cdot \mathbf{A}$.

2-28. $\mathbf{A} = 3\mathbf{i} + 4\mathbf{j}$ and $\mathbf{B} = -2\mathbf{i} - 5\mathbf{j}$. What are the directions of the vectors $\mathbf{A} \times \mathbf{B}$ and $\mathbf{B} \times \mathbf{A}$?

2-29. $\mathbf{A} = 4\mathbf{i} + 6\mathbf{j} - 5\mathbf{k}$ and $\mathbf{B} = -12\mathbf{i} - 18\mathbf{j} + 15\mathbf{k}$. Evaluate $\mathbf{A} \times \mathbf{B}$. What does the result indicate regarding the directions of **A** and **B**?

2-30. $\mathbf{A} = 3\mathbf{i} - 2\mathbf{j} + 4\mathbf{k}$, $\mathbf{B} = 6\mathbf{i} + 5\mathbf{j} - 2\mathbf{k}$, and $\mathbf{C} = -5\mathbf{i} - 3\mathbf{j} + 6\mathbf{k}$. Determine: (*a*) $\mathbf{A} \times (\mathbf{B} \times \mathbf{C})$; (*b*) $(\mathbf{A} \times \mathbf{B}) \times \mathbf{C}$; (*c*) $\mathbf{A} \cdot (\mathbf{B} \times \mathbf{C})$; (*d*) $(\mathbf{A} \times \mathbf{B}) \cdot \mathbf{B}$.

2-31. Repeat Prob. 2-30 for $\mathbf{A} = 5\mathbf{i} - 2\mathbf{j} - 4\mathbf{k}$, $\mathbf{B} = -3\mathbf{i} - 5\mathbf{j} + 6\mathbf{k}$, and $\mathbf{C} = 3\mathbf{i} + 5\mathbf{j} + 4\mathbf{k}$.

2-32. If the vectors **A** and **B** of Prob. 2-30 form two edges of a parallelogram, find the area of the parallelogram.

2-33. If the vectors **A**, **B**, and **C** of Prob. 2-31 form three edges of a parallelepiped, what is the volume?

2-34. Verify Eq. (2-11) by expressing **A**, **B**, and **C** in rectangular form and expanding the terms.

Section 2-6

2-35. At a point in space $\mathbf{A}(t) = 3t^2\mathbf{i} + t\mathbf{j} - \mathbf{k}$, where t represents time. (*a*) Find the precise values of **A** at $t = 1$ and also at $t = 1.01$. (*b*) If $\Delta\mathbf{A}$ represents the increase in **A** as t increases from 1 to 1.01, determine $\Delta\mathbf{A}$. (*c*) Calculate $\Delta\mathbf{A}/\Delta t$. (*d*) Evaluate $d\mathbf{A}/dt$ at $t = 1$. Is this exactly equal to $\Delta\mathbf{A}/\Delta t$? Explain. (*e*) Find the smaller angle between the vectors **A** and $d\mathbf{A}/dt$, when $t = 1$.

2-36. $\mathbf{A} = xyz\mathbf{i} + x^2\mathbf{j} + yz^2\mathbf{k}$. Evaluate $\partial\mathbf{A}/\partial x$ at $(x, y, z) = (1, 2, 3)$. Determine the smaller angle between **A** and $\partial\mathbf{A}/\partial x$ at the specified point.

2-37. Find $\partial\mathbf{A}/\partial y$ if $\mathbf{A} = (x + y^2)\mathbf{i} + (x^2z + y)\mathbf{j} + x^2yz\mathbf{k}$.

2-38. If each of the components of a vector **A** varies sinusoidally with time, with each component containing the term $\sin \omega t$, show that $\ddot{\mathbf{A}} = -\omega^2\mathbf{A}$.

2-39. If $\mathbf{A} = (2 + 4t)\mathbf{i} + (8 - 5t)\mathbf{j} + (1 + t - 8t^2)\mathbf{k}$, find $\dot{\mathbf{A}}$ and $\ddot{\mathbf{A}}$.

2-40. If $\mathbf{A} = 3 \sin 100t\, \mathbf{i} + 5 \sin 100t\, \mathbf{j} - 10 \sin 100t\, \mathbf{k}$, show that **A** and $\dot{\mathbf{A}}$ are in the same or opposite directions at every instant of time.

2-41. Verify Eq. (2-16).

2-42. Verify Eq. (2-17).

2-43. Verify Eq. (2-18).

2-44. Verify Eq. (2-19).

Sections 2-7 and 2-8

2-45. If the line integral $\int_C \mathbf{A} \cdot d\mathbf{l}$ is evaluated along the x-axis, show that $d\mathbf{l} = dx\, \mathbf{i}$ for both increasing and decreasing values of x. On the other hand, when the integral $\int_C \mathbf{A}\, dl$ is evaluated along the x-axis, show that $dl = \pm dx$, with the sign depending on whether or not x is increasing or decreasing.

2-46. If $\mathbf{A} = 3\mathbf{i}$, evaluate the line integral of **A** along the x-axis from (*a*) $x = 0$ to $x = 2$, and (*b*) $x = 5$ to $x = 1$.

2-47. If $\mathbf{A} = 5\mathbf{i}$, evaluate the line integral of **A** (*a*) along the x-axis from the origin to $x = -5$ and back to the origin; and (*b*) along the y-axis from the origin to $y = 4$.

2-48. Evaluate the line integral of **A** along each side of the unit square of Fig. 2-9, in the counterclockwise direction, if $\mathbf{A} = (4 + x^2)\mathbf{i} + xy\mathbf{j}$.

2-49. Evaluate the line integral of **A** along the path $x = y^3$ from (0, 0) to (1, 1) if $\mathbf{A} = (x + y^2)\mathbf{i} + (x^2 + y^2)\mathbf{j}$.

2-50. Evaluate the circulation of **A** around the circle $x = \cos t$, $y = \sin t$, if

$\mathbf{A} = 5y\mathbf{i} + 2x\mathbf{j}$. There are two possible answers, depending on the direction of integration.

2-51. The radius vector **r** at the point (x, y, z) is directed radially outward from the origin of the coordinate system, with magnitude equal to the distance from the origin to the point. Using Eq. (2-21), evaluate the line integral of **r** from the origin to the point (1, 1, 1). Does the path of integration affect the result? What kind of field is the vector field of **r**?

2-52. The circulation of **A** around a circular path of radius 2 is equal to 10. Along the path the magnitude of **A** is constant and the direction of **A** corresponds to the direction of $d\mathbf{l}$ at each point. Determine A. What is the circulation of **A** about the path if the direction of integration is reversed?

2-53. At a point P, $\mathbf{A} = (1/r^2)\mathbf{a}_r$. The distance r is the distance from the origin of the coordinate system to P, and $\mathbf{a}_r$ is a unit vector along r, directed radially outward. Find the line integral of **A** along r, (*a*) from $r = 1$ to $r = 10$; and (*b*) from $r = 100$ to $r = 10$. In both cases note that $d\mathbf{l} = dr\,\mathbf{a}_r$, as dr is positive when r is increasing and dr is negative when r is decreasing.

2-54. Evaluate both $\oint_C d\mathbf{l}$ and $\oint_C dl$ around a circle of radius 4.

2-55. Evaluate both $\int_C dx$ and $\int_C dl$ along the x-axis from $x = 1$ to $x = 0$ and explain the difference between the two integrals.

2-56. $\mathbf{A} = x^2\mathbf{i} + xy\mathbf{j} + xyz\mathbf{k}$. Evaluate $\int_C \mathbf{A}\,dl$ along the x-axis between the origin and $x = -5$.

2-57. If $\mathbf{A} = x^2\mathbf{i} + xyz\mathbf{j} + 2\mathbf{k}$, evaluate $\oint_C \mathbf{A}\,dl$ around the circle $x = \cos t$, $y = \sin t$ in the plane $z = 1$. Solve this problem by expressing **A** and dl in terms of the parameter t.

Sections 2-9 and 2-10

2-58. If $\mathbf{A} = 2\mathbf{i}$, find the flux of **A** over a unit area of a plane surface that is (*a*) normal to the x-axis at $x = 1$; and (*b*) normal to the y-axis at $y = 1$. The positive sides of the surfaces are the sides away from the origin.

2-59. A spherical surface of radius 5 has its center at $r = 0$. If $\mathbf{A} = 1/(4\pi r^2)\,\mathbf{a}_r$, determine the flux of **A** over the spherical surface. What is the source strength of **A** inside the sphere?

2-60. If $\mathbf{A} = 3\mathbf{i} + 4\mathbf{j} - z^2\mathbf{k}$, find the flux of **A** over the surface of the unit cube of Fig. 2-11.

2-61. Repeat Prob. 2-60 with $\mathbf{A} = xyz^2\mathbf{i} - y^2\mathbf{j} - x^2\mathbf{k}$.

2-62. Suppose that Eq. (2-27) applies to any surface in space. When applied to the northern hemisphere of the earth with the contour C being the equator, state whether the circulation of **A** around the equator should be taken eastwardly or westwardly. The upper side of the earth's surface is taken as the positive side. Repeat for the surface of the southern hemisphere. By adding the surface integrals over the northern and southern halves of the earth, show that the flux of **B** over the entire surface of the earth must be zero.

2-63. If two vectors **A** and **B** satisfy Eq. (2-27) where S is any two-sided surface, show that the flux of **B** is zero if the surface S is closed.

Concepts and Units

CHAPTER 3

3-1. SPACE, MASS, TIME, AND CHARGE

A *fundamental concept* of a physical quantity is one not defined in terms of simpler concepts. In mechanics it is usually convenient to regard as fundamental the concepts of *space* (*length*), *mass*, and *time*. In order to measure length, mass, and time, a *unit* of measure must be selected for each. These units can, of course, be selected arbitrarily. In the mks (meter-kilogram-second) system the meter is the unit of length, the kilogram is the unit of mass, and the second is the unit of time. These are called *fundamental units*.

The *meter* is officially defined by the National Bureau of Standards as a length equal to 1,650,763.73 wavelengths of the orange-red radiation in vacuum of krypton 86, a rare gas extracted from the atmosphere. The *kilogram* is defined as the mass of a certain platinum-iridium body kept at the National Bureau of Standards, and the *second* is 1/31,556,925.9747 of the tropical year 1900. Active research is being pursued with the view of enabling the adoption of a definition of the second based on an atomic standard.

For our study of the science of electricity and magnetism we shall select a fourth fundamental concept,* and *electric charge* q appears to be a logical choice. Electric charge cannot be conveniently defined in terms of

* It is not necessary that four fundamental concepts be chosen. See W. K. H. Panofsky and M. Phillips, *Classical Electricity and Magnetism*, Addison-Wesley Publishing Co., Reading, Mass., 1955, Appendix 1.

space, mass, or time. Some of the basic properties of charge were mentioned in the historical sketch of Chapter 1, and these will be discussed more fully in the development of the mathematical theory. The sign of charge q is not restricted. As the early electrical experimenters observed, q may be either positive or negative. The fundamental unit of charge is the *coulomb*, which is the charge of 6.25×10^{18} electrons. As the coulomb is legally defined in terms of its magnetic properties when in motion, this definition is given later, at the end of Sec. 8-5.

Thus for this presentation of the science of electromagnetism, the fundamental concepts are selected as length, mass, time, and electric charge. The units of measure are the meter, kilogram, second, and coulomb, and the system of units that is used is known as the *mks* (*rationalized*) *system*.

In addition to the fundamental concepts we shall use many *secondary*, or *derived*, concepts. These are defined in terms of fundamental concepts and other secondary concepts. Each secondary concept can be expressed dimensionally in terms of length L, mass M, time T, and charge Q, and the secondary units can be defined in terms of the fundamental units. An example of a secondary concept is velocity, which has the dimensions L/T and the mks unit of meter-per-second.

Whenever a general equation is written, both sides must have the same dimensions. If the equation involves terms that are added to one another, each of the terms must have the same dimensions, or otherwise the equation is not generally correct. The dimensional check of an equation is frequently helpful in detecting errors. However, the fact that an equation checks dimensionally is not proof that it is correct. The dimensional check is a necessary, but not a sufficient, condition for correctness.

3-2. SECONDARY MECHANICAL UNITS

Electromagnetic fields exert forces on electric charges and currents, and they store, propagate, and dissipate energy. Consequently, a study of electromagnetism requires a knowledge of the fundamentals of mechanics. Let us now review the definitions of some especially important mechanical concepts, with dimensions in terms of L, M, and T given in brackets.

Velocity $\mathbf{v}$ is defined by

$$\mathbf{v} = d\mathbf{l}/dt \text{ m/sec } [L/T] \tag{3-1}$$

Velocity is a vector quantity, having both magnitude and direction.

Acceleration $\mathbf{a}$ is defined by

$$\mathbf{a} = d\mathbf{v}/dt \text{ m/sec}^2 \ [L/T^2] \tag{3-2}$$

Clearly, acceleration equals the second derivative of length $\mathbf{l}$ with respect to time.

The *momentum* $\mathbf{p}$ of a body is defined as the product of the mass m and the velocity $\mathbf{v}$. Thus

$$\mathbf{p} = m\mathbf{v} \text{ kg-m/sec } [LM/T] \tag{3-3}$$

A *force* that acts on a body causes a change in its momentum. Force is defined as the time rate of change of momentum. Its dimensions are those of momentum divided by time, or LM/T^2, and its mks unit is the *newton.* Mathematically

$$\mathbf{F} = d\mathbf{p}/dt \text{ newtons } [LM/T^2] \tag{3-4}$$

If the mass of a body is invariant with time, this becomes

$$\mathbf{F} = m\mathbf{a} \tag{3-5}$$

This is valid, of course, only if the mass m is constant. We note that a force of one newton is required to accelerate a kilogram of mass at the rate of one meter per second per second. A newton is equivalent to 10^5 dynes and is approximately equal to 0.225 pound of force.

When a force acts on a body, causing it to move through a distance, work is performed. In fact, *work* or *energy* can be defined in terms of the action of a force. If the body moves in a direction other than that of the applied force, only the component of the force in the direction of motion should be considered. Suppose a body that is acted upon by a force $\mathbf{F}$ moves through a differential vector distance $d\mathbf{l}$. The differential work dW done by the force is $F \cos \theta \, dl$, with θ denoting the angle between the vectors $\mathbf{F}$ and $d\mathbf{l}$. In vector notation $dW = \mathbf{F} \cdot d\mathbf{l}$. The work done by the force when the body moves along some path C is

$$W = \int_C \mathbf{F} \cdot d\mathbf{l} \text{ joules } [L^2M/T^2] \tag{3-6}$$

Thus work is defined as the line integral of force, with dimensions of force times distance. Its mks unit is the *joule*, and one joule of energy is expended when a force of one newton acts through a distance of one meter.

In order for energy to be expended, a source of *power* p is required. Suppose a small amount of work ΔW is done in the elemental time Δt. The ratio $\Delta W/\Delta t$ is the average work per unit time, in joules per second, during the time interval Δt. The limit of this ratio as Δt approaches zero is the work per unit time at a particular instant, and this is the instantaneous power. Power has dimensions of work divided by time, or L^2M/T^3, and its mks unit is the *watt*. Clearly, one watt represents an energy expenditure of one joule per second. Mathematically

$$p = dW/dt \text{ watts } [L^2M/T^3] \tag{3-7}$$

A watt corresponds to a joule per second. Therefore, a joule denotes the energy expended in one second when the power is one watt. Accordingly, a watt-second is a unit of energy equivalent to a joule. A *kilowatt-hour* is a unit of energy extensively employed in electrical power engineering.

3-3. KINETIC ENERGY

According to relativity theory, the mass m of a body moving with velocity v is

$$m = m_0(1 - v^2/c^2)^{-1/2} \tag{3-8}$$

with m_0 denoting the *rest mass* of the body and c denoting the velocity of light in free space, which is approximately 3×10^8 m/sec.

Suppose a force $\mathbf{F} = F\mathbf{i}$ is applied to a stationary mass m that is perfectly free to move. The mass accelerates in the x-direction, acquiring a velocity $\mathbf{v}$ and a momentum $m\mathbf{v}$. As force is the time rate of change of momentum, it follows from this and Eq. (3-8) that

$$F = m_0(1 - v^2/c^2)^{-3/2}\,(dv/dt)$$

The energy expended by the force equals the line integral of $\mathbf{F}$, and this energy is converted into kinetic energy K. Therefore, the kinetic energy of the accelerating mass is

$$K = \int m_0(1 - v^2/c^2)^{-3/2}\,(dv/dt)\,dx$$

As $dx/dt = v$, this can be written in terms of the variable v, giving

$$K = \int m_0 v(1 - v^2/c^2)^{-3/2}\,dv$$

By integrating from zero to v and utilizing Eq. (3-8), we obtain

$$K = c^2(m - m_0) \tag{3-9}$$

The kinetic energy of a mass moving with velocity v is $c^2(\Delta m)$, with Δm denoting the increase $(m - m_0)$ in the mass due to its velocity. If $v = c$, the mass m is infinite, and the kinetic energy is also infinite. Clearly, no massive object can go that fast.

The expression for K can be converted into another useful form. From Eqs. (3-8) and (3-9) it follows that

$$K = m_0c^2[(1 - v^2/c^2)^{-1/2} - 1]$$

Application of the binomial expansion to the term in parentheses gives

$$K = m_0c^2(\tfrac{1}{2}v^2/c^2 + \tfrac{3}{8}v^4/c^4 + \cdots)$$

For values of v/c small compared with unity, this becomes

$$K \approx \tfrac{1}{2}m_0v^2 \tag{3-10}$$

In conclusion, the kinetic energy of a mass m moving with velocity v is exactly $c^2(m - m_0)$, and this is approximately equal to $\frac{1}{2}m_0v^2$ provided $v \ll c$.

Of special interest is the case of the photon. The velocity v of a photon is c. From Eq. (3-8) we deduce that the rest mass m_0 of a photon is zero, for otherwise its mass m would be infinite. As m_0 is zero, the kinetic energy of a photon is mc^2.

3-4. CONSERVATION OF CHARGE, ENERGY, AND MASS

The early electrical experimenters found that the two kinds of electric charge are always created in equal amounts. By giving unlike signs to these two kinds of charge, we can state that *a net charge is neither created nor destroyed.* When equal positive and negative charges are combined, the effects of both disappear. However, the conservation law is not violated, for the *net* charge is zero before and after combination. In Sec. 11-1 it is shown that the conservation of charge is a logical consequence of the fundamental electromagnetic laws.

The kinetic energy of an object depends on its mass, and we know from relativity theory that this mass varies with velocity. Even the rest mass of a body is not invariable. For example, the rest mass of an object may increase during an inelastic collision, with a corresponding decrease in the kinetic energy of the object. The conversion between mass and energy is given by $W = mc^2$, with W denoting the energy of the mass m. A fundamental law of physics is the conservation of energy, with the understanding that mass is a form of energy. Energy can be transformed from one form to another, but in this transformation process it is neither created nor destroyed. The total energy of any closed system remains constant.

Whenever an object is moving with a velocity considerably less than the velocity c of light, its mass is approximately equal to its rest mass. For example, at a velocity of $0.1c$, which is over 18,000 miles per second, the increase in the mass is only one-half of one per cent. In this book mass is treated as though it is conserved, an assumption that places a restriction on some of the equations to be presented. Equations that are so restricted must be modified by relativity theory when applied to particles moving with velocities near the speed of light.

In this presentation of nonrelativistic electromagnetism we assume, without proof, that charge, energy, and mass are conserved. In fact, experimental proof is impossible, for the conservation laws are too comprehensive for direct verification. They are based on innumerable observations that support their validity for macroscopic phenomena not involving objects moving at high speeds. Thus the conservation laws are *postulates*.

In Chapter 8 we shall, in addition, postulate the general laws of electromagnetic induction, also based on countless observations. We then proceed to deduce from the postulates the many specific and useful electromagnetic relations that can be verified directly by experiment, often referred to as *experimental laws*. This is the essence of the *scientific method.*

In the next section and in Chapters 4, 5, 6, and 7 we shall consider the definitions of many secondary electrical concepts. Occasionally, an experimental law will be mentioned, but *only for the purpose of clarifying a definition.* However, after the remaining postulates have been presented in Chapter 8, we shall rather rigorously derive the many electromagnetic equations so useful to the engineer and scientist. It is hoped that the student will carefully note the logical development of electromagnetic field theory by the scientific method.

3-5. ELECTRIC CHARGE DENSITY

In mechanics the concept of mass density is quite useful. We frequently refer to the mass density at a point. Actually, we know that mass is not distributed throughout all the space of a region within a solid. Rather it is concentrated into particles, such as protons, neutrons, and electrons, and these particles are separated by space. However, if our "point" is considered to occupy a volume that is very small with respect to the important dimensions of the particular problem but large compared with the atomic dimensions, then this point contains large numbers of the elementary particles. In this case the discrete nature of these particles is not significant, and the assumption of a continuous mass density is valid from an engineering viewpoint.

In a similar manner the concept of a *charge density* is a valid and useful one, even though electric charge exists in discrete units. In most engineering problems this discrete nature of electric charge is insignificant. Consequently, the concept of a charge density at a point is justifiable. In classical electromagnetism, as in classical mechanics, *a point is a very small region having dimensions that are large compared with atomic dimensions,* containing perhaps 10,000 atoms.

The average value of the charge per unit volume in an elemental volume ΔV containing an elemental charge Δq is $\Delta q/\Delta V$. If the elemental volume shrinks into a point, the ratio becomes the charge per unit volume at the point, called the *charge density* ρ. Mathematically, ρ is defined as

$$\rho = \lim_{\Delta V \to 0} \frac{\Delta q}{\Delta V} \text{ coulombs/m}^3 \; [Q/L^3] \tag{3-11}$$

It is understood that the charge distribution at the point is a continuous function of the space coordinates, for otherwise the limit does not exist.

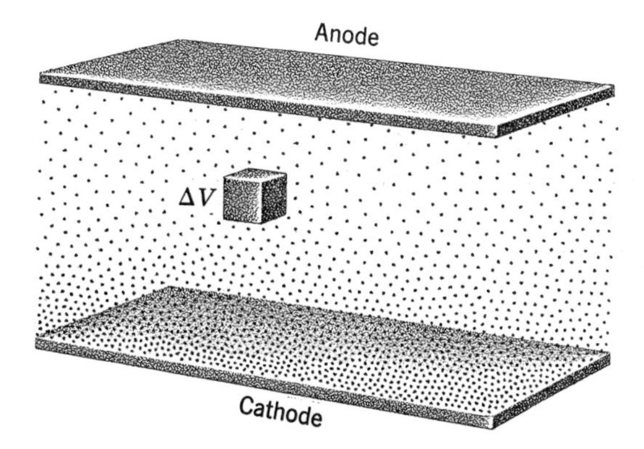

FIG. 3-1. Charge distribution between the plates of a parallel-plate vacuum tube.

Furthermore, the zero limit is interpreted as being macroscopically small but microscopically large; that is, ΔV shrinks to a point. Shown in Fig. 3-1 is the volume charge density in the region between the plates of a parallel-plate vacuum tube. The elemental volume ΔV, though very small, contains large numbers of electrons.

In many cases electric charge will be found to be distributed over a surface, as shown in Fig. 3-2. In terms of the elemental charge Δq on the

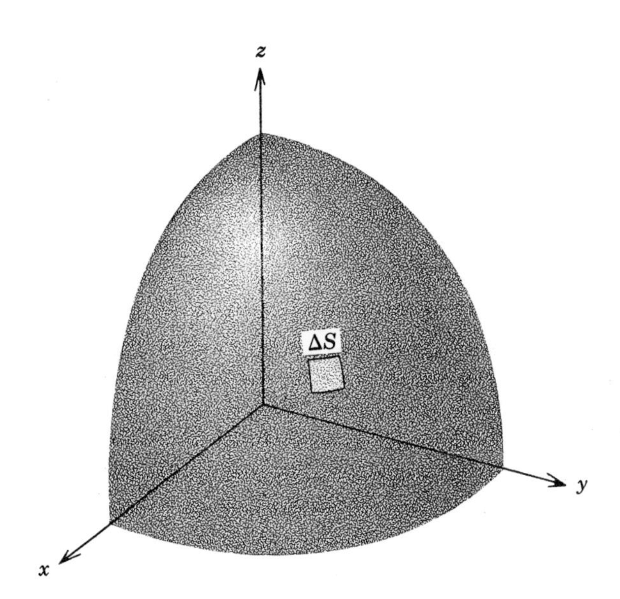

FIG. 3-2. A portion of a charged spherical surface.

elemental surface area ΔS, the *surface charge density* ρ_s at a point is

$$\rho_s = \lim_{\Delta S \to 0} \frac{\Delta q}{\Delta S} \text{ coulombs/m}^2 \, [Q/L^2] \tag{3-12}$$

In other cases charge may be distributed along a line, and the charge per unit length, referred to as the *linear charge density* ρ_l, is defined as

$$\rho_l = \lim_{\Delta l \to 0} \frac{\Delta q}{\Delta l} \text{ coulombs/m} \, [Q/L] \tag{3-13}$$

with Δq denoting the charge in the elemental length Δl.

Finally, we may have electric charge concentrated at a point. It is evident that the total charge in a region is

$$q = \int_V \rho \, dV + \int_S \rho_s \, dS + \int_C \rho_l \, dl + q_1 + q_2 + \cdots \tag{3-14}$$

The volume integral yields the charge due to the volume charge densities; the surface integral yields the charge due to any surface charge densities that may be present; the line integral accounts for the possible linear charge densities; and the terms q_1, q_2, etc., represent all point charges. Usually the relation

$$q = \int_V \rho \, dV \tag{3-15}$$

is understood to imply Eq. (3-14). The volume integral of ρ is interpreted to represent the total charge in the volume V, including surface charge densities, linear charge densities, and point charges.

Electric charge is often expressed in microcoulombs (μc), or micro-microcoulombs ($\mu\mu c$). The prefix *micro-* means *one millionth.* Therefore, a microcoulomb is 10^{-6} coulomb, and a micromicrocoulomb is 10^{-12} coulomb.

REFERENCES

Cullwick, E. G., *The Fundamentals of Electro-magnetism*, Cambridge University Press, London, 2nd ed., 1949, Appendices I and II.

Frank, N. H., *Introduction to Electricity and Optics*, McGraw-Hill Book Co., New York, 2nd ed., 1950, Appendix I.

Hayt, W. H. Jr., *Engineering Electromagnetics*, McGraw-Hill Book Co., New York, 1958, Appendix B.

Panofsky, W. K. H., and M. Phillips, *Classical Electricity and Magnetism*, Addison-Wesley Publishing Co., Reading, Mass., 1955, Appendix 1.

Sommerfeld, A., *Electrodynamics*, Academic Press, New York, 1952, Secs. 2, 7, 8 of Part I.

PROBLEMS

Section 3-2

3-1. The force between two point charges q_1 and q_2 separated a distance r is $F = q_1q_2/(4\pi\epsilon r^2)$. Determine the dimensions of ϵ in terms of L, M, T, and Q.

3-2. If **E** denotes the force per unit charge at a point, determine the dimensions of $\mathbf{E} \cdot d\mathbf{l}$, $\mathbf{E} \cdot d\mathbf{S}$, $d\mathbf{E}/dx$, $\partial^2\mathbf{E}/\partial x^2$, and $q\mathbf{E}$.

3-3. The force per unit charge that acts on a certain charge moving with velocity $\mathbf{v}$ is $\mathbf{v} \times \mathbf{B}$. Determine the dimensions of **B**.

3-4. Under what condition is velocity correctly expressed as distance divided by time? Also, when is force equal to the product of mass and acceleration?

3-5. Determine the weight in pounds of a kilogram at sea level. Also, express a newton in terms of dynes and pounds, and express a joule in terms of ergs, foot-pounds, and kilowatt-hours.

3-6. A constant force of 5 newtons acts vertically downward on a certain object. If the object is moved vertically upward 10 meters and then horizontally another 10 meters, what work is done by the specified force?

3-7. A constant force of 10 newtons acts on an object that moves in a direction making a 30° angle with the force vector. How far does the object move during the expenditure of 25 joules?

3-8. The force acting on a certain object is $\mathbf{a}_r/r^2$, with r denoting the distance from the origin of a rectangular coordinate system and $\mathbf{a}_r$ denoting a unit vector along r directed radially outward. Determine the energy expended by the force when the object is moved from the point (1, 0, 0) to (1, 1, 0). Note that $\mathbf{a}_r/r^2 = \mathbf{r}/r^3$, with $\mathbf{r} = x\mathbf{i} + y\mathbf{j} + z\mathbf{k}$.

3-9. Repeat Prob. 3-8, except let the object be moved from (1, 1, 1) directly to (3, 3, 3).

3-10. Calculate the work done by the force $\mathbf{F} = 2y^2\mathbf{i} - 3xy\mathbf{j}$ acting along the path $y = 2x$ from (2, 4) to (0, 0).

Section 3-3

3-11. The rest mass of an electron is 9.11×10^{-31} kg. Calculate the momentum of an electron with a velocity of $0.999c$.

3-12. A particle with a rest mass of 10^{-14} kg has a kinetic energy of 225 joules. Determine its velocity.

3-13. An electron traveling at a velocity equal to $0.999c$ is acted upon by a force in the direction of its motion. Discuss the effect of this force on the velocity, mass, and momentum of the electron.

3-14. When a certain object moves from rest to a velocity of 2×10^8 m/sec, its mass increases by 10^{-15} kg. Determine the mass and the kinetic energy of the object when its velocity is 2×10^8 m/sec.

3-15. Find the mass and kinetic energy of a photon with a momentum of 10^{-28} kg-m/sec.

3-16. Find the mass and kinetic energy of a photon with a wavelength λ of 10^{-4} m. The momentum mc of a photon equals h/λ, with h denoting Planck's constant 6.625×10^{-34} joule-sec.

Section 3-5

3-17. A charge of 10 μc is uniformly distributed throughout the volume of a sphere of radius 3 m. Determine ρ.

3-18. A charge of $-2\ \mu c$ is uniformly distributed over the surface of a sphere of radius 0.5 m. Find the surface charge density.

3-19. A 500-meter length of wire has a linear charge density of

$$2 \times 10^{-12} \sin 0.002\pi x \text{ coulomb/m}$$

with x denoting the distance measured from one end. Find the total charge on the wire.

3-20. The charge density within a vacuum diode with parallel-plate electrodes is $-2 \times 10^{-6} x^{-2/3}$ coulomb/m^3, with x denoting the distance from the cathode. The cathode and the plate are square plates of 1-cm side length, separated 0.5 cm. Find the total charge in the region between the plates.

3-21. A sphere of radius 2 m has a charge density ρ that is directly proportional to the distance r from the center. If the total charge is 3 μc, find the charge density at a radius of 1.5 m. Note that the differential volume dV of a spherical shell of thickness dr is $4\pi r^2\, dr$.

3-22. Suppose the plane $z = 0$ contains a charge density $\rho_s = x^2 + y^2 - 1$. Determine the total charge in the region of the plane within a square of unit side length, centered at the origin.

Electric and Magnetic Fields

CHAPTER 4

Two secondary concepts of primary importance in electromagnetic theory are the electric and magnetic fields. These quantities are very closely related. For example, an electric charge moving in a region containing electric and magnetic fields is acted upon by both electric and magnetic forces. The current in the conductors of the moving armature of an electric generator is the result of an imbalance between opposing electric and magnetic forces on the free electrons. Both types of fields are propagated in radio waves and other electromagnetic radiation. Furthermore, time-changing electric and magnetic fields always exist together, one producing the other. Thus it seems desirable to introduce and define these quantities together. We shall begin with a discussion of field lines, so helpful in describing vector fields.

4-1. FIELD LINES

A vector field exists in a region when some vector quantity is associated with each point of the region. An example is the gravitational field of force around the earth. Other examples are the velocity field of the water particles in a stream, the electric field about an electric charge, and the magnetic field surrounding a moving charge.

From an arbitrary point in a vector field it is possible to trace a curve in such a manner that the vector at each point is tangent to the curve. The tangent at any point on the curve coincides with the direction of the field vector at that point. Any number of such curves can be drawn in the region. These curves do not cross one another except at points of sources or sinks or at points where the vector field is zero, for only at these points can the field have more than one direction. Curves with field vectors everywhere tangent are called *field lines*. They are also often called *flux lines*, *direction lines*, *stream lines*, and *lines of force*. Figure 4-1 shows the field lines of a positive point charge, in a plane containing the charge.

Let us consider a region with a vector field **A**. At an arbitrary point in the region the vector $\mathbf{A} = A_x\mathbf{i} + A_y\mathbf{j} + A_z\mathbf{k}$, and the differential vector length of the field line passing through the point is $d\mathbf{l} = dx\,\mathbf{i} + dy\,\mathbf{j} + dz\,\mathbf{k}$. The vectors **A** and $d\mathbf{l}$, having the same direction at the point, have identical

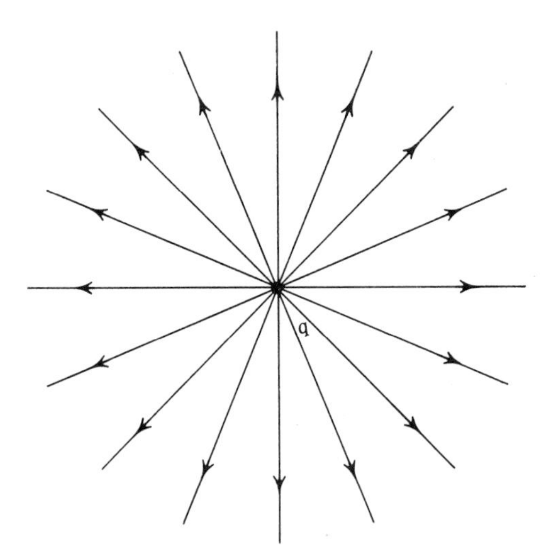

FIG. 4-1. Field lines of a positive point charge.

direction cosines. Therefore, $dx/dl = A_x/A$, or $dx/A_x = dl/A$. Similarly, it can be shown that dy/A_y and dz/A_z are also equal to dl/A. Hence

$$dx/A_x = dy/A_y = dz/A_z \tag{4-1}$$

These are the differential equations of the field lines. An application of Eq. (4-1) to an elementary two-dimensional example follows.

EXAMPLE. Find the equations of the field lines in the xy-plane for $\mathbf{A} = y\mathbf{i} - x\mathbf{j}$.

Solution. Substitution for A_x and A_y into Eq. (4-1) gives $dx/y = -dy/x$. The slope of the field lines is $dy/dx = -x/y$. Separating variables and integrating yield the equation of a circle, $x^2 + y^2 = a^2$, with a denoting an arbitrary constant. There are, of course, an infinite number of field lines corresponding to all possible values of a. Each line in the xy-plane is a circle of radius a having its center at the origin, as shown in Fig. 4-2. These circular field lines may be visualized as a representation of the direction of the vector field at each point of the region.

In addition to representing the direction of the vector field, field lines can be utilized to indicate the strength of the field. Suppose we agree to let the number of lines per unit area, crossing a small area transverse to the direction of the lines, be proportional to the field strength. If this is done, then the density of the lines denotes the field strength. In regions where the lines are closely spaced the field is intense, and in regions where the lines are relatively far apart, the field is weak. The constant of proportionality relating the line density to the field strength is an arbitrary

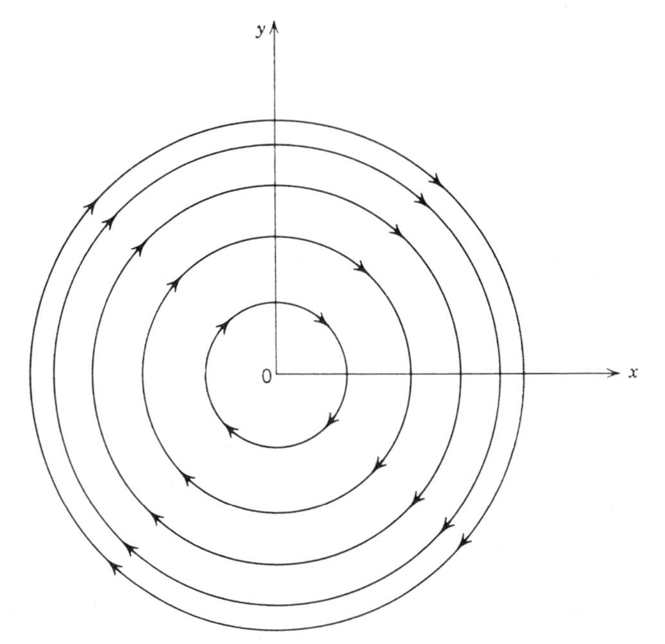

FIG. 4-2. Circular field lines of $\mathbf{A} = y\mathbf{i} - x\mathbf{j}$.

selection. Note that the field of Fig. 4-1 is intense in the region near the point charge, whereas the field of Fig. 4-2 is weak at the origin.

Field lines are used extensively in mapping electric and magnetic fields. Michael Faraday emphasized the importance of these lines in electromagnetic theory, and James Clerk Maxwell developed this concept more fully. Many find it helpful to visualize field lines when working with electric and magnetic fields, but these lines should not be given too concrete an entity.

4-2. ELECTRIC FIELD INTENSITY

An earth satellite is held in its orbit by the gravitational pull of the earth. If somehow this gravitational pull could suddenly be eliminated, the satellite would fly off on a tangent, for there would be no force producing acceleration toward the earth. How can we describe this pull? We know that two masses attract one another, although we do not know why.

It is convenient to associate a vector field—the gravitational field—with the earth. This field exerts a force on every object in it. We visualize the earth as being surrounded by a gravitational field that pervades all space, although the field becomes very weak at great distances. The field is invisible and cannot be observed directly. However, its effect on another mass is readily apparent. The gravitational field lines are radially inward from outer space toward the center of the earth, except for small deviations due to the nonuniformity of the earth's mass, and a mass released at a point in this field is pulled toward the earth. The gravitational field with its lines of force is a concept used to describe this pull. The satellite also has a gravitational field about it, and so does every other mass.

The early electrical experimenters observed that electric charges exert forces on one another. Just as the forces between masses are regarded as due to the action of a gravitational field, the forces between charges are regarded as due to the action of an electrical field. *The concept of electric field is introduced for the purpose of describing the forces between charges, the precise mechanism producing these forces being unknown.* As every charge is surrounded by an electric field, it is reasonable to consider charges as sources that produce the fields. Maxwell showed us that electric fields are also produced by time-changing magnetism. The equations relating the field to its sources will be examined in later chapters. The purpose here is to describe and define the electric field.

The gravitational field at a point is the force per unit mass that would act on a mass placed at the point. It might be expressed in newtons per kilogram. The *electric field intensity* **E** at a point P is defined as the force per unit charge that would act on a stationary test charge placed at the point. **E** is a vector. Its direction is the same as that of the force on a positive test charge, and opposite to the direction of the force on a negative test charge. The presence of the test charge is not necessary, of course, for **E** to exist. The test charge merely provides a way of determining the magnitude and direction of **E** at P. Electric field intensity can be expressed in newtons per coulomb. However, its mks unit is the *volt per meter.* As the *volt* is an mks unit equivalent to the joule per coulomb, it is evident that the volt per meter and the newton per coulomb are equivalent units.

The test charge used to measure **E** at a point in a region should be very small. Otherwise, the forces it exerts on other charges in the region may cause them to move, thus changing the field we wish to measure. With the understanding that the test charge q is sufficiently small to avoid this difficulty, we define the electric field intensity **E** as

$$\mathbf{E} = \mathbf{F}/q \text{ volts/m } [LM/T^2Q] \tag{4-2}$$

with **F** denoting the force on the test charge q. The dimensions are, of course, those of force divided by charge. Obviously, the dimensions of the unit *volt* are L^2M/T^2Q.

The electric field **E** at a point P exerts a force $q\mathbf{E}$ on any charge q placed at P. If q is positive, the electric force is in the direction of **E**, but if q is negative, the force is opposite the direction of **E**. The electric force on q is independent of the motion of the charge. However, if the charge carrier at P is moving, there may also be a magnetic force acting on the charge, and the total force is then the sum of the electric and magnetic forces. Consequently, a stationary charge should be used to measure **E**. We shall now discuss the magnetic field.

4-3. THE MAGNETIC FIELD

In 1820 Oersted found that a wire carrying an electric current produces a magnetic field that exerts a force on a nearby magnetized needle. He determined that the direction of this force is along a circular path around the wire. Shortly thereafter, Ampère discovered that electric currents exert forces on one another. He found that each elemental section of a system of current-carrying conductors exerts a force on every other elemental section.

The forces between electric charges are described in terms of electric fields. Each charge produces an electric field that acts on every other charge. In a similar manner the forces between electric currents are described in terms of magnetic fields. Each differential current element $i\,d\mathbf{l}$ produces a magnetic field that exerts a force on every other current element. *Thus the magnetic field is a concept introduced for the purpose of describing the forces between electric currents.*

Magnetic fields are produced by electric currents. A moving electric charge, which is equivalent to an electric current, also produces a magnetic field. In addition, time-changing electric fields generate magnetic fields. This was first stated by Maxwell, who deduced that a time-changing electric field produced a *displacement current* with the same magnetic effects as a current of moving charge. The precise relationships between magnetism and its sources are discussed in Chapter 8. The purpose here is to define the magnetic field.

The magnetic field is, in many respects, similar to the gravitational and electric fields. The gravitational field exerts forces on masses; the electric field exerts forces on electric charges, regardless of their motion; and the magnetic field exerts forces on moving charges and electric currents. As electric current has not yet been precisely defined, the magnetic field will be defined in terms of the force acting on a moving charge, which is equivalent to an electric current. In Sec. 7-6 the field is expressed in terms of the force on a current element.

The magnetic force on a moving charge is a function of the velocity of the charge. Both the magnitude and direction of this force depend upon both the magnitude and direction of the velocity vector. The magnitude of the force is proportional to the charge q, to its velocity v, to the strength of the field $\mathbf{B}$, and to the sine of the angle θ between the velocity vector and

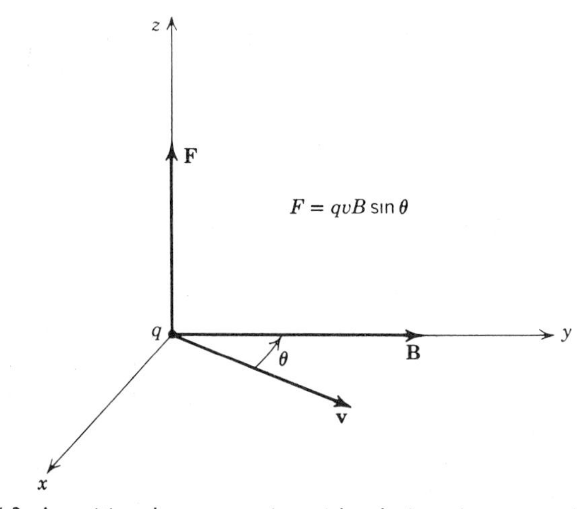

FIG. 4-3. A positive charge q moving with velocity $\mathbf{v}$ in a magnetic field $\mathbf{B}$.

the vector field, as shown in Fig. 4-3. If the charge is moving along a field line, the magnetic force is zero. The direction of the force is always normal to the velocity $\mathbf{v}$ and also normal to the field, as indicated in the illustration. This is true regardless of the orientation of $\mathbf{v}$. Because of these properties, the magnetic field is not so easily defined as is the electric field. However, as is shown in the following section, the essential information can be given in the form of a simple vector equation.

4-4. MAGNETIC FLUX DENSITY

The forces exerted on moving charges, and hence on electric currents, because of the velocity of the charges or the magnitude of the currents, are called magnetic forces. We have learned that the electric field intensity at a point is the force per unit charge $\mathbf{F}/q$ that acts on a stationary test charge at the point. Actually, the electric force on the charge is the same regardless of its motion. However, if the charge is moving, there may also be a magnetic force. The magnetic force per unit charge and the velocity **v** of a moving test charge are employed in the definition of the magnetic field. First, let us consider a region in which the electric field is zero. For such a region the force per unit charge is entirely magnetic, and the magnetic field **B** is defined implicitly by the relation

$$\mathbf{F}/q = \mathbf{v} \times \mathbf{B} \tag{4-3}$$

Note that the magnitude of the magnetic force per unit charge equals $vB \sin \theta$, with θ denoting the angle between the vectors **v** and **B**. The direction of the vector $\mathbf{F}/q$ is normal to both **v** and **B**, with sense determined by the right-hand rule. Refer to Fig. 4-3.

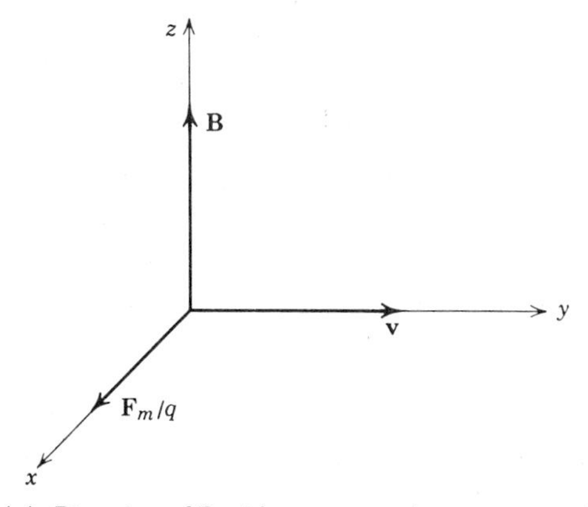

FIG. 4-4. Direction of **B** with respect to the vectors **v** and $\mathbf{F}_m/q$.

Suppose the moving charge is directed so that the magnetic force is zero. In this case the velocity **v** and the field **B** have either the same or opposite directions. If the velocity vector is rotated through an angle θ, the force per unit charge increases as the sine of θ. For $\theta = \frac{1}{2}\pi$, the force per unit charge is a maximum $\mathbf{F}_m/q$. For this case the vectors $\mathbf{F}_m/q$, **v**, and **B** are mutually perpendicular to one another, with directions as shown in Fig. 4-4. A right-hand rectangular coordinate system is oriented in the illustration so that the three axes coincide with the three vectors.

The magnitude of the magnetic force per unit charge can be regarded as the product of $v \sin \theta$ and B. Clearly, $v \sin \theta$ is the component of **v** normal to **B**. Only this normal component contributes to the magnetic force. The component of **v** in the direction of **B** has absolutely no effect on the force.

In Chapter 2 the flux of any vector **A** was defined as the surface integral of **A** over a specified surface S. Thus $\mathbf{A} \cdot d\mathbf{S}$ is referred to as the differential *flux* of **A** over $d\mathbf{S}$. It follows that any vector could, with some logic, be referred to as a *flux density*. The magnetic field **B** is usually called the *magnetic flux density*, although it is frequently referred to as the *magnetic induction*. Magnetic flux density **B** has the dimensions of force-per-unit-charge divided by velocity and, therefore, its units are volts per meter divided by meters per second, or volt-seconds/m^2. The *weber* is an mks unit equivalent to a volt-second. Thus the mks unit of **B** is the *weber per square meter*, also known as the *tesla*. As the volt-second, or weber, is a unit whose dimensions are L^2M/TQ, the dimensions of **B** are M/TQ.

Let us now consider a region with both electric and magnetic fields. A moving test charge experiences both electric and magnetic forces. The force per unit charge due to the electric field is **E**, and the force per unit charge due to the motion of the charge in the magnetic field is $\mathbf{v} \times \mathbf{B}$. Consequently, the total force per unit charge that acts on the test charge is

$$\mathbf{F}/q = \mathbf{E} + \mathbf{v} \times \mathbf{B} \tag{4-4}$$

This is known as the *Lorentz force equation*, and it may be regarded as the defining equation for both the electric field intensity **E** and the magnetic flux density **B**. The electric force is independent of the motion of the charge, whereas the magnetic force depends on the magnitude and orientation of the velocity vector. There is no magnetic force, of course, on a stationary charge.

If an electric charge is accelerating, there is energy radiated, and as a consequence, a *radiation force* acts on the charge. This radiation force, which is in addition to the electric and magnetic forces, is negligible unless the acceleration is very great.

We have agreed to classify a force that acts on a stationary charge as electric. If the charge moves with constant velocity, any additional force is said to be magnetic, and if the charge accelerates, the still additional force is the radiation force. It should be noted that *no other type of force can possibly act on a charge*, because the electric, magnetic, and radiation forces include all possibilities. Although the force on a charge is transmitted to the mass of the charge carrier, we should be careful not to confuse forces on charges with those that act directly on the charge carriers. A gravitational field pulls downward on an electron, but it is the mass that is attracted, not the charge. A mechanical force on a charged copper ball acts on the mass of the ball. In particular, diffusion forces within semiconductor junctions, batteries, and contacts of different metals are forces on the *carriers* of the charges.

It should be mentioned that some prefer to define electric and magnetic fields in terms of the forces on the charge carriers. However, these definitions lead to results inconsistent with the electromagnetic laws. For example, the line integral of the electric field around a closed path that passes through a battery is not zero if the chemical diffusion forces are included in the definition of **E**. Yet Maxwell's equations require the static electric field to have zero circulation.

EXAMPLE. A small test charge is employed in an experiment to determine the static electric and magnetic fields at a point in space. The magnitude and direction of the velocity of the test charge are varied, and the resulting force acting on the charge is measured. In a particular direction, which is selected as the x-direction of a rectangular coordinate system, the force is found to be independent of the magnitude of **v**, with the force per unit charge equal to $1000\mathbf{i} - 2000\mathbf{j} - 1200\mathbf{k}$. With $\mathbf{v} = 10{,}000\mathbf{j}$, the force per unit charge is $1000\mathbf{i} - 2000\mathbf{j} - 800\mathbf{k}$. Find **E** and **B**.

Solution. Clearly, the x-axis of the coordinate system is oriented parallel to the magnetic field. Thus B_y and B_z are zero. With **v** directed along the x-axis, the force is due entirely to the electric field and, therefore, $\mathbf{E} = 1000\mathbf{i} - 2000\mathbf{j} - 1200\mathbf{k}$ volts/m.

With $\mathbf{v} = 10{,}000\mathbf{j}$, the force per unit charge is the sum of **E** and $\mathbf{v} \times \mathbf{B}$. As $\mathbf{F}/q$ and **E** are known, we readily determine $\mathbf{v} \times \mathbf{B}$ to be $400\mathbf{k}$. Therefore, $(10{,}000\mathbf{j}) \times (B_x\mathbf{i}) = 400\mathbf{k}$. It follows that $B_x = -0.04$, and $\mathbf{B} = -0.04\mathbf{i}$ weber/m^2.

4-5. THE PARADOX OF RELATIVE MOTION

It is interesting to note that two observers in motion relative to one another may correctly measure different electric fields. If their relative velocity is small compared with the speed of light, it can be shown* that both will observe approximately the same total force acting on a charge moving in an electromagnetic field, but they will disagree on the division of this force into its electric and magnetic components. We shall now examine this apparent paradox in detail.

Shown in Fig. 4-5 is a test charge moving with velocity **v** in a region containing an electric field **E** and a magnetic field **B**. A stationary observer notes a force per unit charge of $\mathbf{E} + \mathbf{v} \times \mathbf{B}$. From the viewpoint of a second observer, moving with velocity $\mathbf{v}_1$, the velocity of the test charge is $\mathbf{v} - \mathbf{v}_1$. Therefore, the force per unit charge noted by this moving observer is $\mathbf{E}_1 + (\mathbf{v} - \mathbf{v}_1) \times \mathbf{B}_1$, with $\mathbf{E}_1$ and $\mathbf{B}_1$ representing the fields measured by this moving observer. As both observers measure approximately the same force, we have

$$\mathbf{E} + \mathbf{v} \times \mathbf{B} = \mathbf{E}_1 + (\mathbf{v} - \mathbf{v}_1) \times \mathbf{B}_1$$

Rearranging terms gives

$$\mathbf{E} + \mathbf{v}_1 \times \mathbf{B}_1 = \mathbf{E}_1 + \mathbf{v} \times (\mathbf{B}_1 - \mathbf{B})$$

* P. Moon and D. E. Spencer, *Foundations of Electrodynamics*, D. Van Nostrand, Princeton, N.J., 1960, Chapter 12.

Clearly, the velocity $\mathbf{v}$ of the test charge can be changed without having any effect on any of the other quantities of the equation. It follows that $\mathbf{B}_1$ must equal $\mathbf{B}$, and *both observers view the same magnetic field.* The preceding equation becomes

$$\mathbf{E}_1 = \mathbf{E} + \mathbf{v}_1 \times \mathbf{B} \qquad (4\text{-}5)$$

with $\mathbf{v}_1$ denoting the velocity of the observer. Thus the electric field $\mathbf{E}_1$ viewed by an observer with velocity $\mathbf{v}_1$ is equal to the vector sum of $\mathbf{E}$ and $\mathbf{v}_1 \times \mathbf{B}$, with $\mathbf{E}$ denoting the electric field viewed by a stationary observer.

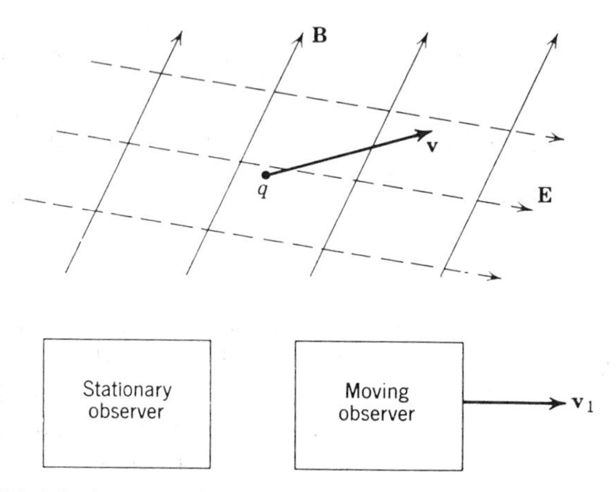

FIG. 4-5. A moving charge, and observers with relative motion.

We conclude that two observers with relative motion in a region containing an electromagnetic field observe different electric and magnetic forces on the same test charge, although both observe the same total force for ordinary velocities. The two observers note different electric fields, different velocities for the test charge, and the same magnetic field. Let us now consider two illustrative examples.

EXAMPLE 1. A stationary observer views a 10-μc charge moving with a velocity v of 10^6 meters/sec normal to a magnetic field B of 0.1 weber/m^2. From his viewpoint the electric field is zero. A second observer moves along with the charge with the same velocity. Determine the electric and magnetic forces acting on the charge, from the viewpoint of each. Refer to Fig. 4-6.

Solution. According to the stationary observer, the electric force is zero, and the magnetic force qvB is 1 newton, directed out of the paper. From the viewpoint of the moving observer, the charge is stationary. Consequently, he regards the total force of 1 newton as an electric force, with the magnetic force equal to zero. He detects an electric field of vB, or 10^5 volts/m, directed out of the paper.

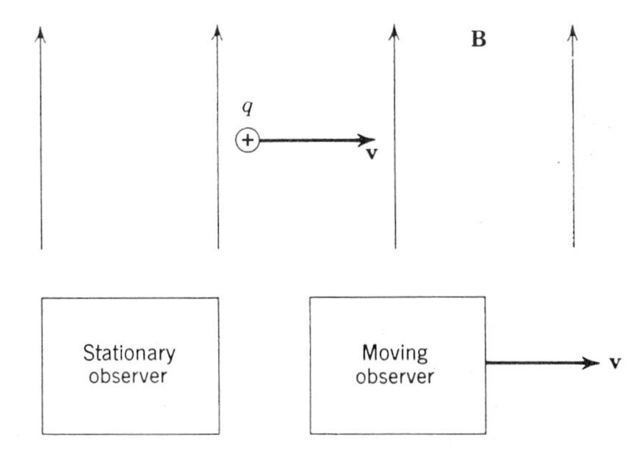

FIG. 4-6. Two observers with relative motion, and a charge moving in a magnetic field **B**.

EXAMPLE 2. A stationary observer views a stationary 10-μc charge in a magnetic field B of 0.1 weber/m^2, the electric field being zero. A second observer is moving with a velocity **v** of 10^6 meters/sec, as shown in Fig. 4-7. From the viewpoint of each, determine the electric and magnetic forces that act on the charge.

Solution. According to the stationary observer, both the electric and magnetic forces are zero. From the viewpoint of the moving observer, however, the charge is moving in a region containing electric and magnetic fields, and there are electric and magnetic forces acting on it. The moving observer detects an electric field $\mathbf{v} \times \mathbf{B}$ equal to 100,000 volts/m directed out of the paper. The electric force on the charge is 1 newton out of the paper. The magnetic force is also 1 newton. However, the magnetic force is directed into the paper, for the motion of the charge relative to this observer is to the left. The total force is, of course, zero.

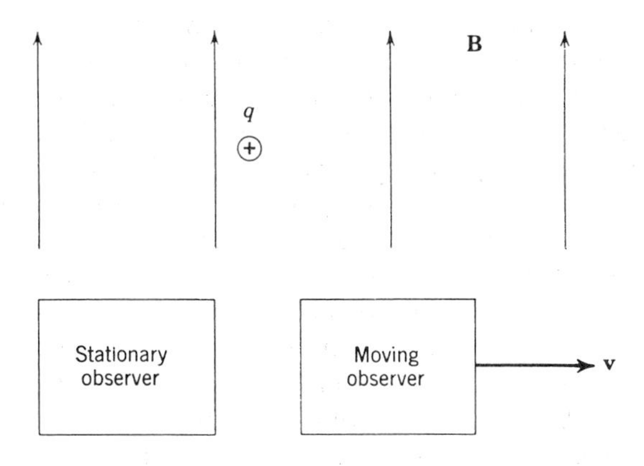

FIG. 4-7. Two observers with relative motion, and a stationary charge in a magnetic field **B**.

4-6. MAGNETIC FLUX

The flux of any vector **A** over a surface S has been defined as the surface integral of **A** over S. In accordance with this definition of flux, the *magnetic flux* Φ over a surface S is

$$\Phi = \int_S \mathbf{B} \cdot d\mathbf{S} \text{ webers } [L^2M/TQ] \tag{4-6}$$

As **B** is expressed in webers/m^2, the mks unit of magnetic flux is the weber. Magnetic flux is a scalar quantity.

Before the surface integral of Eq. (4-6) can be evaluated over some specified surface in a given field, one side of the surface S must be designated the positive side. This is an arbitrary selection. Frequently, an arrow is

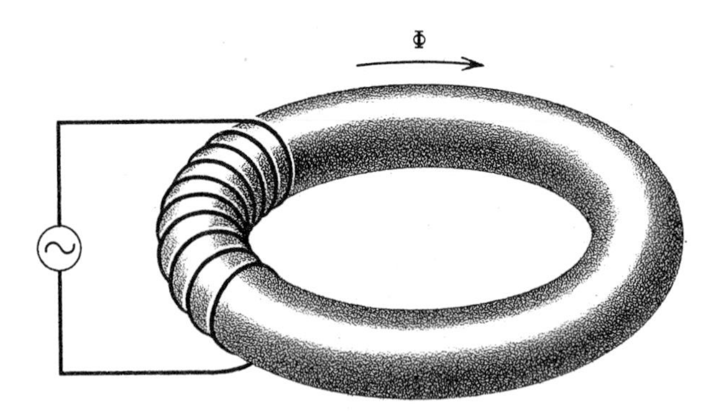

FIG. 4-8. Arrow indicating arbitrarily selected positive direction of Φ.

shown on an illustration to indicate this selection, with the arrow regarded as pointing out of the positive side. For example, in Fig. 4-8 the flux Φ is the magnetic flux over a cross-sectional surface of the iron core, and the arrow alongside the symbol Φ denotes that the positive side of each cross-sectional surface is the side facing in the clockwise direction. This arrow is usually referred to as indicating *the positive, or reference, direction of the magnetic flux* Φ, even though Φ is actually a scalar.

The magnetic flux density **B** is a vector. Therefore, field lines can be drawn or imagined in a region containing **B**. The field line at any point in the region has the direction of **B** at the point. As previously stated, the number of lines per unit area, crossing an area transverse to the direction of the lines, can be made to represent the magnitude of **B**. For example, we might let one million lines per square meter correspond to a magnetic flux of one weber/m^2. Having selected some line density to denote a certain magnetic flux density, we could, if we wished, express **B** in terms of the number of lines per square meter. As magnetic flux Φ is the surface integral of **B**, it follows that the total number of lines over a surface is a measure of Φ. Accordingly, when referring to Φ, the expression *lines of magnetic flux* is often used. Many engineers and scientists find it helpful to visualize these flux lines, always oriented in the direction of **B** with a density at each point proportional to the magnitude of **B**. Michael Faraday referred to these lines as "magnetic lines of force."

In conclusion, the magnetic flux Φ over a surface S is the surface integral of **B** over S. The mks unit of magnetic flux is the weber, with dimensions L^2M/TQ. One side of the surface S is selected as the positive side, and this selection is usually indicated by means of an arrow shown on a sketch. The selection, which is arbitrary, determines whether Φ is positive or negative at a particular instant of time. Magnetic flux is a scalar quantity that is sometimes expressed in terms of lines of magnetic flux. These lines are, of course, imaginary.

PROBLEMS

Section 4-1

4-1. If the electric field **E** in the xy-plane is $(x\mathbf{i} + y\mathbf{j})/(x^2 + y^2)^{3/2}$ volts/m, deduce from Eq. (4-1) the equations of the field lines and sketch these lines. Include arrowheads.

4-2. The magnetic field of a long straight wire with a steady current is directed along circular paths around the wire, with the planes of the circles normal to the wire. The strength of the field is inversely proportional to the distance from the wire. In a plane normal to the wire, sketch the field lines so as to show the direction and relative magnitude of the magnetic field. Assume a clockwise direction.

4-3. If $\mathbf{A} = 10\mathbf{i} + 5\mathbf{j}$ at all points of a region, find the equations of the field lines, and sketch these lines in the xy-plane.

4-4. If $\mathbf{A} = y\mathbf{i} + x\mathbf{j}$ in the xy-plane, find the equations of the field lines, and sketch these lines. Include arrowheads.

Section 4-2

4-5. Determine the magnitude and direction cosines of the electric force on a charge of $-5\ \mu c$ in an electric field $\mathbf{E} = 6\mathbf{i} - 4\mathbf{j} + 3\mathbf{k}$ volts/m.

4-6. Determine the magnitude and direction angles of the electric force on a charge of $-8\ \mu c$ in an electric field $\mathbf{E} = 100\mathbf{i} + 200\mathbf{j} - 300\mathbf{k}$ volts/m.

Section 4-4

4-7. At a point P in a region containing a static magnetic field a test charge with a velocity of 10^5 m/sec in the x-direction has a force per unit charge of $2\mathbf{j} - 3\mathbf{k}$ newtons/coulomb. When the test charge is given a velocity of 10^5 m/sec in the y-direction, the force per unit charge at P is $-2\mathbf{i} - 4\mathbf{k}$. In terms of the unit vectors, find the magnetic flux density **B** at P and calculate the magnitude and direction cosines of **B**.

4-8. A charge of $-2\ \mu c$ has a velocity of $200\mathbf{i} - 400\mathbf{j} - 300\mathbf{k}$ m/sec at a point P. If the magnetic field at P is $-0.01\mathbf{i} + 0.03\mathbf{j} - 0.02\mathbf{k}$ weber/m^2, find the magnetic force on the charge and calculate the force per unit charge. Express your answers in terms of the unit vectors.

4-9. At a certain instant a charge is at a point P with velocity $\mathbf{v} = 100\mathbf{i} + 50\mathbf{j} - 200\mathbf{k}$, and the magnetic field at P is $-0.1\mathbf{i} + 0.2\mathbf{j}$ weber/m^2. If no net force acts on the charge, determine the electric field intensity at P.

4-10. An elemental charge is placed at a point P in a region containing static fields. The force per unit charge acting on the stationary charge is $2\mathbf{i} + 4\mathbf{j} - 5\mathbf{k}$ newtons/coulomb. Next the charge is given a velocity of $-2\mathbf{i} - 4\mathbf{j} + 3\mathbf{k}$ at P, and the force per unit charge is observed to be $-5\mathbf{i} + 15\mathbf{j} + 5\mathbf{k}$. Finally the charge is given a velocity of $3\mathbf{i} - 2\mathbf{j} + 5\mathbf{k}$ at P, and the observed force per unit charge is $9\mathbf{i} - 3\mathbf{j} - 12\mathbf{k}$. Find $\mathbf{E}$ and $\mathbf{B}$ in terms of the unit vectors.

4-11. A stationary 4-μc charge is at a point P in an electric field of $10\mathbf{i} - 5\mathbf{j} - 8\mathbf{k}$ volts/m and a magnetic field of $\mathbf{i} + 2\mathbf{j}$ webers/m^2. Determine the magnitude and the direction angles of the force on the charge.

4-12. At a certain instant a 0.006-c charge is moving in the y-direction at 1000 m/sec in an electric field $\mathbf{E} = 8\mathbf{i} - 6\mathbf{j} - 7\mathbf{k}$ and a magnetic field $\mathbf{B} = 0.001\mathbf{i} - 0.004\mathbf{j} - 0.003\mathbf{k}$. In terms of the unit vectors find the force on the charge and also the force per unit charge.

4-13. A 0.002-c charge is moving in the z-direction at 5000 m/sec in a magnetic field $\mathbf{B} = 0.04\mathbf{k}$. Find the force on the charge.

4-14. Show that Eq. (4-4) is dimensionally correct.

4-15. A charged particle of mass m and charge q is moving in the xy-plane with velocity v in a region containing a magnetic field $\mathbf{B} = B\mathbf{k}$, with B constant. Show that the particle moves in a circular path, and find the radius of this path in terms of q, m, v, and B by equating the centrifugal and centripetal forces. Recall that the inward acceleration of a particle in circular motion with constant velocity is v^2/r. Also, find the time it takes the particle to complete one circuit. How does the velocity of the particle affect this time? Does the magnetic field affect the kinetic energy of the particle?

4-16. An electron is released at the origin of a coordinate system with zero initial velocity in a region containing an electric field of $10{,}000\mathbf{i}$ volts/m. A short time later the electron reaches the point P located at $x = -0.1$ m. Determine the acceleration of the electron, its velocity at P, the time it took the electron to move from the origin to P, and the electron's kinetic energy at P.

4-17. An electron of charge $-e$ and mass m enters at time zero a uniform electric field $-E\mathbf{j}$ volts/m at the origin of a coordinate system with an initial velocity of $v_0\mathbf{i}$. Determine the acceleration of the electron in terms of E, e, and m, and find v_x and v_y in terms of E, e, m, v_0, and time t. Also, find x and y as functions of time t and eliminate t to obtain the equation of the parabolic path of the electron.

4-18. A charged particle of mass m and charge q is released at time zero with zero initial velocity at the origin of a coordinate system in a region with an electric field $E\mathbf{i}$ and a magnetic field $-B\mathbf{k}$, with E and B constants. Show that

$$qE - qv_yB = m\,dv_x/dt$$
$$qv_xB = m\,dv_y/dt$$

From these deduce that $d^2v_x/dt^2 = -(qB/m)^2v_x$, and noting that $v_x = v_y = 0$ at

$t = 0$, show that $v_x = E/B \sin (qB/m)t$. From this find v_y, and integrate v_x and v_y to obtain x and y as functions of time. For q, m, E, and B each equal to unity, plot the path of the particle.

Section 4-5

4-19. A satellite is encircling the earth at the equator from east to west with a velocity of 11,000 m/sec relative to the earth's surface. The earth's magnetic field is 3×10^{-5} weber/m^2, parallel to the surface and directed from south to north. Determine the magnitude and direction of the electric field intensity, measured by an instrument on the satellite, if this field is entirely due to the motion of the satellite through the magnetic field.

4-20. A satellite, encircling the earth with a velocity of 11,000 m/sec, is directly over the equator moving from southeast to northwest. An instrument on the satellite measures an electric field intensity of 0.2 volt/m, this field being the result of the motion of the satellite through the earth's magnetic field. Find the magnetic field **B**, assuming it is parallel to the surface and directed from south to north.

4-21. The electric and magnetic fields at a point P are 1000**i** volts/m and 0.04**j** weber/m^2. A test charge at P is moving with a velocity of 100,000**k** m/sec. Observers 1, 2, and 3 are moving with respective velocities of 1000**j**, 5000**k**, and 400(**i** + **j** − **k**) m/sec. From the viewpoints of these observers determine the electric and magnetic forces, on a per-unit-charge basis, acting on the test charge.

Section 4-6

4-22. Find the magnetic flux Φ over a unit area of the plane surface $x = 1$, with the positive side facing away from the origin, if (*a*) $\mathbf{B} = 0.1\mathbf{j} + 0.2\mathbf{k}$, and (*b*) $\mathbf{B} = -0.1\mathbf{i} + 0.1\mathbf{j} + 0.2\mathbf{k}$.

4-23. If **B** is tangent to a surface at every point, show that the magnetic flux Φ over the surface is zero. If **B** is everywhere normal to a surface, with a magnitude independent of the space coordinates, show that $\Phi = BS$, with S denoting the surface area.

4-24. At a certain instant the magnetic field in a region is $0.01 \sin y\, \mathbf{k}$ weber/m^2. With the side facing the positive z direction selected as positive, find the magnetic flux over the plane area of a square loop in the xy-plane, centered at the origin, and of side length one meter.

Electromotive Force

CHAPTER 5

In general, an electric generator supplies voltage and current to a load connected across its terminals. When the terminals are open, there is no current, and only voltage is generated. When the terminals are shorted, there is no voltage, and only current is generated. For all other loads, both voltage and current are produced. Basically, an electric generator is a source of electric power. We may, if we wish, regard it as a "voltage source" that generates a voltage, which in turn produces a current. Or we may regard it as a "current source" that generates a current, which in turn produces a voltage. Either viewpoint is equally acceptable. However, we should understand that both voltage and current are generated whenever electrical power is delivered to a load, with the nature of the load determining the ratio of voltage to current.

Electromotive force and voltage drop are synonymous.* If an electromotive force, or simply *emf*, is impressed on an electric circuit, current

* Electromotive force does not have the dimensions of force and it affects the electric charge of a body, whereas mechanical force acts on the mass of a body. Hence, many engineers object to the use of the term, preferring *voltage* instead. However, there is considerable disagreement and confusion with regard to the usage of the term *voltage*. Although it is usually understood to be synonymous with emf, some interpret voltage to be the negative of emf; others regard it as synonymous with electric potential difference, discussed in Chapter 13, and a few give it even other meanings. Thus it seems desirable to retain the term *electromotive force*. It is desirable also to use both *voltage drop* and *voltage rise*, rather than simply *voltage* (and negative voltage), because voltage means *voltage drop* to some and *voltage rise* to others. Thus the addition of *drop* or *rise* eliminates ambiguity.

results. Conversely, if a current is impressed on the circuit, an emf results. The electromotive force along the path of the circuit is the work done by the electromagnetic fields on a unit positive charge that is moved along the path. Thus a specified emf gives certain useful information about the fields. In many engineering problems a knowledge of the voltage is of more importance than a knowledge of the actual fields at points along the path.

The primary purpose of this chapter is to define electromotive force, with an explanation of its significance. In addition, a means of utilizing mechanical energy to maintain a voltage along the path of an electric circuit is considered, and the important *generator law* is developed.

5-1. A MASS IN THE GRAVITATIONAL FIELD

A brief investigation of the work done by the earth's gravitational field on a mass moved along a path in space will prepare us for the definition of emf presented in the next section. Therefore, let us consider a body of mass m in this gravitational field of force. Suppose the mass is located at a point beyond the earth's atmosphere. Because of its position in the gravitational field, the body is said to have a certain *potential energy* that is regarded as residing in the field. Now suppose the mass falls toward the earth. As it falls, its potential energy decreases and, consequently, the energy stored in the gravitational field decreases. The loss of field energy is accounted for by the increase in the kinetic energy of the body. When the body enters the atmosphere its acceleration will decrease because of air friction. However, its potential energy is still decreasing, and energy is, therefore, still being taken from the field. At least part of this energy is now being converted into heat, increasing the temperature of the air and mass. The body may become so hot that it disintegrates in flames. The falling mass is moving in the direction of the field force, and the work done on the mass by the field is *positive.*

Next, suppose a mechanical force pushes the mass upward in the gravitational field. The increase in potential energy is, of course, an increase in the stored energy of the field. Consequently, when the body is moved against the gravitational force, work is done on the body by the mechanical force that moves it in opposition to the field. The field energy increases as the body is raised, and the work done *by the field* is regarded as *negative.* It is important that the student clearly understands this concept of negative work.

The body may be moved in directions other than up and down. If moved horizontally, the potential energy and, therefore, the field energy remain unchanged, and the field does no work. In general, when the body is moved along some path C, the work W done on the body by the field is

$$W = \int_C \mathbf{F} \cdot d\mathbf{l} \tag{5-1}$$

with $\mathbf{F}$ denoting the gravitational force on the mass. The line integral of $\mathbf{F}$ may be positive or negative, depending on the path C. As $\mathbf{F}$ is directed downward, the integral is positive if the path C generally slopes downward, and it is negative if the path slopes upward. In any event the line integral gives the work done on the body by the gravitational field, with the understanding that negative work signifies energy is actually given to the field by the mass.

5-2. A CHARGE IN ELECTROMAGNETIC FIELDS

A charge in a region containing electric and magnetic fields is acted upon by a force $\mathbf{F}$ due to these fields. Of course, the magnetic field contributes to the force only if the charge is moving. Suppose the charge q is moved along some path C. The work done on the charge by the fields is given by Eq. (5-1) with $\mathbf{F}$ denoting the field force on q. Clearly, this work may be positive or negative. If negative, the movement of the charge along C is generally against the force of the fields, and the stored energy of the electromagnetic field is increased.

Equation (5-1) can be put on a per-unit-charge basis by dividing both sides by q, giving the work W/q per unit charge equal to the line integral of the force $\mathbf{F}/q$ per unit charge. This gives us more general information about the fields along the path C, for the value of the line integral is now independent of the actual charge. There is, however, a difficulty in using a charge of appreciable magnitude, for such a charge has a field that might affect the other charges and currents, causing a change in their fields. Certainly, we should not want our test charge to disturb the fields of interest along the path C. Consequently, if we were to measure the work per unit charge along C, we should use a very small test charge q. The field force acting on this small charge is $\mathbf{F}$, and the work done by the fields on the test charge moved along C is W. For a sufficiently small charge the work per unit charge W/q, known as the *electromotive force* (*emf*), or *voltage drop*, is

$$\text{emf} = \frac{W}{q} = \int_C \frac{\mathbf{F}}{q} \cdot d\mathbf{l} \text{ volts } [L^2M/T^2Q] \tag{5-2}$$

This equation precisely defines electromotive force. The choice of the *volt* as the mks unit of emf is obviously logical, for $\mathbf{F}/q$ has the dimensions of electric field intensity and can be expressed in volts per meter.

In words, the electromotive force, or voltage drop, along some specified path C is defined as *the work per unit charge done by the fields on a small test charge moved along C.* Emf is a scalar quantity measured in volts, with one volt equivalent to a work-per-unit-charge of a joule per coulomb. It is not a true force in the mechanical sense. Its sign may be positive or negative, depending on the fields and the path. However, its sign does *not* depend on the sign or magnitude of the test charge. To show this clearly, let us consider a very elementary example. Suppose a test charge of 1 μc is moved along a path C, and the work done by the fields on the charge is found to be -2 μjoules. The work per unit charge is -2 volts. Now suppose the test charge is -4 μc. Obviously, the work done by the fields on this negative charge is $+8$ μjoules, and the work per unit charge is again -2 volts. Thus the emf is the same for both cases, even though charges of unlike sign and magnitude were used as test charges. In the next section we shall express emf directly in terms of the fields.*

5-3. EMF AND ELECTRIC AND MAGNETIC FIELDS

We have learned that the force per unit charge that acts on a charge in a region containing an electric field $\mathbf{E}$ and a magnetic field $\mathbf{B}$ is $\mathbf{E} + \mathbf{v} \times \mathbf{B}$ newtons per coulomb, with $\mathbf{v}$ denoting the velocity of the charge. Clearly, this expression can be substituted for $\mathbf{F}/q$ in Eq. (5-2), giving

$$\text{emf} = \int_C (\mathbf{E} + \mathbf{v} \times \mathbf{B}) \cdot d\mathbf{l} \tag{5-3}$$

This equation correctly expresses the emf in terms of the $\mathbf{E}$ and $\mathbf{B}$ fields. However, we need to investigate the term $\mathbf{v} \times \mathbf{B}$.

Suppose the path C is a *stationary* path in space. Then the velocity $\mathbf{v}$ of the test charge and each differential path length $d\mathbf{l}$ have the same direction at each point of the path C. As the vector $\mathbf{v} \times \mathbf{B}$ is normal to $\mathbf{v}$, it is also normal to $d\mathbf{l}$. Consequently, $(\mathbf{v} \times \mathbf{B}) \cdot d\mathbf{l}$ is zero at each point along C, and Eq. (5-3) becomes

$$\text{emf} = \int_C \mathbf{E} \cdot d\mathbf{l} \tag{5-4}$$

* Some authors define emf as the work per unit charge done by the fields and certain *impressed forces* in moving a charge carrier along a path. These impressed forces are chemical diffusion forces, mechanical forces, etc., and they act on the carriers, not the charge. When included in the definition of emf, it is no longer correct to say that the emf around a closed path equals the time derivative of the magnetic flux linkages, yet this is a well-accepted statement of Faraday's law. Because of this and because the impressed forces are not electromagnetic, they are not included in emf as used in this text.

This is the electromotive force, or voltage drop, along a *stationary* path in space. The velocity of the test charge along C does not affect the work per unit charge, for the force exerted on the charge by virtue of its motion in the magnetic field is normal to the differential path length at each point of C. Equation (5-4) is a special case of Eq. (5-3). Obviously, its use is not restricted to stationary paths if the region has no magnetic field.

Next, suppose the path C is a *moving* path in space. For example, the path may be along a wire that is moving with respect to our coordinate system. The velocity $\mathbf{v}$ of the test charge is no longer in the same direction as $d\mathbf{l}$, and the vector product $\mathbf{v} \times \mathbf{B}$ will now have a component in the direction of $d\mathbf{l}$. Therefore, Eq. (5-3) must be used whenever the path C is moving in a region containing a magnetic field. Of course, the component of the velocity in the direction of $d\mathbf{l}$ contributes nothing to the emf. Only the sideways component due to the motion of the path makes a contribution. Clearly, the velocity $\mathbf{v}$ of Eq. (5-3) should be interpreted as *the velocity of the differential vector path length* $d\mathbf{l}$. The test charge is assumed to be moved instantly over the path C in determining the emf at a particular instant, and emf is, in general, a function of time.

An example of a moving path of practical importance is the path along the conductors of a rotating armature of an electric machine. These conductors move in a magnetic field, resulting in a magnetic force on the free electrons. The voltage and current depend on both the electric and magnetic forces. Equation (5-3) properly expresses the emf along this moving path, and an application is discussed in Sec. 5-5. Let us now consider two examples involving stationary paths.

EXAMPLE 1. In the region between the plates of a certain parallel-plate vacuum tube the electric field intensity is $-400{,}000x^{1/3}\mathbf{i}$ volts/m, with x denoting the

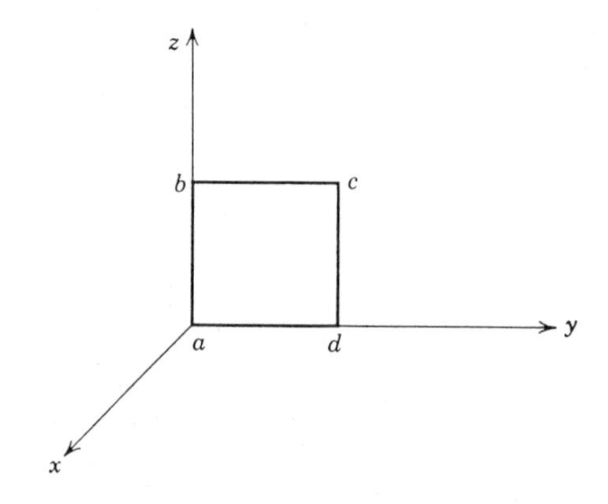

FIG. 5-1. Square path *abcda*.

distance from the cathode. The distance between the plates is 0.5 cm. Find the emf along a direct path from the anode to the cathode.

Solution. The vector path length $d\mathbf{l}$ is directed opposite to $\mathbf{i}$. However, $d\mathbf{l} = dx\,\mathbf{i}$ along the path, for x is decreasing, and dx is negative. The scalar product $\mathbf{E} \cdot d\mathbf{l}$ becomes $-400{,}000x^{1/3}\,dx$. Integration from 0.005 to 0 gives an emf of 257 volts.

EXAMPLE 2. In the dielectric of a certain hollow-pipe waveguide the electric field is

$$\mathbf{E} = 100 \cos 100x \cos (\omega t - 15\pi z)\,\mathbf{j}$$

At time zero find the emf around the square path *abcda* of Fig. 5-1. The length of each side is 0.1 m.

Solution. For $x = t = 0$, the field is $100 \cos 15\pi z\,\mathbf{j}$. Along *ab* the emf is zero, for $\mathbf{E}$ and $d\mathbf{l}$ are everywhere normal. From *b* to *c* the emf is also zero, as $\mathbf{E}$ is zero at each point. Along *cd* the field and the path are normal, and the emf is again zero. From *d* to *a* the field is $100\mathbf{j}$, and $d\mathbf{l} = dy\,\mathbf{j}$ as y decreases from 0.1 to zero. Therefore, the total emf is the integral of $100\,dy$ from 0.1 to 0, or -10 volts.

5-4. VOLTAGE

It has become fairly common practice to refer to electromotive force as *voltage drop*. Therefore, the voltage drop along a path C is the work per unit charge done by the fields on a small test charge moved along C. Voltage drop may, of course, be positive or negative. Some engineers and scientists prefer using the term electromotive force only with reference to energy sources or when referring to *closed* paths. However, there is no particular advantage in restricting the use of the term in this manner. As used in this text, electromotive force and voltage drop are synonymous.

A negative voltage drop is often referred to as a *voltage rise*. Thus the voltage rise along a path C is the work per unit charge done by an external force in moving a small test charge along C against the force of the fields. In terms of the fields the voltage rise is

$$\text{voltage rise} = -\int_C (\mathbf{E} + \mathbf{v} \times \mathbf{B}) \cdot d\mathbf{l} \tag{5-5}$$

If there is no magnetic field in the region or if the path C is stationary, this becomes the negative of the line integral of $\mathbf{E}$. A negative voltage rise is, of course, equivalent to a voltage drop.

A volt is equivalent to a joule per coulomb. If we interpret a coulomb-volt as the work done when one coulomb moves through a voltage of one volt, then a coulomb-volt is an energy of one joule. An *electron-volt*, often abbreviated *ev*, is the work done when an electron moves through one volt. As the electronic charge is 1.602×10^{-19} coulomb, it follows that the electron-volt is a unit of energy equal to 1.602×10^{-19} joule. This unit is frequently used when dealing with very small energies.

Voltage must not be regarded as energy. When a charge q moves through a voltage v, the work done is qv joules. However, if there is no movement of charge, there is no energy involved. For example, there is voltage between the terminals of a battery, but there is no expenditure of energy unless charge carriers flow through an electric circuit connected to these terminals. Voltage is often expressed in terms of *kilovolts* (kv), *millivolts* (mv), and *microvolts* (μv). A kilovolt is a thousand volts; a millivolt is one-thousandth of a volt; and a microvolt is one-millionth of a volt.

Shown in Fig. 5-2 is a method commonly used to indicate voltage on a circuit diagram. Such a diagram is an idealized representation of the actual physical circuit, with the circuit parameters regarded as lumped at points. By restricting integration paths to those external paths between

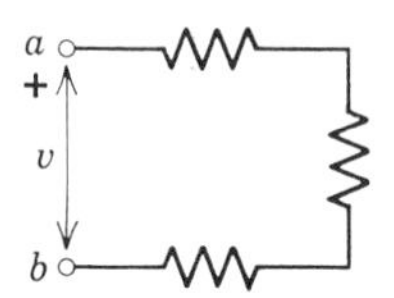

FIG. 5-2. A method of indicating the voltage v.

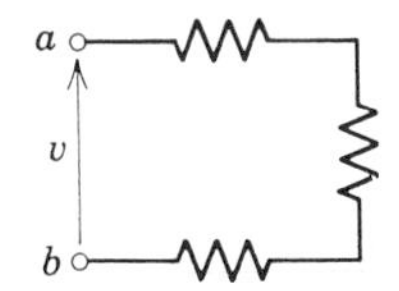

FIG. 5-3. Alternate method.

the terminals of these lumped elements, the voltage between two points becomes independent of the path of integration. This is discussed in detail in Chapter 14. Thus the double-headed arrow of Fig. 5-2 indicates the two end points of the integration path to which the voltage v is referred. The plus sign at terminal a informs us that v is the voltage drop from a to b. Of course, v also represents the voltage rise from b to a. At any instant v may be positive or negative, and as time varies, the sign of v may alternate. If v represents a d-c voltage that does not vary with time, a minus sign is often placed at terminal b in addition to the plus sign at terminal a, and usually the symbol V is used. Sometimes the plus sign on Fig. 5-2 is carelessly omitted. The doubled-headed arrow, alone without the plus sign, fails to indicate whether v is the voltage drop or voltage rise from a to b, and there is ambiguity.

Figure 5-3 shows a second method sometimes used to indicate voltage. The single-headed arrow replaces the double-headed arrow and plus sign. The voltage v represents the voltage drop from a to b, as before. The notation of Figs. 5-2 and 5-3 is said to indicate the *reference direction*, or *positive direction*, of v. We should keep in mind, however, that voltage is a scalar, and that the symbols are used to inform us whether v denotes the voltage drop or rise when integrating from one point to another. Frequently, double subscripts are utilized in place of arrows, with the voltage drop from a to b denoted by the symbol v_{ab}.

It should be emphasized that the selection of the reference direction of voltage is arbitrary. The terminal voltage of an a-c generator is alternately positive and negative no matter which way the reference direction is specified. For a 2-volt battery, if the reference direction is selected so that v denotes the voltage drop from the positive to the negative terminal, then $v = +2$. However, if the reference direction is selected so that v denotes the voltage drop from the negative to the positive terminal, then $v = -2$. Either choice is acceptable, and both are absolutely correct. Some refer to the reference direction as the *assumed direction*, but *there is really nothing assumed.* Only a choice is made from two possible selections, and one choice is as reasonable and logical as the other.

Whenever a charge q moves through a voltage drop v, the work done by the fields is qv. This energy must come from some source, and the source

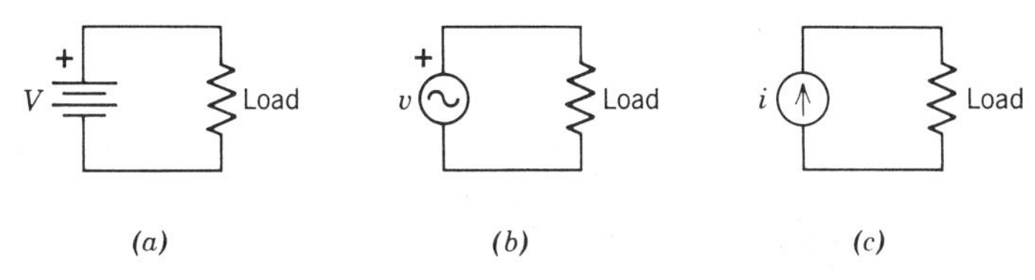

FIG. 5-4. (*a*) Ideal d-c voltage source. (*b*) Ideai a-c voltage source. (*c*) Ideal current source.

must supply energy continuously if a steady flow of charge is to be maintained. Some examples of such energy sources are batteries, generators, thermocouples, and photocells, which respectively convert chemical energy, mechanical energy, heat energy, and light energy into electrical form. The work done on the charges by the fields results in a withdrawal of energy from the energy source. The source receives energy, of course, when the charges are driven through it in the reverse direction, as in a battery being charged, but much of this energy may be lost as heat.

In electric circuit diagrams energy sources are often represented as ideal voltage or current sources. An *ideal voltage source* supplies a voltage that is unaffected by the load connected between its terminals, and an *ideal current source* supplies a current that is unaffected by the load. Neither exists, but many generators approximate one or the other for restricted load conditions. Shown in Figs. 5-4(*a*), (*b*), and (*c*) are symbols often employed to represent an ideal d-c voltage source, an ideal a-c voltage source, and an ideal current source, respectively. The plus signs on the voltage sources denote the reference directions of the voltages, as previously explained. The arrow on the current source has a similar meaning with respect to current, and this is discussed in Sec. 7-5. Incidentally, the reference directions of the voltage and current of an electric circuit are selected independently. Each selection is an arbitrary choice.

Let us consider briefly the voltage drop along a stationary path in a static electric field. Such a field is produced by static electric charges. Later it will be shown that the *electrostatic field is a conservative field*, having zero circulation. In Sec. 2-7 it was shown that the line integral of a conservative vector depends only on the end points of the path of integration, being independent of the actual path selected for evaluation of the integral. Therefore, in a region containing a *static* electric field the voltage

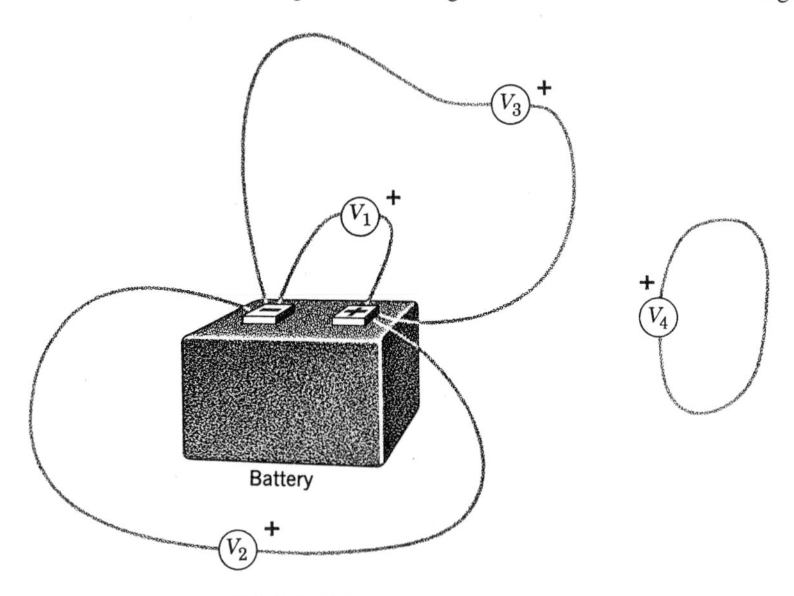

FIG. 5-5. Voltmeters in a static field.

along any stationary path depends entirely upon the end points of the path, and if the path is closed, the voltage is zero. For such regions it is proper to refer to the voltage between two points, without specifying any particular path. In Fig. 5-5 the positive and negative charges on the terminals of the battery produce an electrostatic field. As this field is conservative, voltmeters V_1, V_2, and V_3 read the same, and voltmeter V_4 reads zero.

In the general case of time-varying fields the electric field is not conservative, and the voltage around a closed stationary path is not zero. Also, when the fields vary with time, the voltage between two points depends on the path of integration. In "low-frequency" circuits the fields vary rather slowly with respect to time, and usually, voltages are measured along paths selected so that the electric field is approximately conservative. This will be discussed in more detail later.

5-5. MOTIONAL EMF AND THE GENERATOR LAW

A conductor contains charge carriers called *free electrons*. If a conductor is in an electric field **E**, or if it is moving in a magnetic field **B**, a force acts on these electrons, causing them to drift in the direction of the force. Such a motion of charge carriers constitutes an electric current. The moving charges acquire energy from the fields, and this energy is converted into heat by means of *collisions* between the electrons and the atoms.

Let us consider a circuit consisting of metallic wires that form a closed path. Suppose a portion of this circuit is somehow moved, without opening the circuit, so that the force per unit charge due to $\mathbf{v} \times \mathbf{B}$ is directed along the moving conductor. Obviously, the free electrons will drift along the path of the wires, causing the wires to heat. The source of energy is mechanical, for a mechanical force moves the wire. This principle is utilized to convert mechanical energy into electrical energy.

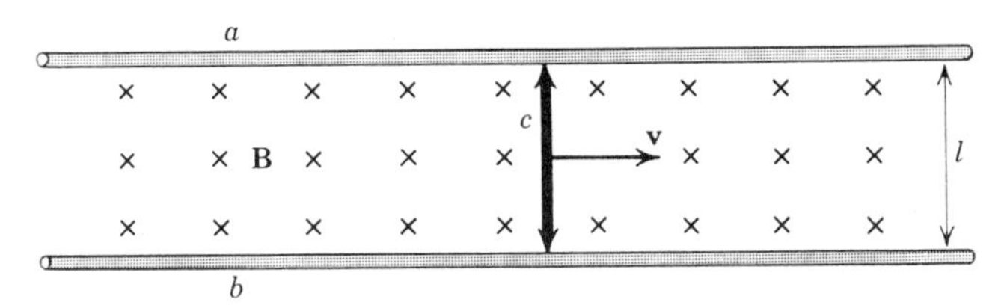

FIG. 5-6. An elementary electric generator.

Shown in Fig. 5-6 is a simple electric generator. The wires labeled a and b are stationary conductors separated a distance l, whereas wire c is moving from left to right with constant velocity $\mathbf{v}$. Conductor c is connected electrically to conductors a and b by means of sliding contacts. A uniform magnetic field **B** is directed into the paper, with the crosses of the illustration denoting the tail ends of arrows directed along lines of magnetic flux.

The circuit of Fig. 5-6 is open. Therefore, under equilibrium conditions there cannot possibly be an electric current. As the free electrons do not have a drift velocity, the net force acting on these charge carriers is zero, and so is the force per unit charge $\mathbf{F}/q$. Clearly, the voltage drop, which is the line integral of $\mathbf{F}/q$, is zero along any path C that is wholly within the conducting material of wires a, b, and c.

At each point of the moving conductor c the force per unit charge, which equals $\mathbf{E} + \mathbf{v} \times \mathbf{B}$, is zero. It follows that $\mathbf{E} = -\mathbf{v} \times \mathbf{B}$. The vector product $\mathbf{v} \times \mathbf{B}$ has magnitude vB and direction along the moving wire from conductor b to conductor a. Let us investigate the source of the electric field.

Initially, with wire c stationary, there is no electric field, and $\mathbf{v} \times \mathbf{B}$ is zero. As the velocity of the conductor increases, the magnetic force on the charge carriers increases, and a separation of charge results. Conductor a acquires a net positive charge, and conductor b acquires a net negative charge. These charges produce an electric field in the region. In the moving wire the electric force on the charge carriers, due to the field $\mathbf{E}$, opposes the magnetic force due to $\mathbf{v} \times \mathbf{B}$. As has been shown, under equilibrium conditions there is no current, the net force on the free electrons of the moving wire is zero, and $\mathbf{E}$ is exactly equal to $-\mathbf{v} \times \mathbf{B}$.

Next, let us consider the line integral of the electric field $\mathbf{E}$ along the path C of the moving wire from conductor a to conductor b. At points along this path the magnitude of the electric field is vB, and $\mathbf{E}$ is directed from conductor a to conductor b. Therefore, the line integral of $\mathbf{E}$ from a to b is the product of vB and the path length l, or vBl. Of course, the line integral of $\mathbf{v} \times \mathbf{B}$ along this same path is $-vBl$, and the total voltage drop is zero.

The electric field intensity is the field of the static charges on conductors a and b. The electrostatic field is conservative. Therefore, the line integral of $\mathbf{E}$ from a to b equals vBl regardless of the path selected. This is the voltage drop from a to b along *any stationary path*. Thus we see that the magnetic force on the charge carriers in the moving wire causes an initial separation of charge, with conductor a charged positively and conductor b charged negatively. These equal and opposite charges produce an electric field. Within the moving wire the electric force on the charge carriers opposes the magnetic force, and consequently, the voltage drop along the moving wire is zero. However, along any *stationary* path from a to b the voltage drop is vBl. This would be the reading of a stationary voltmeter connected between the conductors. The relation

$$\text{emf} = vBl \tag{5-6}$$

is known as the *generator law*.

In order to put the emf to work, let us connect between conductors a and b a stationary wire with appreciable resistance to the flow of electric charge. This resistance wire closes the circuit of Fig. 5-6, and a steady electric current results. The moving charges in the resistance produce heat. The source of energy is the mechanical work done in moving wire c. There is now a small emf along conductors a, b, and c, resulting from the force per unit charge required to move the charge carriers of these conductors. Consequently, the voltage along the path of the resistance wire is somewhat less than vBl. The charges on conductors a and b are reduced, and the magnitude of $\mathbf{E}$ at points of the moving wire is slightly less than the magnitude of $\mathbf{v} \times \mathbf{B}$. The greater magnetic force moves the charge carriers in the direction opposite to the smaller electric force. Of course, there is no magnetic force on the free electrons of the stationary conductors.

Around the closed metallic circuit the voltage drop is

$$\text{emf} = \oint_C \mathbf{E} \cdot d\mathbf{l} + \oint_C (\mathbf{v} \times \mathbf{B}) \cdot d\mathbf{l} \tag{5-7}$$

The line integral of **E** around the closed path C is often referred to as the *transformer emf.* In this static problem the field is conservative, and the transformer emf is zero. The line integral of $\mathbf{v} \times \mathbf{B}$ is called the *motional emf,* or *speed emf.* The motional emf around the closed path C is, of course, equal to vBl. Most of this voltage appears across the resistance wire, provided conductors a, b, and c offer relatively little resistance to the flow of the free electrons. The motional-emf principle is utilized in commercial electric generators to convert mechanical energy into electrical energy, and we shall examine this in more detail in Sec. 7-7. Electrical energy can be efficiently transported over considerable distances by means of transmission lines and then converted into the energy form that is desired.

REFERENCE

Booker, H. G., *An Approach to Electrical Science*, McGraw-Hill Book Co., New York 1959, Chap. 3 of Part 4.

PROBLEMS

Section 5-4

5-1. A test charge q is moved along a path C in a region containing electromagnetic fields, and the work done on the test charge by the fields is W. Determine the emf, the voltage drop, and the voltage rise along C if (*a*) $q = +2\ \mu\text{c}$, $W = +4\ \mu\text{joules}$; (*b*) $q = -3\ \mu\text{c}$, $W = 9\ \mu\text{joules}$; (*c*) $q = +4\ \mu\text{c}$, $W = -36\ \mu\text{joules}$; (*d*) $q = -5\ \mu\text{c}$, $W = -50\ \mu\text{joules}$.

5-2. A small particle with charge q is moved along a path C in a region containing electromagnetic fields, and the work done on the particle by the mechanical force that moves it against the field force is W. Determine the emf and the voltage rise along C if (*a*) $q = +4\ \mu\text{c}$, $W = +40\ \mu\text{joules}$; (*b*) $q = -4\ \mu\text{c}$, $W = +24\ \mu\text{joules}$; (*c*) $q = +5\ \mu\text{c}$, $W = -100\ \mu\text{joules}$; (*d*) $q = -1\ \mu\text{c}$, $W = -100\ \mu\text{joules}$.

5-3. A test charge q is moved along a path C in a region containing electromagnetic fields, resulting in the field energy being increased by an amount W. Determine the emf and the voltage rise if (*a*) $q = +1\ \mu\text{c}$, $W = +150\ \mu\text{joules}$; (*b*) $q = -2\ \mu\text{c}$, $W = +200\ \mu\text{joules}$; (*c*) $q = +3\ \mu\text{c}$, $W = -60\ \mu\text{joules}$; (*d*) $q = -4\ \mu\text{c}$, $W = -1000\ \mu\text{joules}$.

5-4. A test charge of $+2\ \mu\text{c}$ is moved along the x-axis from the origin to $x = 2$. $\mathbf{E} = -10\mathbf{i} + 5\mathbf{j} - 25\mathbf{k}$ volts per meter. (*a*) Find the work done by **E** on the test charge. (*b*) Determine the work per unit charge done by **E** on the test charge.

(*c*) What is the emf along the path traversed by the test charge? (*d*) What is the voltage rise along this path?

5-5. Repeat Prob. 5-4, except let the test charge be $-2\ \mu c$.

5-6. An electric field $\mathbf{E} = (100/r^2)\mathbf{a}_r$ volts/meter, where r represents the distance from the origin of a coordinate system and $\mathbf{a}_r$ represents a unit vector along r directed away from the origin. (*a*) Find the emf along a path C from infinity directly toward the origin to $r = 2$. (*b*) Find the voltage rise along a path C from $r = 2$ radially outward to $r = 5$.

5-7. Repeat Prob. 5-6, except let $\mathbf{E} = -(50/r^2)\mathbf{a}_r$.

5-8. A circular loop of metallic wire, with a loop radius of 1 m, has an electromotive force induced by a time-changing magnetic field. If the electric field intensity $\mathbf{E}$ along the path C of the wire has a magnitude of 2 v/m and if $\mathbf{E}$ is directed along the path C in a clockwise direction, find (*a*) the emf around C in a clockwise direction; (*b*) the voltage rise around C in a counterclockwise direction; (*c*) the voltage rise around one-half of the loop in a clockwise direction; and (*d*) the voltage rise around one-half of the loop in a counterclockwise direction.

5-9. An electric charge of $+0.2$ c is moved through a voltage rise of 50 v. What work is done by (*a*) the mechanical force that moves the charge carrier, and (*b*) the field?

5-10. An electric charge of $+2\ \mu c$ "falls" freely through a voltage drop of 100 volts. What kinetic energy does the charge carrier acquire?

5-11. An electric charge of $-5\ \mu c$ "falls" freely through a voltage rise of 50 volts. What kinetic energy does the charge carrier acquire?

5-12. In a resistance wire a charge of 10 coulombs moves through a voltage of 100 volts at a constant drift velocity. What is the heat energy supplied to the wire?

5-13. In a resistance wire there is a steady flow of electric charge at a rate of 10 coulombs per second through a voltage of 500 volts. What power is supplied to the wire by the electric field, causing the wire to heat?

5-14. A vacuum tube has a voltage rise of 200 volts from the cathode to the plate. An electron, emitted by the cathode with negligible emission velocity, is accelerated by the electric field present in the vacuum. Find the kinetic energy and the velocity of the electron immediately before it strikes the plate. What heat energy is supplied by the electron to the plate?

5-15. An electron with zero initial velocity moves freely through a voltage rise of 1,000,000 volts. Determine the kinetic energy and the velocity acquired by the electron.

5-16. A voltage of 100 exists between two parallel plates 1 cm apart in vacuum. Determine the electric field intensity E in the region between the plates, if E is assumed to be a constant, independent of position. Find the acceleration of an electron moving freely in the region between the plates.

5-17. At a certain instant of time, the electric field intensity $\mathbf{E} = \cos x \sin y\ \mathbf{i} - \sin x \cos y\ \mathbf{j}$ in a region. Find the voltage rise along a path C that starts at the origin and extends directly to the point (1, 1, 0).

5-18. Repeat Prob. 5-17, except let the path C extend from the origin directly to the point (1, 0, 0) and from there directly to the point (1, 1, 0).

5-19. If $\mathbf{E} = 100\mathbf{i} - 50\mathbf{j} + 200\mathbf{k}$ in a region, determine the emf along a path C, if C is a path (a) along the x-axis from the origin to $x = 3$, (b) along the y-axis from the origin to $y = 5$, (c) along the path $x = y = z$ from the origin to the point (1, 1, 1).

Section 5-5

5-20. In Fig. 5-6, suppose a voltmeter, consisting of a high resistance in series with a galvanometer, is inserted in the moving wire between the sliding taps. If $B = 0.01$ weber/m^2, $l = 0.2$ m, and $v = 100$ m/sec, what does the voltmeter read?

5-21. In Fig. 5-6 suppose a stationary voltmeter is inserted between wires a and b. If $B = 0.01$ weber/m^2, $l = 0.2$ m, and $v = 100$ m/sec, what does the voltmeter read?

5-22. A thin copper disk of radius 0.2 m is rotating about an axis through its center at a rate of 1200 revolutions per minute. A uniform magnetic field of 0.5 weber/m^2 is directed normal to the plane of the rotating disk. Determine the reading of a voltmeter which has one terminal connected to the center of the disk and the other terminal connected to the rim of the disk, these connections being made by means of sliding contacts. (To solve this problem consider a path directly between the sliding contacts. The motional emf of a differential path length is $vB\,dl$. The velocity v of dl is equal to ωr, where ω is the angular velocity in radians per second and r is the distance from the center of the disk.)

Physical Media

CHAPTER 6

Physical media are believed to be composed of discrete particles containing discrete charges, with the particles separated from one another by intervening spaces. The variation of the fields from point to point in these media is considerable. The number, arrangement, and behavior of the particles of a medium may appreciably affect the electric and magnetic fields and their associated currents. However, by utilizing the concepts of *permittivity*, *permeability*, and *conductivity*, we can regard media as continuous, with the effects of the multitudinous charged particles described by these concepts. This enables us to state the field equations so as to include the electric and magnetic effects of physical media without considering the individual action of each charged particle. Classical electromagnetic theory treats each point of a region as a small volume containing thousands of individual atoms, and only the *average* fields are of interest. In this chapter the three concepts used to describe the electrical properties of physical media are briefly discussed.

6-1. PERMITTIVITY OF FREE SPACE

In the 1780's the French physicist, Charles Coulomb, investigated the law of force between electric charges. In one of his experiments he measured the force on a small charged body held near the surface of a charged conductor. He ascertained that this force and, therefore, the electric field intensity are proportional to the surface charge density ρ_s.

Shown in Fig. 6-1 are two closely spaced conducting plates separated by free space, or vacuum. The plates are charged with equal and opposite charges, with the force of attraction causing surface charge densities ρ_s and $-\rho_s$ to appear on the sides of the plates facing each other. The electric field **E** is directed from the positive plate to the negative plate, and the magnitude E is proportional to ρ_s. This relationship is defined as $\epsilon_0 E = \rho_s$, with ϵ_0 representing the constant of proportionality. This constant may be regarded as one of the universal physical constants, having a value of 8.854×10^{-12} in the rationalized mks system of units. Both sides of the equation $\epsilon_0 E = \rho_s$ must, of course, have the same dimensions. As E is measured in volts per meter and ρ_s is measured in coulombs per square meter, it is evident that ϵ_0 is expressed in coulombs per volt per meter.

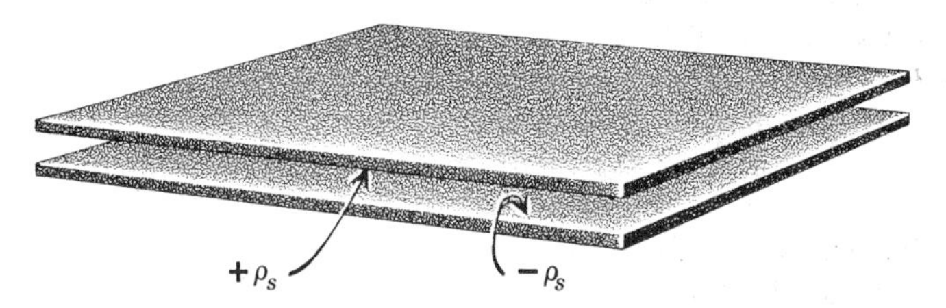

FIG. 6-1. Parallel conducting plates with uniform surface-charge densities ρ_s and $-\rho_s$ on the sides of the plates facing each other.

The *farad* is an mks unit defined as a coulomb per volt. Therefore, ϵ_0 has the mks unit *farad per meter*.

The constant ϵ_0, called the *permittivity of free space*, appears in many equations of electromagnetic theory. The equation relating E and ρ_s of the charged plates is but one example. Accordingly, we define the permittivity ϵ_0 of free space as

$$\epsilon_0 = 8.854 \times 10^{-12} \text{ farad/m} \quad [T^2Q^2/L^3M] \tag{6-1}$$

6-2. PERMITTIVITY

Suppose the region between the conducting plates of Fig. 6-1 is now occupied by some insulating material. The charges on the conducting plates exert forces on the charged particles of the atoms of the physical medium. The forces on the positive nuclei and the forces on the surrounding negative electron clouds, being oppositely directed, cause the electron clouds to be slightly displaced relative to their respective nuclei. Consequently, each atom appears to have two equal charges of opposite sign, with a small distance between them. These atomic charges produce an electric field that is directed opposite to the field of the charges on the conducting plates. Therefore, the effect of the medium is to *reduce* the total field.

It is not the purpose here to discuss the electric theory of materials from the microscopic viewpoint, but rather to define the *macroscopic* concept of *relative permittivity*. This concept is employed to describe the large-scale observable effect of a medium on the electric field produced by a system of charges and currents, *without considering the effects of the individual atomic particles*. The macroscopic and microscopic views are carefully related in Sec. 18-9.

Let us refer again to Fig. 6-1. If the region between the plates is a vacuum, the magnitude E_v of the electric field in the vacuum is ρ_s/ϵ_0. Now suppose a dielectric slab is inserted between the plates. Although the surface charge density ρ_s remains unchanged, the magnitude E of the field is less because of the effect of the atomic charges of the medium. The ratio E_v/E, with constant charge, is known as the *relative permittivity* ϵ_r of the medium. Thus

$$\epsilon_r = E_v/E \qquad (q \text{ constant}) \tag{6-2}$$

E_v is the field with vacuum, or free space, between the plates, and E is the field with the physical medium present, the surface charge density being the same for both cases. The relative permittivity ϵ_r, defined by Eq. (6-2), is also frequently called the *dielectric constant* of the medium.

Obviously, ϵ_r is dimensionless. Its value depends on the intricate atomic structure of the medium. The dielectric constant of a given material depends on the temperature, pressure, frequency, and other variables that affect the atomic structure. As the field E of Eq. (6-2) is less than the field E_v, the relative permittivities of materials are greater than unity. Most commercial insulating materials have relative permittivities between 1 and 10. *The dielectric constants of metallic conductors are not precisely known*, being very difficult to measure, but the range of dielectric constants of conductors is about the same as for dielectrics, or insulators. Some oxides of titanium have relative permittivities as high as 10,000. The dielectric constant of air is 1.0006, and that of free space is, of course, unity.

Equation (6-2) can be used as a basis for direct measurement of ϵ_r. The voltage between the charged plates is proportional to the field E, for the field is approximately uniform in the region between the plates except near the edges. Therefore, the relative permittivity equals v_v/v, with v_v and v denoting the voltages corresponding to E_v and E, respectively. By measuring the voltages with and without the dielectric, while maintaining the charges on the plates constant, we can determine ϵ_r. Actually it is not necessary to keep the charge constant, provided the charge-voltage ratio is measured. This is discussed further in Sec. 18-9. Also, refer to Probs. 6-1 and 6-2.

The product $\epsilon_r\epsilon_0$ appears frequently in electromagnetic equations. For example, the field E_v in the vacuum between the conducting plates of Fig. 6-1 is ρ_s/ϵ_0. With a dielectric of relative permittivity ϵ_r between the plates, with ρ_s unchanged, the field E is E_v/ϵ_r, or $\rho_s/(\epsilon_r\epsilon_0)$. For free space the electric field intensity and the surface charge density are related by the constant ϵ_0 of proportionality, but with the medium present the constant of proportionality is $\epsilon_r\epsilon_0$, with ϵ_r describing the electrical effect of the medium. The product $\epsilon_r\epsilon_0$ is called the *permittivity* ϵ of the medium. In terms of ϵ, the field between the parallel plates is ρ_s/ϵ, with the permittivity defined as

$$\epsilon = \epsilon_r\epsilon_0 \text{ farad/meter} \quad [T^2Q^2/L^3M] \tag{6-3}$$

Both ϵ and ϵ_0 have the mks unit *farad per meter*, whereas ϵ_r is dimensionless and has no unit. Permittivity is sometimes referred to as *capacitivity*.

6-3. ELECTRIC FLUX DENSITY

In the region between the charged plates of Fig. 6-1 the field and the surface charge density are related by the equation $\epsilon\mathbf{E} = \rho_s\mathbf{a}$, with $\mathbf{a}$ denoting a unit vector directed from the positive to the negative plate. Both sides of the equation are measured in coulombs per square meter. The vector $\epsilon\mathbf{E}$ is called the *electric flux density* $\mathbf{D}$, and so by definition we have

$$\mathbf{D} = \epsilon\mathbf{E} \text{ coulombs/m}^2 \quad [Q/L^2] \tag{6-4}$$

For the special case of the charged parallel plates the electric field intensity $\mathbf{E}$ between the plates is $(\rho_s/\epsilon)\mathbf{a}$, and the electric flux density $\mathbf{D}$ is $\rho_s\mathbf{a}$. Therefore, at points between the plates the magnitude of the vector $\mathbf{D}$ equals ρ_s *regardless of the physical medium present*. Although $\mathbf{D}$ and $\epsilon\mathbf{E}$ are equal, the vectors $\mathbf{D}$ and $\mathbf{E}$ are fundamentally different concepts, having different magnitudes and dimensions.

Previously, we defined the flux of any vector over a surface S as the surface integral of the vector over the surface. Accordingly, the *electric flux* ψ over a surface S is defined as the flux of $\mathbf{D}$ over S. As $\mathbf{D}$ has the dimensions Q/L^2, the scalar product $\mathbf{D} \cdot d\mathbf{S}$ has the dimension of charge Q, and the mks unit of electric flux is the *coulomb*. Therefore, electric flux is

$$\psi = \int_S \mathbf{D} \cdot d\mathbf{S} \text{ coulombs } [Q] \tag{6-5}$$

In evaluating the surface integral of Eq. (6-5), one side of the surface is taken as the positive side. This is often indicated on a sketch by means of an arrow pointing out of the positive side. The arrow is referred to as the *reference direction* of the scalar ψ. If the direction of $\mathbf{D}$ reverses periodically, the sign of ψ alternates with time.

The concepts of electric flux density and electric flux are quite useful in electromagnetism. We shall learn that every charge is either a source or sink of electric flux. Also, we shall find that a time-changing electric flux has precisely the same magnetic properties as a current of moving charges. These and other important properties of electric flux are discussed in later chapters.

EXAMPLE. Shown in Fig. 6-2 is a cross section of a coaxial transmission line. The radius a of the inner conductor is 0.5 cm, and the inner radius b of the outer conductor is 1.5 cm. The relative permittivity of the dielectric is 8. It will be shown later in the text that charges $+q$ and $-q$ coulombs per meter on the inner

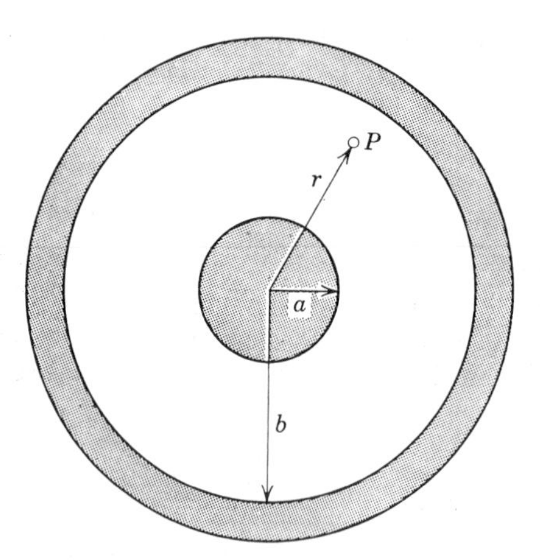

FIG. 6-2. Cross section of coaxial line.

and outer conductors, respectively, produce at a point P in the dielectric the field $\mathbf{E} = q/(2\pi\epsilon r)\,\mathbf{a}_r$, with r denoting the distance from the axis to P and with $\mathbf{a}_r$ denoting a unit vector at P directed radially outward. For $q = 5 \times 10^{-9}$ coulomb/m, determine the electric field intensity, the electric flux density, and the surface charge density at the surface of the inner conductor. Also, find the electric flux leaving the inner conductor in a length of one meter.

Solution. As $\epsilon = 8\epsilon_0 = 70.83 \times 10^{-12}$ and $q = 5 \times 10^{-9}$, it follows that $\mathbf{E} = 11.2/r\,\mathbf{a}_r$. At the surface of the inner conductor, $r = 0.005$, and $\mathbf{E} = 2240\mathbf{a}_r$ volts/m. The electric flux density $\mathbf{D} = \epsilon\mathbf{E} = 0.159\mathbf{a}_r$ μc/m^2. The surface charge density is found by dividing q by the surface area in one meter of length. This area is 0.01π, and the surface charge density is 0.159 μc/m^2. It should be noted that ρ_s and the magnitude of $\mathbf{D}$ at the surface are equal.

The electric flux ψ leaving the inner conductor in one meter of length is the surface integral of $\mathbf{D}$ over this surface. $\mathbf{D}$ and $d\mathbf{S}$ have the same direction at each point, and D is constant at points on this surface. Therefore, the surface integral equals the product of D and the surface area. As $D = \rho_s$, we deduce that the electric flux ψ leaving a unit length of the inner conductor equals the charge q per unit length. Thus $\psi = 5 \times 10^{-9}$ coulomb for a length of one meter.

6-4. PERMEABILITY OF FREE SPACE

In Sec. 6-1 we defined the permittivity ϵ_0 of free space as a certain number with certain dimensions. *To help us appreciate the significance of this selection* we considered the special case of two closely spaced parallel plates, charged with equal and opposite charges. The constant ϵ_0 was given as the proportionality constant relating the electric field and the surface charge density with a dielectric of free space. When a physical medium was introduced, we included an additional constant ϵ_r to allow for the effect of the medium on the field. We shall follow a similar procedure in discussing permeability.

In Fig. 6-3 is shown a small section of a long cylindrical coil of wire carrying a current that is steady with time. The turns of the wire are so

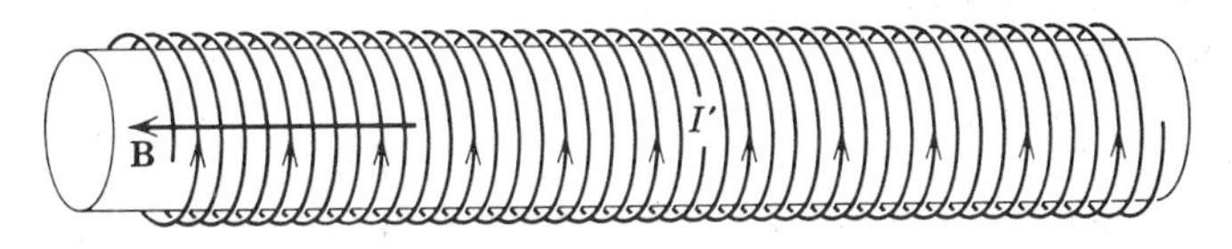

FIG. 6-3. A section of a long cylindrical coil of wire carrying a steady current I'.

close together that we can regard the coil as a continuous *current sheet* with charge carriers flowing circumferentially around the conducting sheet. Let us designate the current in one meter of length by the symbol I. Then I has units of amperes per meter. If the current in each individual turn is I' and if N denotes the number of turns of wire in the length l, the current I per unit length equals NI'/l amperes per meter.

Inside the coil the magnetic flux density **B** is directed parallel to the axis of the coil, with the magnitude B proportional to the current I per unit length. If the current is positive, the extended thumb of the right hand gives the direction of **B** inside the coil provided the fingers are curled around the coil in the direction of the current reference arrow. This is another useful right-hand rule. The relationship between **B** and I is supported by experimental observation, and later we shall deduce this relationship by application of Maxwell's equations. If the medium inside the coil is free space, the constant μ_0 of proportionality in the equation $B = \mu_0 I$ is called the *permeability of free space*.

The constant μ_0 may be regarded as one of the universal physical constants, having a value of $4\pi \times 10^{-7}$ in the rationalized mks system of units. The dimensions of μ_0 must satisfy dimensionally the equation relating B and I. As B and I are measured in webers per square meter and amperes per meter, respectively, it follows that μ_0 could be expressed in terms of webers per ampere per meter. A weber per ampere, with dimensions of L^2M/Q^2, is called a *henry* and, therefore, μ_0 has the mks unit of *henry per meter*. Thus the permeability of free space is defined as

$$\mu_0 = 4\pi \times 10^{-7} \text{ henry/m} \quad [LM/Q^2] \tag{6-6}$$

6-5. PERMEABILITY

Suppose the region inside the coil of Fig. 6-3 is now occupied by some physical medium. The orbiting and spinning electrons of the atoms have associated magnetic fields. In the absence of an applied magnetic field there is normally no net magnetization resulting from these atomic particles, for the fields of the individual atoms or groups of atoms are randomly oriented, thus canceling one another. However, when a magnetic field is applied, the orientations may be affected, inducing a net magnetization. The total field is the vector sum of the applied and induced fields, and this total field may be less than or greater than the applied field.

It is not the purpose here to discuss the magnetic theory of materials from the atomic viewpoint, but rather to define the *macroscopic* concept of relative permeability. This concept is employed to describe the large-scale observable effect of a medium on the magnetic field produced by a system of charges and currents, without considering the effects of the individual atomic particles. The macroscopic and microscopic views are carefully related in Secs. 17-4, 17-5, and 17-6.

Let us refer again to the coil of Fig. 6-3. For free space $B_v = \mu_0 I$, with the subscript v denoting vacuum. When a physical medium is present, the relation becomes $B = \mu_r \mu_0 I$, with μ_r introduced to describe the magnetic effect of the medium. Its value is determined by the large-scale effect of the many atomic magnets, and its use in the field equations of electromagnetism enables us to neglect the individual microscopic effects of the atoms. As B_v equals $\mu_0 I$ and as B equals $\mu_r \mu_0 I$, it is evident that

$$\mu_r = B/B_v \qquad (I \text{ constant}) \tag{6-7}$$

The field B in the medium and the field B_v in a vacuum are understood to be produced by the same current I per unit length. Equation (6-7) defines relative permeability. Obviously, μ_r is dimensionless, with a value in free space of unity.

The relative permeabilities of materials, excepting the *ferromagnetic metals* and alloys containing these metals, are approximately unity. The ferromagnetic elements are iron, cobalt, and nickel. These metals and alloys of these metals have relative permeabilities that range from several hundred to several million. The magnetic flux density inside the coil of

Fig. 6-3 will be very much greater in an iron core than in a nonferromagnetic core. The relative permeability of a material is a function of temperature, pressure, frequency, and any other variable that affects the atoms of the medium. *For nonferromagnetic materials the assumption of a relative permeability of unity is usually a reasonable engineering approximation.*

The product $\mu_r\mu_0$, which appears in the expression relating B and I, is called the *permeability* μ of the medium. As μ_r is dimensionless, μ and μ_0 have the same dimensions and are measured in the same units. Therefore, permeability μ is

$$\mu = \mu_r\mu_0 \text{ henry/m} \quad [LM/Q^2] \tag{6-8}$$

Permeability is sometimes referred to as *inductivity*.

6-6. MAGNETIC FIELD INTENSITY

In terms of the permeability μ of the medium, the magnitude B of the magnetic field inside the coil of Fig. 6-3 is equal to the product μI, with I denoting the current per unit length in amperes per meter. Clearly, the vector $\mathbf{B}/\mu$ has a magnitude equal to the magnetizing current I per unit length, regardless of the physical medium present. The ratio $\mathbf{B}/\mu$ is called the *magnetic field intensity*. It is designated by the symbol $\mathbf{H}$, and its mks unit is the *ampere per meter*. The defining equation is

$$\mathbf{H} = \mathbf{B}/\mu \text{ amperes/m} \quad [Q/LT] \tag{6-9}$$

Inside the coil of wire carrying a current I per unit length, the magnitude H equals I. As $\mathbf{H}$ is so closely related to the magnetizing current, it is sometimes called the *magnetizing force*, and the magnetic flux density $\mathbf{B}$ at a point in a medium is often thought of as the result of the action of the magnetizing force $\mathbf{H}$ on the medium. The magnetic field intensity $\mathbf{H}$ is directly related to the electric currents of a region. This relationship is discussed in Chap. 8. If $\mathbf{H}$ is known, the magnetic flux density $\mathbf{B}$ can be determined from the relation $\mathbf{B} = \mu\mathbf{H}$. Although $\mathbf{B}$ and $\mathbf{H}$ are simply related, they are fundamentally different concepts, having different magnitudes and different dimensions.

The unit of $\mathbf{H}$, the *ampere per meter*, is frequently called the *ampere-turn per meter*. This latter name is derived from the fact that intense magnetic fields are obtained by coiling current-carrying conductors so as to form a great many closely spaced turns. However, the addition of the dimensionless unit *turn* seems illogical when applied to the magnetic field intensity in the space between transmitting and receiving antennas or in the dielectric of a hollow-pipe waveguide. Thus the unit *ampere per meter* is preferred.

The line integral of the magnetic field intensity along a path C is called the *magnetomotive force*, or *mmf*, along the path. As **H** has the dimensions Q/LT, the line integral of **H** has the dimensions Q/T, and therefore, the mks unit of magnetomotive force is the *ampere*. The defining equation is

$$\text{mmf} = \int_C \mathbf{H} \cdot d\mathbf{l} \text{ amperes } [Q/T] \tag{6-10}$$

Magnetomotive force is sometimes expressed in *ampere-turns*, with *turn* being a dimensionless unit. Although the electromotive force along a path is defined as the work per unit charge done by the fields on an electric charge moved along the path, mmf is not similarly defined, because magnetic charges do not exist.

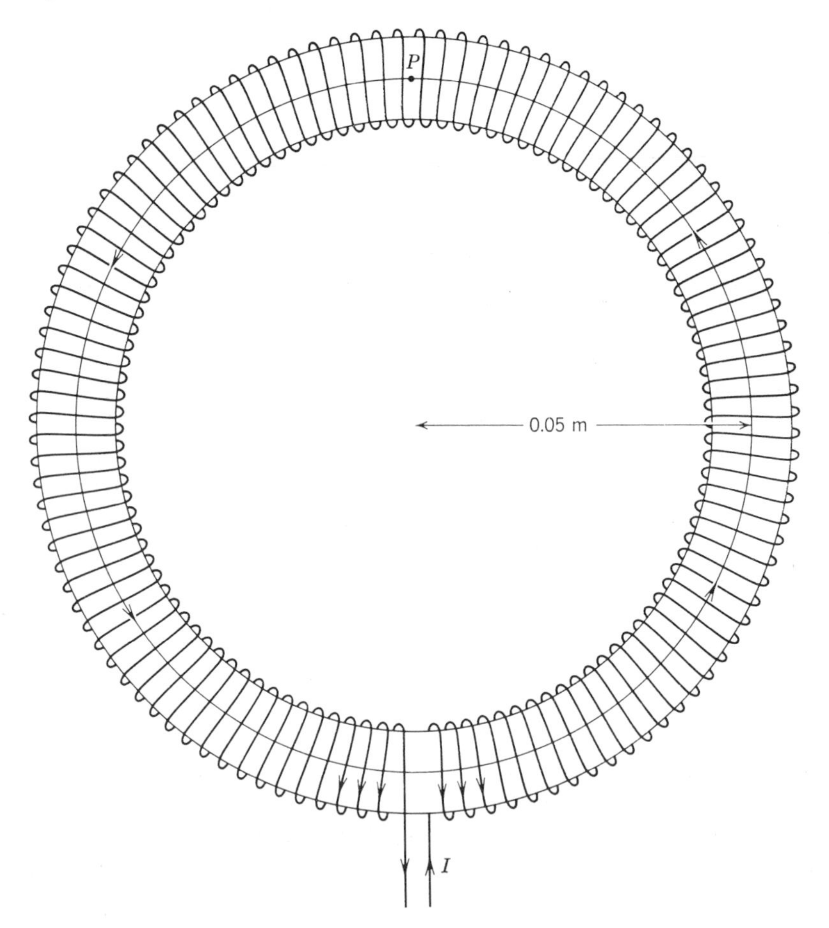

FIG. 6-4. Ferromagnetic toroid of circular cross section. The circular line through P represents a line of magnetic flux.

EXAMPLE 1. Shown in Fig. 6-4 is a ferromagnetic toroid of circular cross section. The current in the wire coiled about the toroid produces a magnetomotive force of 100 amperes around the ring. Passing through the point P is a circular line of magnetic flux of radius 0.05 m. Assuming a relative permeability of 400, determine the magnetic field intensity and the magnetic flux density at P.

Solution. The 100-ampere mmf equals the line integral of $\mathbf{H}$ around a path around the ring. Consider the path of the illustrated flux line. At points along this path $\mathbf{H}$ and $d\mathbf{l}$ have the same direction, and the magnitude of $\mathbf{H}$ is constant from symmetry considerations. Therefore, the 100-ampere mmf equals the product of H and the path length of 0.1π. It follows that H is $100/(0.1\pi)$, or 318 amperes per meter. The magnetic flux density $\mathbf{B} = \mu\mathbf{H}$. As $\mu = 400\mu_0$, the magnitude of $\mathbf{B}$ is readily determined to be 0.16 weber/m^2. The direction of the magnetic field at P is that of the illustrated flux line.

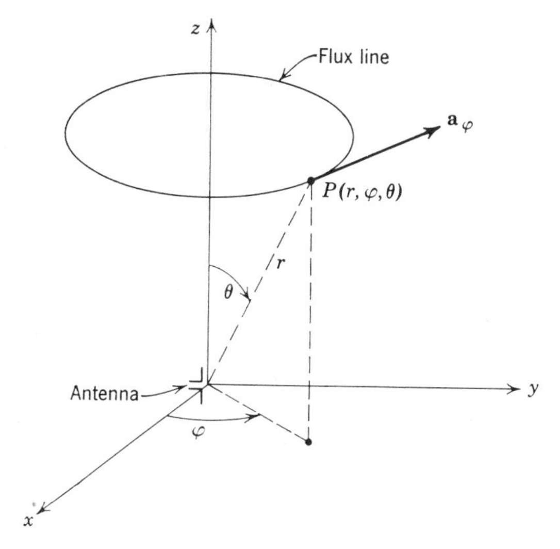

FIG. 6-5. A magnetic flux line through the point P, due to an antenna at the origin of the coordinate system.

EXAMPLE 2. A center-fed straight-wire antenna, a half wavelength long, is located in free space at the origin of a spherical coordinate system. The magnetic field intensity at a point $P(r, \varphi, \theta)$ at time t is

$$\mathbf{H} = \frac{2 \cos (90^\circ \cos \theta)}{r \sin \theta} \cos (6\pi \times 10^8 t - 2\pi r)\, \mathbf{a}_\varphi$$

Determine the magnetic field intensity and the magnetic flux density at the point $P_1(100, 50^\circ, 30^\circ)$, and find the mmf around the closed path of a flux line passing through P_1. Refer to Fig. 6-5.

Solution. The magnetic field intensity at P_1 is found by substituting the coordinates of P_1 into the expression for $\mathbf{H}$, giving

$$\mathbf{H} = 0.00836 \cos (6\pi \times 10^8 t)\, \mathbf{a}_\varphi$$

The magnetic flux density $\mathbf{B} = \mu_0\mathbf{H}$, for the medium is free space. We obtain $B_\varphi = 1.05 \times 10^{-8} \cos(6\pi \times 10^8 t)$ weber/m^2.

As the magnetic field at an arbitrary point P has only the component H_φ, the flux line through P_1 is circular about the z-axis as shown in Fig. 6-5. All points on this path have the same r and θ coordinates. As the magnitude of **H** is independent of φ, the expression for **H** at P_1 applies to all points on this path. It is evident that the mmf equals the product of H and the path length $2\pi(100 \sin 30°)$, or 100π meters. Therefore, the mmf is $2.63 \cos(6\pi \times 10^8 t)$ amperes.

6-7. CONDUCTIVITY

When an electric field **E** is applied to a physical medium, a force is exerted on the charges present. If the carriers of these charges were perfectly free to respond to the force, they would, of course, accelerate. However, there is a collisional force in the medium that increases with the velocity of the carriers. This restraining force stabilizes the carriers at a particular *drift velocity* **v**, whose magnitude is normally proportional to the electric field. The product of charge density ρ and drift velocity **v**, with the dimensions Q/L^2T, represents the flow of electric charge per unit area in coulombs per second per square meter. The area referred to is, of course, transverse to the velocity vector. As a coulomb per second is an ampere, the product $\rho\mathbf{v}$ is measured in amperes per square meter.

In general, the product $\rho\mathbf{v}$ is called the *convection current density* **J**. If the convection current density is in a conductor and if the motion of the charge carriers is due entirely to the force of an electric field, the convection current density is usually referred to as *drift current density*. Drift currents can be described in terms of the concept of conductivity, which we are now ready to define.

The drift current density in a conductor is

$$\mathbf{J} = \rho\mathbf{v} \text{ amperes/m}^2 \qquad [Q/L^2T] \tag{6-11}$$

If ρ is positive, the vectors **J** and **v** have the same direction; but if ρ is negative, their directions are opposite. The ratio of the magnitude J of the drift current density to the magnitude E of the applied electric field is called the *conductivity* σ of the medium. This is the drift current density per unit electric field. As **J** has units of amperes per square meter and **E** has units of volts per meter, the ratio J/E has units of amperes per volt per meter. The *mho* is an mks unit equivalent to an ampere per volt, with dimensions TQ^2/L^2M. Accordingly, we have

$$\sigma = J/E = \rho v/E \text{ mhos/m} \qquad [TQ^2/L^3M] \tag{6-12}$$

J and E denote the magnitudes of the drift current density and the electric field intensity, respectively, at a point in a medium.

The vectors **J** and **E** have the same direction. When the charge carriers are positive, they drift in the direction of **E**, and $\rho\mathbf{v}$ has the direction of **E**. On the other hand, when the charge carriers are negative, they drift in the direction opposite to **E**. However, the vector $\rho\mathbf{v}$ still has the direction of **E**, for ρ is negative. As $J = \sigma E$ from Eq. (6-12) and as **J** and **E** are in the same direction, it is evident that

$$\mathbf{J} = \sigma\mathbf{E} \text{ amperes/m}^2 \tag{6-13}$$

An electric field in a conducting medium causes the atomic charge carriers to drift, thereby producing an electric current. The drift current density is given in Eq. (6-13) directly in terms of the applied field and the conductivity, which depends on the atomic structure and the density of the free charge carriers. As might be expected, the conductivity is a function of temperature, pressure, and other variables that affect the atomic structure. Equation (6-13) enables us to utilize drift currents in our equations without considering each atomic charge carrier individually. Utilizing the product $\rho\mathbf{v}$ for this purpose is not as satisfactory, for the drift velocity **v** depends on the electric field.

6-8. FREE CHARGE CARRIERS

Any charged particle that is free to move in response to an applied electric field constitutes a free charge carrier. An example is an ionized atom in a gas. In solids there are two kinds of free charge carriers that are of particular importance. One of these is called a *hole*, and the other is called a *free electron*. A hole has a positive charge e, and a free electron has a negative charge $-e$, with the electronic charge $e = 1.602 \times 10^{-19}$ coulomb. In metals the charge carriers are free electrons, but in other materials both holes and free electrons may be present.

If a medium contains holes and free electrons, both types of charge carriers contribute to the conductivity. Let ρ_p and $\mathbf{v}_p$ denote the charge density and drift velocity, respectively, of the positive holes, and let ρ_n and $\mathbf{v}_n$ denote the corresponding quantities of the negative free electrons. The drift current density at a point in the medium is

$$\mathbf{J} = \rho_p\mathbf{v}_p + \rho_n\mathbf{v}_n \tag{6-14}$$

The positive holes drift in the direction of the electric field **E**, whereas the negative free electrons drift in the opposite direction. However, both $\rho_p\mathbf{v}_p$ and $\rho_n\mathbf{v}_n$ are vectors in the direction of **E**, for ρ_n is negative. It follows that the magnitude of the current density is

$$J = \rho_p v_p + |\rho_n| v_n \tag{6-15}$$

The conductivity J/E becomes

$$\sigma = (\rho_p v_p + |\rho_n| v_n)/E \tag{6-16}$$

Both holes and free electrons contribute positively to the conductivity.

We can put Eq. (6-16) into another common and useful form. In terms of the *carrier densities* p and n of the holes and electrons, respectively, the hole charge density ρ_p is pe, and the magnitude $|\rho_n|$ of the free-electron charge density is ne. Equation (6-16) becomes

$$\sigma = pe(v_p/E) + ne(v_n/E) \tag{6-17}$$

The drift velocity per unit electric field is known as *mobility* μ. The hole mobility $\mu_p = v_p/E$, and the electron mobility $\mu_n = v_n/E$. In terms of the carrier mobilities, the conductivity is

$$\sigma = pe\mu_p + ne\mu_n \tag{6-18}$$

This equation is of particular importance in the field of semiconductor electronics. The mks unit of mobility is the *meter²/volt-sec*, with the dimensions TQ/M. It should be noted that mobility and permeability, although different concepts, are designated by the same symbol μ. The carrier densities p and n are the number of carriers per cubic meter, with the dimensions $1/L^3$. Let us now take a very brief look into the process of conduction in solids.

6-9. ELECTRON ENERGY BANDS

Most conducting materials of interest to electrical engineers have their atoms arranged in an orderly array. Such materials are called *crystals*. Metals and semiconductors are examples of crystals, whereas important noncrystalline materials are concrete, glass, and plastics. The electrons in a crystalline solid determine its electric and magnetic properties, and the behavior of these electrons is governed by the laws of quantum mechanics. According to quantum-mechanical theory, the electrons are in certain *allowed energy bands*, these bands being separated by *forbidden energy gaps*. Each energy band contains an enormous number of *discrete* energy levels. No more than one electron in the entire crystal can occupy one of these discrete levels, and this is known as the *Exclusion Principle*.

If each discrete energy level in an allowed energy band is occupied by an electron, the electrons of this band cannot participate in the conduction process. They are unable to absorb energy from an applied electric field, because there are no higher energy levels to which they can go, all energy levels in the band being occupied. Consequently, *the electrons in a filled energy band do not contribute to conduction.* Such electrons are often referred to as *bound electrons*, although no one electron is actually bound to any particular atom.

The highest energy band that contains electrons at absolute zero of temperature is called the *valence band*, and its electrons are *valence electrons*. All bands of lower energy are completely filled and, therefore, need not be considered. All bands of higher energy are completely devoid of electrons at zero degrees Kelvin.

Suppose the valence band of a solid is completely filled at absoute zero. Such a solid has no free charge carriers and is a perfect insulator, with a conductivity of zero. However, at temperatures above absolute zero, some of the valence electrons acquire thermal energy sufficient to enable them to jump the forbidden energy gap to the next highest allowed band. The valence band is no longer filled, and the next highest band, called the *conduction band*, is no longer empty. The electrons in the partially filled conduction band are free electrons, capable of responding to an applied electric field.

Each electron that jumps from the valence band to the conduction band leaves a vacant energy level behind. These vacancies are called *holes*. A hole represents a positive electronic charge, for it is actually the absence of a negative electron from a region that was electrically neutral. If an electron in the valence band jumps into the vacant energy level of the hole, the hole is filled. However, a new hole appears at the location and energy level of the electron that jumped into the hole. In this manner the holes can respond to an applied electric field, and consequently, the positive holes are free charge carriers. If the forbidden energy gap separating the valence and conduction bands is large, very few free electrons and holes are thermally generated, and the solid is an *insulator*. However, if the forbidden gap is small, many free electrons and holes are thermally generated at room temperature, and the solid is a *semiconductor*.

Shown in Fig. 6-6 is the energy-band structure of a semiconductor. The symbols $+$ and $-$ denote thermally generated holes and free electrons, respectively, in the valence and conduction bands.

The preceding discussion infers that free electrons and holes are created in pairs. This is not always the case. Impurities in the semiconductor may donate electrons to the conduction band without creating holes. Such impurities are called *donors*, for they donate free electrons. Each donor atom that has given an electron to the conduction band has an allowed empty energy level that is just below the conduction band but is considerably higher than the valence band. Thus the valence band does not acquire holes corresponding to the free electrons given to the conduction band by the donor atoms.

Other impurities, called *acceptors*, may accept electrons from the valence band, resulting in the generation of holes without corresponding free electrons. The accepted electrons are in energy states just above the valence band but well below the conduction band and, consequently, these electrons cannot participate in the conduction process. Depending on the amount and kind of impurities, the charge carriers of a semiconductor may be predominantly either holes or free electrons. If positive

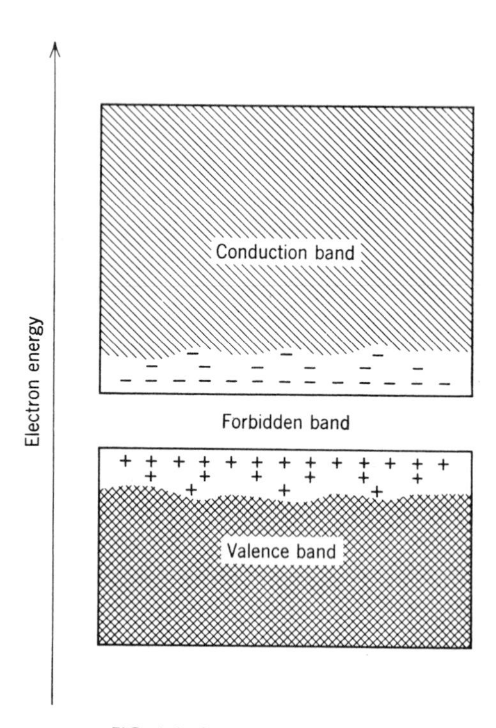

FIG. 6-6. Semiconductor bands.

holes are the majority carriers, the conductor is said to be a *P-type* semiconductor. If negative electrons are the majority carriers, the semiconductor is *N-type*. A semiconductor with equal numbers of holes and free electrons is said to be *intrinsic*. Obviously, a semiconductor without impurities is intrinsic.

A *PN junction* is a junction between P-type and N-type semiconductors. Such a junction passes electric current more easily in one direction, called the *forward* direction, than it does in the *reverse* direction. A PN junction is a solid-state rectifier. A *PNP* or *NPN transistor* consists of two rectifier junctions, which can be used to amplify electrical signals.

6-10. THE CONDUCTION PROCESS IN METALS

A metallic solid nearly always consists of large numbers of small crystals. Most of the electrical properties are determined by the properties of the individual crystals. Each crystal has a partially filled valence band, regardless of the temperature. Therefore, all the valence electrons are free electrons, and metals are good conductors. At 0°Kelvin (−273°C), the periodic array of a pure crystal is perfect, with every atom in precisely the correct place in the crystal lattice. Now it is well known that waves can propagate through a lossless periodic structure without attenuation or reflection. The quantum-mechanical equation that governs the motion of the electrons is a wave equation. Consequently, the free electrons travel through the periodic structure of the crystal without being reflected, or *scattered*, by the individual atoms. When an electric field is applied, the free electrons flow, and the crystal structure offers absolutely no resistance to the current. Therefore, a pure metal at absolute zero degrees is a *perfect conductor*, with an infinite conductivity. The flow of the free electrons within the conductor is unaffected by the presence of the atoms.

When the temperature of the conductor is raised, the thermal energy causes the individual atoms to vibrate. This vibration disturbs the periodic structure, and as a result, the free electrons are reflected, or scattered, after traveling a certain distance. The electrons are said to have *collisions*, but these collisions are not actual impacts of solid particles. At room temperature each free electron may travel an average distance of about 1000 atomic diameters before suffering a collision. This would not be possible if electrons were the solid round balls that many people like to visualize. The motion of the free electrons is random. They move at high velocities, usually about a million meters per second, and they suffer frequent collisions. The average distance between collisions is called the *mean free path*. As the temperature is raised, the thermal vibrations of the atoms increase, collisions are more frequent, and the mean free path decreases. The mean free path of a pure metal at absolute zero degrees is, of course, infinite.

When an electric field is applied, the electric force accelerates the free electrons, and they absorb energy from the field. This absorbed energy is imparted to the atoms during collisions, resulting in increased thermal vibrations. The electrons drift under the influence of the electric field. Their drift velocity is always very small compared with their large thermal velocity. For example, the drift velocity of the free electrons in an ordinary house wire supplying power to a 100-watt lamp is approximately 0.005 centimeter per second. Over three minutes are required for the electrons to drift through a distance of one centimeter! As the atoms absorb energy from the electrons during the collision process, the solid offers resistance to the flow of electrons, and this resistance increases with temperature.

The distribution of the free electrons within a metal is always approximately uniform. Usually one or more electrons of each atom has become a free electron, and each atom is, therefore, a positive ion. Electric neutrality must be maintained in each small region of the metal. Suppose a wire carrying a current of free electrons is in a magnetic field. The magnetic force on the moving electrons is at right angles to their motion, and this force tends to move the free electrons toward one side of the wire. However, *there is no appreciable displacement of the free electrons*, because the attractive forces between the positive ions and the negative electrons strongly oppose this separation of charge. The magnetic force on the moving electrons is conveyed to the fixed ions through these attractive forces, and the wire tends to move sideways.

6-11. THE CONDUCTION PROCESS IN SEMICONDUCTORS

The free electrons of a semiconductor behave similarly to the free electrons of a conductor. It can be shown from quantum mechanics that the holes act very much like free electrons with positive charges. The holes have a random motion, move at high velocities, suffer collisions, and drift under the influence of an electric field. At zero degrees Kelvin a semiconductor has no free charge carriers and is a perfect insulator. As the temperature is raised, however, holes and free electrons are thermally generated, and the conductivity increases. If the impurity atoms are predominantly donors, the free electron is the majority charge carrier; but if the impurity atoms are predominantly acceptors, the hole is the majority carrier. At sufficiently high temperatures the thermal generation of hole-electron pairs is so great that the densities of the two types of charge carriers become nearly equal, and the semiconductor is intrinsic.

The conductivity of a semiconductor depends very much on the amount of impurity present and on the temperature. At room temperature (300°K) the conductivity is usually between 1 and 10,000 mhos per meter, a range of values that are considerably greater than those of good insulators and considerably less than those of good conductors. The semiconducting material used in transistors is usually germanium or silicon in the form of a single crystal with carefully controlled impurities.

We have learned that the conductivity of a conductor is infinite at zero degrees Kelvin and that this conductivity decreases as the temperature is raised. In comparison, the conductivity of a semiconductor is zero at absolute zero degrees, increasing as the temperature rises. An insulator is similar to a semiconductor, but its forbidden energy gap between the valence and conduction bands is much greater. These are important differences between conductors, semiconductors, and insulators.

6-12. OHM'S LAW

The drift current density **J** at a point in a medium is equal to $\sigma\mathbf{E}$, with σ denoting the conductivity. In general, any variable that affects the structure of a medium would be expected to affect its conductivity; for example, we know that σ may vary considerably with temperature. It may also depend on the applied electric field **E**. However, *most engineering materials have conductivities that are very nearly independent of the applied electric field intensity* **E**, except for unusually intense fields. This was first stated by Georg Simon Ohm in 1826.

If the conductivity of a medium is essentially independent of the electric field, then the drift current density **J** is directly proportional to the electric field **E**. As the current i of a conductor is proportional to the current density, and the voltage v along the path of the conductor is proportional to the electric field, it follows that the drift current is proportional to the voltage. The relation $v = iR$, with R denoting a constant independent of v and i, is commonly known as *Ohm's law*. The constant R is the *resistance* of the conductor. The relation $\mathbf{J} = \sigma\mathbf{E}$, with σ independent of **E**, is referred to as the *point form of Ohm's law*. The conductivity may vary with temperature, pressure, and other variables, but a medium is said to obey Ohm's law *provided σ is independent of* **E**. The law is based on experiment, and theoretical verification for actual materials is extremely difficult.

There are important exceptions to Ohm's law, and several are mentioned in Sec. 15-3. For these exceptions the equations $v = iR$ and $\mathbf{J} = \sigma\mathbf{E}$ still apply, but the values of σ and R depend on the magnitude of the applied field. The drift current density and the electric field are not proportional, and neither are the current and voltage. Ohm's law does not apply to such *nonlinear* media, for σ and R are not constants.

Frequently, it is convenient to work with the reciprocal of conductivity, referred to as *resistivity*. The mks unit of resistivity is the *ohm-meter*. As conductivity is measured in mhos per meter, it is evident that the *ohm* and the reciprocal mho are equivalent. Thus an ohm is equivalent to a volt per ampere.

Resistivity is usually denoted by the symbol ρ, which is also used to represent electric charge density. Mathematically, resistivity is defined as

$$\rho = 1/\sigma = E/J \text{ ohm-meter} \qquad [L^3M/TQ^2] \qquad (6\text{-}19)$$

If a medium is linear, Ohm's law applies, and ρ is independent of E and J.

Ohm's law is basic to the study of electric circuits. When written in the form

$$v = iR \tag{6-20}$$

it is important to understand that v denotes the voltage drop along the path of the element *in the direction of the reference current i*. This is usually illustrated as in Fig. 6-7, with the resistance R represented as a lumped element. The product vi gives the power p in watts supplied to the resistance R, for v is the work per unit charge and i is the charge per

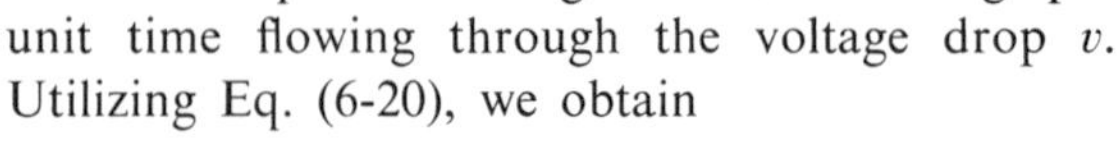

unit time flowing through the voltage drop v. Utilizing Eq. (6-20), we obtain

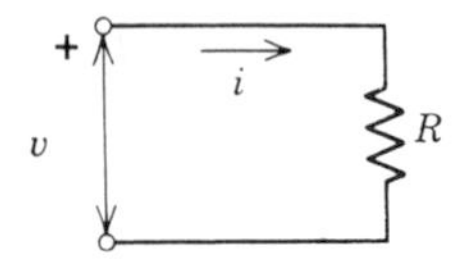

FIG. 6-7. Circuit with resistance.

$$p = vi = i^2R \text{ watts} \tag{6-21}$$

The power to the resistance is due to the collisional force that opposes the drift of the free charge carriers. The collisions tend to increase the thermal vibrations of the atoms, and the electrical energy withdrawn from the electromagnetic field appears as heat. If the reference direction of the current i of Fig. 6-7 is reversed, Eq. (6-20) becomes $v = -iR$. The power supplied to R is $-vi$, which equals i^2R as before. Clearly, this power is positive regardless of the sign of i.

6-13. LINEAR, ISOTROPIC, HOMOGENEOUS MEDIA

The field vectors are related by the expressions

$$\mathbf{D} = \epsilon\mathbf{E} \qquad \mathbf{B} = \mu\mathbf{H} \qquad \mathbf{J} = \sigma\mathbf{E}$$

with ϵ, μ, and σ denoting the permittivity, permeability, and conductivity, respectively. The drift current density $\mathbf{J}$ at a point is a convection current density $\rho\mathbf{v}$ due to charges of density ρ moving in response to an applied field $\mathbf{E}$.

Suppose ϵ, μ, and σ are independent of the *magnitudes* E and H of the fields. Then D is proportional to E, B is proportional to H, and J is proportional to E. Of course, plots of D versus E, B versus H, and J versus E are *straight lines*. Such physical media are said to be *linear*. *In a linear medium the equations of force are independent of the magnitudes of the forces.*

If the equations of force are independent of the *orientations* of the forces, the medium is *isotropic*. In an isotropic medium the vectors $\mathbf{D}$ and $\mathbf{E}$ are in the same direction, the vectors $\mathbf{B}$ and $\mathbf{H}$ are in the same direction, and so are the vectors $\mathbf{J}$ and $\mathbf{E}$. The parameters ϵ, μ, and σ are independent of the directions of the field vectors.

Each force in a medium that is linear and isotropic can be determined independently of the existence of other forces. In other words, each effect can be obtained from its cause and the superposition principle can be utilized to find the total effect. Consequently, the principles of vector algebra are applicable. The parameters ϵ, μ, and σ are, of course, independent of the magnitudes and orientations of the electric and magnetic fields in a region containing linear isotropic media.

A *homogeneous* medium is one in which the equations of force are the same at each point of the medium, *regardless of location*. Therefore, the parameters ϵ, μ, and σ are independent of the space coordinates within the boundaries of the medium. Inhomogeneous and anisotropic media are not considered in this book. Nonlinear media are treated briefly in several places, but in most cases ϵ, μ and σ are treated as constants that are independent of the magnitudes and directions of the fields and independent of the space coordinates. This places restrictions on some of the equations that we shall encounter.

REFERENCES

Dekker, A. J., *Electrical Engineering Materials*, Prentice-Hall, Englewood Cliffs, N.J., 1959, Chaps. 5, 6.

Ham, J. M., and G. R. Slemon, *Scientific Basis of Electrical Engineering*, John Wiley and Sons, New York, 1961, Chaps. 5, 6.

Ramey, R. L., *Physical Electronics*, Wadsworth Publishing Co., Belmont, Calif., 1961, Chaps. 3, 4, 6.

PROBLEMS

Sections 6-2 and 6-3

6-1. In the region between the parallel plates of Fig. 6-1, separated a distance d, the electric field **E** is directed from the positive to the negative plate, with a magnitude equal to ρ_s/ϵ. The charge q of a plate is the product of the surface charge density ρ_s and the plate area S. In terms of ϵ, d, and S, find the *capacitance* $C = q/v$, with v denoting the voltage between the plates. What is the capacitance per unit area for $d = 1$?

6-2. Using the result of Prob. 6-1, show that the dielectric constant equals the ratio of the capacitances of the parallel plates with and without the dielectric.

6-3. Suppose the voltage between two charged plates is 100 volts with a dielectric of air, and 25 volts with the space between the plates filled with an insulator, with constant equal and opposite charges. Calculate the permittivity and dielectric constant of the insulator.

6-4. A 100-volt battery is connected to two parallel plates and the charge on the positive plate is 9 μc. When the dielectric between the plates is removed, leaving free space, this charge is only 0.7 μc. Find the relative permittivity of the dielectric.

6-5. At a point in a medium $\mathbf{E} = 50{,}000\mathbf{i}$ volts/m and $\mathbf{D} = 5\mathbf{i}$ μc/m^2. Determine the permittivity and the relative permittivity of the medium, and find **E** if **D** is increased to $15\mathbf{i}$ μc/m^2.

6-6. Two parallel plates have charges $\pm q$. Find the total electric flux leaving each plate.

6-7. The inner and outer conductors of a coaxial transmission line (Fig. 6-2) have charges q and $-q$ coulombs per meter, respectively, and the electric field **E** in the dielectric is $q/(2\pi\epsilon r)\,\mathbf{a}_r$. Find the voltage drop v from the inner conductor to the outer one, and determine the *capacitance C per unit length*, with $C = q/v$. Calculate C for $a = 0.5$ cm, $b = 1.5$ cm, and $\epsilon_r = 8$, and compare this with the capacitance per unit length for a dielectric of air.

6-8. The electric field intensity at a point in free space is $10\mathbf{i} - 5\mathbf{j} - 4\mathbf{k}$ volts/m. Find the magnitude and direction cosines of the electric flux density.

6-9. At a point in a medium the z component of the electric field intensity is $100 \sin \omega t$ volts/m and the z component of the electric flux density is $7 \times 10^{-9} \sin \omega t$ coulomb/m^2. Determine the relative permittivity.

6-10. A straight wire of infinite length has a uniform linear charge density of ρ_l coulombs/m, and the electric flux density in the dielectric is $\rho_l/(2\pi r)\,\mathbf{a}_r$. Find the total electric flux over the surface of a concentric cylinder of radius a and unit length.

6-11. The total electric flux leaving a point charge q is equal to q. Find the electric flux density at points on a spherical surface with center at q and with radius r. Also, determine the electric field **E** a distance r from q in a dielectric of permittivity ϵ.

6-12. If $\mathbf{D} = 0.1\mathbf{i} + 0.4\mathbf{j} - 0.3\mathbf{k}$ coulomb/m^2, find the electric flux over a unit area of the xy-plane, with the positive side taken as that side facing the negative z direction.

6-13. The electric flux density in a certain region is $q/(4\pi r^2)\,\mathbf{a}_r$, with r denoting the distance from the origin of the coordinate system. Recalling that $\mathbf{a}_r = \mathbf{r}/r$, with $\mathbf{r} = x\mathbf{i} + y\mathbf{j} + z\mathbf{k}$, evaluate the surface integral of **D** over one side of a cube centered on the origin and having a side length of 4 m, and deduce that the electric flux leaving the cube equals q.

Sections 6-5 and 6-6

6-14. Suppose a long cylindrical coil of wire has 400 turns per meter of length and carries a current I' of 5 amperes. Assuming the coil approximates a continuous current sheet, calculate the circumferential current I per unit length. Also, determine the flux density B for a ferromagnetic core with a relative permeability of 200.

6-15. A long cylindrical coil of wire, with a ferromagnetic core whose relative permeability is 400, has a coil current I' of 2 amperes that produces a magnetic flux density of 0.5 weber/m^2 in the core. Find the number of turns of wire per meter, assuming the coil approximates a current sheet, and determine the current required to produce the same flux density in a nonferromagnetic core.

6-16. A long cylindrical coil of wire with a current I per unit length of 1000 amperes per meter approximates a current sheet. Find the magnetic field intensity and the magnetic flux density in the core of relative permeability 500. Repeat for a nonferromagnetic core. What effect does the medium have on **H**?

6-17. Suppose the coil of the ferromagnetic toroid of Fig. 6-4 approximates a continuous current sheet that produces a magnetomotive force around the ring equal to 200 amperes. In the ring of relative permeability 500, points P_1 and P_2 are located 5 and 5.3 cm, respectively, from the center of the toroid. Find B and H at points P_1 and P_2.

6-18. The magnetic field intensity in a certain region is

$$\mathbf{H} = -1.25 \sin 40x \sin(\omega t - 50z)\,\mathbf{i} + \cos 40x \cos(\omega t - 50z)\,\mathbf{k}$$

Find the mmf along the path $x = z$ in the xz-plane from the origin to the point $x = z = 0.01$ at time $t = 0$.

6-19. In the free space about a long straight wire carrying a steady current the magnetic field lines are circular around the wire. If the magnetic flux density is $10^{-7}/r$ weber/m^2, with r denoting the distance from the wire, determine the mmf around a circular path of radius r.

Sections 6-7 and 6-8

6-20. In the region between the plates of a certain parallel-plate vacuum tube the convection current density J is 500 amperes/m^2, and the velocity v of the electrons is $3 \times 10^8 x^{1.5}$ meters per second, with x denoting the distance from the cathode. Determine the charge density ρ as a function of x, and plot on the same axes the quantities J, v, and ρ versus x for values of x between zero and 0.005 m.

6-21. Assuming 8×10^{28} free electrons per cubic meter in copper, determine the drift velocity in a copper wire with a current density of 5×10^5 amperes/m^2. If $E = 0.009$ volt/m, what is the conductivity?

6-22. The charge density of the free charge carriers in a conducting wire with a cross-sectional area of 0.02 cm^2 is -7×10^9 coulombs/m^3, and the drift velocity is 10^{-4} meter/sec. Find the current.

6-23. An electric field of 0.01 volt/m is applied to a conductor with $\sigma = 4 \times 10^7$ mhos/m. The charge density of the free electrons is -5×10^9 coulombs/m^3. Find the current density and the drift velocity of the electrons.

6-24. A semiconductor has 10^{21} free electrons/m^3, with a mobility of 0.39 m^2/volt-sec, and 7.5×10^{17} holes/m^3, with a mobility of 0.19 m^2/volt-sec. Find the conductivity. Is this semiconductor P-type or N-type?

6-25. Find the conductivity of a P-type semiconductor with 3.3×10^{17} holes/cm^3 and 10^9 free electrons/cm^3. The carrier mobilities are given in Prob. 6-24.

6-26. In a P-type semiconductor with a conductivity of 90 mhos/cm, the hole mobility is 1900 cm^2/volt-sec. Assuming the free-electron density is very small compared with the hole density, find the hole density.

Sections 6-11 and 6-12

6-27. The conductivity of a semiconductor increases with temperature over most temperature ranges. However, over some limited temperature range the conductivity may decrease as the temperature increases. Explain.

6-28. What are the conductivities and resistivities of pure copper and pure germanium at absolute zero of temperature?

6-29. Determine the intrinsic conductivity and resistivity of an intrinsic semiconductor with a hole density of 1.5×10^{10} holes/cm^3, if the hole and electron mobilities are 500 and 1200 cm^2/volt-sec, respectively.

6-30. From the point form $\mathbf{J} = \sigma\mathbf{E}$ of Ohm's law, deduce that the voltage drop in a length l of wire with cross-sectional area S is $v = (l/\sigma S)i$, *provided* the current density $\mathbf{J}$ has the same value at each point within the wire. The expression $l/(\sigma S)$ is the *d-c resistance* of the wire.

6-31. In terms of L, M, T, and Q, what are the dimensions of $(\mu/\epsilon)^{1/2}$ and $(\mu\epsilon)^{-1/2}$? Also, compare the dimensions of $\dot{\mathbf{D}}$ with those of $\mathbf{J}$.

6-32. A round wire having a diameter of 0.5 cm and a conductivity of 5×10^7 mhos/m has a current $i = 8$ amperes. Find the voltage drop in a 100-meter length (*a*) in the direction of the reference current i, and (*b*) in the direction opposite to the reference current i. (*c*) Also determine the power that heats the wire, and calculate the energy dissipated in one hour. Refer to Prob. 6-30.

Electric Current

CHAPTER 7

Several years after Volta made his battery, Oersted discovered that an electric current produces a magnetic field, and Ampère showed that currents exert forces on one another. The early electrical experimenters believed that the current in a conductor *consists of electric charge in motion.* Their belief was strengthened in 1876 when Rowland showed that a moving charge produces a magnetic field. The success of the modern electron theory and quantum mechanics is convincing evidence that this is correct.

In order to resolve certain inconsistencies in the field equations Maxwell proposed that magnetic fields are produced by time-changing electric fields as well as by currents of moving charges. Accordingly, he introduced into the electromagnetic equations the concept of *displacement current*, and his theory was later substantiated by Hertz's experimental work. Displacement currents and currents of moving charges exhibit similar magnetic effects. Indeed, it is this similarity that led to the classification of current into these two basic types.

The main purpose of this chapter is to define electric current precisely. We shall examine briefly the different types of current, and we shall consider an alternate definition of magnetic flux density, with **B** expressed in terms of the force acting on a current element. The chapter concludes with a summary of definitions of the electric and magnetic quantities.

7-1. ELECTRIC CURRENT DENSITY

There are basically two kinds of electric current density, *convection current density* and *displacement current density.* Both have the same dimensions and the same magnetic effect.

Convection current density consists of electric charge in motion. Suppose the charge carriers at a point have charge density ρ and move with velocity $\mathbf{v}$. As previously defined, the convection current density $\mathbf{J}$ at the point is

$$\mathbf{J} = \rho\mathbf{v} \text{ amperes/m}^2 \qquad [Q/L^2T] \tag{7-1}$$

Displacement current density is due to a time-changing electric field, being defined as the time derivative of the electric flux density $\mathbf{D}$. If $\mathbf{D}$ at a point P is changing with time, there is a displacement current density $\mathbf{J}_d$ at P, with $\mathbf{J}_d$ equal to $\partial\mathbf{D}/\partial t$. As $\mathbf{D}$ has the dimensions Q/L^2, $\mathbf{J}_d$ has the dimensions Q/L^2T, which are the same as those of convection current density. Accordingly, the mks unit of $\mathbf{J}_d$ is the *ampere per square meter*. Using a dot over the vector $\mathbf{D}$ to denote the partial time derivative, we have

$$\mathbf{J}_d = \dot{\mathbf{D}} \text{ amperes/m}^2 \qquad [Q/L^2T] \tag{7-2}$$

Displacement currents are present whenever electric fields are changing with time. When electromagnetic waves are propagated from a transmitting antenna to a receiving antenna, there are time-changing fields present; consequently, there are displacement current densities at points in the space between the antennas. Other examples are the displacement currents in the dielectric between the plates of a capacitor being charged and between the wires of an open-wire telephone line.

The sum of the convection and displacement current densities is the *total current density* $\mathbf{J}_t$, which is

$$\mathbf{J}_t = \mathbf{J} + \mathbf{J}_d = \rho\mathbf{v} + \dot{\mathbf{D}} \tag{7-3}$$

An example that consists of both types is that at a point inside a vacuum tube used to amplify time-varying signals. The movement of the electrons in the space between the electrodes gives a convection current density; the time-changing voltage implies a time-changing electric field that produces a displacement current density. At high frequencies the fields are changing rapidly, and the displacement current density is appreciable. Another example is the current density in a leaky dielectric between the plates of a capacitor being charged. Still another is $\mathbf{J}_t$ in a conductor carrying an alternating current. The time-changing electric field at a point gives a displacement current density as well as a convection current density of moving charges. However, *in good conductors the displacement currents are negligible compared with the convection currents*, because the conductivities are very large.

7-2. DRIFT CURRENT DENSITY

When charge carriers drift in a conducting medium *in response to the force of an electric field* $\mathbf{E}$, the convection current density is usually referred to as *drift*, or *conduction, current density*. This was discussed briefly in Chapter 6. There we learned that a drift current density can be expressed as either $\rho\mathbf{v}$ or $\sigma\mathbf{E}$, with $\mathbf{v}$ denoting the drift velocity of the free charge carriers in the medium of conductivity σ. Let us bear in mind that convection currents in conductors are not always entirely drift currents. For example, when a conductor moves in a magnetic field, there are magnetic forces on the charge carriers in addition to electric forces that may be present. Within certain regions between the electrodes of a battery the charge carriers are acted upon by both chemical and electrical forces. In transistors the free electrons and holes move by the diffusion process, discussed in the next section, as well as by the drift process. A charged conducting plate that is rapidly rotated will cause a magnetic needle to deflect; in this case the current is the direct result of the mechanical force producing the rotation. However, in most engineering problems the currents in conductors are the result of *electric forces on the charge carriers*.

It is frequently convenient to incorporate the term $\sigma\mathbf{E}$ into the expression for $\mathbf{J}_t$. When this is done, Eq. (7-3) is written as

$$\mathbf{J}_t = \sigma\mathbf{E} + \dot{\mathbf{D}} + \rho\mathbf{v} \tag{7-4}$$

with the understanding that $\rho\mathbf{v}$ now denotes only the convection current density, if any, *in excess of the drift term* $\sigma\mathbf{E}$. In Eq. (7-4) the convection current density is the sum of the terms $\sigma\mathbf{E}$ and $\rho\mathbf{v}$, whereas in Eq. (7-3) it is denoted by the single term $\rho\mathbf{v}$. Equation (7-4) is often written with $\rho\mathbf{v}$ replaced by $\mathbf{J}$, giving

$$\mathbf{J}_t = \sigma\mathbf{E} + \dot{\mathbf{D}} + \mathbf{J} \tag{7-5}$$

The drift current density is $\sigma\mathbf{E}$, the displacement current density is $\dot{\mathbf{D}}$, and the convection current density, excluding that due to the drift process, is denoted in Eq. (7-5) by the symbol $\mathbf{J}$.

EXAMPLE. The field $\mathbf{E}$ at a point in a copper wire having a conductivity of 5.8×10^7 mhos/m is $0.02 \sin 10^5 t\, \mathbf{i}$ ampere/m^2. Determine the drift and displacement current densities, assuming a dielectric constant of unity.

Solution. The drift current density $\sigma\mathbf{E}$ is $1.16 \times 10^6 \sin 10^5 t\, \mathbf{i}$. The displacement current density $\dot{\mathbf{D}}$ equals $\epsilon_0\, \partial\mathbf{E}/\partial t$, or $1.77 \times 10^{-8} \cos 10^5 t\, \mathbf{i}$, and this is certainly negligible.

7-3. DIFFUSION CURRENT DENSITY

Using a familiar example to illustrate the diffusion process, let us consider the effect of releasing a small quantity of some pungent gas, such as sulfur dioxide, in a corner of a room. We all know that someone on the other side of the room would soon smell the gas, even in the absence of circulating air currents. It is the random thermal motion of the gas molecules that causes the sulfur dioxide gas to spread, or *diffuse*, away from the region of concentration. This net flow across a specified surface constitutes a current of sulfur dioxide molecules. After a period of time the gas density becomes uniform, and the current no longer exists.

Shown in Fig. 7-1 is a PNP transistor with bias voltages. It consists of a solid piece of semiconducting material, such as silicon or germanium, with impurities added to make P-type regions for the emitter e and the collector c and an N-type region for the base b. Positive holes are constantly injected from the emitter into the base, producing and maintaining

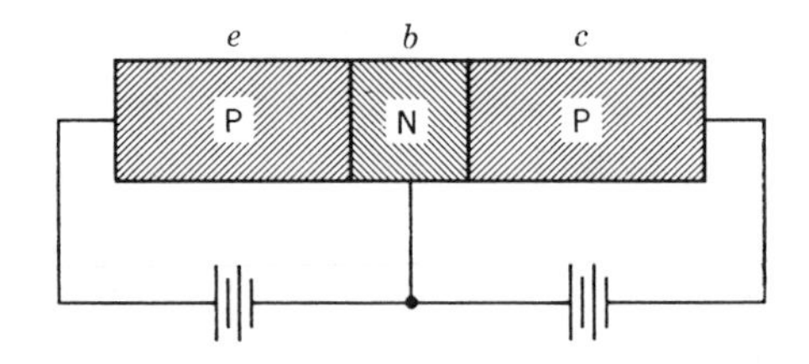

FIG. 7-1. PNP transistor.

in the base a concentration of holes near the emitter-base junction. A similar concentration of free electrons also occurs, for the free electrons of the base move into the region of hole concentration to neutralize the charge. If the net charge is very small, there are no appreciable repulsion forces, and such is frequently the case. However, the holes have random thermal motion and, consequently, they diffuse through the base, flowing to the collector. New holes are injected from the emitter into the base as fast as they diffuse away from the emitter-base junction, maintaining the hole gradient. This diffusion process is similar to that of the sulfur dioxide molecules in the example considered.

The flow of holes through the base constitutes a flow of electric charge. At each point there is a convection current density $\rho\mathbf{v}$ because of hole diffusion, and this is usually called the *diffusion current density*. It is independent of any electric field that may be present. If the holes are not completely neutralized by the electrons of the base region, there will be repulsion forces that cause the holes to drift away from the concentration. However, this is a drift current, which we discussed in the preceding section. Both drift and diffusion currents may be appreciable, though in special cases one or the other may be negligible.

In general, whenever a charge concentration exists in a conductor, there is a diffusion current density at points of the region. If the concentration is one of positive holes, the holes diffuse away from the concentration, and the current density is similarly directed. If the concentration consists of negative electrons, the electrons also diffuse away from the concentration, but the current density is, of course, in the opposite direction. The magnitude of the diffusion current density at a point is proportional to the space rate of change of the charge density, or *charge density gradient*, at the point; the constant of proportionality is known as the *diffusion constant*.

In Chapter 10 the gradient of a scalar point function, such as electric charge density, is discussed and expressed in mathematical form. The expression for diffusion current density and an example illustrating its use are presented at the end of Sec. 10-2.

It is important to note that diffusion currents in resistive materials, being independent of electric fields, do not produce voltage drops. As previously mentioned, however, a region may have both diffusion and drift currents, with the drift current associated with a voltage drop. To the electronics engineer diffusion currents in transistors are of special importance.

Let us now consider an example in which diffusion and drift current densities are everywhere equal in magnitude but opposite in direction. Suppose a solid conducting sphere has a net negative charge. The excess electrons exert repelling forces on one another by means of the electric fields produced by the charges. As a result the excess charge tends to distribute itself over the surface of the sphere. At each point inside the conductor there is a charge density gradient $d\rho/dr$, with r denoting the distance from the center. Associated with this gradient is a diffusion of negative electrons toward the center of the ball, giving a diffusion current density directed radially outward. Mathematically, this current density is $-D_n \, d\rho/dr \, \mathbf{a}_r$, with D_n denoting the *diffusion constant* for the electrons and with $\mathbf{a}_r$ denoting a unit vector directed radially outward. The negative sign cancels that associated with ρ. This current density is greatest, of course, near the surface where the charge density gradient is large.

We are dealing with a static situation; the net current must be zero everywhere. Therefore, there is a drift current density $\sigma\mathbf{E}$ at each point of the ball that exactly cancels the diffusion current density. Clearly, the field $\mathbf{E}$ equals the negative of the diffusion current density divided by σ, or

$$\mathbf{E} = (D_n/\sigma) \, d\rho/dr \, \mathbf{a}_r$$

For good conductors the ratio D_n/σ is so small that the field $\mathbf{E}$ inside the conductor is negligible. For example, if the ball is copper with $D_n = 0.0001$ and $\sigma = 5.8 \times 10^7$, the electric field is approximately 1.7×10^{-12} times the charge gradient. The charge gradient is always very small at distances greater than several atomic diameters from the surface. Consequently, practically all of the excess charge resides in a surface layer not more than a few atomic diameters in thickness, and the electric field inside the ball is zero for all practical purposes. Even for rather poor conductors a static charge is almost entirely contained within a very thin surface layer. When dealing with charged conductors, it is usually convenient to utilize the concept of surface charge density with the unit coulomb-per-square-meter. If there is no net current, the electric field within the conductor is negligibly small.

Both drift and diffusion currents are special cases of convection current. These are not the only kinds, however. For example, the electron flow in a vacuum tube is a convection current that is neither drift nor diffusion. Even in a metallic conductor other kinds may exist; this was discussed briefly in the preceding section.

EXAMPLE 1. A PN junction rectifier made of germanium has a rectangular cross section of area 10^{-6} m^2. Let x represent the distance from the junction to an arbitrary point in the N-type region. The hole density p in the N region is $[1.8 + 400 \exp(-x/0.0005)]\,10^{18}$ holes per cubic meter, and the free electron density n is $[320 + 400 \exp(-x/0.0005)]\,10^{18}$ electrons/m^3. If the hole mobility μ_p is 0.19 m^2/volt-sec and the electron mobility μ_n is 0.39 m^2/volt-sec, determine the conductivity as a function of x.

Solution. By Eq. (6-18) the conductivity σ is the sum of $pe\mu_p$ and $ne\mu_n$, with e representing the electronic charge 1.6×10^{-19} coulomb. Adding these terms together, after substituting the values given for p, n, and the mobilities, gives

$$\sigma = 20 + 37.1 \exp(-x/0.0005) \text{ mhos/m}$$

EXAMPLE 2. In the rectifier of Example 1 the hole diffusion current density $\mathbf{J}_p$ is $-0.005e\, dp/dx\, \mathbf{i}$ amperes/m^2, and the electron diffusion current density $\mathbf{J}_n$ is $0.01e\, dn/dx\, \mathbf{i}$. If the total current density, consisting of both drift and diffusion current densities, is everywhere equal to $1000\mathbf{i}$ amperes/m^2, determine the voltage drop v from $x = 0$ to $x = 0.0015$ m.

Solution. In Example 1, p and n are given as functions of x. Differentiation of these expressions shows that $dp/dx = dn/dx = -8 \times 10^{23} \exp(-x/0.0005)$. From this result we find $\mathbf{J}_p$ to be $640 \exp(-x/0.0005)\,\mathbf{i}$ and $\mathbf{J}_n$ to be $-1280 \times \exp(-x/0.0005)\,\mathbf{i}$. Therefore, the total *diffusion* current density is $-640 \times \exp(-x/0.0005)\,\mathbf{i}$. As the sum of the drift and diffusion current densities is everywhere equal to $1000\mathbf{i}$, it follows that the *drift* current density is $[1000 + 640 \times \exp(-x/0.0005)]\,\mathbf{i}$.

The drift current density equals $\sigma\mathbf{E}$. Therefore, E_x is $1/\sigma$ times the magnitude of the drift current density. Using the conductivity calculated in Example 1, we obtain

$$E_x = \frac{1000 + 640 \exp(-x/0.0005)}{20 + 37.1 \exp(-x/0.0005)}$$

The voltage drop v is found by integrating E_x with respect to x from 0 to 0.0015. The integration is readily performed by changing variables, with $y = -x/0.0005$, and referring to integral tables. The result shows that the voltage drop is 59 millivolts.

The current over a cross section of the rectifier equals the current density of 1000 amperes/m^2 multiplied by the area of 10^{-6} m^2. This gives a current of 0.001 ampere, or 1 ma. The ratio of the voltage drop v to the current is 59 ohms.

It should be noted that the diffusion current densities are not related to the electric field and, consequently, do not contribute to the voltage drop. The voltage drop is due entirely to the drift current densities.

7-4. ELECTRIC CURRENT

In a great many types of engineering problems the *electric current* over a surface S is of greater interest than the current density at points on the surface. *Electric current is defined as the surface integral of the electric current density.* For example, the current in a conducting wire is the surface integral of the current density taken over a cross-sectional surface area. As current density has the dimensions Q/L^2T, electric current has the dimensions Q/T, and the *ampere* is its mks unit.

If the current density is a convection current density, the *convection current* i is

$$i = \int_S \mathbf{J} \cdot d\mathbf{S} = \int_S \rho\mathbf{v} \cdot d\mathbf{S} \tag{7-6}$$

This current over the surface S represents the flow of electric charge, in coulombs per second, through S. To verify this, let us consider the scalar product $\mathbf{J} \cdot d\mathbf{S}$, which equals $J_n\, dS$ with J_n denoting the component of $\mathbf{J}$ normal to the differential surface area. Only this normal component of $\mathbf{J}$ contributes to the charge passing through dS, the tangential component contributing nothing. Clearly, $\mathbf{J} \cdot d\mathbf{S}$ represents the flow of charge in amperes, or coulombs per second, through $d\mathbf{S}$, and the integral of Eq. (7-6) gives the charge per unit time through the entire surface.

It is sometimes convenient to express i in terms of the differential charge dq that flows through the stationary surface S in the differential time dt. The charge flow in coulombs per second, or amperes, is dq/dt. A difficulty arises in applying this to a surface in motion. The question is whether or not to include in the current the flow of charge through S due to the motion of S, and the answer is negative. To justify this let us consider a surface S moving in a region containing charges at rest. From the viewpoint of a stationary observer the current density $\mathbf{J}$ is everywhere zero, and consequently, the surface integral of $\mathbf{J}$, which defines the current i, is zero. Furthermore, the static charges do not produce a magnetic field. The absence of a magnetic field is, of course, a positive indication of no current. We conclude that simply moving a surface through a region with a static charge distribution does not create a current. The expression

dq/dt does not, therefore, include any charge that passes through S as a result of the motion of the surface. To indicate this, it is conventional to utilize the partial time derivative, giving

$$i = \partial q/\partial t = \dot{q} \tag{7-7}$$

with the partial derivative signifying that motion of the surface is not to be considered in evaluating i.

It is interesting to note that the preceding discussion also applies, at least approximately, to an observer in motion with a velocity that is small when compared with that of light. In Sec. 4-5 it was shown that such an observer would note approximately the same magnetic field as a stationary observer, and for a system of static charges this magnetic field is zero. Suppose the observer in motion is moving along with the surface S in a region with positive static charges, with a velocity that is less than, say, ten per cent of that of light. The magnetic force on a test charge employed by this observer to measure the fields is negligible compared with the electric force. If the concentration of positive charge were great enough to produce an appreciable electric current relative to this observer, the electrostatic forces would be enormous. Usually, convection currents are in conductors containing equal amounts of positive and negative charge. For such cases the charge passing though a surface S *due to its motion alone* is precisely zero.

Suppose a region has a time-changing electric field, producing a displacement current density $\mathbf{J}_d$. The displacement current i_d is defined as

$$i_d = \int_S \mathbf{J}_d \cdot d\mathbf{S} = \int_S \dot{\mathbf{D}} \cdot d\mathbf{S} \tag{7-8}$$

This is the flux of $\mathbf{J}_d$, or $\dot{\mathbf{D}}$, over the surface S; although measured in amperes, it does not, of course, represent a flow of charge. The flux of $\dot{\mathbf{D}}$ over S equals the partial time derivative of the flux of $\mathbf{D}$ over S. Consequently,

$$i_d = \frac{\partial}{\partial t} \int_S \mathbf{D} \cdot d\mathbf{S} = \frac{\partial \psi}{\partial t} = \dot{\psi} \tag{7-9}$$

with ψ denoting the electric flux over the surface. Again, the partial time derivative is used to signify that the motion of the surface is not to be considered in evaluating i_d. For example, when a surface moves through a static electric field, the electric flux over the surface may vary with time, but there is no displacement current. The *partial* time derivatives of both $\mathbf{D}$ and ψ are zero.

The *total electric current* i_t is the sum of the convection current i and the displacement current i_d, giving

$$i_t = i + i_d \tag{7-10}$$

In terms of the current densities, the total current i_t is

$$i_t = \int_S \mathbf{J}_t \cdot d\mathbf{S} = \int_S (\mathbf{J} + \mathbf{J}_d) \cdot d\mathbf{S} \tag{7-11}$$

Clearly, the total current represents the spatial average of the current densities at all points of the cross section. Equation (7-11) can be written

$$i_t = \int_S (\rho\mathbf{v} + \dot{\mathbf{D}}) \cdot d\mathbf{S} \tag{7-12}$$

Also, we can utilize Eqs. (7-7) and (7-9) to obtain

$$i_t = \dot{q} + \dot{\psi} \tag{7-13}$$

From Eq. (7-13) it is evident that the electric current over a surface equals one ampere if electric charge flows through the surface at the rate of one coulomb per second, or if the electric flux over the surface is changing at the rate of one coulomb per second.

Electric current is called *drift current* if the current density is a drift current density. It is called *diffusion current* if the current density is due to diffusion. Both types may be present in the same region. A drift current can be expressed in terms of the conductivity σ, for $\rho\mathbf{v}$ is equal to $\sigma\mathbf{E}$, and Eq. (7-6) becomes

$$i = \int_S \sigma\mathbf{E} \cdot d\mathbf{S} \tag{7-14}$$

This is, of course, a special case.

7-5. THE POSITIVE DIRECTION OF ELECTRIC CURRENT

The flux of any vector over a surface is a scalar. Electric current is the flux of current density and, therefore, is a scalar. However, electric current density is a vector.

In order to evaluate a surface integral, one side of the surface must be selected as the positive side, and this choice is arbitrary. Current is the surface integral of current density. When we refer to the current over some surface, we should state which side is designated the positive side. If the current density at points on the surface is directed out of this side, the surface integral yields a positive value. On the other hand, if the current density at points on the surface is directed out of the negative side, the integral yields a negative value, and the current is negative. Of course, the current density at some points may be directed out of the positive side and at other points may be directed out of the negative side. The integral always gives, however, the net current over the surface.

In electric circuit theory an arrow is commonly used to indicate the positive side of a cross section of the circuit. *The side facing in the direction of the arrow is the designated positive side.* Although current is a scalar, it is customary to refer to the direction of the arrow as the *positive*, or *reference, direction of the current*. This custom will be adhered to in this text, but the student should understand that the arrow actually shows the selected positive side of the cross-sectional surface.

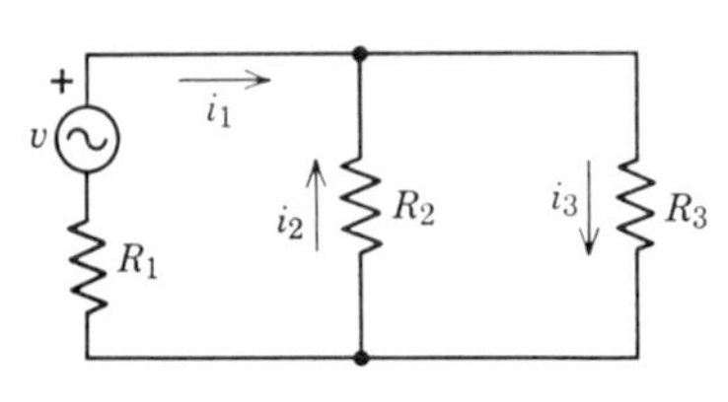

FIG. 7-2. Electric circuit.

Figure 7-2 shows an electric circuit with arrows indicating the positive directions of the branch currents. The selections of these reference directions were arbitrary. Suppose that the currents i_1, i_2, and i_3 are equal to -2, $+5$, and $+3$ amperes, respectively, at a certain instant. If the positive directions of the currents had been selected opposite to the directions indicated by the arrows, the currents would be $+2$, -5, and -3 amperes.

The fact that current is a scalar follows directly from its definition, and it is futile to attempt to regard it as a vector. For example, consider the current entering the cylindrical cathode of a vacuum tube from a larger cylindrical anode surrounding it. The current densities at points on the cathode surface have *different directions at different points* about the cathode. The convection current is the flow of electric charge across this surface, and at any instant of time this quantity has magnitude only.

Electric current usually varies with time. The equations that have been presented apply at each and every instant. The symbols $\mathbf{J}$ and i denote the instantaneous current density and the instantaneous current, respectively, and are commonly expressed as functions of time t.

EXAMPLE 1. Illustrated in Fig. 7-3 is a conducting rod with a circular cross section of radius 2.1 centimeters. The current i varies sinusoidally with time at a frequency of 1590 cycles per second, and its positive direction is specified by the arrow on the illustration. Inside the wire the drift current density $J_z\mathbf{k}$ varies with respect to the distance r from the center of the wire because of a phenomenon known as *skin effect*. The current density J_z is given by the approximate expression

$$J_z = 0.001e^{\pi r} \sin(\omega t + \pi r) \text{ amperes/cm}^2$$

with $\omega = 10^4$ and with r measured in centimeters. Determine the current i as a function of time.

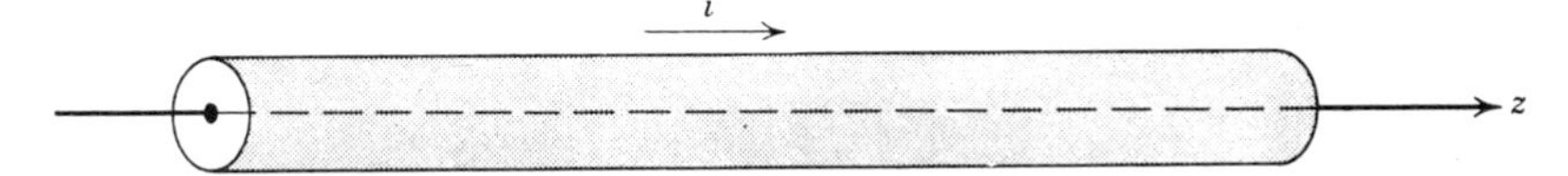

FIG. 7-3. Cylindrical conductor.

Solution. As J_z depends only on the distance r from the center of the wire and time t, it is clear that a differential area of a cross-sectional surface can be taken as the area between two circles of radii r and $r + dr$. This is $2\pi r\,dr$ square centimeters. The current arrow on the illustration specifies the positive side of the surface as the side facing in the positive z-direction. Therefore, the vector differential area is $2\pi r\,dr\,\mathbf{k}$, and $\mathbf{J} \cdot d\mathbf{S}$ equals $J_z 2\pi r\,dr$. The current i is

$$i = \int_0^{2.1} J_z 2\pi r\,dr$$

Substitution for J_z gives

$$i = 0.002\pi \int_0^{2.1} re^{\pi r} \sin(\omega t + \pi r)\,dr$$

A change of variable from r to x, with $x = \pi r$, yields the equation

$$i = \frac{0.002}{\pi} \int_0^{2.1\pi} xe^x \sin(\omega t + x)\,dx$$

By integrating by parts one can readily show that

$$\int xe^x \sin(\omega t + x)\,dx = [\tfrac{1}{2}e^x][(x \cos x + x \sin x - \sin x) \times \sin \omega t + (x \sin x - x \cos x + \cos x) \cos \omega t] \quad (7\text{-}15)$$

Utilizing Eq. (7-15), we find the current i to be

$$i = 1.87 \sin \omega t - 0.769 \cos \omega t$$

This can be expressed as

$$i = 2.024 \sin(\omega t - 22.3°) \text{ amperes}$$

by application of the trigonometric identity given as Eq. (12-22). The sign of the current is alternately positive and negative as time varies.

EXAMPLE 2. The rod of Example 1 is made of brass having a conductivity of 1.57×10^7 mhos per meter. Determine the displacement current i_d as a function of time. Assume $\epsilon_r = 1$.

Solution. The displacement current density $\mathbf{J}_d$ is $\dot{\mathbf{D}}$, or $\epsilon\dot{\mathbf{E}}$. As $\mathbf{E} = \mathbf{J}/\sigma$, it follows that $\mathbf{J}_d$ equals $(\epsilon/\sigma)\dot{\mathbf{J}}$. The ratio ϵ/σ is $8.854 \times 10^{-12}/1.57 \times 10^7$, or 5.64×10^{-19} second, and

$$\mathbf{J}_d = 5.64 \times 10^{-19} \dot{J}_z \mathbf{k}$$

The drift current density J_z is given in Example 1. Its partial time derivative equals J_z multiplied by ω, or 10^4, with the angle of the sine function increased by 90°. Thus

$$J_d = 5.64 \times 10^{-18} e^{\pi r} \sin (\omega t + 90° + \pi r) \text{ ampere/cm}^2$$

with r measured in centimeters. Comparison of this with the expression for the drift current density J_z reveals that J_d can be found from J_z by multiplying J_z by 5.64×10^{-15} and by increasing its angle by 90°. We deduce that the displacement current can be found from the drift current i by multiplying i by 5.64×10^{-15} and by adding 90° to its angle. This gives

$$i_d = 1.14 \times 10^{-14} \sin (\omega t + 67.7°) \text{ ampere}$$

It should be noted that the displacement current is negligible compared with the drift current. This is true in all good conductors.

7-6. THE ELECTRIC CURRENT ELEMENT

Determination of the electric and magnetic fields produced by a system of currents is often accomplished with the aid of the superposition principle. The conductors are regarded as made up of a great many extremely small current elements, each of which occupies an infinitesimal volume. The fields of the entire system are found by adding together, or integrating, the fields of the individual elements. In a somewhat similar manner we often find the magnetic force on a conductor by adding the forces on the small current elements. This method will be utilized in various sections of later chapters. Thus the concept of a current element of differential dimensions is of engineering importance, even though a single isolated element does not exist.

By definition a *current element*, or *current moment*, is

$$\text{current element} = \mathbf{J}\, dV \text{ ampere-meter} \tag{7-16}$$

with $\mathbf{J}$ representing the convection current density in the volume dV within a conductor. The magnitude of the vector current element is the differential quantity $J\, dV$, and its direction is that of $\mathbf{J}$. If the magnitude and direction of $\mathbf{J}$ vary with time, the magnitude and direction of the current element also vary with time.

$\mathbf{J}\, dV$ can be written as $\rho\mathbf{v}\, dV$, or $(\rho\, dV)\mathbf{v}$. Clearly, $\rho\, dV$ is the differential charge dq of the free charge carriers in dV, which have drift velocity $\mathbf{v}$. We obtain

$$\mathbf{J}\, dV = dq\, \mathbf{v} \tag{7-17}$$

This shows that *a current element can be regarded as a moving charge insofar as its electric and magnetic effects are concerned*, provided the effects of the bound charges, if important, are also considered.

The product $dq\,\mathbf{v}$ can be written as $dq\,d\mathbf{l}/dt$, or $(dq/dt)\,d\mathbf{l}$. But dq/dt is the flow of charge in coulombs per second through a cross section of the element, and this is the current i. Consequently,

$$\mathbf{J}\,dV = i\,d\mathbf{l} \tag{7-18}$$

with the understanding that i is the current over the small cross-sectional area of dV. When dealing with *filamentary* conductors, which have small cross sections, i is the total current. We select the reference direction of i arbitrarily. Then if i is positive, the direction of the current element $i\,d\mathbf{l}$ corresponds with this reference direction; but if i is negative, the vector $i\,d\mathbf{l}$ has the opposite direction. In the usual case the current is alternating, and its sign alternates with time.

In good conductors currents that change rapidly with time are mostly confined to thin surface layers. This is referred to as *skin effect*, which is discussed in Chapter 14. In many cases involving high frequencies the assumption of *surface current densities* is a reasonable engineering approximation. We previously defined the convection current density $\mathbf{J}$ as the product $\rho\mathbf{v}$. However, suppose the moving charges are confined to the surface of a conductor. In this case the current density is a *surface current density* $\mathbf{J}_s$, defined as the product of the surface charge density ρ_s of the moving charges and the drift velocity $\mathbf{v}$ of the charge carriers. Thus

$$\mathbf{J}_s = \rho_s\mathbf{v} \text{ amperes/m} \tag{7-19}$$

It should be noted that surface current density $\mathbf{J}_s$ is expressed in amperes per meter, whereas current density $\mathbf{J}$ is expressed in amperes per square meter.

Let us consider an example. Suppose the current of a cylindrical wire of radius r is confined to a thin surface layer. If the surface charge density $\mathbf{J}_s$ directed along the length of the wire is uniform around the circumference of the wire, the current i in the wire is $2\pi rJ_s$ amperes.

We are now prepared to express a current element in terms of a surface current density $\mathbf{J}_s$. By multiplying both sides of Eq. (7-19) by dS and replacing the product $\rho_s\,dS$ with dq, we obtain

$$\mathbf{J}_s\,dS = dq\,\mathbf{v} \tag{7-20}$$

with dq denoting the charge of the free charge carriers of the differential surface area dS. It is evident that $\mathbf{J}_s\,dS$ represents a current element in terms of a surface current density.

When a charge moves in a magnetic field $\mathbf{B}$, a force acts on it, and the differential force $d\mathbf{F}$ on the differential charge dq is $dq\,\mathbf{v} \times \mathbf{B}$. The current in a wire consists of moving charges. If the wire is in a magnetic field, the field exerts a force on each of the moving charges, and this force is transmitted to the atoms of the wire. Let dq denote the charge moving with drift velocity $\mathbf{v}$ in the differential length dl of the wire. The differential force $d\mathbf{F}$ that acts on this length is $dq\, \mathbf{v} \times \mathbf{B}$. By utilizing Eqs. (7-17) and (7-18) we can express this force in terms of the current element $i\, d\mathbf{l}$, and the important result is

$$d\mathbf{F} = i\, d\mathbf{l} \times \mathbf{B} \tag{7-21}$$

A wire with a current i consists of a large number of differential current elements in series. Equation (7-21) gives the force that acts on each of these elements.

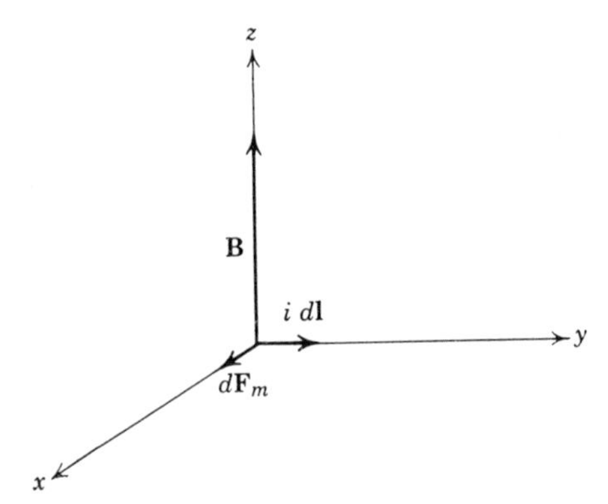

FIG. 7-4. Direction of **B** with respect to the differential vectors $i\, d\mathbf{l}$ and $d\mathbf{F}_m$.

The magnetic flux density **B** was defined in terms of the force on a moving charge. However, a current element is equivalent to a moving charge, and the magnetic flux density **B** exerts a force on a current element in accordance with Eq. (7-21). In fact, Eq. (7-21) is frequently selected as the defining equation for **B**.

We note that the magnetic force on a current element is always at right angles to each of the vectors $d\mathbf{l}$ and **B**. If $d\mathbf{l}$ is oriented so that $d\mathbf{F}$ is a maximum $d\mathbf{F}_m$, then the magnitude of **B** is $dF_m/(i\, dl)$. Consequently, the magnitude of **B** at a point is the maximum possible force per unit current element. With $d\mathbf{l}$ oriented so that the force is a maximum, **B** is directed perpendicular to the plane of $d\mathbf{F}_m$ and $i\, d\mathbf{l}$, with sense as illustrated in Fig. 7-4. These statements concerning the magnitude and direction of **B** could have been selected for defining **B**.

Although a single current element cannot be physically realized, a small length of wire carrying a current i is sometimes employed as a substitute. The connections to the short wire must be made so as to prevent any undesirable effects. This approximation of a current element can be used to test for and to measure the magnetic field in a region of space.

A current-carrying conductor in a magnetic field is acted upon by a magnetic force, provided the conductor is not parallel to the field lines. There is a force acting on each current element in accordance with Eq. (7-21). In general, magnetic fields exert forces on moving charges and electric currents; on the other hand, electric fields exert forces on charges, regardless of their motion.

The magnetic force on each differential volume dV of a conductor is determined from Eq. (7-21) with $i\,d\mathbf{l}$ replaced by $\mathbf{J}\,dV$. This gives a differential force of $\mathbf{J} \times \mathbf{B}\,dV$, and *the force per unit volume is* $\mathbf{J} \times \mathbf{B}$. The force

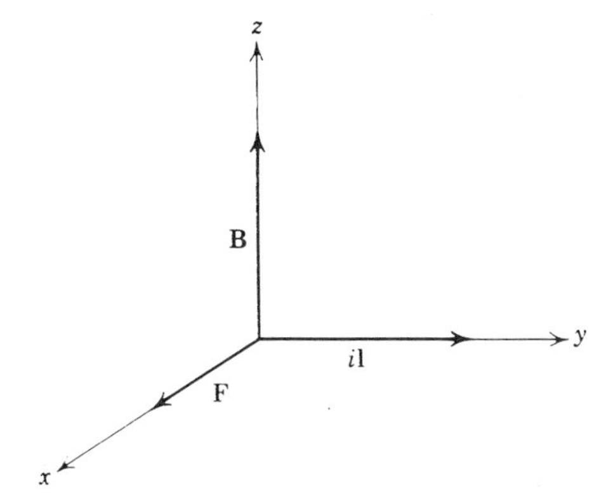

FIG. 7-5. Force **F** on $i\mathbf{l}$ oriented normal to field **B**.

per unit area on the differential surface dS of a conductor with a surface current density $\mathbf{J}_s$ is obviously $\mathbf{J}_s \times \mathbf{B}$.

Let us apply Eq. (7-21) to an important special case. Suppose a length l of straight wire with a current i is oriented at right angles to a magnetic field of uniform density **B**. The magnitude of the vector $d\mathbf{l} \times \mathbf{B}$ is $B\,dl$, and the force acting on the wire is

$$F = \int_0^l Bi\,dl = Bi\int_0^l dl = Bil \tag{7-22}$$

The direction of the force is normal to the plane containing the wire and **B**, with sense determined by the equation $\mathbf{F} = i\mathbf{l} \times \mathbf{B}$. These relations are illustrated in Fig. 7-5.

The relation $F = Bil$ is often referred to as the *motor law*. It applies only if the magnetic field **B** is uniform, if the current i is the same for all current elements, and if the conductor is a straight wire normal to **B**.

It is a restricted form of the general relation of Eq. (7-21). In many electric motors wires are oriented perpendicular to a magnetic field. When a current is passed through these wires, a force results, causing the *armature* supporting the wires to rotate. This principle is utilized to convert electrical energy into mechanical energy. We shall discuss this further in the next section.

EXAMPLE. The magnetic flux density **B** in a region around a straight conducting wire with a current of 500 amperes is given by

$$\mathbf{B} = \frac{0.0001(y\mathbf{i} - x\mathbf{j})}{x^2 + y^2}$$

The magnetic flux lines represented by this mathematical expression are circles about the z-axis, which coincides with the wire.

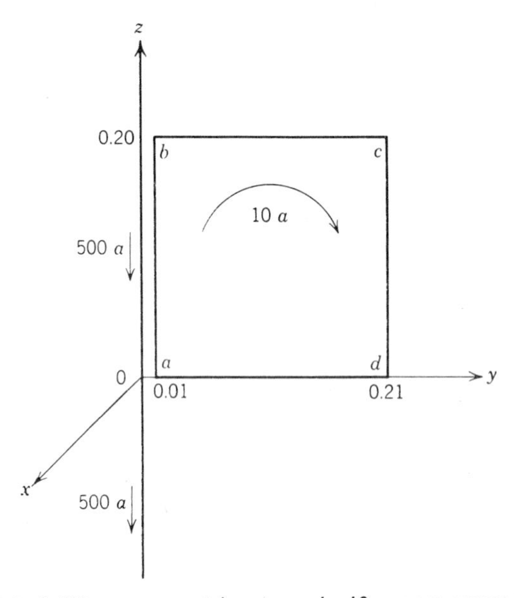

FIG. 7-6. A 500-ampere straight wire and a 10-ampere square loop.

Suppose a square conducting loop, with side length equal to 0.2 meter and with a current of 10 amperes, is placed in the region as indicated by Fig. 7-6. Determine the net force acting on this square loop.

Solution. In the plane of the loop, $x = 0$ and the 500-a current produces a magnetic flux density $\mathbf{B} = 0.0001/y\ \mathbf{i}$. In Fig. 7-6 the flux lines are directed out of the paper, for positive y. It is evident from Eq. (7-21) that the specified magnetic field produces forces on the sides of the square loop with each force vector being normal to its side, lying in the plane of the loop, and directed toward the inside of the loop.

Along path ab, y is 0.01 and $\mathbf{B}$ is 0.01$\mathbf{i}$. The force $\mathbf{F}_{ab}$ is $Bil\mathbf{j}$, or $0.01 \times 10 \times 0.2\mathbf{j}$, or 0.02$\mathbf{j}$ newton.

Along path bc, $\mathbf{B}$ varies with y, and we must use Eq. (7-21). A current element along this path is $10\,dy\,\mathbf{j}$, and the force on a current element is $(10\,dy\,\mathbf{j}) \times (0.0001/y\,\mathbf{i})$, or $-0.001\,dy/y\,\mathbf{k}$. The total force on this side is

$$\mathbf{F}_{bc} = -0.001 \int_{0.01}^{0.21} 1/y\,dy\,\mathbf{k} = -0.00304\mathbf{k}$$

Along path cd, y is 0.21 and $\mathbf{B}$ is 0.00048$\mathbf{i}$. The force $\mathbf{F}_{cd}$ is $-Bil\mathbf{j}$, or $-0.00096\mathbf{j}$.

Along path da, a current element is $10\,dy\,\mathbf{j}$, with dy negative, and the force on a current element is $-0.001\,dy/y\,\mathbf{k}$. For negative dy the limits of the integral are taken with y decreasing from 0.21 to 0.01, and evaluation of the integral gives a force $\mathbf{F}_{da}$ of 0.00304$\mathbf{k}$.

The net force acting on the square loop is the vector sum of $\mathbf{F}_{ab}$, $\mathbf{F}_{bc}$, $\mathbf{F}_{cd}$, and $\mathbf{F}_{da}$. This gives a net force $\mathbf{F}$ equal to 0.019$\mathbf{j}$ newton. If the loop were rigid but free to move, the magnetic force would move the loop of Fig. 7-6 from left to right. It should be mentioned that the current of the loop produces a magnetic field which we have neglected. Although this field contributes to the force on each side of the loop, these force components obviously cancel when the net force is computed.

7-7. A SIMPLE ELECTRIC DYNAMO

A device that transmits energy from one system to another is known as a *transducer*. An *electromechanical transducer* is one that transforms energy from the electrical state to the mechanical state, or vice versa. The electric machine, or *dynamo*, is an example of such a transducer. We shall first investigate the behavior of a current-carrying conductor in a uniform magnetic field, after which we shall consider an elementary dynamo of more practical design.

Shown in Fig. 7-7 is an electric circuit located in a uniform magnetic field $\mathbf{B}$, which is directed into the paper. The rod with sliding contacts can move sideways without opening the circuit. There is, however, some friction at the sliding contacts. When the switch S is closed, the current i in the rod rises rapidly from zero to a large value which is determined by the applied voltage V and the small resistance of the electric circuit. This is a drift current due to the electric field $\mathbf{E}$. The magnetic force on the rod is Bil by Eq. (7-22), and this force is directed from left to right.

The rod accelerates to the right; its velocity v, initially zero, is now increasing. Because the rod is moving in a magnetic field, there is now a magnetic force acting *along the wire* on the free charge carriers present. The magnetic force per unit charge, equal to vB, is directed opposite to the electric force per unit charge of magnitude E. Therefore, the net force per unit charge is $E - vB$. As v increases, the force acting on the charge

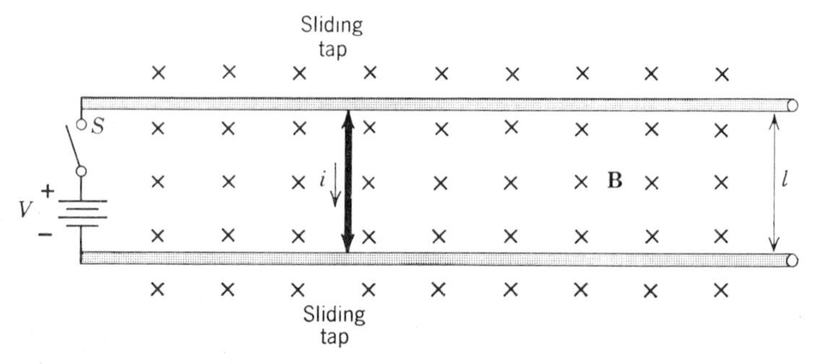

FIG. 7-7. An electric circuit containing a rod with sliding taps located in a uniform magnetic field **B**.

carriers decreases. Consequently, the drift velocity of the charge carriers decreases, and the current i decreases. Thus the current i and the force F acting on the rod decrease as the velocity of the rod increases. Equilibrium is reached when the magnetic force on the rod has lowered to the value of the frictional force of the sliding taps. At equilibrium, both the velocity of the rod and the current are steady.

At points inside the moving rod the force per unit charge is $E - vB$. The quantities E, v, and B do not vary along the path of the rod. Therefore, the voltage drop along this moving rod, in the direction of the positive current, is $El - vBl$. If the circuit between the battery and the rod is lossless, then El obviously equals the applied terminal voltage V, and the voltage drop becomes $V - vBl$. The voltage V is that component of the emf due to the electric field, and the voltage vBl is that component due to the magnetic field. As the effect of the motional-emf component is opposite to that of the applied voltage, the term vBl is often referred to as a *back emf*, or a *counter emf*.

Suppose the rod is made of a good conducting material, such as copper. If the current i is not excessively large, the force per unit charge acting on the charge carriers is small, and the voltage drop along the rod is small. In this case the applied voltage V and the motional emf vBl are approximately equal, and the velocity v is nearly $V/(Bl)$.

The force opposing the motion of the rod constitutes the mechanical load. We assumed only a frictional force. However, some other mechanical force might also be present. In any event, under equilibrium conditions the magnetic force Bil must equal the total mechanical force opposing the motion of the rod. If this mechanical force is large, the current i is large; and if this mechanical force is small, the current is small.

The device just described is a simple, though crude, electric motor. It draws electrical energy from the electric source and converts it into mechanical energy. The same device can be employed as an electric generator by application of the proper mechanical force. For example, suppose a mechanical force pushes the rod of Fig. 7-7 to the right at a velocity v such that the motional emf vBl is now greater than the applied voltage V. The magnetic force vB per unit charge acting on the charge carriers is larger than the electric force E per unit charge. The flow of charge is now reversed, and electric power is delivered to the electric circuit connected across the terminals of the moving rod. Under equilibrium conditions the magnetic force Bil equals the mechanical force F, provided we understand that F includes the effect of both the applied and frictional forces. It follows that the current i delivered to the external circuit is F/Bl.

Regardless of the way the mechanical force acts on the rod, both motor and generator action are present. If the current from the electric source produces a magnetic force that drives the rod of Fig. 7-7 to the right in opposition to a mechanical force, the device is a motor. However, generator action is present, for the motion of the rod in the magnetic field yields a motional emf that opposes the applied voltage V. If the rod is driven to the right by a mechanical force, mechanical power is converted into electrical power, and the device is a generator. In this case the motional emf is greater than the terminal voltage, and the current i is reversed. There is motor action, however, for the magnetic force Bil opposes the driving mechanical force.

Shown in Fig. 7-8 is a sketch of the end view of a more practical electric dynamo. The *yoke*, *poles*, and *armature* are ferromagnetic, and the current-carrying coils on the poles produce intense magnetic fields directed as indicated by the several magnetic flux lines illustrated. It should be noted that the flux lines leave the surface of the *north pole* and enter the surface of the *south pole*. Later, magnetic circuits such as this one will be analyzed in some detail. For the purposes of this analysis we shall assume that the magnetic field in the air gaps between the armature and the poles of the electromagnets is nearly uniform and radial.

The iron armature is a cylinder of radius r and axial length l, and this cylinder is free to rotate on its axis. At the surface of the cylinder are many axial slots, each containing a number of insulated conductors, also of length l. These conductors are connected to the external circuit in various ways which will not be discussed here. However, the connections are made so that the positive currents of those conductors on the *right side* of the armature are in one direction and the positive currents of those conductors on the *left side* of the armature are in the other direction. A mechanical switching arrangement rapidly reverses the current of a conductor as it passes from one side to the other.

Let us consider operation of the dynamo as a motor. The external electric circuit supplies a current i to each armature conductor. Suppose the currents of those conductors on the right side of the armature of Fig. 7-8 are directed into the paper and the currents of those on the left side are directed out of the paper. As the current elements are normal to the magnetic flux density $\mathbf{B}$, the magnetic force on each armature conductor is Bil. This force is directed tangential to the surface of the armature in a counterclockwise direction, and the resulting torque T produces a counterclockwise rotation. As B is proportional to the total magnetic flux φ of a

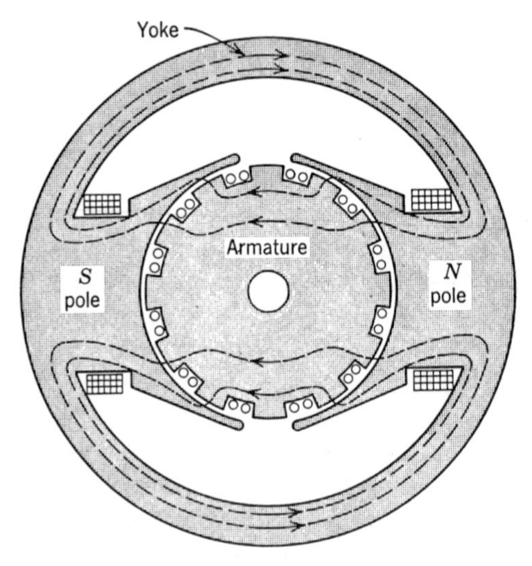

FIG. 7-8. End view of electric dynamo. Several magnetic flux lines are shown as dashed lines.

pole and as the current of each conductor is proportional to the total current supplied by the external circuit, it follows that the magnetic torque is proportional to the product φi, with i now representing the total current. Thus

$$T \propto \varphi i \tag{7-23}$$

The mechanical power developed is the product of the torque T and the angular velocity ω of the armature. A portion of this power is used to supply the frictional losses and the remainder is supplied to the mechanical load on the shaft.

The motion of the armature conductors through the magnetic field results, of course, in a motional emf that acts in opposition to the applied current. The motional emf of each conductor is Blv, with v denoting the velocity of the conductor. As v is proportional to the speed of rotation in revolutions per minute (rpm), it is evident that the motional emf is proportional to the product of the pole flux φ and the rpm, giving

$$\text{motional emf} \propto \varphi \, (\text{rpm}) \tag{7-24}$$

For motors this motional emf is a back, or counter, emf. Equations (7-23) and (7-24) are important relations that are utilized in the analysis and design of electric machinery.

The dynamo of Fig. 7-8 can also be operated as a generator. In this case mechanical power must be applied to the shaft of the armature, producing rotation. The motional emf produces a current i in the external electrical circuit. This motional emf is now greater than the terminal voltage, and the magnetic force acting on the free charge carriers of the conductors is greater than the electric force. The applied mechanical torque on the armature equals the sum of the frictional torque and the magnetic torque, given by Eq. (7-23). The product of the applied torque and the angular velocity ω gives the input mechanical power, and the product of the magnetic torque and ω gives the developed electrical power. The difference is the frictional power loss.

A generator supplies voltage, current, and power to the electric circuit connected to its terminals. If the external terminals are open, the current and power are zero, and the generator supplies a voltage only. On the other hand, if the terminals are shorted, the generator supplies a current only. These are special cases. In general, the values of the generated voltage, current, and power are determined by the characteristics of the machine and its external circuit. The voltage and current may be d-c or a-c, and this depends on the manner in which the armature conductors are connected to the terminals.

EXAMPLE. The armature of a d-c motor is 12 cm long and 8 cm in diameter and contains 400 conductors connected in series between the external electrical terminals. When the motor is connected across a 110-volt supply, the air-gap flux density is 0.3 weber per square meter, the current is 2 amperes, and the speed is 1700 rpm. Determine the back emf and the mechanical power developed.

Solution. The angular velocity is 1700 rpm, or 178 radians per second. The velocity v of each conductor is $r\omega$, or 7.12 m/sec. It follows that the motional emf Blv per conductor is 0.256 volt. The back emf of the 400 conductors is 102.5 volts.

The magnetic force acting on each conductor is Bil, or 0.072 newton. The magnetic torque is obtained by multiplying this force by the radius of the armature and by the number of conductors. This gives a torque of 1.15 newton-m. Multiplication by the angular velocity gives 205 watts. This is the mechanical power developed, including that power used to overcome friction. As 746 watts is one horsepower, the mechanical power developed is 0.275 hp.

The difference between the applied voltage and the back emf is 7.5 volts. This is the voltage drop between the terminals of the motor along the path of the moving conductors of the armature. If the armature conductors were perfect, this voltage would be zero.

7-8. MAGNETIC CURRENT

The total electric current over a surface S is equal to the flow of electric charge through S plus the partial time derivative of the electric flux over S. Magnetic charges do not exist, and consequently, there is no magnetic current of moving magnetic charges. However, the partial time derivative of the magnetic flux over S corresponds to the electric displacement current. Accordingly, magnetic current is defined as the partial time derivative of the magnetic flux Φ.

As magnetic flux Φ has units of webers, magnetic current has units of webers per second. A weber per second is dimensionally equivalent to the volt. Therefore, the mks unit of magnetic current is the *volt*, and we have

$$\text{magnetic current} = \frac{\partial \Phi}{\partial t} \text{ volts} \tag{7-25}$$

An alternate form is

$$\text{magnetic current} = \int_S \dot{\mathbf{B}} \cdot d\mathbf{S} \tag{7-26}$$

Obviously, the magnetic current density at a point is $\dot{\mathbf{B}}$ volts per square meter.

Although the electric and magnetic fields have been defined, the manner in which these fields are produced has not yet been precisely stated. In the next chapter we shall learn that electric currents produce magnetic fields and magnetic currents produce electric fields. Electric fields are also produced by electric charges, whereas magnetic charges do not exist.

7-9. SUMMARY OF DEFINITIONS

In Chapters 3 through 7 the various electric and magnetic quantities, and also some important mechanical quantities, have been defined. It is essential that the student understand the meaning of these concepts before proceeding to the study of the fundamental laws of electromagnetic induction. These laws are presented in the next chapter.

Table 7-1 briefly summarizes the definitions, units, and dimensions of most of the quantities that have been considered.

TABLE 7-1
Summary of Definitions, Units, and Dimensions

Name	Defining Equation	Unit	Dimension
length	l	meter	L
mass	m	kilogram	M
time	t	second	T
charge	q	coulomb	Q
velocity	$\mathbf{v} = d\mathbf{l}/dt$	m/sec	L/T
acceleration	$\mathbf{a} = d\mathbf{v}/dt$	m/sec^2	L/T^2
momentum	$\mathbf{p} = m\mathbf{v}$	kg-m/sec	LM/T
force	$\mathbf{F} = d\mathbf{p}/dt$	newton	LM/T^2
work (energy)	$W = \int_C \mathbf{F} \cdot d\mathbf{l}$	joule	L^2M/T^2
power	$p = dW/dt$	watt	L^2M/T^3
electric charge density	$\rho = \lim_{\Delta V \to 0} \Delta q/\Delta V$	coulomb/m^3	Q/L^3
surface charge density	$\rho_s = \lim_{\Delta S \to 0} \Delta q/\Delta S$	coulomb/m^2	Q/L^2
linear charge density	$\rho_l = \lim_{\Delta l \to 0} \Delta q/\Delta l$	coulomb/m	Q/L
electric field intensity	$\mathbf{E} = \mathbf{F}/q$ (q stationary)	volt/m	LM/T^2Q
magnetic flux density	$d\mathbf{F} = dq\,\mathbf{v} \times \mathbf{B}$ $d\mathbf{F} = i\,d\mathbf{l} \times \mathbf{B}$	weber/m^2	M/TQ
magnetic flux	$\Phi = \int_S \mathbf{B} \cdot d\mathbf{S}$	weber	L^2M/TQ
electromotive force (voltage drop)	$\text{emf} = \int_C (\mathbf{F}/q) \cdot d\mathbf{l}$ $= \int_C (\mathbf{E} + \mathbf{v} \times \mathbf{B}) \cdot d\mathbf{l}$	volt	L^2M/T^2Q
free space permittivity	$\epsilon_0 = 8.854 \times 10^{-12}$	farad/m	T^2Q^2/L^3M
free space permeability	$\mu_0 = 4\pi \times 10^{-7}$	henry/m	LM/Q^2
relative permittivity	$\epsilon_r = E_v/E$ (q constant)		
relative permeability	$\mu_r = B/B_v$ (i constant)		
permittivity	$\epsilon = \epsilon_r\epsilon_0$	farad/m	T^2Q^2/L^3M
permeability	$\mu = \mu_r\mu_0$	henry/m	LM/Q^2
electric flux density	$\mathbf{D} = \epsilon\mathbf{E}$	coulomb/m^2	Q/L^2
magnetic field intensity	$\mathbf{H} = \mathbf{B}/\mu$	ampere/m	Q/LT
convection current density	$\mathbf{J} = \rho\mathbf{v}$	ampere/m^2	Q/L^2T
conductivity	$\sigma = J/E$	mho/m	TQ^2/L^3M

TABLE 7-1
(*Continued*)

Name	Defining Equation	Unit	Dimension
resistivity	$\rho = 1/\sigma$	ohm-m	L^3M/TQ^2
drift current density	$\mathbf{J} = \sigma\mathbf{E}$	ampere/m²	Q/L^2T
electric flux	$\psi = \int_S \mathbf{D} \cdot d\mathbf{S}$	coulomb	Q
displacement current density	$\mathbf{J}_d = \dot{\mathbf{D}}$	ampere/m²	Q/L^2T
total current density	$\mathbf{J}_t = \mathbf{J} + \mathbf{J}_d$	ampere/m²	Q/L^2T
convection current	$i = \int_S \mathbf{J} \cdot d\mathbf{S}$	ampere	Q/T
displacement current	$i_d = \int_S \mathbf{J}_d \cdot d\mathbf{S}$	ampere	Q/T
total electric current	$i_t = i + i_d$	ampere	Q/T
magnetomotive force	$\text{mmf} = \int_C \mathbf{H} \cdot d\mathbf{l}$	ampere	Q/T
magnetic current	magnetic current $= \dot{\Phi}$	volt	L^2M/T^2Q

PROBLEMS

Sections 7-1 and 7-2

7-1. The charge density of the free electrons in a metal of conductivity 5×10^7 mhos/m is -8×10^9 c/m³. If $J = 500{,}000$ amperes/m², find the drift velocity v and the mobility μ of the free electrons.

7-2. The electron density at a point P is 6×10^{28} electrons/m³. If the electrons are moving with a velocity of 4×10^{-6} m/sec in the positive x direction, determine the vector current density $\mathbf{J}$ at P.

7-3. At a point P in a copper conductor having a conductivity of 5.8×10^7 mhos/m, the drift current density $\mathbf{J} = 10^6 \sin 10^5 t\, \mathbf{i}$ amperes/m². Determine the displacement current density $\mathbf{J}_d$ and the total current density $\mathbf{J}_t$ at the point, assuming a dielectric constant of unity.

7-4. A 100-megacycle radio wave has an electric field intensity of one millivolt per meter maximum value at a point in air. Consequently, $E = 0.001 \sin (2\pi \times 10^8 t)$. Determine J_d.

7-5. The electric field intensity in a region is $\mathbf{E} = \cos x \cos \omega t\, \mathbf{j}$. If the dielectric constant of the medium is 9 and if the angular frequency ω is 10^8, determine the displacement current density as a function of x and t.

7-6. Two large parallel plates are separated by a distance of 0.002 m. The voltage drop from A to plate B is $100 \sin 10^8 t$. Assuming a uniform electric field in the region between the plates, determine the displacement current density in the direction from A to B, if the dielectric constant is 10.

7-7. In the free-space dielectric of a hollow-pipe waveguide the electric field intensity is $\mathbf{E} = 1000 \sin 20\pi x \cos (\omega t - 55.4z)\,\mathbf{j}$. The angular frequency ω is $8\pi \times 10^9$. Determine the displacement current density at the point (0.01, 0.01, 0.01) as a function of time.

Section 7-3

7-8. For the PN junction rectifier of Examples 1 and 2 of Sec. 7-3, determine the drift velocities $\mathbf{v}_p$ and $\mathbf{v}_n$ of the holes and free electrons, respectively, at $x = 0$ and also at $x = 0.0015$ m. Recall that mobility equals the drift velocity per unit electric field intensity.

7-9. For the PN junction rectifier of Examples 1 and 2 of Sec. 7-3, determine as functions of x the hole component $\mathbf{J}_p'$ and the free-electron component $\mathbf{J}_n'$ of the drift current density. These components are $\sigma_p\mathbf{E}$ and $\sigma_n\mathbf{E}$, respectively, with $\sigma_p = pe\mu_p$ and $\sigma_n = ne\mu_n$. On the same axes plot as functions of x, from $x = 0$ to $x = 0.0015$ m, the x components of the diffusion current densities $\mathbf{J}_p$ and $\mathbf{J}_n$ and the drift current densities $\mathbf{J}_p'$ and $\mathbf{J}_n'$.

Sections 7-4 and 7-5

7-10. The anode of a vacuum tube is a metal cylinder of radius 0.01 m and length 0.04 m. The electron density at points just off the anode is 3×10^{12} electrons/m^3, and the electrons strike the anode with a velocity of 8×10^6 m/sec directed normal to the surface. Determine the electric current i over the anode surface, with the inner surface taken as the positive side. How many electrons strike the anode per second?

7-11. For the conducting rod of Example 1 of Sec. 7-5, determine the drift current density at $r = 2$ cm and also at $r = 1$ cm at the instant of time when the current i is zero and going negative.

7-12. For the conducting rod of Example 1 of Sec. 7-5, determine the drift current density as a function of r at the instant of time when the current i is zero and going positive. Plot this current density as a function of r for this instant of time.

7-13. Assume that the conducting rod of Example 1 of Sec. 7-5 has a radius of only 1.5 cm and determine the current i as a function of time.

7-14. Assume that the conducting rod of Example 1 of Sec. 7-5 has a radius of 2.5 cm and determine the current i as a function of time.

7-15. If $\mathbf{E} = 8000 \sin 10\pi x \sin (\omega t - 27.5z)\,\mathbf{j}$ in the free-space dielectric of the rectangular waveguide of Fig. 7-9, with $\omega = 12.5 \times 10^9$, show by evaluation of the surface integral of the current density that the displacement current leaving the bottom side of the guide from $z = 0$ to $z = 0.1$ m is $4.02 \sin (\omega t + 11.2°)$. The inside dimensions of the cross section are 0.1 by 0.05 meter.

7-16. Two parallel conducting plates, each with an area of 0.01 m^2, are separated 0.5 cm by a leaky dielectric with $\epsilon_r = 5$ and $\sigma = 5 \times 10^{-5}$ mho/m. Assume that the electric field intensity $\mathbf{E} = 2000 \sin 10^6 t\,\mathbf{i}$, normal to the plates, and determine the total current and voltage as functions of time.

7-17. A point charge q is moving between two parallel conducting plates A and B, separated a distance d, with velocity v directed from plate A to plate B. The total electric flux ψ leaving q is equal to q, and each flux line leaving q terminates on one of the two plates. The number of flux lines terminating on plate B is directly proportional to the distance x of the charge from plate A, and the number of flux lines terminating on plate A is similarly proportional to the distance $(d - x)$ of

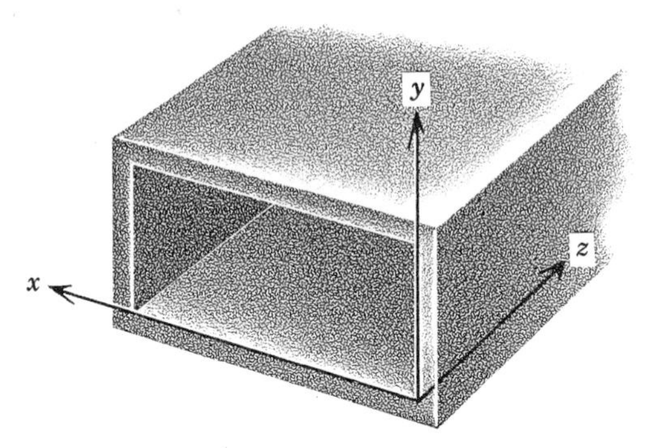

FIG. 7-9. Rectangular waveguide.

the charge from plate B. Show that the flux ψ_B entering plate B is qx/d and that the displacement current entering plate B is qv/d.

7-18. The cathode and anode of a certain vacuum diode consist of parallel conducting plates spaced 1 cm apart. A battery connected across the plates produces a voltage rise of 150 volts from the cathode to the anode. An electron, emitted with negligible kinetic energy from the cathode, accelerates through the voltage rise toward the anode. Determine the anode current due to this electron immediately before it strikes the plate, with the positive side of the anode selected as the side facing the cathode. Refer to Prob. 7-17.

7-19. Assuming 10^{29} free electrons per cubic meter, find the drift velocity of the free electrons in a No. 10 (AWG) copper wire with a current of 1 ampere. The diameter of the wire is 0.102 inch.

7-20. A metallic wire with a radius of 0.001 m has 10^{29} free electrons per m^3. The free charge carriers are drifting along the wire with a drift velocity v of one-millionth of a meter per second. Determine: (*a*) the charge q per unit length due to the free electrons; (*b*) the product qv; (*c*) the current i.

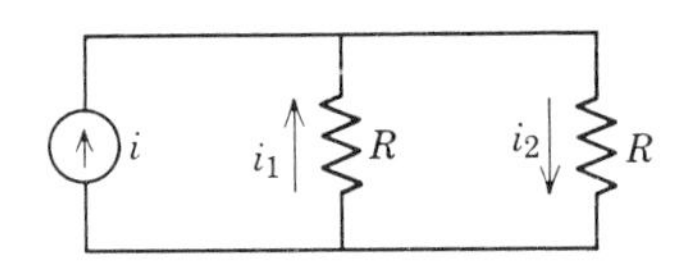

FIG. 7-10. Electric circuit.

7-21. Shown in Fig. 7-10 are two identical resistance wires, each with resistance R, connected across the terminals ab of the ideal current generator whose current i is $10 \sin 377t$. The flow of charge from the generator is divided equally between the two resistance wires. Determine the currents i_1 and i_2 at time $t = 0.0005$ sec and also at $t = 0.001$ sec.

7-22. A square in the xy-plane has its corners at the points (0, 0), (0, 8), (8, 8), and (8, 0). If $\mathbf{D} = 10^{-8} \sin (10^7 t - 0.034x)\, \mathbf{k}$, determine the displacement current, in the positive z direction, over the surface of the square at time zero.

7-23. Let S denote the surface of the anode of a vacuum diode, with the positive side of S selected as the side *facing* the cathode. The electric field in the vacuum is always directed from the anode to the cathode, but the magnitude of this field pulsates with time. As a consequence, the negative electrons emitted by the cathode strike the anode at a rate that varies with time, this rate being $(31.2 - 3.12 \sin 10^8 t)\, 10^{16}$ electrons per sec. Also, the electric flux ψ over S varies with time, with $\psi = (20 - 2 \sin 10^8 t)\, 10^{-11}$ coulomb. Determine the *total* electric current over S as a function of time.

Section 7-6

7-24. A current-carrying wire of radius 0.0002 m is parallel to the x-axis of a coordinate system. The free electron density is 8×10^{28} electrons per m^3, and these charge carriers are drifting along the wire with a drift velocity $\mathbf{v} = -0.0001\mathbf{i}$ meter/sec. Determine the current density $\mathbf{J}$ and the current i, with the positive side of a cross-sectional surface selected as the side facing the direction of increasing x. For a differential length dx of the wire, find dV, $d\mathbf{l}$, and dq in terms of dx. Using these results show that $\mathbf{J}\, dV = i\, d\mathbf{l} = dq\, \mathbf{v}$.

7-25. A conducting wire lies along the x-axis and carries a current of 5 amperes in the positive x direction. If a uniform magnetic field, of density $\mathbf{B} = 0.05\mathbf{i} + 0.2\mathbf{j} - 0.4\mathbf{k}$ weber/m^2, exists in the region, determine the vector force per unit length acting on the wire.

7-26. A conducting wire lies along the x-axis and carries a current of -3 amperes in the positive x direction. If $\mathbf{B} = 0.2 \cos x \cos \omega t\, \mathbf{j}$ in the region, determine the vector force acting on the section of the wire between the origin and $x = 1$. What is the maximum value of this force as time varies?

7-27. A closed metallic circuit carries a current i in a *uniform* magnetic field of density $\mathbf{B}$. If the current i is the same over each cross-sectional surface of the circuit, prove that the net force acting on the entire circuit is zero. Use the relation

$$\int (i\, d\mathbf{l} \times \mathbf{B}) = \left(\int i\, d\mathbf{l} \right) \times \mathbf{B},$$

provided $\mathbf{B}$ is uniform. This relation follows from the distributive rule of Sec. 2-4.

7-28. Repeat Prob. 7-27, except prove that the force is zero by expressing $i\, d\mathbf{l}$ and $\mathbf{B}$ in rectangular form, taking the cross product, and integrating the resulting terms around a closed path.

7-29. Shown in Fig. 7-11 is a moving-coil galvanometer used to measure steady electric currents. The magnetic force on the current of the coil exerts a torque on the armature. A retarding torque, proportional to the deflection angle θ, is exerted by a mechanical spring. Attached to the armature is a pointer that indicates the current on a suitable scale. Assume that the magnetic flux density $\mathbf{B}$ is directed normal to the surface of the ferromagnetic armature, and deduce that the deflection angle θ is directly proportional to the current i. The magnitude B of the flux density is uniform in the air gap.

7-30. If the restoring torque of the spring of Prob. 7-29 is $k\theta$, determine the deflection angle θ in terms of k, the number of coil turns n, the magnetic flux density B, and the area S of the coil.

Section 7-7

7-31. A sudden decrease in the pole flux φ of a d-c motor has what immediate effect on the back emf? Note that the inertia of a motor prevents abrupt changes in speed.

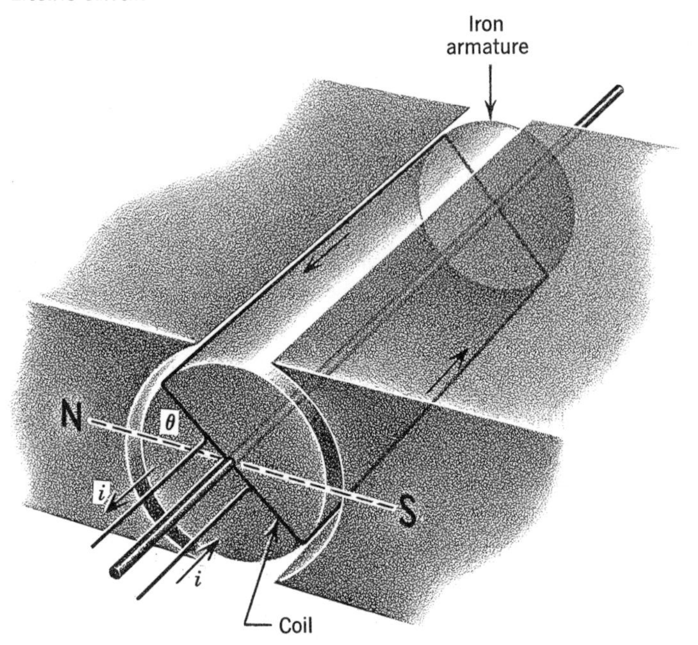

FIG. 7-11. Moving-coil galvanometer.

7-32. A d-c motor with a pole flux φ and an armature current i develops a magnetic torque T. If the flux is decreased to 0.1φ and the current is increased to $50i$, determine the new magnetic torque.

7-33. The armature current i of a d-c motor equals the difference between the applied voltage V and the back emf, divided by the resistance R of the armature winding. A d-c motor of the type described in Sec. 7-7 has an applied voltage V maintained constant at 240 volts and an armature resistance of one ohm. The armature current i is 4 amperes, and the pole flux φ is 0.2 weber. Suppose the pole flux is suddenly reduced to 0.02 weber at time t_1. At this instant determine the new armature current and the percentage change in the magnetic torque T. What effect does the decrease in φ have on the speed?

7-34. The magnetic torque developed in a 1200-rpm motor is 1.5 newton-meters. If the frictional losses are 10 watts, determine the mechanical torque and power, in mks units, applied to the load. Recall that power equals $T\omega$. Also, express the load torque and power in pound-feet and horsepower, respectively.

7-35. The armature of a d-c generator is driven by a motor at angular velocity ω. The n armature conductors of the generator are connected in series. Consequently, the total current i that is generated equals the current of each conductor, and the total motional emf equals the sum of the motional emfs of the conductors. Assuming a uniform flux density B in the air gaps, deduce that the magnetic torque T opposing the driving torque is $nBilr$ and that the motional emf developed is $nBlr\omega$, with l and r denoting the length and radius, respectively, of the armature. From these results show that $T\omega = (motional\ emf)i$. This is the electrical power developed.

7-36. A d-c generator, driven at 1000 rpm, generates a motional emf of 200 volts and a current of 5 amperes. The frictional loss is 50 watts. (*a*) Using the results of Prob. 7-35, determine the electrical power developed and the mechanical power input. (*b*) Determine the electrical power developed and the mechanical power input if the speed of the generator is doubled. Assume the pole flux and the frictional loss remain unchanged, and also assume that the generated current is proportional to the motional emf.

Section 7-8

7-37. If $\mathbf{B} = 10^{-9} \sin (10^8 t - 0.35x)\,\mathbf{k}$, determine the magnetic current, as a function of time, through the square loop having corners at (0, 0, 0), (5, 0, 0), (5, 5, 0), and (0, 5, 0). The positive side of the surface faces in the positive z direction.

Electromagnetic Laws I

CHAPTER 8

In the first seven chapters we studied the historical development of electromagnetism, some background mathematics, and the definitions of many electrical concepts. Except for brief mention in the historical sketch, the experimental laws of Coulomb, Ampère, Faraday, Henry, and others have not been considered. James Clerk Maxwell showed that these numerous experimental laws can be expressed by means of a few general equations, known today as Maxwell's equations.

A primary purpose of this entire book is to give the student a thorough understanding of Maxwell's equations. If students contemplate doing creative work in electrical research, development, or design, they most certainly should study carefully these fundamental equations of electromagnetism—examining these equations in different forms and applying them to many different situations. We shall do this here and in later chapters. In fact, a large portion of the remainder of this book is devoted to a study of Maxwell's equations and their applications.

Earlier we discussed the conservation of electric charge. We do not know that charge is always conserved. We cannot directly verify that the conservation law is valid, even within limits of experimental error, for the law is too general. We do know, however, that charge appears to be conserved in all electrical experiments ever performed. Thus it seems reasonable to assume that charge is neither created nor destroyed. This assumption, being a generalization of experimental evidence, is called a *postulate*.

In this presentation of electromagnetism two of Maxwell's equations, expressed in integral form, are selected as additional postulates. These equations are broad mathematical statements of general electromagnetic relations. Although they are too comprehensive for direct experimental verification, innumerable logical deductions have been verified within the limits of experimental error. The classical theory of electromagnetism is based on the validity of our postulates.

From these postulates we shall develop the mathematical theory of electromagnetism. We shall derive the experimental laws discovered by the early electrical experimenters, and we shall deduce the equations basic to the study of electrostatics, magnetostatics, electric and magnetic circuits, transmission lines, waveguides, and antennas. These derivations and deductions should reveal a clear and unmistakable *unity* among the many equations utilized in the various areas of electromagnetism, and this unity should greatly aid the student's understanding of electrical science.

8-1. THE FUNDAMENTAL LAWS

The fundamental laws of electromagnetism, which we shall employ as postulates, were presented by James Clerk Maxwell in 1873. Maxwell studied the ideas and the equations of Ampère, Ohm, Kirchhoff, Faraday and others of his predecessors, and he formulated these ideas into clear mathematical form. His concept of displacement current was introduced into his equations in order to resolve certain inconsistencies. The logic employed by Maxwell is discussed in Sec. 1-7, and a review of this discussion should prove helpful.

We have learned that electric fields exert forces on electric charges and that magnetic fields exert forces on moving charges and current elements. The fields were defined in terms of these forces. However, the manner in which the electric and magnetic fields are produced has not yet been carefully considered. It has been mentioned that electric fields are produced by electric charges and magnetic currents, and that magnetic fields are produced by electric currents. The precise relationships between the fields and the charges and currents that produce them are given by Maxwell's equations.

Maxwell's first equation is often called the *Maxwell-Faraday law*, or the *first law of electromagnetic induction*. The integral form of this law states that the circulation of the electric field intensity **E** around any closed path C is equal to the negative of the magnetic current $\partial\Phi/\partial t$ over any surface

S which has the path C as its boundary. Three equivalent mathematical statements of this law are

$$\oint_C \mathbf{E} \cdot d\mathbf{l} = -\int_S \frac{\partial \mathbf{B}}{\partial t} \cdot d\mathbf{S} \tag{8-1a}$$

$$\oint_C \mathbf{E} \cdot d\mathbf{l} = -\frac{\partial}{\partial t} \int_S \mathbf{B} \cdot d\mathbf{S} \tag{8-1b}$$

$$\oint_C \mathbf{E} \cdot d\mathbf{l} = -\frac{\partial \Phi}{\partial t} \tag{8-1c}$$

The surface S is any two-sided surface having the contour C. **B** is the magnetic flux density, and Φ represents the flux of **B** over the surface S. The right-hand integration rule of Sec. 2-10 applies. According to this rule, if the right hand is oriented so that the extended thumb points out of the arbitrarily selected positive side of the surface S, then the curled fingers indicate the direction of integration around the contour C.

Equations (8-1b) and (8-1c) involve the partial time derivative of the magnetic flux over the surface S. The *partial* time derivative of this magnetic flux Φ denotes the time rate of increase of Φ *due only to the time-changing magnetic field*, and it is important that this be clearly understood. In particular, a time rate of change of the magnetic flux over S, due to motion of the surface S in a magnetic field, is *not* included in the *partial* time derivative of Φ. If the surface is a moving surface, the space limits of integration vary with time. However, the *partial* time derivative denotes that these limits are treated as constants, and consequently, $\partial\Phi/\partial t$ is exactly equivalent to the surface integral of $\partial\mathbf{B}/\partial t$ in all cases.

Maxwell's second equation is often called the *Maxwell-Ampère law*, or the *second law of electromagnetic induction*. The integral form of this law states that the circulation of the magnetic field intensity **H** around any closed path C is equal to the total electric current over any two-sided surface S which has the path C as its boundary. Three equivalent mathematical statements of this law are

$$\oint_C \mathbf{H} \cdot d\mathbf{l} = \int_S \mathbf{J}_t \cdot d\mathbf{S} \tag{8-2a}$$

$$\oint_C \mathbf{H} \cdot d\mathbf{l} = \int_S \left(\rho\mathbf{v} + \frac{\partial \mathbf{D}}{\partial t}\right) \cdot d\mathbf{S} \tag{8-2b}$$

$$\oint_C \mathbf{H} \cdot d\mathbf{l} = i_t \tag{8-2c}$$

It should be recalled that the fields are related by the expressions $\mathbf{D} = \epsilon\mathbf{E}$ and $\mathbf{B} = \mu\mathbf{H}$.

The Maxwell-Faraday and Maxwell-Ampère laws are presented below for comparison.

$$\oint_C \mathbf{E} \cdot d\mathbf{l} = -\int_S \dot{\mathbf{B}} \cdot d\mathbf{S} \tag{8-3}$$

$$\oint_C \mathbf{H} \cdot d\mathbf{l} = \int_S \mathbf{J}_t \cdot d\mathbf{S} \tag{8-4}$$

$\dot{\mathbf{B}}$ is the magnetic current density, and $\mathbf{J}_t$ is the total electric current density, equal to $\rho\mathbf{v} + \dot{\mathbf{D}}$. If we had agreed upon a left-hand integration rule, the negative sign of Eq. (8-3) would become a positive sign, and Eq. (8-4) would then have a negative sign. However, the right-hand integration rule is a well-established convention. It should be noted that the signs would be ambiguous were it not for our integration rule.

An example of a surface S and its contour C is the surface of this page and the path around its borders. Another example is the surface of the northern hemisphere of the earth and the path around the equator. If the line integrals are applied to the closed path of an electric circuit in three-dimensional space, the surface S is any surface that has this path as its boundary.

It should be emphasized that the fundamental laws are unrestricted with regard to the surface, its boundary path, and time. The surface S may be very large or very small, and it may have portions in different physical media. The contour C may be a moving path with different parts of the path having different velocities and with the surface S changing with time as the path moves. The equations are valid at each and every instant of time.

Equations (8-1c) and (8-2c) are presented below for comparison.

$$\oint_C \mathbf{E} \cdot d\mathbf{l} = -\dot{\Phi} \tag{8-5}$$

$$\oint_C \mathbf{H} \cdot d\mathbf{l} = i_t \tag{8-6}$$

The magnetic current $\dot{\Phi}$ and the total electric current i_t are the currents over any surface bounded by the path C. The electric current includes, of course, both convection and displacement currents, if both are present. Equation (8-5) implies that a time-changing magnetic field always has an electric field associated with it. Equation (8-6) implies that an electric current, whether consisting of moving charges or time-changing electric flux, always has a magnetic field associated with it. Our fundamental laws inform us that electric fields are produced by time-changing magnetic fields, and magnetic fields are produced by moving electric charges and also by time-changing electric fields. As we shall see later, these laws implicitly infer that electric fields are also produced by electric charges. Electric and magnetic fields were defined in Chapter 4. The fundamental laws tell us how these fields can be obtained.

If the magnetic flux density **B** varies with time and is not a linear function of time, then $\dot{\mathbf{B}}$ varies with time, and we deduce from Eq. (8-1) that the electric field **E** changes with time. If **E** varies with time and is not a linear function of time, then $\dot{\mathbf{E}}$ and $\dot{\mathbf{D}}$ vary with time, and we deduce from Eq. (8-2) that the magnetic field **H** changes with time. Therefore, *time-changing electric and magnetic fields exist together*, provided neither is a linear function of time. Certainly an electric or a magnetic field could neither increase nor decrease linearly with time for a very long time interval.

Maxwell's equations are the mathematical foundation of electricity and magnetism. The behavior of electric circuits, electric machinery, the radio, the telephone, lightning, and nearly all other electrical equipment and phenomena is governed by these fundamental laws. The only exceptions that have ever been found are the electrodynamics of rapidly moving systems and phenomena involving the intimate electrical structure of matter, such as the photoelectric effect.

8-2. THE MAXWELL-FARADAY LAW

In order to illustrate the meaning and use of the Maxwell-Faraday law, let us consider several simple examples.

EXAMPLE 1. Shown in Fig. 8-1 is a circular metallic loop having a radius of one meter. Suppose a time-varying magnetic field exists in the region such that the magnetic flux density at points of the circular area is approximately

$$\mathbf{B} = 10^{-8}\,(1 - r^2/4 + r^4/64) \sin 3 \times 10^8 t\, \mathbf{k}$$

with r denoting the distance from the center of the loop and **k** representing a unit vector directed out of the paper. Find the counterclockwise voltage drop around the loop.

Solution. Let the positive side of the plane surface S bounded by the path C of the loop be the side facing the reader. By the right-hand integration rule the line integral of **E** is taken in the counterclockwise direction. Thus the counterclockwise voltage drop v is found by differentiating **B** with respect to time and substituting into the Maxwell-Faraday equation. Noting that the unit vector **k** and each differential vector area $d\mathbf{S}$ have the same direction, we obtain

$$v = -\int_S 3(1 - r^2/4 + r^4/64) \cos 3 \times 10^8 t\; dS$$

As the integrand is a function of the space coordinate r, a convenient differential area is that between two circles of radii r and $r + dr$. This area is $2\pi r\,dr$, and the limits of r are zero and one. Consequently,

$$v = -6\pi \cos 3 \times 10^8 t \int_0^1 (r - r^3/4 + r^5/64)\,dr$$

Evaluation of the integral yields a counterclockwise voltage drop v equal to $-8.3 \cos 3 \times 10^8 t$ volts.

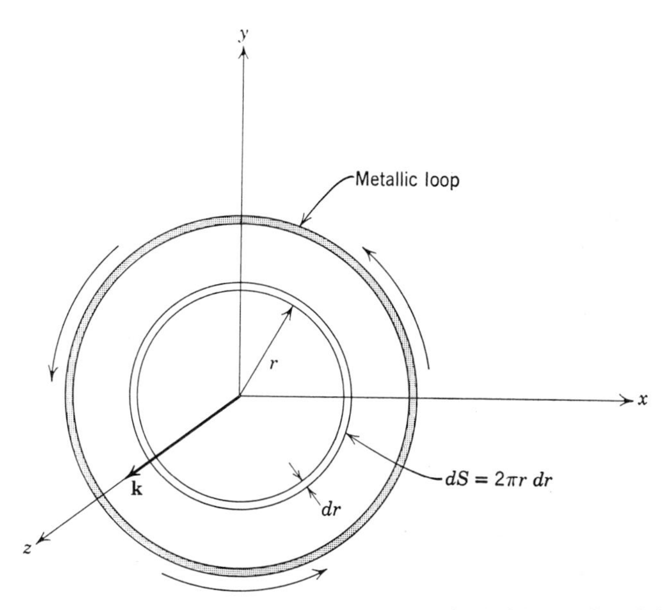

FIG. 8-1. Metallic loop of unit radius in a magnetic field of density $\mathbf{B} = B_z\mathbf{k}$.

The electric field lines in the plane area are circles concentric with the metallic loop. Because of the circular symmetry, the field intensity equals the voltage drop divided by the circumference of the loop. Therefore, at points on the conductor the counterclockwise electric field intensity is $-1.32 \cos 3 \times 10^8 t$ volts/m.

EXAMPLE 2. Shown in Fig. 8-2 is a simplified sketch of an electric transformer consisting of two coils of wire on a ferromagnetic core. A current i supplied to the primary winding produces a magnetic flux φ in the iron core. The two-turn secondary coil is connected to a resistance R. Assuming a core flux of 0.001 sin $377t$ weber, with the indicated positive direction, determine the voltage drop counterclockwise around the closed secondary circuit.

Solution. The counterclockwise emf equals the negative of the partial time derivative of the magnetic flux over S, whose positive side faces the reader. It is evident from Fig. 8-2 that the core flux φ passes through the surface S *two* times. Therefore, the flux over S is 2φ, or 0.002 sin $377t$. The negative of the time derivative of this flux is $-0.754 \cos 377t$ volt, and this is the counterclockwise voltage drop around the closed metallic circuit. If the resistance of the secondary coil is small compared with the resistance R, this voltage appears across R.

It should be noted that the flux over a surface bounded by the two-turn coil of Example 2 is 2φ, with φ denoting the core flux. In general, if a coil has N turns, the flux over a surface bounded by the N-turn coil and its external circuit is $N\varphi$. This assumes that each magnetic flux line of the core links each turn of the coil. When applied to coils of wire, the Maxwell-Faraday law is often written as

$$\oint_C \mathbf{E} \cdot d\mathbf{l} = -N \frac{\partial \varphi}{\partial t}$$

with φ denoting the flux linking each of the N turns of the coil. Of course,

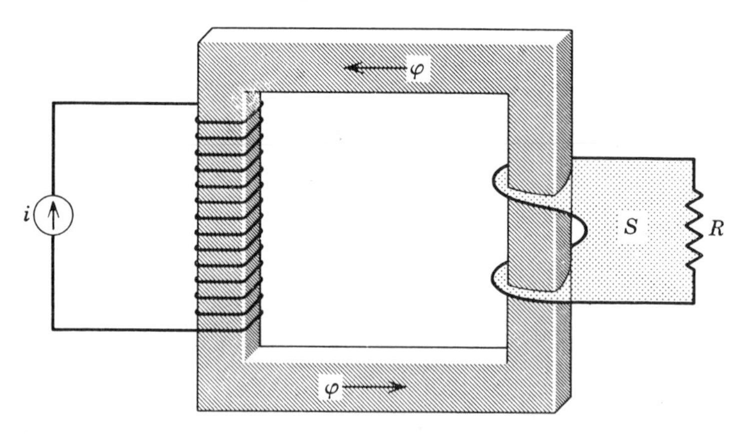

FIG. 8-2. Transformer.

the product $N\varphi$ represents the total flux Φ over any surface bounded by the coil. This product is frequently referred to as the *flux linkages* of the coil. Coils of many turns are utilized when a great many flux linkages are desired.

EXAMPLE 3. Shown in Fig. 8-3 is a slot cut in a copper plate. A sinusoidal voltage v, equal to $10 \sin 10^9 t$ volts, is applied across the center of the slot as indicated. Such a center-fed slot is frequently used as an antenna at very high frequencies. For all practical purposes the copper plate behaves like a perfect conductor at such high frequencies. Find the magnetic flux passing through the left half of the slot, the right half of the slot, and the entire slot.

Solution. Let the plane surface of the slot be divided into surfaces S_1 and S_2 as indicated, with the positive sides of these surfaces selected as the sides facing the reader. Application of the Maxwell-Faraday law to the surface S_1 and its contour C_1 counterclockwise around S_1 gives

$$\oint_{C_1} \mathbf{E} \cdot d\mathbf{l} = -\frac{\partial \Phi_1}{\partial t}$$

with Φ_1 denoting the magnetic flux out of the paper over the surface S_1. The voltage drop along the path *bafe* just inside the conducting material is negligibly small, for the copper plate of this example can be regarded as a perfect conductor. Electric fields do not exist in perfect conductors. A finite electric field in a conductor with no resistance would result in the absurdity of an infinite current. It follows that the voltage drop around the closed path C_1 equals the voltage drop along that portion of the path from e to b, and this voltage drop is $-v$. Therefore, $-v$ equals $-\partial\Phi_1/\partial t$, or

$$-10 \sin 10^9 t = -\partial\Phi_1/\partial t$$

Integration with respect to time gives

$$\Phi_1 = -10^{-8} \cos 10^9 t \text{ weber}$$

The constant of integration is zero if the magnetic field has no steady component.

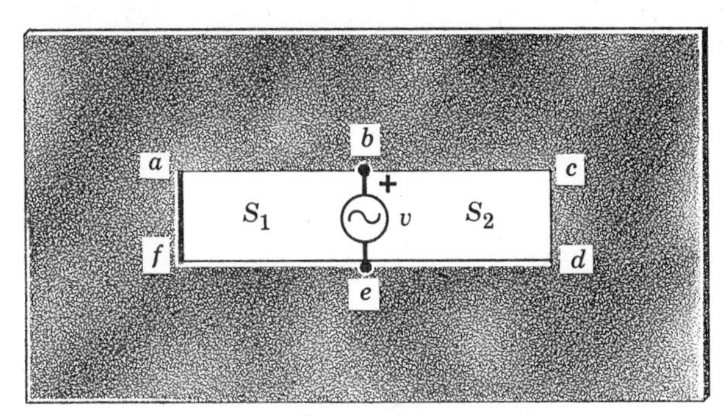

FIG. 8-3. A slot antenna.

The voltage drop counterclockwise around the path C_2 that bounds the surface S_2 is obviously equal to v. Therefore, v equals $-\dot{\Phi}_2$, with Φ_2 denoting the magnetic flux out of the paper over the surface S_2. We deduce that Φ_2 is the negative of Φ_1, or

$$\Phi_2 = 10^{-8} \cos 10^9 t \text{ weber}$$

The total magnetic flux over the area of the slot is the sum of Φ_1 and Φ_2, and this sum is zero. Thus the total flux is zero at every instant of time.

EXAMPLE 4. Shown in Fig. 8-4 is a copper loop around a cylindrical ferromagnetic core. Suppose that the region contains a magnetic field that varies sinusoidally with time, inducing a voltage rise v equal to $0.001 \sin 1000t$ in the loop. The arrow on the sketch denotes the positive direction of v; when v is positive, the voltage rise around the loop in the direction of the arrow is positive; and when v is negative, this voltage rise is negative. The *closed* surface S of the iron core is divided by the loop into the two surfaces S_1 and S_2. With the outer sides of the surfaces designated as positive, determine the magnetic flux over the surfaces S_1, S_2, and S.

Solution. Let us apply the Maxwell-Faraday law to the surface S_1 and its contour, which is the path of the wire loop. The right-hand integration rule requires that we take the voltage drop around this path in the direction of the arrow on the sketch of Fig. 8-4. This voltage drop is $-v$, which must equal $-\dot{\Phi}_1$. Therefore, $\dot{\Phi}_1 = 0.001 \sin 1000t$, and the outward flux Φ_1 is $-10^{-6} \cos 1000t$ weber. The constant of integration is zero, for the magnetic field was specified to be a sinusoidal function of time.

Now let us consider the surface S_2. The contour of this surface is also the path of the loop. The right-hand integration rule requires that we take the voltage drop around the path in the direction opposite to the arrow on the sketch. This

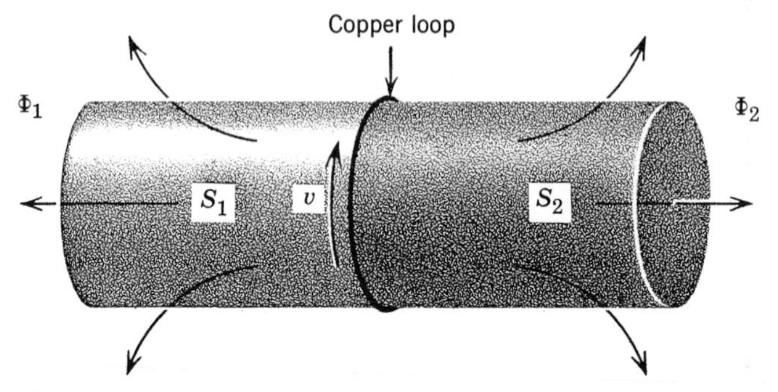

FIG. 8-4. The copper loop divides the closed surface S into surfaces S_1 and S_2. These include the ends of the iron cylinder.

voltage drop is v, which is $0.001 \sin 1000t$, and this must equal $-\dot{\Phi}_2$. It follows that the outward flux Φ_2 is $10^{-6} \cos 1000t$, which is the negative of Φ_1. The total magnetic flux out of the closed surface S is the sum of Φ_1 and Φ_2. As this sum is zero, the outward flux is zero at every instant. In Sec. 8-4 it is shown that the magnetic flux over any closed surface is always zero.

EXAMPLE 5. The electric circuit of Fig. 8-5 shows a battery connected to a loop of conducting wire through a switch. Assume the battery maintains a constant 10 volts across its terminals, regardless of the current. Also assume that the battery connections, the closed switch, and the conducting wire offer no resistance whatever to the flow of electric charge. This is an idealized situation

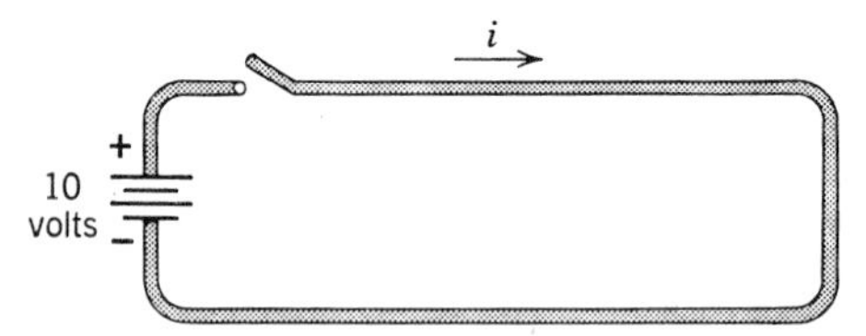

FIG. 8-5. Ideal battery and resistanceless circuit.

which cannot be physically realized. There is no magnetic flux present in the region prior to the closing of the switch at time zero. Determine the magnetic flux Φ out of the back side of the plane surface S bounded by the electric circuit.

Solution. As the positive side of the surface S is the side opposite the reader, the line integral of $\mathbf{E}$ around the closed circuit will be taken clockwise. The voltage drop along the conducting wire is zero, for there can be no electric field within a perfect conductor. The line integral of **E** across the battery terminals from the negative to the positive terminal is -10 volts. Therefore, the clockwise circulation of **E** is -10, and this must equal $-\dot{\Phi}$ by the Maxwell-Faraday law. Integration yields $\Phi = 10t$ webers. The constant of integration is zero, for Φ is zero at time zero.

The magnetic flux Φ entering the side of the surface S facing the reader increases linearly with time. According to the Maxwell-Ampère law, magnetic fields are produced by electric currents. Thus we can regard the flux as produced by the electric current of the circuit, and it follows that the current also varies linearly with time. Even though the wire is assumed to have no resistance, the current does not rise instantaneously to an infinite value. At the instant the switch is closed, the current is zero but increasing. As the magnetic field produced by the current increases, this field induces an electric field in the wire that exactly cancels the applied electric field of the battery. The electromotive force resulting from the time-changing magnetic flux opposes the emf of the battery and, therefore, is called a *counter-emf.*

If the conducting wire in this problem has resistance to the flow of electric charge, then an electric field exists in the wire when there is current. In this case the clockwise circulation of the electric field **E** around the circuit is not -10 volts, but equals -10 plus the voltage drop in the wire. Consequently, $\dot{\Phi}$ equals 10 volts *less* the voltage drop in the wire. As the current rises from zero, $\dot{\Phi}$ decreases due to the increased voltage drop in the wire. Eventually $\dot{\Phi}$ becomes zero and the current becomes steady, the magnitude of the current being determined by the battery voltage and the circuit resistance. In this steady-state condition the circulation of **E** around the closed circuit is zero, and the voltage drop due to the resistance of the circuit equals the battery voltage.

Before leaving this problem let us extend it a step further. Suppose the conducting wire has resistance and the steady-state condition has been reached. Over the surface S enclosed by the circuit of Fig. 8-5 the magnetic flux lines are directed into the paper. Now suppose that the applied voltage is suddenly reduced to zero by means of a fast switching arrangement that removes the battery and simultaneously replaces it with a conducting wire. With the voltage source removed, the current will decrease. As the current decreases, the magnetic flux over S decreases, and $\dot{\Phi}$ is negative because Φ is decreasing with time. The clockwise circulation of **E** around the circuit is $-\dot{\Phi}$, which is a positive quantity as $\dot{\Phi}$ is negative. Thus we see that the decreasing flux induces in the circuit a voltage that tends to maintain the current, preventing the current from decreasing abruptly. The current, due to the electric field induced in the wire by the decreasing magnetic flux, drops gradually to zero.

The preceding problem shows that the current in an electric circuit does not change suddenly from one value to another but varies continuously. This is the result of the emf induced by the time-changing magnetic field. If the current is increasing, the induced emf acts in opposition to the current, preventing a sudden increase. If the current is decreasing, the induced emf acts so as to aid the current, preventing a sudden decrease. The time-changing magnetic field, which is produced by the current, induces an electric field that acts in opposition to the *change* in the current.

It should be emphasized that the voltage magnetically induced by the current of the circuit opposes a *change* in the current. This emf of self-induction opposes an increasing current but aids a decreasing current. The fact that the self-induced emf opposes a change in the current is known as *Lenz's law*.

Let us consider the impossible case of a current changing a finite amount in zero time. According to the Maxwell-Ampère law, this would require a sudden change in the magnetic field, thus making $\dot{\Phi}$ infinite. The opposing emf of self-induction would be infinite, and the entire situation becomes absurd.

EXAMPLE 6. Shown in Fig. 8-6 is a representation of a series electric circuit with a current that alternates at a frequency of 60 cycles per second. The current

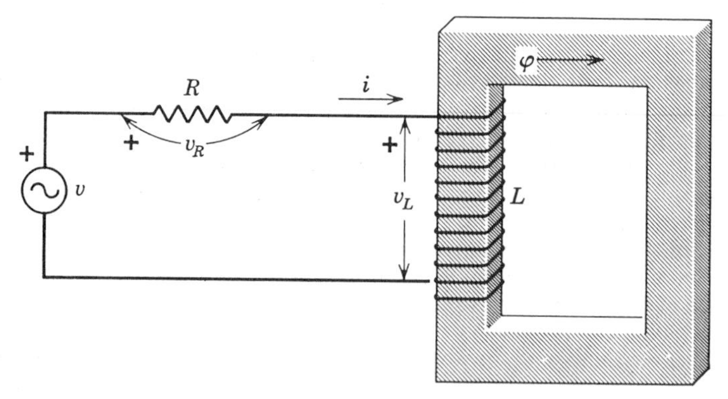

FIG. 8-6. An *RL* circuit.

density **J** is assumed to be uniform, and the current i is the same over all cross sections of the circuit. The distributed resistance R of the actual circuit is regarded as lumped, with v_R denoting the voltage across the terminals of the lumped resistance. This resistive voltage drop, which equals the product iR, is the line integral of the electric field intensity, or $\mathbf{J}/\sigma$, along the metallic wire connected between the terminals of the generator. The magnetic flux of the circuit is regarded as confined to the iron core, and the changing flux linkages produce across the terminals of the coil an emf of self-induction. Let v_L denote this inductive voltage.

Find the relations between the applied voltage v, the resistive voltage drop v_R, and the inductive voltage drop v_L. Also, determine v_L, assuming that the flux linkages $N\varphi$ equal 0.1 sin $377t$ weber.

Solution. In applying the Maxwell-Faraday law, the voltage drop around the circuit will be taken clockwise in accordance with the right-hand rule and the specified positive direction of φ. The clockwise voltage drop across the terminals of the generator and around the metallic path is $-v + v_R$, and this must equal $-N\dot{\varphi}$. Therefore, $v = v_R + N\dot{\varphi}$. The clockwise voltage drop around the closed path across the terminals of the generator, across the terminals of R, and across the terminals of L is zero, for all magnetic flux is assumed to be confined to the magnetic circuit of the coil. Consequently, $v = v_R + v_L$, and we deduce that v_L is $N\dot{\varphi}$. This can be written

$$v_L = N\, d\varphi/dt$$

We note that *the inductive voltage drop in the direction of the positive current is* $+N\, d\varphi/dt$, *provided the reference direction for* φ *is such that* φ *is positive when i is positive.* These reference directions are shown in Fig. 8-6. For the given flux linkages we determine v_L to be 37.7 cos 377t volts.

In linear low-frequency circuits the magnetic flux φ is directly proportional to the current i, *provided* the current density **J** is sufficiently uniform over each cross section so that *skin effect* is negligible. It follows that the flux linkages $N\varphi$ equal Li, with L denoting the constant of proportionality referred to as *inductance.* Thus the inductance L is the flux linkages per unit current $N\varphi/i$ of the circuit. Its mks unit is the *henry.* As the inductive voltage drop is $N\dot{\varphi}$, it is evident that $v_L = L\, di/dt$, with v_L representing *the voltage drop across the inductance L in the direction of the positive current.* Note that the positive directions of i and φ, as indicated on the illustration, were selected so that these quantities are in time phase.

In representations of actual physical circuits it is customary and convenient to utilize ideal lumped circuit elements. By incorporating the effect of $\dot{\varphi}$ into the lumped inductance, *we can equate the voltage drops around the circuit to zero*, provided these drops are taken across the terminals of the elements. This rule, known as *Kirchhoff's voltage law*, is a consequence of the Maxwell-Faraday law. Circuit concepts are discussed with greater rigor and in more detail in Chapters 14 and 15.

Many practical electromagnetic problems deal with static fields. If the electric field in a region is static, the magnetic field is also static, and $\dot{\mathbf{B}}$ is zero. By the Maxwell-Faraday law the circulation of **E** around every possible path in the region occupied by static fields is zero. Thus *the electrostatic field is conservative*, having zero circulation. In a conservative field the line integral along a path between two points is independent of the actual path of integration, depending only on the terminal points. Therefore, the voltage drops along various paths between the same two points are identical, *provided the fields are not changing with time.* The science of electrostatics is discussed in Chapter 18.

The Maxwell-Faraday law is frequently written without the use of vector notation. One such form of the equation is

$$\oint_C E_l\, dl = -\frac{\partial}{\partial t}\int_S B_n\, dS \tag{8-7}$$

E_l denotes the component of $\mathbf{E}$ in the direction of $d\mathbf{l}$, and B_n denotes the component of $\mathbf{B}$ normal to the differential surface area dS and out of its positive side.

8-3. EMF AROUND A CLOSED PATH

The electromotive force, or voltage drop, around a closed path is the work per unit charge done by the fields on a test charge moved around the path. If the path is stationary, this emf is simply the circulation of $\mathbf{E}$, which equals $-\partial\Phi/\partial t$ by the Maxwell-Faraday law. However, if portions of the path are moving in a magnetic field, there is motional emf, and the electromotive force around the closed path is

$$\text{emf} = \oint_C (\mathbf{E} + \mathbf{v} \times \mathbf{B}) \cdot d\mathbf{l} \tag{8-8}$$

$\mathbf{E}$ and $\mathbf{B}$ are, of course, the fields that would be measured by a *stationary* observer.

As the circulation of $\mathbf{E}$ equals $-\dot{\Phi}$, with Φ denoting the magnetic flux over any surface bounded by the path, it follows from (8-8) that

$$\text{emf} = -\frac{\partial\Phi}{\partial t} + \oint_C (\mathbf{v} \times \mathbf{B}) \cdot d\mathbf{l} \tag{8-9}$$

The first term on the right side of Eq. (8-9) represents the voltage induced in the closed loop by the time-changing magnetic field that produces an electric field $\mathbf{E}$. This electric field exerts an *electric* force on any charge carriers present. The second term on the right side denotes the motional emf due to the *magnetic* force on any charge carriers present. If the path is not moving in a magnetic field, this term is, of course, zero.

The expression $(\mathbf{v} \times \mathbf{B}) \cdot d\mathbf{l}$ of Eq. (8-9) can be replaced with $-\mathbf{B} \cdot (\mathbf{v} \times d\mathbf{l})$. This is evident from inspection of the vector identity of Eq. (2-12). Equation (8-9) becomes

$$\text{emf} = -\left[\frac{\partial\Phi}{\partial t} + \oint_C \mathbf{B} \cdot (\mathbf{v} \times d\mathbf{l})\right] \tag{8-10}$$

Let us recall that the partial time derivative of the magnetic flux Φ, over any surface S having the path C as its boundary, represents the time rate of increase of Φ *due only to the time-changing magnetic field.* We shall now verify that the line integral inside the brackets of Eq. (8-10) represents the time rate of increase of Φ *due to the path C cutting lines of magnetic flux* as a result of motion relative to the frame of reference of the observer.

Shown in Fig. 8-7 is an enlarged differential path length $d\mathbf{l}$ of a circuit moving in a magnetic field. The z-axis is oriented so that $d\mathbf{l} = dz\,\mathbf{k}$. Only the component of the velocity vector normal to $d\mathbf{l}$ contributes to the cross product of $\mathbf{v}$ and $d\mathbf{l}$ of Eq. (8-10). Therefore, no generality is sacrificed by orienting the velocity vector normal to $d\mathbf{l}$, with $\mathbf{v} = v_y\mathbf{j}$. Thus $\mathbf{v} \times d\mathbf{l}$ equals $v_y\, dz\, \mathbf{i}$ and, consequently, $\mathbf{B} \cdot (\mathbf{v} \times d\mathbf{l})$ equals $B_x v_y\, dz$.

Now let us suppose that $d\mathbf{l}$ is a portion of a closed circuit in the yz-plane, such as the circuit indicated by the closed path C of Fig. 8-7. With the emf around C taken counterclockwise, the positive side of the plane surface S bounded by C is the side facing the reader. The product $B_x v_y\, dz$ represents the increase in the magnetic flux out of this surface, per unit time,

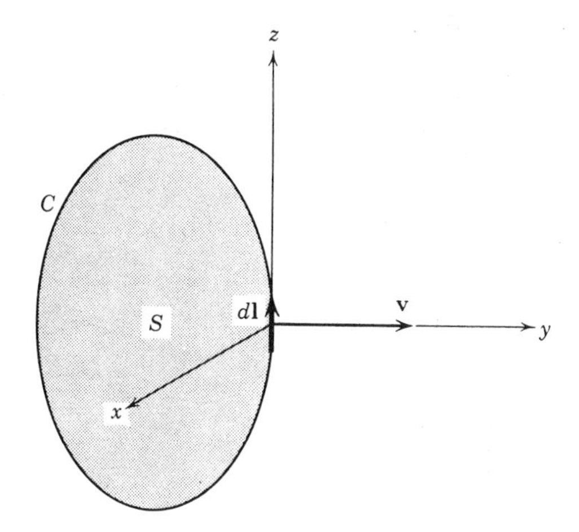

FIG. 8-7. The differential length $d\mathbf{l}$ of the circuit C is moving with velocity $\mathbf{v}$ in a magnetic field.

due to the length dz cutting lines of magnetic flux. This follows from the fact that $v_y\, dz$ equals $dy\, dz/dt$, or dS/dt, which is the time rate of increase of the surface area due to the motion of $d\mathbf{l}$. Multiplication of dS/dt by the normal component of $\mathbf{B}$, this component being B_x, gives the time rate of increase of Φ due to the motion of $d\mathbf{l}$ in the magnetic field. The integral of $\mathbf{B} \cdot (\mathbf{v} \times d\mathbf{l})$ around the closed path C gives the total time rate of increase of Φ *due to the motion of the path* C relative to the frame of reference of the observer. The surface S is not restricted to the plane surface considered, for the flux over every surface bounded by the path is the same. This follows from the Maxwell-Faraday law and is discussed in the next section.

Let us reexamine Eq. (8-10). The first term in the brackets denotes the time rate of increase of the magnetic flux Φ due to the time-changing magnetic field $\mathbf{B}$. The second term in the brackets denotes the time rate of increase of Φ due to the motion of the path C in the magnetic field. If the magnetic field $\mathbf{B}$ is static, the first term is zero. If the path C does not cut lines of magnetic flux, the second term is zero. Equation (8-10) is commonly written in the form

$$\text{emf} = -d\Phi/dt \tag{8-11}$$

with the understanding that $d\Phi/dt$ denotes the time rate of increase of Φ due to a time-changing magnetic field and also due to the path C cutting lines of magnetic flux. *A change in Φ by some other method is not included in the expression $d\Phi/dt$ in Eq.* (8-11). Equations (8-8), (8-9), (8-10), and (8-11) are equivalent.

The difference between the Maxwell-Faraday law and Eq. (8-11) should be carefully noted. In terms of the magnetic flux density **B** the two equations are

$$\oint_C \mathbf{E} \cdot d\mathbf{l} = -\frac{\partial}{\partial t}\int_S \mathbf{B} \cdot d\mathbf{S} \tag{8-12}$$

$$\text{emf} = -\frac{d}{dt}\int_S \mathbf{B} \cdot d\mathbf{S} \tag{8-13}$$

If the surface S is bounded by a moving path C, the limits of the surface integral are functions of time. The *partial* time derivative of the surface

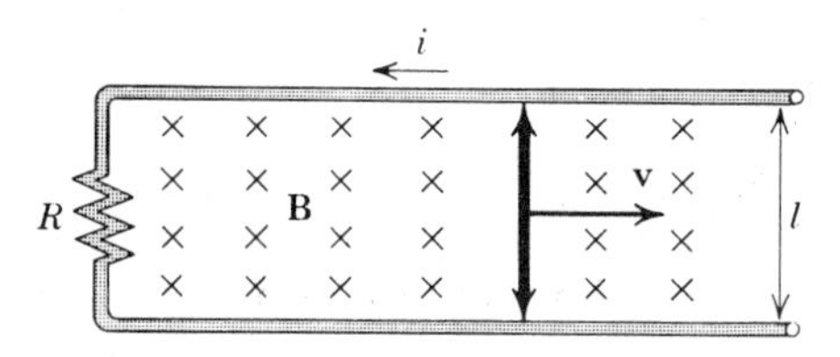

FIG. 8-8. Circuit with moving conductor.

integral of **B** is equal to the surface integral of $\dot{\mathbf{B}}$. but the *total* time derivative of the surface integral involves time derivatives of the limits of integration. Equation (8-13) is Eq. (8-12) with motional emf, if present, included.

Let us consider several illustrative examples.

EXAMPLE 1. Apply Eq. (8-11) to the electric circuit of Fig. 8-8 and determine the counterclockwise voltage drop around the closed metallic circuit. The magnetic flux density **B**, directed into the paper, is uniform and static.

Solution. Let S denote the plane surface bounded by the path C of the metallic circuit. The emf counterclockwise around C equals $-d\Phi/dt$, with Φ denoting the magnetic flux over the surface S, whose positive side faces the reader. Obviously, Φ equals $-BS$, and $-d\Phi/dt$ equals $+B\,dS/dt$. The time rate of increase of the surface area S is vl. It follows that the voltage drop counterclockwise around C is Bvl. The line integral of **E** around the closed metallic path is zero, for $\dot{\mathbf{B}}$ is zero, but the emf is Bvl, this emf being entirely a motional emf. The current i is positive.

In the stationary conductors this current is the result of the electric field produced by the charges stored on the conductors, but in the moving conductor the current is due to the magnetic force that drives the charge carriers in opposition to the electric force.

EXAMPLE 2. Shown in Fig. 8-9 is a *Faraday disc generator*, or *homopolar generator*, connected by means of sliding taps to an electric circuit with a resistance R. The generator consists of a copper disc of radius a, rotating on its axis with angular velocity ω radians per second. A uniform static magnetic field is directed normal to the disc from left to right. Determine the voltage drop around the closed metallic circuit *abcda*, in terms of the radius a, the angular velocity ω, and the flux density B.

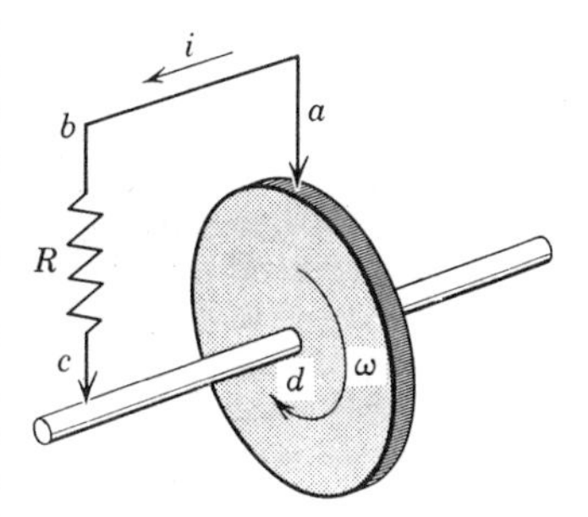

FIG. 8-9. Faraday disc generator.

Solution. The line integral of **E** around any closed path in the region is zero, for $\dot{\mathbf{B}}$ is zero. However, there is definitely a motional emf generated by the moving plate. Consider the path in the copper disc extending directly from d to a. The motional emf of a differential path length is $(\mathbf{v} \times \mathbf{B}) \cdot d\mathbf{l}$, and this equals $vB\, dl$, for $\mathbf{v}$ and $\mathbf{B}$ are normal to one another and their cross product is directed along $d\mathbf{l}$. The velocity v of dl is $r\omega$, and dl equals dr, with r representing the distance from the center of the disk. Therefore, the motional emf of a differential path length is $\omega Br\, dr$. As ω and B do not vary along the path, integration from 0 to a yields a motional emf equal to $\frac{1}{2}a^2\omega B$. This is the voltage drop around the closed metallic circuit *abcda*.

If the resistance of the disc generator is negligible compared with the resistance R of the load, the voltage drop across the load from b to c is equal to the motional emf. This voltage drop is, of course, directly due to the electric field produced by the charges separated by the rotation of the disc in a magnetic field. The voltage along the path from d to a inside the disc is negligibly small, for the electric and magnetic forces on the free charge carriers of the disc oppose one another.

It is not convenient to apply Eq. (8-11) to this problem. However, if Φ denotes the magnetic flux into the paper over the surface S bounded by the path *abcda*, the expression $d\Phi/dt$ is positive, for Φ increases as the moving path from d to a cuts magnetic flux lines. In fact, $d\Phi/dt$ must equal the motional emf. When applied to problems involving static magnetic fields, the expression $d\Phi/dt$ of Eq. (8-11) denotes the time rate of increase of Φ due only to the cutting of magnetic flux lines by the path C that bounds the surface S.

EXAMPLE 3. Shown in Fig. 8-10 is an electric circuit consisting of a voltmeter and a wire coiled about an iron cylinder. The voltmeter is connected to the ends of the coil by means of sliding contacts, with the tap on the right side sliding along a copper ring to which the coil end is soldered. The current I of the second circuit produces a steady magnetic flux φ in the iron cylinder. Although the electric circuits are not in the magnetic field, the flux lines pass through the turns of the coils.

When the end of the coil at A is pulled downward, the cylinder rotates on its axis, and the coil unwinds. Suppose the coil is unwound at a rate that causes the magnetic flux over a surface S bounded by this coil and the voltmeter to decrease at a rate of one weber per minute. What does the voltmeter read?

Solution. The magnetic flux over the surface S is changing with time. However, this change is due neither to a time-changing magnetic field nor to the cutting of flux lines by the path C that bounds the surface S. Therefore, there is no emf, and the voltmeter reads zero. The expression $d\Phi/dt$ of Eq. (8-11) is zero. An emf

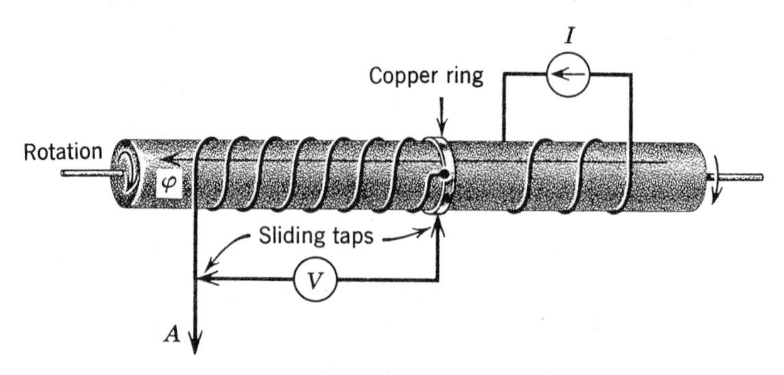

FIG. 8-10. Two coils on an iron core. One is being unwound as the core rotates, and its flux linkages change with time, though φ is steady.

around a closed path exists only if a time-changing magnetic flux density **B** induces a voltage according to the Maxwell-Faraday law, or if there is motional emf.

EXAMPLE 4. A *wavefront* of an electromagnetic wave in a perfect dielectric is shown in Fig. 8-11. The wavefront propagates in a direction normal to its surface with velocity c. Ahead of the wavefront there are no fields. Immediately behind

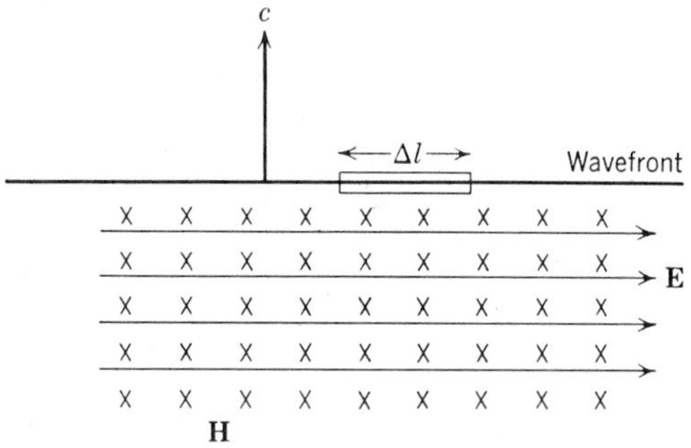

FIG. 8-11. Cross section of the wavefront of an electromagnetic wave.

the wavefront the **E** and **H** fields are parallel to the surface and normal to one another. The crosses of Fig. 8-11 indicate magnetic field lines directed into the paper. Show that $E/H = \mu c$, with μ denoting the permeability of the medium.

Solution. Let us apply the Maxwell-Faraday law to the very small rectangle constructed about a portion of the wavefront, as illustrated in Fig. 8-11. The wavefront is passing through the stationary rectangle at the instant under consideration. The clockwise circulation of **E** around the closed path C of the rectangle is obviously equal to $E\,\Delta l$, with Δl denoting the length of the rectangle. This must equal $-\dot{\Phi}$, with the positive side of the surface S of the rectangle being the side facing the reader. If we select the *back* side of the rectangle as the positive side, then $E\,\Delta l = +\partial\Phi/\partial t$.

The time rate of increase of the magnetic flux out of the back side of the rectangle is $Bc\,\Delta l$, because $c\,\Delta l$ represents the rate of increase of the surface area occupied by the flux density B. Therefore, $E\,\Delta l = Bc\,\Delta l$, or $E = Bc$, or $E/H = \mu c$.

It is easily shown that **E** and **H** must be normal to one another at the surface of a wavefront. Suppose that there is a component of **H** in the direction of **E**. Then the *magnetomotive force* around the path C of the rectangle of Fig. 8-11 has value. This violates the Maxwell-Ampère law, since there is neither convection nor displacement current over the surface S of the rectangle. Therefore, **H** cannot have a component in the direction of **E**.

8-4. MAGNETIC FLUX OVER A CLOSED SURFACE

A closed surface of any size or shape can be divided into two surfaces by a closed path. For example, the surface of the earth is so divided by the equator, or by any other closed path on the earth's surface.

Let Φ represent the net outward magnetic flux over a closed surface S, and suppose the closed path C divides S into two surfaces, designated S_1 and S_2. Each of these are bounded by the same path C. If Φ_1 and Φ_2 denote the outward magnetic fluxes over S_1 and S_2, respectively, then $\Phi = \Phi_1 + \Phi_2$. The Maxwell-Faraday law, applied to surface S_1 bounded by C, gives

$$\oint_C \mathbf{E} \cdot d\mathbf{l} = -\dot{\Phi}_1 \tag{8-14}$$

When this law is applied to surface S_2, the result is

$$\oint_C \mathbf{E} \cdot d\mathbf{l} = -\dot{\Phi}_2 \tag{8-15}$$

The line integrals of Eqs. (8-14) and (8-15) must be taken in *opposite* directions around the path C, in accordance with the right-hand integration rule. For example, suppose S is the closed surface of the earth, with S_1 denoting the surface of the northern hemisphere and S_2 denoting that of the southern hemisphere. The equator is the path C that bounds both S_1 and S_2, with the outer sides selected as the positive sides. If the Maxwell-Faraday law is applied to the northern hemisphere, the right-hand integration rule requires that the circulation of **E** around the equator be taken *eastward*. When applied to the southern hemisphere, the integration rule requires the circulation to be taken *westward*. In Eqs. (8-14) and (8-15) the line integrals of **E** have the same magnitude but opposite signs.

Therefore, the addition of the two equations yields $\dot{\Phi}_1 + \dot{\Phi}_2 = 0$. As Φ is the sum of Φ_1 and Φ_2, it is evident that $\dot{\Phi}$ is zero.

Thus the magnetic current over any closed surface is zero. This implies that the magnetic flux Φ over any closed surface is independent of time. Consider a very small closed surface S surrounding an arbitrary point P in space. Then

$$\oint_S \mathbf{B} \cdot d\mathbf{S} = C_1$$

with C_1 denoting a constant independent of time. Recall that the flux of a vector over a closed surface is a measure of the source strength of the vector in the volume enclosed by the surface. If C_1 is not zero, there must be a source of the magnetic field at the point P. This source may *never* move away from P, and it may *never* change in magnitude. It is fixed in position and invariant with time. Such point sources seem rather absurd and, in fact, no such sources have ever been observed. Accordingly, we postulate a zero value for the constant C_1, and it follows that *the magnetic flux over a closed surface is always zero.* Mathematically,

$$\oint_S \mathbf{B} \cdot d\mathbf{S} = 0 \tag{8-16}$$

Equation (8-16) is a fundamental law of electromagnetism, which is usually classified as one of the equations known as Maxwell's equations. We derived it from the Maxwell-Faraday law, utilizing experimental evidence denying the existence of immobile and invariant magnetic charges acting as sources of the magnetic field. It applies to all closed surfaces, regardless of size or shape, and is valid at each instant of time. It does not, of course, imply that there is no magnetic flux over portions of a surface. However, the net outward flux over an entire closed surface is zero. The flux entering the closed surface equals the flux leaving the surface.

As magnetic flux density has no sources or sinks, it is a solenoidal field. The field lines representing **B** have neither beginning nor end, for there are no sources or sinks of **B**. The lines may close on themselves. They may start and end at infinity. Because a flux line is one-dimensional, occupying zero volume, it is possible for one to be confined to a finite region without closing on itself. In any event, the flux lines of **B** do not start or end at points unless these points are the same. They continue endlessly.

As $\mathbf{B} = \mu\mathbf{H}$, Eq. (8-16) becomes

$$\oint_S \mu\mathbf{H} \cdot d\mathbf{S} = 0 \tag{8-17}$$

If all points of the surface S are in the same physical medium, the permeability μ of Eq. (8-17) is constant and may be dropped. This gives

$$\oint_S \mathbf{H} \cdot d\mathbf{S} = 0 \tag{8-18}$$

Equation (8-18) applies only if the permeability μ is the same at all points of the closed surface S. As Eq. (8-18) is not always valid, it is clear that the magnetic field intensity $\mathbf{H}$ is not, in general, a solenoidal field.

8-5. THE MAXWELL-AMPÈRE LAW

The magnetomotive force along a path is, by definition, the line integral of the magnetic field intensity $\mathbf{H}$ along the path. According to the Maxwell-Ampère law, the magnetomotive force around a closed path equals the

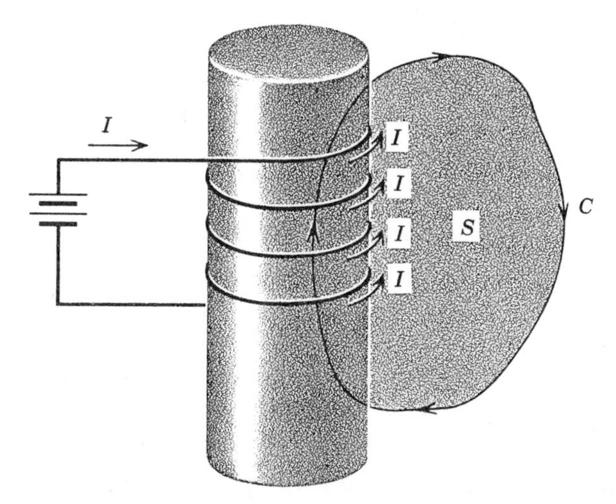

FIG. 8-12. A path C that links a 4-turn coil.

total electric current over any surface bounded by the path. Let us consider several elementary examples involving this law.

EXAMPLE 1. To obtain a large mmf around a closed path, without employing large currents, a coil of wire can be used. Shown in Fig. 8-12 is an electric circuit with a coil of four turns. The battery supplies an electromotive force to the circuit, and a steady current I results. Determine the magnetomotive force around the closed path C that links the four turns of the coil.

Solution. By the Maxwell-Ampère law the mmf clockwise around C equals the total electric current out of the back side of the plane surface S bounded by C. As there are no time-varying fields present, there are no displacement currents, and the only current present is that of the electric circuit. Each of the four turns of wire intersects the surface S. Figure 8-12 clearly shows that the current I in each turn enters the negative side of S and leaves the positive side. Therefore,the total current over the surface is $4I$ amperes, and this is the mmf around the closed path C.

In general, if a coil has N turns and carries an instantaneous current i, the mmf around a closed path that links the N turns of the coil is Ni amperes, provided displacement currents are negligible. The product Ni is usually referred to as the *ampere-turns* of the coil. A current of one ampere in a coil of a thousand turns produces the same magnetomotive force as a current of a thousand amperes in a one-turn loop. The general

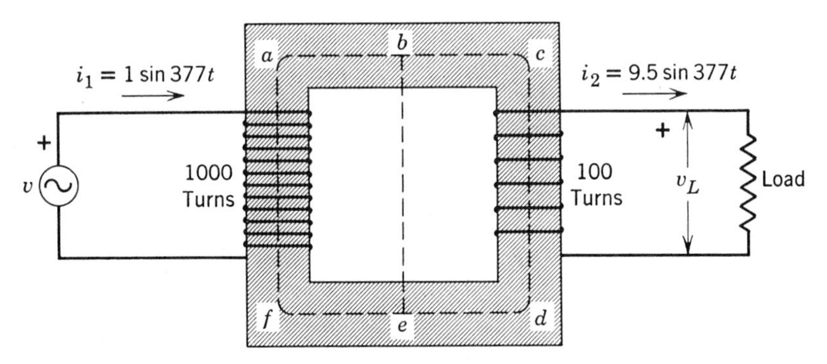

FIG. 8-13. Transformer.

direction of the magnetic flux lines passing through a coil is easily determined by placing the right hand on the coil with the fingers curled around the coil in the direction of the current I. The extended thumb points in the direction of the flux lines. This should be evident from Fig. 8-12. Coils are frequently mounted on ferromagnetic cores with large relative permeabilities in order to obtain intense magnetic flux densities.

EXAMPLE 2. The sketch of Fig. 8-13 represents an iron-core transformer with 1000 primary turns and 100 secondary turns. The manner in which the coils are wound on the core is indicated on the sketch. Assuming a primary current i_1 of sin $377t$ and a secondary current i_2 of 9.5 sin $377t$, with positive directions as shown, determine the magnetomotive forces around the paths *abcdefa*, *abefa*, and *bcdeb*. Displacement currents are negligible.

Solution. Let S denote the plane surface bounded by the path *abcdefa* of the iron core, and let S_1 and S_2 denote the left and right parts of the surface S, bounded by the paths *abefa* and *bcdeb*, respectively. The positive sides of these surfaces are the back sides by the right-hand rule, for the line integrals are to be taken clockwise. The total current over the left-hand surface S_1, which is the mmf around the path *abefa*, is 1000 sin $377t$ amperes. The total current over the right-hand surface S_2, which is the mmf around the path *bcdeb*, is -950 sin $377t$. The sum of these currents is the current over the surface S. Therefore, the mmf around the path *abcdefa* of the iron core is 50 sin $377t$ amperes. In this example the mmfs of the primary and secondary windings, acting around the iron core, are in opposition at each instant of time. The primary and secondary circuits are coupled together by the time-varying lines of magnetic flux around the magnetic circuit.

EXAMPLE 3. A device often used in microwave systems consists of a hollow metallic box known as a *cavity resonator*. Cavity resonators are employed in many high-frequency electron tubes. They may be used as the resonant element that transfers power from an electron stream to a waveguide. Sometimes they serve as waveguide filters that eliminate undesired frequencies.

A simple rectangular resonator is shown in Fig. 8-14. The hollow box is made of copper that shields the inner region from the outside. Electromagnetic fields

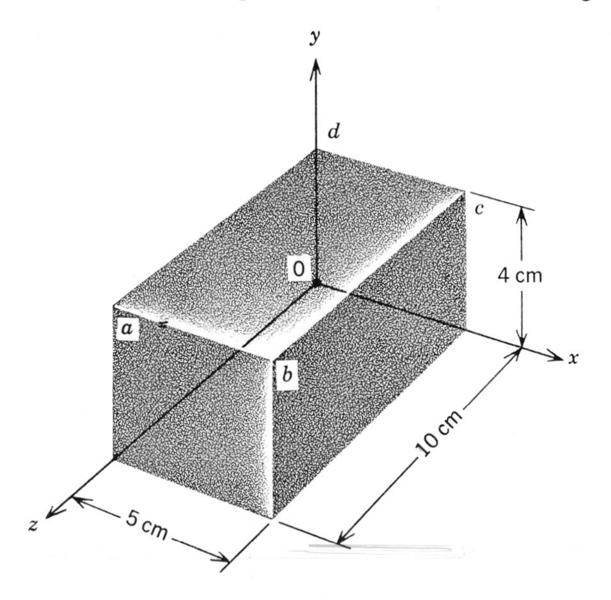

FIG. 8-14. Cavity resonator.

are excited inside the box by a small current-carrying probe inserted through a small opening. Suppose the electric field in the inner region, assumed to have a dielectric constant of 5, is

$$\mathbf{E} = 1000 \sin 20\pi x \sin 10\pi z \sin \omega t\, \mathbf{j}$$

The frequency is 1500 megacycles, which gives an angular frequency ω of $3\pi \times 10^9$. Using the Maxwell-Ampère law, determine the mmf around the rectangular path *abcda, which lies in the inner dielectric* just off the metallic sides.

Solution. The mmf around the specified path equals the total electric current over any surface S bounded by the path. The obvious surface to select is the plane rectangular surface having the path as its contour. By the right-hand rule the positive side of this surface is the top side. As all points on the surface are located in the dielectric, the convection current is zero, and the mmf equals the displacement current over S. The displacement current density has only the y

component J_y, which equals $\epsilon_r\epsilon_0\dot{E}_y$. This gives

$$J_y = 417 \sin 20\pi x \sin 10\pi z \cos \omega t$$

with the number 417 obtained from the product $1000\epsilon_r\epsilon_0\omega$.

The surface integral of J_y over the surface S yields the displacement current i_d. As $dx\, dz$ denotes a differential surface area, the displacement current is

$$i_d = 417 \cos \omega t \int_0^{0.05} \sin 20\pi x\, dx \int_0^{0.1} \sin 10\pi z\, dz$$

Evaluation of the definite integrals gives a current of 0.844 cos ωt ampere. This is the mmf around the specified path. Even though this path does not link a conductor, there is a magnetomotive force present. The selected path actually is along a magnetic flux line of this resonator. In Chapter 11 we shall learn how to find, from the Maxwell equations and the given electric field, the magnetic field intensity at each point of the region.

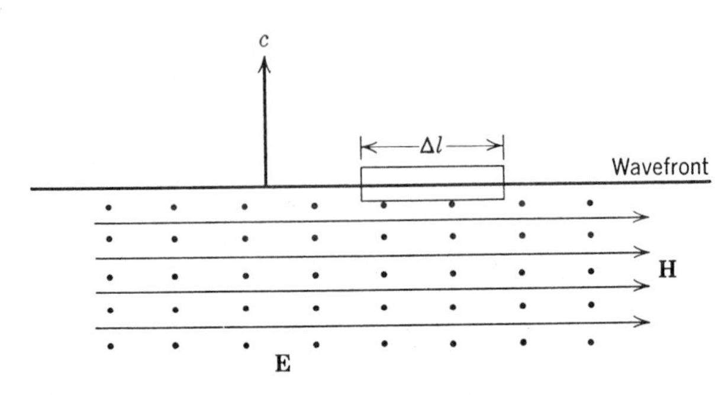

FIG. 8-15. Cross section of the wavefront of an electromagnetic wave.

EXAMPLE 4. Earlier, we applied the Maxwell-Faraday law to the wavefront of an electromagnetic wave in a perfect dielectric. Our problem now is to apply the Maxwell-Ampère law and show that the ratio E/H equals $1/(\epsilon c)$. The wavefront, propagating with velocity c in a dielectric of permittivity ϵ, is sketched in Fig. 8-15. The view is oriented so that the magnetic field is directed from left to right and the electric field is directed out of the paper. At the instant under consideration the wavefront is passing through the small stationary rectangle shown on the sketch.

Solution. The counterclockwise mmf around the rectangle is $H\,\Delta l$. By the Maxwell-Ampère law this equals the total electric current over the plane surface S bounded by the path of the rectangle, with the positive side of S facing the reader. This current is $\dot{\psi}$, with ψ denoting the electric flux over S. The time rate of increase of ψ is the product of the electric flux density D and the time rate of increase of that part of the surface S behind the wavefront. Therefore, the displacement current is $Dc\,\Delta l$ amperes. As this equals the mmf $H\,\Delta l$, it follows that $H = Dc = \epsilon Ec$, and $E/H = 1/(\epsilon c)$.

In Example 4 of Sec. 8-3 we applied the Maxwell-Faraday law to the wavefront and deduced that $E/H = \mu c$, with μ denoting the permeability of the medium. From this and the result of the preceding example it is evident that $\mu c = 1/(\epsilon c)$, or $c = 1/\sqrt{\mu\epsilon}$ meters per second. Thus the application of Maxwell's equations to the wavefront of an electromagnetic wave in a perfect dielectric reveals that the wave propagates at a velocity determined by the permittivity and the permeability of the physical medium, If the medium is free space, this velocity is approximately 3×10^8 meters per second. Also, we note that the ratio of E to H at the wavefront is $\sqrt{\mu/\epsilon}$ ohms, and this is called the *intrinsic impedance* of the perfect dielectric. The intrinsic impedance of free space is approximately 377 ohms.

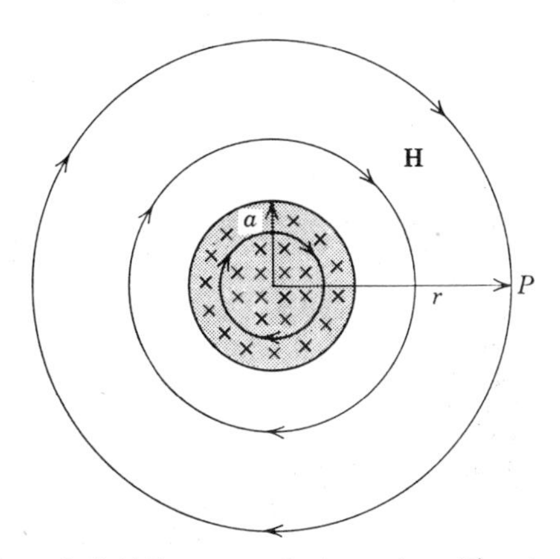

FIG. 8-16. Magnetic field lines around a long wire with a steady current I.

EXAMPLE 5. Shown in Fig. 8-16 is a cross section of a straight wire of infinite length carrying a steady current I into the paper. This current is uniformly distributed over the cross section of radius a. The magnetic field lines are circles centered on the axis of the wire. Find the field **H** at a point P a distance r from the axis of the wire.

Solution. Along the circular path of a field line the scalar product of **H** and $d\mathbf{l}$ equals $H\,dl$. From symmetry it is evident that H is constant along the circular path. Therefore, the line integral of **H** around the closed path of a field line is the product of H and the path length, and this magnetomotive force is $2\pi rH$. For $r > a$ the clockwise mmf equals the current I by the Maxwell-Ampère law. Thus the magnetic field intensity at the point P is

$$H = I/(2\pi r) \text{ amperes/m} \tag{8-19}$$

For $r < a$ the current through the circular area enclosed by the path is Ir^2/a^2, and the magnetic field intensity is

$$H = rI/(2\pi a^2) \text{ amperes/m} \tag{8-20}$$

The circular field lines are directed clockwise according to the right-hand rule. Note that, if our right hand holds the wire with the thumb pointing in the direction of the current, the fingers curled around the wire indicate the direction of the flux lines.

The results of the preceding example can be used to state the basis for the official definition of the coulomb. Suppose a straight filamentary wire parallel to the first is placed so that it passes through the point P of Fig. 8-16. The first wire produces a magnetic flux density $\mathbf{B}$ at P equal to $\mu I/(2\pi r)$ amperes per meter, directed downward. If the second wire also carries a current I, but with the positive direction being out of the paper, a magnetic force $I\,d\mathbf{l} \times \mathbf{B}$ acts on each differential length of this wire. As $I\,d\mathbf{l}$ of the second wire is directed out of the paper and as the magnetic flux density $\mathbf{B}$ at the point P due to the first wire is downward, the differential force on $d\mathbf{l}$ is directed to the right, away from the first wire. The magnitude of this differential force is $BI\,dl$, and the repulsive force *per unit length* is simply BI. Substitution for B gives a repulsive force of

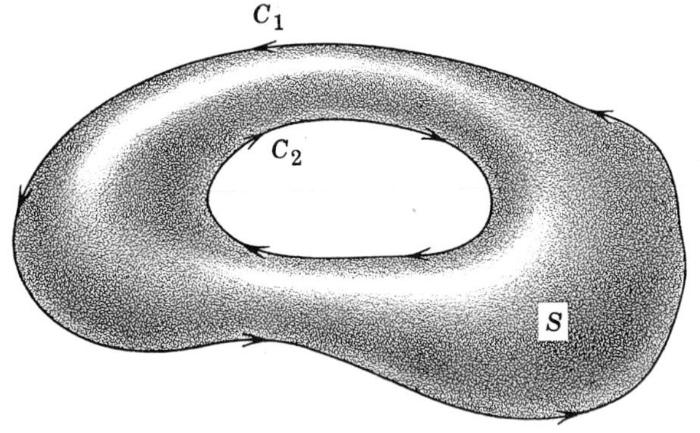

FIG. 8-17. A surface bounded by two paths, C_1 and C_2.

$\mu I^2/(2\pi r)$ newtons per meter. If I is one ampere and the separation r is one meter, this force of repulsion is $\mu/(2\pi)$, or 2×10^{-7} newton per meter for free space.

The result is used to define the coulomb. If parallel wires with equal and opposite currents are placed a meter apart in free space, with the current adjusted to produce a repulsive force of 2×10^{-7} newton per meter, the charge that passes a cross section of the wire in one second is one coulomb. This is the official definition of the coulomb. For purposes of measurement, the force principle is applied to coils instead of straight wires.

8-6. SURFACES WITH SEVERAL BOUNDARY PATHS

Whenever a surface is bounded by two or more closed paths, the line integrals of the Maxwell-Faraday and Maxwell-Ampère laws must include all these paths. To justify this we shall apply these laws to the shaded surface S of Fig. 8-17, with the positive side of S selected as the side facing the reader. In accordance with the right-hand integration rule, applied to the surface S, the line integral around C_1 is taken counterclockwise and the line integral around C_2 is taken clockwise.

By the Maxwell-Ampère law the magnetomotive force counterclockwise around C_1 equals the net outward electric current over the *entire* surface bounded by C_1. The mmf clockwise around C_2 equals the net inward electric current over the *inner* surface bounded by C_2. Obviously, the sum of these two line integrals gives the net outward electric current over the surface S bounded by the closed paths C_1 and C_2. The same reasoning applies to similar application of the Maxwell-Faraday law.

REFERENCES

Bewley, L. V., *Flux Linkages and Electromagnetic Induction*, The Macmillan Co., New York, 1952.

Boast, W. B., *Principles of Electric and Magnetic Circuits*, Harper and Brothers, New York, 2nd ed., 1957, Chap. 15.

Booker, H. G., *An Approach to Electrical Science*, McGraw-Hill Book Co., New York, 1959, Chaps. 2, 3, 4, 5 of Part 4.

Carter, G. W., *The Electromagnetic Field in Its Engineering Aspects*, Longmans, Green and Co., London, 1954, Chap. 8.

Cullwick, E. G., *The Fundamentals of Electro-magnetism*, Cambridge University Press, London, 2nd ed., 1949, Chap. 2.

Fano, R. M., L. J. Chu, and R. B. Adler, *Electromagnetic Fields, Energy, and Forces*, John Wiley and Sons, New York, 1960, Chap. 1.

Ham, J. M., and G. R. Slemon, *Scientific Basis of Electrical Engineering*, John Wiley and Sons, New York, 1961, Chap. 4.

Harnwell, G. P., *Principles of Electricity and Magnetism*, McGraw-Hill Book Co., New York, 2nd ed., 1949, Chap. 10.

Kraus, J. D., *Electromagnetics*, McGraw-Hill Book Co., New York, 1953, Chap. 7.

PROBLEMS

Section 8-1

8-1. Deduce from Eqs. (8-1) and (8-2) that the voltage drop around a closed stationary circuit is zero, *provided* all electric currents are steady with time.

8-2. Let S denote the surface of this page, with the positive side facing the reader, and let C denote the counterclockwise path around S. (*a*) If the magnetic current over S is $5 \sin 1000t$ volts, what is the emf around C? (*b*) If the electric current is $5 \sin 1000t$ amperes, what is the mmf around C?

8-3. A uniform electric field $\mathbf{E}$, equal to $500 \sin 10^6 t\, \mathbf{i}$, is assumed to exist in the region between the plates of a certain parallel-plate capacitor. As $\mathbf{E}$ is independent of the space coordinates, it is evident that the given field is conservative. Show that such a field is incompatible with Maxwell's equations and, therefore, is only an approximation of the actual field.

8-4. Using the data of Prob. 8-3, find the mmf around a closed path C that encircles the dielectric of the capacitor. The dielectric constant is 10, and the area of a plate is 100 square centimeters.

8-5. If the magnetic flux Φ out of the square surface S of Fig. 8-18 equals $\Phi_m \sin \omega t$, determine whether the voltage drop around C is positive, negative, or zero at an instant when (*a*) Φ is positive and increasing, (*b*) Φ is positive and decreasing, (*c*) Φ is negative and increasing (becoming less negative), (*d*) Φ is negative and decreasing (becoming more negative), (*e*) $\omega t = 0$, (*f*) $\omega t = \frac{1}{2}\pi$.

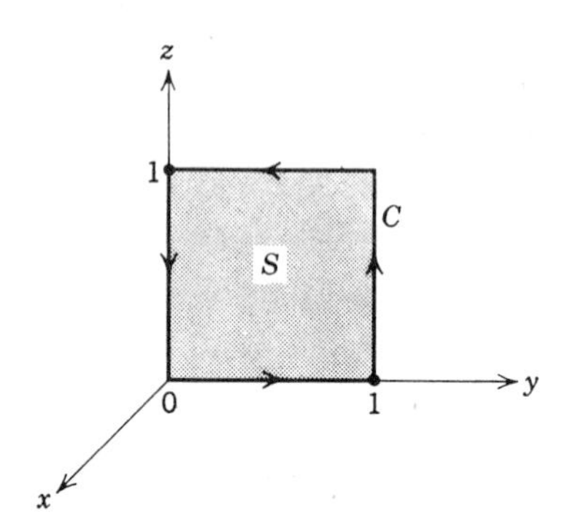

FIG. 8-18. The positive side of S faces the reader.

8-6. Assume that $\mathbf{H} = 0.01 \cos y \cos 3 \times 10^8 t\, \mathbf{i}$ ampere/m in the region of the square path C of Fig. 8-18. The medium is free space. (*a*) Use Eq. (8-1*a*) to find the voltage drop around C. (*b*) Repeat, using Eq. (8-1*b*). (*c*) What is the magnetic current over S?

8-7. Assume that $\mathbf{E} = 1000 \cos y \cos 3 \times 10^8 t\, \mathbf{i}$ volts/m in the region of the square path C of Fig. 8-18. The medium is free space. (*a*) Find the mmf around C. (*b*) What is the total electric current over S?

8-8. The electric and magnetic fields in the region of the square path of Fig. 8-18 vary sinusoidally with time. If $\mathbf{E} = 1000 \sin (3 \times 10^8 t - y)\, \mathbf{k}$, find the magnetic flux out of the square surface S at time $t = 0$.

8-9. In the region of the spherical surface S of Fig. 8-19 the electromagnetic fields vary sinusoidally with time. If the magnetic flux over S_1 is $0.001 \sin 1000t$ weber, determine (*a*) the emf around C, (*b*) the magnetic current over S_2, (*c*) the magnetic flux over S_2, and (*d*) the magnetic flux over S.

8-10. In the region of the spherical surface S of Fig. 8-19 the electromagnetic fields vary sinusoidally with time. If the mmf around C is $2 \cos 377t$, determine the total electric current over each of the surfaces S_1, S_2, and S. If the current over S_1 is entirely a convection current and the current over S_2 is entirely a displacement current, determine the electric flux over the closed surface S.

8-11. In Fig. 8-20, determine the mmfs around each of the paths C_1 and C_2.

Section 8-2

8-12. At points of the plane surface bounded by the circular conductor of Fig. 8-1 the magnetic flux density $\mathbf{B}$ is approximately

$$\mathbf{B} = 10^{-8}(1 - r^2/4 + r^4/64) \sin 3 \times 10^8 t\, \mathbf{k}$$

Utilize the Maxwell-Faraday law and the circular symmetry of the problem to find the electric field intensity as a function of distance r and time t. The radius of the loop is unity.

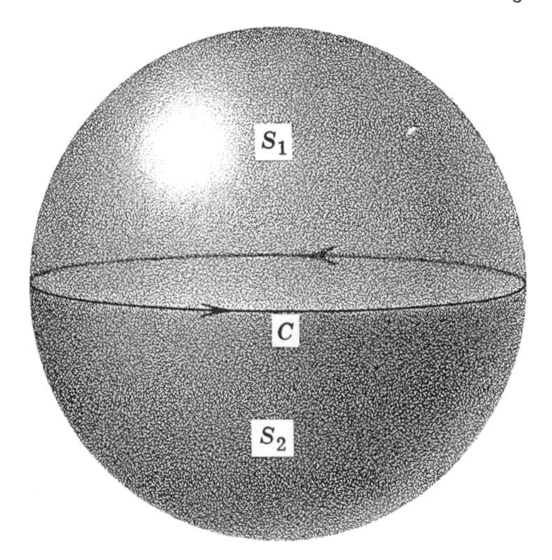

FIG. 8-19. A spherical surface S divided into surfaces S_1 and S_2 by the circular path C. The positive sides of the surfaces are the outer sides.

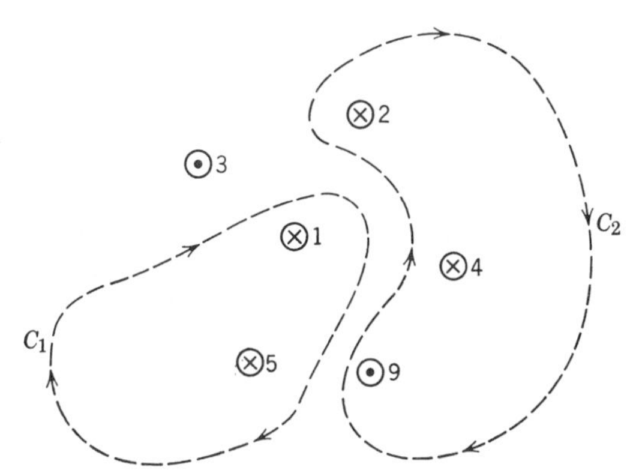

FIG. 8-20. Cross sections of six wires with currents as indicated.

8-13. In the transformer of Fig. 8-21, the flux φ over each cross section of the iron core is assumed to be 0.001 sin 377t weber. The primary and secondary windings, coiled as indicated, have 1000 and 100 turns, respectively. (*a*) Determine the clockwise voltage drops around the closed metallic paths of the primary and secondary circuits. (*b*) Assuming the wires to be perfect conductors, find the voltages v_1 and v_2 and their ratio v_1/v_2. (*c*) What is the voltage along the path of the metallic wire of a coil? (*d*) Determine the primary and secondary flux linkages.

8-14. In the transformer of Fig. 8-21, the flux φ is assumed to be the same over each cross section of the iron core. The primary and secondary windings, coiled as indicated, have 800 and 200 turns, respectively, and their resistances are negligible. If $v_1 = 100 \sin 377t$, find φ, v_2, and v_1/v_2.

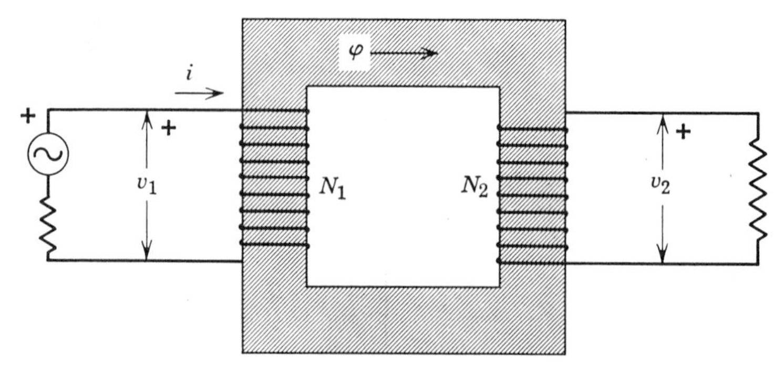

FIG. 8-21. Iron-core transformer.

8-15. When used for receiving, the slot antenna of Fig. 8-3 has a load connected across the gap in place of the power source. Suppose such a receiving antenna is located in an electromagnetic field that yields a magnetic flux Φ_1, out of the left half of the slot, equal to $10^{-14} \sin 10^{10}t$ weber. Determine the voltage drop across the load from b to e.

8-16. A 100-turn coil of wire with a plane area of 0.05 m^2 is oriented normal to the magnetic field of an electromagnetic wave in free space. In the plane of the loop the magnetic field intensity $\mathbf{H}$ is approximately $2 \sin 10^8 t\, \mathbf{i}$ microamperes per meter. Find the voltage induced in the loop by the electromagnetic wave.

8-17. If the connections to the battery of the circuit of Fig. 8-5 are instantly interchanged at one second intervals, determine the magnetic flux out of the paper over the plane surface S bounded by the circuit. The battery is ideal, and the wire is a perfect conductor. Sketch the voltage and the flux versus time.

8-18. Suppose the 10-volt battery of the electric circuit of Fig. 8-5 is replaced with an ideal generator that supplies a voltage of $0.1 \sin 1000t$, whose positive direction is as indicated on the illustrated battery. The switch is closed at time $t = 0$. Assuming perfect conductors, determine the magnetic flux out of the paper over the plane surface S bounded by the circuit.

8-19. Repeat Prob. 8-18, except assume the switch is closed at the instant that makes $\omega t = \frac{1}{2}\pi$.

8-20. In the circuit of Fig. 8-6 the resistance R is 5 ohms, and the inductance L is 10 millihenrys. If i is $4 \sin 377t$ amperes, determine the voltage v and the magnetic flux linkages. Utilize the trigonometric identity of Eq. (12-22).

8-21. Suppose the voltage v of the circuit of Fig. 8-6 is a steady 10 volts impressed on the circuit at time $t = 0$. The inductance L is 0.2 henry. Find the current i as a function of time for (*a*) $R = 0$, and (*b*) $R = 10$ ohms.

Section 8-3

8-22. Verify the identity $(\mathbf{v} \times \mathbf{B}) \cdot d\mathbf{l} = -\mathbf{B} \cdot (\mathbf{v} \times d\mathbf{l})$, thereby proving the equivalence of Eqs. (8-9) and (8-10).

8-23. The resistance R in the circuit of Fig. 8-9 is 1.6 ohms, and the internal resistance of the generator, including the resistance of the sliding contacts, is 0.4 ohm. What are the revolutions per minute required to produce a current i of 40 milliamperes, if the radius a is 20 cm and the magnetic flux density B is 0.0025 weber/m^2?

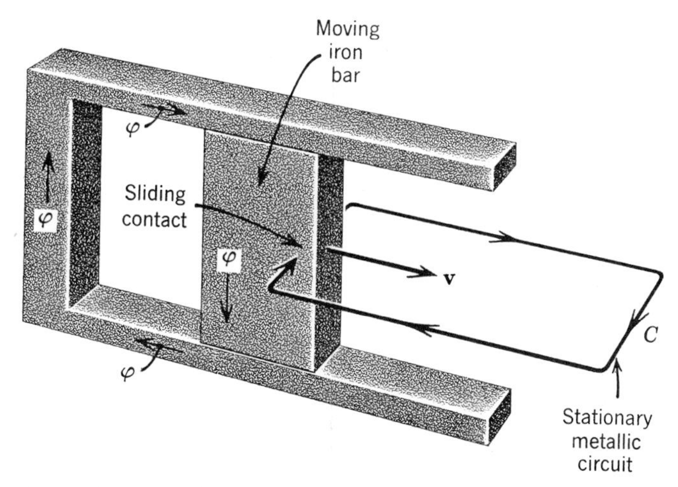

FIG. 8-22. An iron bar moving between the poles of a permanent magnet and a stationary copper loop.

8-24. The iron bar of Fig. 8-22, moving to the right with a velocity v of 2 m/sec, has a magnetic flux φ produced by the permanent magnet. The stationary metallic circuit is connected to the moving bar through sliding contacts spaced 0.1 m apart. The flux density B is 0.2 weber/m^2 inside the bar and zero outside. Noting that the conducting path between the sliding taps is *moving in a magnetic field*, determine the motional emf clockwise around the closed path C. Also, noting that the flux density at points on a portion of the plane surface S bounded by C is *changing with time*, determine the clockwise circulation of **E** around C. What is the total emf around C?

Section 8-5

8-25. Without using vector notation, write the Maxwell-Ampère law in terms of H_l, J_n, and D_n. The subscripts have the same significance as those of Eq. (8-7).

8-26. The primary and secondary windings of the transformer of Fig. 8-21 are assumed to have 500 turns and 100 turns, respectively. The primary current i is 0.2 sin 377t. If the closed secondary circuit has no resistance whatsoever, what are the ampere turns of each of the coils, and what is the flux φ in the core?

8-27. In the transformer of Fig. 8-13, the path *abcdefa*, of length 0.5 m, coincides with a magnetic field line. Each cross section of the core has an area of 0.001 m^2, and the magnetic field is approximately uniform over this area. The relative permeability of the iron is assumed to be 5000. (*a*) Determine the magnetic field intensity in the core. (*b*) What is the flux φ of the core? (*c*) If the iR drop of each winding has a maximum value of 5 volts, find the voltages v and v_L.

8-28. Determine the clockwise mmfs around the paths C_1, C_2, and C_3 of the magnetic circuit of Fig. 8-23. The coils are wound as indicated, and the currents i_1, i_2, i_3, and i_4 are 2, 5, -6, and 4 amperes, respectively.

8-29. If the clockwise mmfs around the paths C_1, C_2, and C_3 of the magnetic circuit of Fig. 8-23 are -6, 12, and 28 amperes, respectively, find the currents, assuming $i_1 = -i_2$.

8-30. The electric field is $E_y = \sin 20\pi x \sin 10\pi z \sin \omega t$ in the cavity resonator of Fig. 8-14. The magnetic field lines, lying in planes normal to the y-axis, form closed loops around the electric field lines. Using dots to denote E-lines out of the surface, sketch the E- and H-lines in a top view of one of these planes, at $\omega t = \pi/4$. Indicate the direction of the H-lines, and note that each H-line encircles a displacement current.

8-31. Calculate the intrinsic impedance and wave velocity in a glass dielectric with a relative permittivity of 5. Assume negligible conductivity.

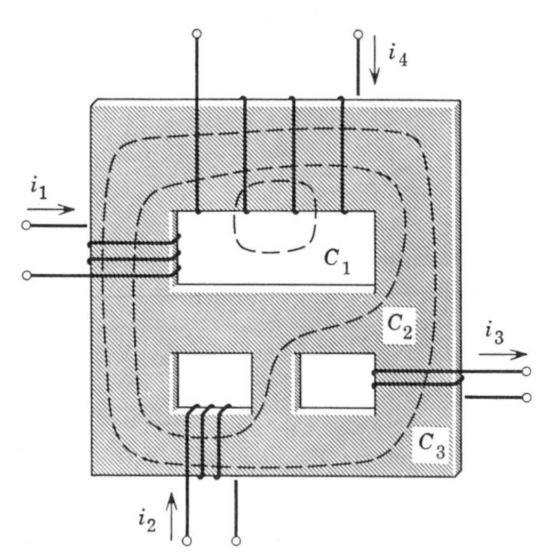

FIG. 8-23. Four coils on a core.

8-32. From symmetry considerations and the solenoidal nature of the magnetic field, deduce that the magnetic field of the current of an infinite straight wire cannot have a radial component.

8-33. Given in Example 1 of Sec. 7-5 are the approximate current density J_z and current i of a certain long straight wire. We note that i is zero at the instant of time t_1 that makes $\omega t = 22.3°$. On an enlarged sketch of a cross section, plot the field lines of J_z at time t_1, using crosses and dots to denote lines into and out of the paper, respectively. Also, sketch the magnetic field lines at this instant and indicate their directions. If the wire were not straight, why would you expect a magnetic field outside the wire, as well as inside, at the instant when the sinusoidal current i is zero?

8-34. The radius of the inner conductor of a coaxial transmission line is 0.5 cm, and the inner radius of the outer conductor is 1.5 cm. If the equal and opposite currents are each one ampere, determine the magnetic flux Φ per unit length, in the free-space dielectric, that links the one-ampere current of the inner conductor.

8-35. A ferromagnetic toroid of circular cross section has an inner radius of 4 cm and an outer radius of 6 cm. Such a toroid is shown in Fig. 6-4. The coil has 1000 turns that are so closely spaced that the coil approximates a current sheet. The current is 0.2 ampere, and the relative permeability of the iron is 500. Determine the maximum and minimum values of the magnetic field intensity in the iron. Also, find the approximate magnetic flux φ in the core.

8-36. Due to a stroke of lightning, two conductors of a power transmission line carry currents of 50,000 and 10,000 amperes in the same direction. The wires are two meters apart. What is the magnitude and direction of the force acting on a 100-meter length of one of the conductors?

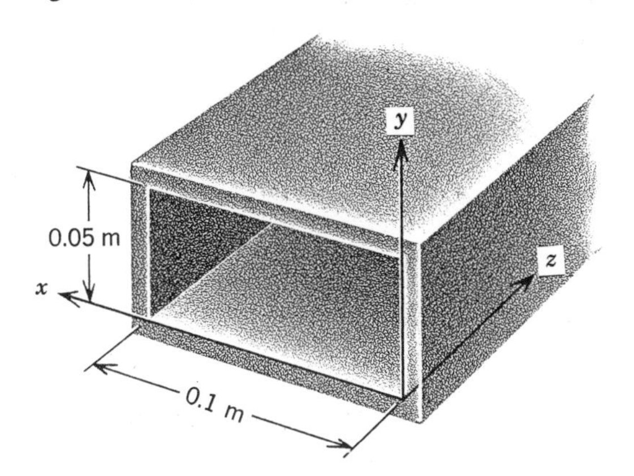

FIG. 8-24. Rectangular waveguide.

8-37. A TM_{11} wave is propagating along the rectangular waveguide of Fig. 8-24. The magnetic field is

$$H_x = 2 \sin 10\pi x \cos 20\pi y \cos (\omega t - \beta z)$$

$$H_y = -\cos 10\pi x \sin 20\pi y \cos (\omega t - \beta z)$$

with $\omega = 3 \times 10^{10}$ and $\beta = 71.2$. The dielectric is free space. Find the maximum value, as time varies, of the displacement current over a cross section.

Electromagnetic Laws II

CHAPTER 9

This chapter continues the discussion of the basic electromagnetic laws. The conservation of charge has already been postulated. However, if we are to use this postulate to full advantage, we must express it in mathematical language The result is employed in conjunction with the Maxwell-Ampère law to derive the relationship between electric flux and charge known as Gauss's law. Application of Gauss's law to an isolated electric charge yields Coulomb's law. Finally, the fields in the region of a boundary between two physical media are investigated.

The basic electromagnetic laws of this and the preceding chapter are studied and applied to many practical problems throughout the remainder of the text. Their importance cannot be overemphasized.

9-1. THE ELECTRIC CURRENT OVER A CLOSED SURFACE

From the Maxwell-Faraday law we found that the magnetic current over a closed surface is always zero. In a similar manner we shall determine, utilizing the Maxwell-Ampère law, that the total electric current is likewise zero.

A closed surface S, with its outer side taken as positive, is divided into two surfaces S_1 and S_2 by any closed path C on S. By the Maxwell-Ampère law, the total electric current over S_1 equals the mmf around the path C in the direction specified by the right-hand integration rule; the current over S_2 equals the mmf around C in the opposite direction. Thus the two magnetomotive forces and, therefore, the two currents are equal in magnitude but opposite in sign. Consequently, the sum of the two outward currents is zero, and we have deduced from the Maxwell-Ampère law that *the total electric current over a closed surface is zero.* The current is zero at every instant of time, regardless of the size or shape of the closed surface and regardless of the physical media present. There may be a net convection current and a net displacement current, but their sum must be zero if the surface is closed. Mathematically

$$\oint_S (\rho \mathbf{v} + \dot{\mathbf{D}}) \cdot d\mathbf{S} = 0 \tag{9-1}$$

Several examples will now be considered.

Shown in Fig. 9-1 is a simple series circuit consisting of a generator connected to a resistance R. The generator impresses on the circuit a sinusoidally time-varying electromotive force that produces sinusoidal currents i_1 and i_2. The specified positive directions of these currents are indicated by arrows on the illustration. Recall that these arrows actually indicate the positive sides of the cross-sectional surfaces. We shall investigate the relationship between i_1 and i_2.

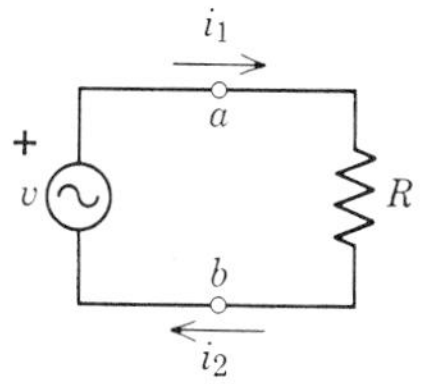

FIG. 9-1. Series electric circuit.

Imagine a closed surface S that encloses the resistance R, cutting the electric circuit only at points a and b. The total current over S is $i_d + i_2 - i_1$, with i_d denoting the net outward displacement current. Of course, this total current is zero, and the difference $i_1 - i_2$ equals the displacement current over S. If the circuit is a "low-frequency" circuit, with dimensions that are very small compared with the wavelength of the exciting source, the displacement current is negligible, and the currents i_1 and i_2 are practically equal. Ordinary *electric circuit theory* is restricted to such "low-frequency" circuits. On the other hand, the frequency may be so high that the dimensions of the circuit are appreciable compared with the wavelength. Displacement currents are no longer negligible, and the conduction currents i_1 and i_2 may differ appreciably.

Shown in Fig. 9-2 is a junction of three wires assumed to have currents i_1, i_2, and i_3, with positive directions as indicated. Imagine a small closed surface S surrounding the junction. If there are no displacement currents entering or leaving the junction, the total inward current is the sum of the three currents, and

$$i_1 + i_2 + i_3 = 0$$

Note that at least one of these currents must be negative at each instant. The general statement of this relation is known as *Kirchhoff's junction rule*, which states that the *net* current entering a junction, with due regard for sign, is zero. The current entering the junction equals the current leaving the junction. The junction currents must include displacement currents if they are appreciable. In low-frequency circuits the currents and fields vary rather slowly with respect to time, and displacement currents at junctions are usually negligible.

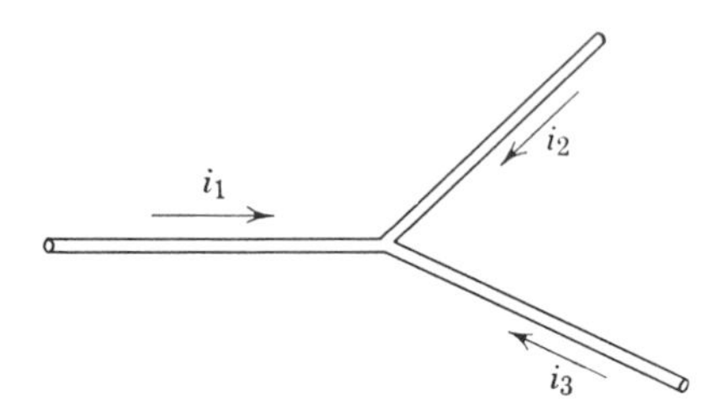

FIG. 9-2. Junction of conducting wires.

Figure 9-3 illustrates a current generator supplying a steady current I to a capacitor C. The capacitor consists of parallel conducting plates separated by a perfect dielectric. Because of the current I, the charge on the positive plate increases linearly with time; the charge on the negative plate is equal and opposite, for charge is conserved. The time-changing charges produce a time-changing electric field in the dielectric between the plates and, consequently, there is a displacement current. Our problem is to determine the value of this displacement current.

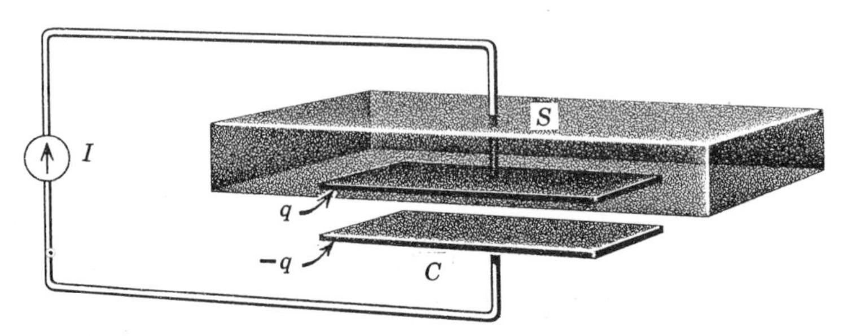

FIG. 9-3. Parallel-plate capacitor. The top plate is within the closed surface S.

Consider a closed surface S around the positive plate of the capacitor, with the surface passing between the plates and cutting the conducting wire leading to the positive plate. The convection current entering this closed surface is I. As the total current over S is zero, there must be a displacement current $\dot{\psi}$ equal to I and leaving the surface. Therefore, the displacement current in the dielectric from the positive to the negative plate equals the charging current I. Thus the current into a capacitor passes through the dielectric in the form of displacement current. There is no flow of charge between the plates, however.

Shown in Fig. 9-4 is a section of a wire with currents i_1 and i_2 through the two cross sections S_1 and S_2, respectively. We wish to find the displacement current leaving the wire between the surfaces S_1 and S_2.

Consider the *closed* surface S consisting of the surfaces S_1, S_2, and the curved cylindrical surface of the wire between S_1 and S_2. The conduction current that enters this surface has a net value of $i_1 - i_2$. Therefore, the displacement current that leaves S equals $i_1 - i_2$. This displacement current leaves the surface of the wire and, of course, it is zero if i_1 and i_2

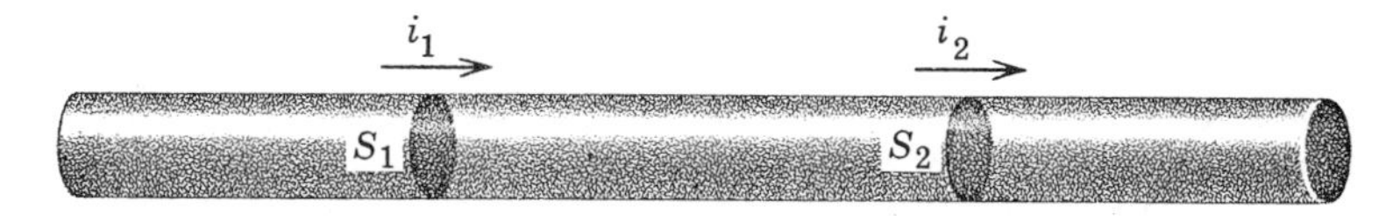

FIG. 9-4. Currents i_1 and i_2 over cross sections S_1 and S_2 of a wire.

are equal. In open-wire telephone lines, and other types of transmission lines as well, there are displacement currents between the conductors, causing the current along the line to vary with distance as well as with time.

9-2. THE EQUATION OF CONTINUITY

We have learned that the total electric current over a closed surface S is zero. Therefore, the net outward convection current equals the net inward displacement current, or

$$\oint_S \mathbf{J} \cdot d\mathbf{S} = -\frac{\partial}{\partial t} \oint_S \mathbf{D} \cdot d\mathbf{S} \tag{9-2}$$

Equation (9-2) follows directly from Eq. (9-1).

The outward convection current is the charge flow, in coulombs per second, across S. As charge is conserved, the outward flow of charge must be accompanied by a decrease in the charge inside the volume V enclosed by the surface S. In fact, the outward flow of charge must exactly equal the time rate of decrease of the total charge q_t inside V, for otherwise the conservation law would be violated. As the charge q_t in the volume V is the volume integral of the charge density ρ, it is clear that

$$\oint_S \mathbf{J} \cdot d\mathbf{S} = -\frac{\partial}{\partial t} \oint_V \rho \, dV \tag{9-3}$$

This is the integral form of the *equation of continuity. It is a formal statement of the law of conservation of charge.*

If the closed surface S of Eq. (9-3) is in motion relative to the frame of reference of the observer, the charge within the volume V might change with time even if the charge distribution is static, with current densities and currents being zero. The *partial* time derivative of Eq. (9-3) implies that this effect is *not* included. The partial time derivative of the volume integral of ρ equals the volume integral of $\dot{\rho}$, even though the limits of the volume integral may be functions of time.

In the next section we shall deduce the important Maxwell equation known as Gauss's law by comparison of Eqs. (9-2) and (9-3).

EXAMPLE. The current i fed to a certain antenna consisting of a vertical tower above ground is $10 \cos 10^7 t$ amperes. Determine the total *time-varying* charge q on the radiator.

Solution. As charge is conserved, the convection current i supplied to the antenna must equal the time rate of increase of the charge q. Therefore, $\dot{q} = 10 \cos 10^7 t$, and $q = 10^{-6} \sin 10^7 t$ coulomb. It should be noted that the displacement current $\dot{\psi}$ leaving the radiator equals i, or $\dot{q}$.

9-3. GAUSS'S LAW

It is evident from Eqs. (9-2) and (9-3) that

$$\frac{\partial}{\partial t} \oint_S \mathbf{D} \cdot d\mathbf{S} = \frac{\partial}{\partial t} \int_V \rho \, dV \tag{9-4}$$

with V denoting any volume in space enclosed by the surface S. The left side of Eq. (9-4) is the net displacement current out of the surface S, and the right side is the time rate of increase of the total charge in the volume V. Each of these expressions is equal to the net convection current inward over the surface. Equation (9-4) was derived directly from the Maxwell-Ampère law and the conservation of charge.

We note that the electric flux ψ over S and the total charge q_t inside S have time rates of change that are always equal. It follows that ψ and q_t may differ only by a constant C_1 that is independent of time. If C_1 were not zero, there would be sources of the field that *are rigidly fixed in position and absolutely invariant with time.* As such sources have never been observed, we postulate their nonexistence, making C_1 zero. Consequently, ψ and q_t are equal, and we have

$$\oint_S \mathbf{D} \cdot d\mathbf{S} = \int_V \rho \, dV \tag{9-5}$$

Equation (9-5), known as *Gauss's law*, states that the electric flux over a closed surface S equals the total charge in the volume V bounded by S. The law applies to all closed surfaces, large or small, at every instant of time, and the volume integral includes all charges in V. Different parts of the region may be occupied by different physical media. In fact, there are no restrictions. Gauss's law is a basic equation of electromagnetic theory, and it is classified as one of Maxwell's equations. Sometimes Gauss's law is referred to as the integral form of Coulomb's law, for Coulomb's law is easily deduced from it, as we shall see in the next section.

In Sec. 8-4 we learned that the magnetic field of flux density **B** is a solenoidal field, having no sources or sinks. Gauss's law informs us that the electric field of flux density **D** is, in general, a nonsolenoidal field. The sources and sinks of **D** are electric charges, with positive charges acting as sources that produce the field and with negative charges acting as sinks that absorb the field. Field lines of **D** may begin and end on positive and negative charges, respectively. In a region devoid of charge, the electric flux over any closed surface is zero. In this case the electric flux density is solenoidal, having no sources or sinks.

From the Maxwell-Faraday law we learned that a time-changing magnetic field produces an electric field. Gauss's law tells us that electric fields are also produced by charges. Magnetic fields are, of course, produced by electric convection and displacement currents.

When Gauss's law is applied to a closed surface, the surface is referred to as a *Gaussian surface*. Thus a Gaussian surface is simply any closed surface to which Gauss's law is applied. Applications of Gauss's law, as well as the other Maxwell equations, are given throughout the remainder of the text. In particular, several illustrative examples are discussed in the next section. At the end of this chapter the four Maxwell equations are presented together. These are the Maxwell-Faraday law, the Maxwell-Ampère law, the equation stating that the magnetic flux density is solenoidal, and Gauss's law.

9-4. COULOMB'S LAW

The electric field in the region about a stationary point charge q, located in an infinite medium of permittivity ϵ, is readily deduced from Gauss's law. Consider a spherical surface with radius r and with center at q. In accordance with Gauss's law the outward electric flux ψ over the Gaussian surface equals the charge q.

The flux ψ is the surface integral of the electric flux density **D**. It is evident from the symmetry of the problem that the field lines are radial. Therefore, **D** equals $D\mathbf{a}_r$, with $\mathbf{a}_r$ denoting a unit vector directed radially outward. If the charge is positive, the field lines are outward, and D is also positive. On the other hand, if the charge is negative, the lines are directed inward, and D is likewise negative. As each differential vector area $d\mathbf{S}$ of the Gaussian surface is directed radially outward, the scalar product of $\mathbf{D}$ and $d\mathbf{S}$ is $D\,dS$, and we have

$$\oint_S D\,dS = q$$

The magnitude of the flux density is the same at all points on the spherical surface S, for each point is equidistant from q. Thus D can be taken outside the integral, and the outward flux is the product of D and the integral of dS over the Gaussian surface. As this integral is the surface area $4\pi r^2$, the flux is $4\pi r^2 D$. Consequently, D equals $q/(4\pi r^2)$. In terms of vectors

$$\mathbf{D} = \frac{q}{4\pi r^2}\,\mathbf{a}_r \tag{9-6}$$

The electric flux density at a point located a distance r from q is directly proportional to the charge and inversely proportional to the distance squared. If q is positive, $\mathbf{D}$ is directed radially outward; if q is negative, $\mathbf{D}$ is directed radially inward. The flux density is independent of the permittivity of the infinite medium. As $\mathbf{D}$ equals $\epsilon\mathbf{E}$, the field intensity is

$$\mathbf{E} = \frac{q}{4\pi\epsilon r^2}\,\mathbf{a}_r \tag{9-7}$$

We note that $\mathbf{E}$ depends on the permittivity, being inversely proportional to ϵ.

Equation (9-7) can be utilized to determine the force between two point charges q_1 and q_2, separated a distance r in an infinite medium of permittivity ϵ. At the point occupied by q_2 the electric field $\mathbf{E}$ due to q_1 is $q_1\mathbf{a}_r/(4\pi\epsilon r^2)$. The force that acts on q_2 is $q_2\mathbf{E}$, for $\mathbf{E}$ is the force per unit charge. Therefore,

$$\mathbf{F} = \frac{q_1 q_2}{4\pi\epsilon r^2}\,\mathbf{a}_r \text{ newtons} \tag{9-8}$$

The unit vector $\mathbf{a}_r$ at the point occupied by q_2 is directed away from q_1. Obviously, the force that acts on q_1 due to the charge q_2 is also given by Eq. (9-8), with $\mathbf{a}_r$ at q_1 being directed away from q_2.

Equation (9-8), known as *Coulomb's law*, states that electric charges exert forces on one another. If the two point charges have like signs, the force is one of repulsion. If the two point charges have unlike signs, the product $q_1 q_2$ is negative, and the force is one of attraction. The magnitude of the force is proportional to the product of the charges and inversely proportional to the permittivity ϵ of the medium and the distance squared.

The force of attraction or repulsion between stationary charges is explained in terms of the electric field. A point charge produces an electric field according to Eq. (9-7), and this field exerts a force on a second charge located in the field. If more than two charges are present, each exerts a force on every other charge. It is interesting to note that the Coulomb-law force between two point charges of one coulomb each, located a meter apart in free space, is over a million tons. A point charge of one coulomb is far too enormous to be practical. Let us consider several examples illustrating the use of Coulomb's and Gauss's laws.

EXAMPLE 1. Three point charges of 100 μc, -200 μc, and 400 μc are located in a medium having a relative permittivity of 3 at the points $(3, -2, 2)$, $(-1, -3, -2)$, and $(2, 4, -4)$, respectively. The force on the 400-μc charge is desired.

Solution. The force on the 400-μc charge due to the point charge of 100 μc will be determined first. Let $\mathbf{r}$ denote the vector drawn from the point $(3, -2, 2)$ to the point $(2, 4, -4)$. The rectangular components of $\mathbf{r}$ are found by subtracting the coordinates at the point of the tail of the vector from the respective coordinates of the point at the head of the vector. This gives $\mathbf{r} = -\mathbf{i} + 6\mathbf{j} - 6\mathbf{k}$, and the magnitude r is 8.54 m. As the unit vector $\mathbf{a}_r$ is $\mathbf{r}/r$, we can determine the force on the 400-μc charge, due to the 100-μc charge, by substitution into the equation

$$\mathbf{F} = \frac{q_1 q_2 \mathbf{r}}{4\pi\epsilon r^3} \tag{9-9}$$

The result is

$$\mathbf{F} = -0.19\mathbf{i} + 1.15\mathbf{j} - 1.15\mathbf{k}$$

Similarly, the force on the 400-μc charge due to the -200-μc charge is found to be

$$\mathbf{F} = -1.48\mathbf{i} - 3.44\mathbf{j} + 0.98\mathbf{k}$$

Utilization of the superposition principle gives the total force on the 400-μc charge. The result is

$$\mathbf{F} = -1.67\mathbf{i} - 2.29\mathbf{j} - 0.17\mathbf{k}$$

The magnitude of this force is 2.84 newtons, its direction cosines are -0.588, -0.806, and -0.060, and its direction angles are 126°, 144°, and 93.4°.

EXAMPLE 2. A copper ball of radius a has a uniform surface charge density ρ_s coulombs/m^2. The net charge at points inside the copper ball is zero. Determine the electric flux density $\mathbf{D}$ as a function of the distance r from the center of the ball.

Solution. Consider a concentric spherical Gaussian surface of radius r. The outward flux of $\mathbf{D}$ over this surface equals the total charge enclosed, by Gauss's law. From symmetry, $\mathbf{D}$ is radial, and the magnitude of $\mathbf{D}$ is the same at all points of the Gaussian surface. Therefore, the outward flux is the product of D and the area $4\pi r^2$ of the sphere, or $4\pi r^2 D$. If r is less than a, the charge enclosed by the Gaussian surface is zero, and D is zero. If r is greater than a, the charge enclosed is $4\pi a^2 \rho_s$ and, consequently, D is $\rho_s a^2/r^2$. $\mathbf{D}$ is directed radially outward for positive ρ_s and radially inward for negative ρ_s. At the surface of the ball D equals ρ_s.

In terms of the total charge q on the surface of the copper ball, the electric flux density $\mathbf{D}$ outside the ball is $q/(4\pi r^2)\,\mathbf{a}_r$, with $\mathbf{a}_r$ denoting a unit vector directed radially outward. This is the same flux density that would result from a charge q located at the center of the ball. We conclude that, if a charge q is uniformly distributed over a spherical surface, the electric field in the volume enclosed by the surface is zero, the electric flux density at the surface equals the surface charge density, and the field outside the surface is the same as that which would be produced by a charge q located at the center of the sphere.

EXAMPLE 3. A straight cylindrical wire of infinite length has a uniform linear charge density ρ_l coulombs per meter. Determine the electric flux density in the region about the wire.

Solution. A suitable Gaussian surface is a coaxial cylinder of radius r, of unit length, and with closed ends. The electric flux ψ over this surface equals the total charge enclosed, by Gauss's law. Therefore, $\psi = \rho_l$.

From symmetry we deduce that the flux lines are radial, with no flux out of the ends of the Gaussian cylinder. Also from symmetry, the magnitude of $\mathbf{D}$ is constant over the curved surface of the cylinder. Consequently, the outward electric flux ψ is the product of D and the area $2\pi r$ of the curved surface of the cylinder. It follows that $2\pi r D$ equals the charge ρ_l in a meter of length of the wire. In terms of the unit vector $\mathbf{a}_r$ directed radially outward, the electric flux density is

$$\mathbf{D} = \frac{\rho_l}{2\pi r}\,\mathbf{a}_r \tag{9-10}$$

EXAMPLE 4. A small conducting ball with a charge q is placed in the dielectric inside an uncharged closed copper box. Determine the charges induced on the inner and outer surfaces of the box. Also find these charges if the outer surface is momentarily connected to ground, followed by removal of the ball.

Solution. Consider a Gaussian surface surrounding the inner region of the box, having all points in the metal between the inner and outer surfaces. The electric flux over this Gaussian surface is zero, for there is no electric field within the copper. We deduce from Gauss's law that the total enclosed charge is zero. Therefore, the induced charge on the inner surface of the box is $-q$. As the total charge of the metallic box is zero, the charge on the outer surface is $+q$.

If the outer surface is momentarily grounded, the charge q on this surface is neutralized. The charge on the inner surface is still $-q$, and the charge on the outer surface is zero. If the ball is removed from the box, application of Gauss's law to the Gaussian surface shows that the charge on the inner surface of the box is now zero. The net charge $-q$ resides on the outer surface. This example illustrates the principle of charging by induction.

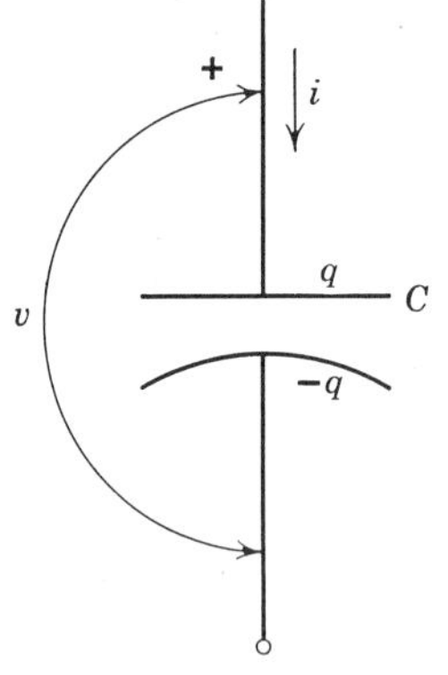

FIG. 9-5. Capacitor.

EXAMPLE 5. A capacitor, consisting of two conducting plates separated by a perfect dielectric, has charges q and $-q$ on its plates. The voltage drop from the positive to the negative plate is v, and the current in the direction of this voltage drop is i, as shown in Fig. 9-5. Deduce that $i = C\,dv/dt$, with C denoting the ratio q/v. C is the *capacitance*, in farads, of the capacitor.

Solution. By Gauss's law the electric flux from the positive to the negative plate equals q. The electric field lines emitted by the positive charges terminate on the negative charges, and the field intensity at each point of the dielectric is proportional to q. As the voltage drop v is the line integral of $\mathbf{E}$, this voltage is also proportional to q. It follows that the capacitance C, equal to q/v, is a constant independent of the magnitudes of these quantities.

The current i, which may be regarded as either the charging current or the displacement current of the capacitor, causes q and v to vary with time. However, C is constant and, consequently, $dq/dt = C\,dv/dt$. As charge is conserved, the time rate of increase of q, in coulombs per second, equals the charging current i. This gives

$$i = C\frac{dv}{dt}$$

Integrating with respect to time yields

$$v = \frac{1}{C}\int_{-\infty}^{t} i\,dt$$

These equations are basic to the study of electric circuits. We note that the current i through a capacitor depends on the time rate of change of the voltage v. If the voltage is not changing with time, there is no current. The voltage drop across the capacitor *in the direction of the reference current i* is $1/C$ multiplied by the time integral of i. The limit $-\infty$ denotes any time in the past before the current was initiated, and t is the present time. Clearly, the time integral of i is the charge q of the capacitor.

EXAMPLE 6. Shown in Fig. 9-6 is a charge q moving with velocity v between large parallel conducting plates A and B separated a small distance d. The

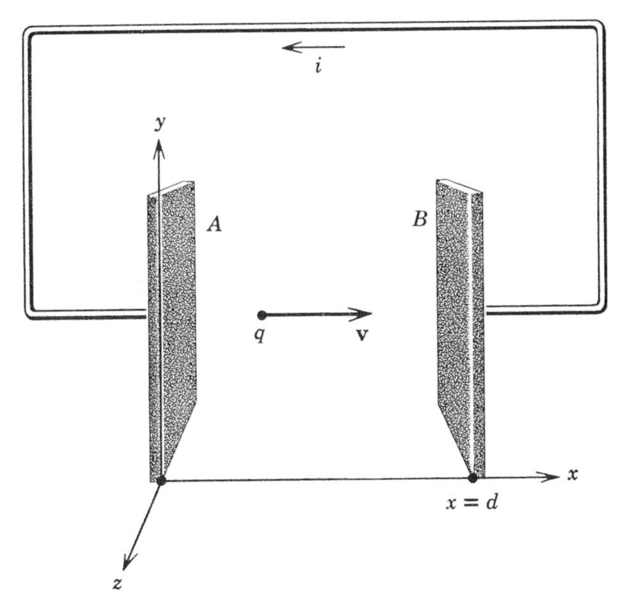

FIG. 9-6. A charge moving between metal plates.

number of electric flux lines from q that terminate on plate B is proportional to the distance x of the charge from plate A. This time-changing flux constitutes a displacement current entering the inner side of plate B, whereas the current leaving the outer side of B is the convection current i in the copper wire connecting the plates. We wish to determine i.

Solution. The electric flux ψ_B entering the inner surface of plate B equals C_1x, with C_1 the constant of proportionality. When q is half-way between the plates, at $x = \frac{1}{2}d$, the total flux ψ leaving q goes half to plate A and half to plate B, from symmetry considerations. As $\psi_B = \frac{1}{2}\psi$ when $x = \frac{1}{2}d$, the constant C_1 is ψ/d. Thus $\psi_B = \psi x/d$. By Gauss's law the flux leaving q equals q and, therefore, the electric flux entering the inner surface of plate B is qx/d coulombs.

The displacement current entering plate B is $\dot{\psi}_B$, or $q\dot{x}/d$. As $\dot{x}$ is the velocity v of the charge, this displacement current is qv/d amperes, which is also the current over any cross section between the plates. It is likewise the current i of the copper wire, for the convection current leaving plate B must equal the displacement current entering the plate. The current i is positive or negative depending on the sign of the charge q.

In a vacuum tube the charge carriers are electrons, each with a charge of $-e$. If the cathode and anode are closely spaced parallel plates, the current in the external circuit due to a single electron is ev/d, with the positive current around the circuit directed opposite to the motion of the electron.

9-5. BOUNDARY CONDITIONS

At the surface whose points lie on the boundary between two different physical media, the permittivity, permeability, and conductivity are discontinuous. These quantities change abruptly from one side of the surface to the other. Consequently, the electric and magnetic fields are discontinuous. The manner in which the fields vary from one side of a boundary to the other can be determined from Maxwell's equations. Not only is the application of these equations to this problem interesting and informative but the results are of considerable importance and will be used frequently in the chapters that follow.

Figure 9-7 represents a side view of the boundary between two media. Shown at this boundary is a rectangle, having a small length Δl and a differential height dh that approaches zero. By the Maxwell-Faraday law the circulation of $\mathbf{E}$ around the closed path C of this rectangle equals the negative of the magnetic current $\dot{\Phi}$ over the plane surface S bounded by C. There is no current, however, because the area of the rectangle approaches zero as dh approaches zero. Therefore, the circulation of $\mathbf{E}$ is zero. As the length Δl of the rectangle is so small that $\mathbf{E}$ can be regarded as constant, the line integral of $\mathbf{E}$ around C is $E_{t1}\,\Delta l - E_{t2}\,\Delta l$, and this must be zero. It follows that $E_{t1} = E_{t2}$. *The tangential component of the electric field intensity is continuous across the boundary of two different physical media.*

Next, the Maxwell-Ampère law will be applied. The mmf around C equals the total electric current over the surface S. *If neither medium is a perfect conductor*, there is no surface current density, and the total electric current over S approaches zero as dh approaches zero. Consequently, the

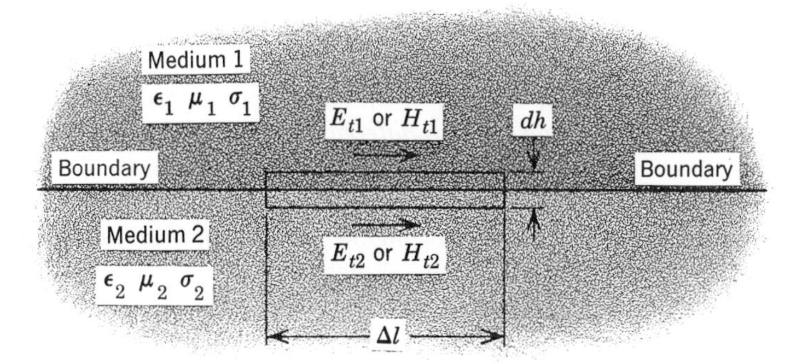

FIG. 9-7. Side view of the boundary between two media.

circulation of **H** is zero, and $H_{t1} = H_{t2}$. *The tangential component of the magnetic field intensity is continuous across the boundary of two different physical media, provided neither is a perfect conductor.*

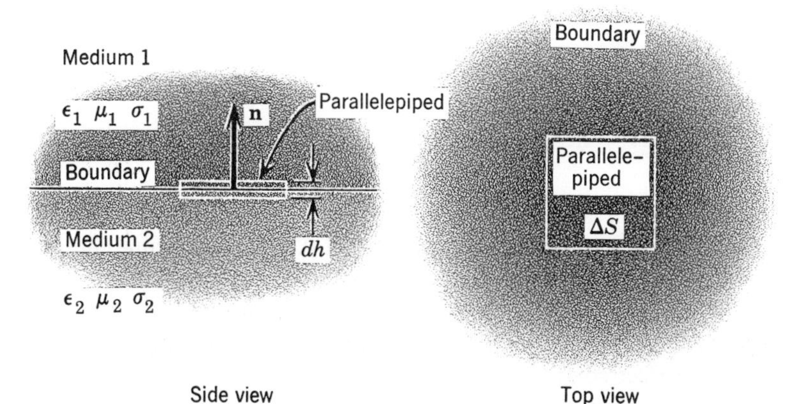

FIG. 9-8. Side and top views of the surface between two media, with a parallelepiped constructed at the boundary.

In order to determine the relationships between the normal components of the electric and magnetic fields across a boundary, we shall utilize a small parallelepiped that encloses a small portion of the surface between the two media. Side and top views of the parallelepiped are shown in Fig. 9-8. The top and bottom elemental areas are each ΔS, and the differential height dh approaches zero. The unit vector **n** normal to the surface is directed into medium 1, and the subscript n will be used to denote the component of a vector in the direction of **n**.

As the magnetic flux density **B** is solenoidal, the surface integral of **B** over the closed surface of the parallelepiped is zero. The flux of **B** through the sides of the parallelepiped is negligible, because dh is a very small height that approaches zero. Therefore, $B_{n1}\,\Delta S - B_{n2}\,\Delta S = 0$, and consequently, $B_{n1} = B_{n2}$. *The normal component of the magnetic flux density is continuous across the boundary of two different physical media.*

Next, Gauss's law will be applied to the parallelepiped. The surface integral of **D** over the closed surface is $D_{n1}\,\Delta S - D_{n2}\,\Delta S$, because the flux of **D** over the sides becomes negligible as dh approaches zero. The total charge in the volume of the parallelepiped is $\rho_s\,\Delta S$, with ρ_s denoting the surface charge density. By Gauss's law the electric flux equals the enclosed charge. It follows that $D_{n1} - D_{n2} = \rho_s$. *The normal component of the electric flux density is discontinuous across the boundary of two different physical media by an amount equal to the surface charge density* ρ_s.

The four boundary conditions, deduced by application of Maxwell's equations, are

$$E_{t1} = E_{t2} \tag{9-11}$$

$$H_{t1} = H_{t2} \tag{9-12}$$

$$B_{n1} = B_{n2} \tag{9-13}$$

$$D_{n1} - D_{n2} = \rho_s \tag{9-14}$$

The subscripts t and n denote the tangential and normal components, respectively, of the field vectors. In Eq. (9-14), D_n is the normal component of **D**, taken in the direction from medium 2 to medium 1, and the equation simply states that *the net outward electric flux per unit area equals the surface charge per unit area.* Equation (9-12) does not apply if either medium is a perfect conductor.

The relations $\mathbf{D} = \epsilon\mathbf{E}$ and $\mathbf{B} = \mu\mathbf{H}$ can be applied to Eqs. (9-11) through (9-14) to obtain the relationships between the tangential components of **D** and **B** and the normal components of **E** and **H** across the boundary between two media. This is left as an exercise for the student.

9-6. THE SURFACE OF A PERFECT CONDUCTOR

We need to investigate the tangential component of the magnetic field intensity at the surface of a perfect conductor, defined as a medium of infinite conductivity, or zero resistivity. Although all conductors, excluding the *superconductors*, have some resistance, it is frequently convenient to assume the existence of an ideal conductor. In many engineering problems good conductors can be regarded as perfect with negligible error. Frequently, such an assumption enables us to determine with ease the approximate fields, currents, and voltages in a region. Then the finite resistivities can be utilized to find the approximate power losses. Thus the concept of a perfect conductor has engineering importance.

The electric field inside a perfect conductor is zero, for otherwise there would be the absurdity of an infinite drift current. We know from Maxwell's equations that time-varying electric and magnetic fields always accompany one another and, consequently, a time-varying magnetic field cannot exist in a perfect conductor. An electric current always has a magnetic field according to the Maxwell-Ampère law. As time-varying magnetic fields cannot exist in perfect conductors, neither can time-varying electric currents. However, we know that good conductors readily carry alternating currents. Clearly, the time-varying current of a perfect conductor must reside *on the surface*, in a layer of zero thickness. The current density is a surface current density $\mathbf{J}_s$, equal to $\rho_s\mathbf{v}$, with ρ_s denoting the charge density of the moving surface charges and $\mathbf{v}$ denoting their drift velocity. The surface current density $\mathbf{J}_s$ is measured in amperes per meter.

To determine the tangential component of the magnetic field intensity $\mathbf{H}$, we shall apply the Maxwell-Ampère law to the rectangle of Fig. 9-7, with medium 2 regarded as a perfect conductor. Time-varying fields are assumed, and the surface current density $\mathbf{J}_s$ is directed into the paper.

The mmf around the path of the rectangle in a clockwise direction is $H_{t1}\,\Delta l$, because $\mathbf{H}$ is zero inside the perfect conductor. This equals the current into the surface of the rectangle, and this current is $J_s\,\Delta l$ amperes. Therefore, $H_{t1} = J_s$.

The component of H_t in the direction of $\mathbf{J}_s$ is zero, for if the rectangle is constructed with its length in this direction, no current passes through it. The normal component of $\mathbf{H}$ is zero at the surface. This follows from the fact that the normal component of $\mathbf{B}$ is continuous, by Eq. (9-13); as B_n is zero inside the conductor, B_n and H_n are zero just outside the conductor.

In conclusion, at the surface of a perfect conductor the time-varying magnetic field intensity $\mathbf{H}$ is tangential to the surface, normal to $\mathbf{J}_s$, and equal to $\mathbf{J}_s$. The sense of $\mathbf{H}$ is illustrated in Fig. 9-9. The crosses at the surface denote a surface current density directed into the paper. If $\mathbf{n}$ represents a unit vector, normal to the conductor and directed outward, the magnitude and direction of **H** at the surface are completely specified by the relation

$$\mathbf{n} \times \mathbf{H} = \mathbf{J}_s \tag{9-15}$$

When the fields are static, surface current densities are nonexistent even in the best conductors, and Eq. (9-15) does not apply. In such cases, of course, the tangential component of **H** is continuous across the boundary, in accordance with Eq. (9-12). Usually, actual conductors are regarded as perfect only if the currents are confined to thin surface layers. As we shall see in Chapter 14, the depth of penetration of a sinusoidally time-varying current density depends on *the product of the conductivity and the frequency with which the current alternates.* Therefore, conductors with currents produced by slowly varying or static fields are not considered perfect, regardless of their conductivities. Exceptions are the superconductors.

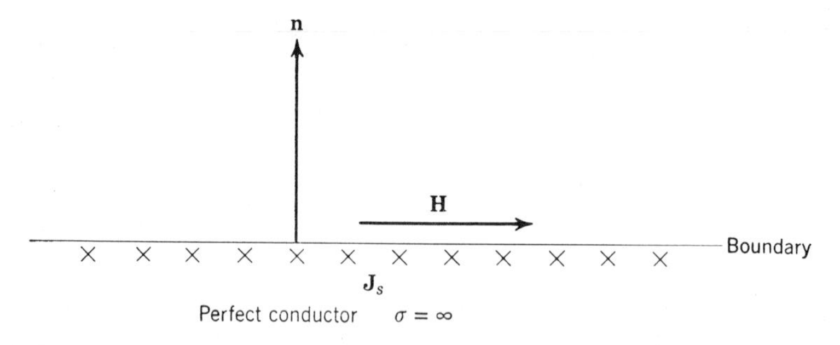

FIG. 9-9. Relation between **H** and $\mathbf{J}_s$ at the surface of a perfect conductor. The surface current density is into the paper.

The electric field at the surface of a perfect conductor is readily determined from Eqs. (9-11) and (9-14). Inside the conductor the electric field is zero. As the tangential component of **E** is continuous across a boundary, it is clear that E_t is zero at the surface. The normal component of the electric flux density at a boundary is discontinuous by an amount equal to the surface charge density ρ_s. Therefore, D_n equals ρ_s. In conclusion, the electric field at the surface of a perfect conductor is normal to the surface, with the outward electric flux density D equal to the surface charge density ρ_s. In terms of the unit vector **n** directed out of the surface of the perfect conductor, we have

$$\mathbf{D} = \rho_s \mathbf{n} \tag{9-16}$$

If ρ_s is negative, **D** is directed into the surface. Equations (9-15) and (9-16) completely specify the boundary conditions at the surface of a perfect conductor.

9-7. SUMMARY OF ELECTROMAGNETIC LAWS

Maxwell's equations in integral form are

$$\oint_C \mathbf{E} \cdot d\mathbf{l} = -\int_S \dot{\mathbf{B}} \cdot d\mathbf{S} \tag{9-17}$$

$$\oint_C \mathbf{H} \cdot d\mathbf{l} = \int_S (\mathbf{J} + \dot{\mathbf{D}}) \cdot d\mathbf{S} \tag{9-18}$$

$$\oint_S \mathbf{B} \cdot d\mathbf{S} = 0 \tag{9-19}$$

$$\oint_S \mathbf{D} \cdot d\mathbf{S} = \int_V \rho \, dV \tag{9-20}$$

Also, we have the relations $\mathbf{D} = \epsilon\mathbf{E}$ and $\mathbf{B} = \mu\mathbf{H}$, and the Lorentz force equation $\mathbf{F}/q = \mathbf{E} + \mathbf{v} \times \mathbf{B}$. The Maxwell-Faraday and Maxwell-Ampère laws were presented as postulates, and Eqs. (9-19) and (9-20) were derived from these postulates and the conservation of charge. Equation (9-19) is sometimes referred to as the *magnetic-field Gauss's law*, and Eq. (9-20) is Gauss's law.

The integral form of the equation of continuity, which states mathematically that electric charge is conserved, is

$$\oint_S \mathbf{J} \cdot d\mathbf{S} = -\frac{\partial}{\partial t}\int_V \rho \, dV \tag{9-21}$$

This is one of our postulates.

The electromotive force, or voltage drop, around a closed path is the circulation of the electric field $\mathbf{E}$, provided the path is stationary. If the path is moving in a magnetic field, however, there is also a motional emf, and the total emf is

$$\text{emf} = \oint_C (\mathbf{E} + \mathbf{v} \times \mathbf{B}) \cdot d\mathbf{l} \tag{9-22}$$

$$\text{emf} = -\frac{\partial \Phi}{\partial t} + \oint_C (\mathbf{v} \times \mathbf{B}) \cdot d\mathbf{l} \tag{9-23}$$

$$\text{emf} = -\frac{d\Phi}{dt} \tag{9-24}$$

Equations (9-22), (9-23), and (9-24) are equivalent with the understanding that the total time derivative of Φ in Eq. (9-24) represents the time rate of change of the magnetic flux due only to a time-changing magnetic flux density and to the cutting of magnetic flux lines by the moving path C. If the path C is stationary, these equations are equivalent to the Maxwell-Faraday law.

Coulomb's inverse-square law is

$$\mathbf{F} = \frac{q_1 q_2}{4\pi\epsilon r^2}\,\mathbf{a}_r \tag{9-25}$$

This gives the force between two stationary point charges in an infinite medium. It was derived from Gauss's law.

Application of Maxwell's equations to the boundary between two physical media enabled us to deduce important relations between the fields on opposite sides of the boundary. If neither medium is a perfect conductor, we found that

$$E_{t1} = E_{t2} \qquad B_{n1} = B_{n2}$$
$$H_{t1} = H_{t2} \qquad D_{n1} - D_{n2} = \rho_s$$

with D_n denoting the normal component taken in the direction from medium 2 to medium 1. At the surface of a perfect conductor

$$\mathbf{D} = \rho_s \mathbf{n} \qquad \mathbf{n} \times \mathbf{H} = \mathbf{J}_s$$

From the Maxwell-Ampère law we deduced that the total electric current over a closed surface is always zero. Neither the convection current nor the displacement current over a closed surface is necessarily zero, but their sum is zero at every instant of time.

The integral forms of Maxwell's equations and the equation of continuity relate the fields, currents, and charges of certain paths, surfaces, and volumes in space. By applying the equations to regions of infinitesimal dimensions, we can obtain differential equations relating the fields, currents, and charges at points. These equations will prove invaluable in our further investigations in electromagnetism. In the next chapter we shall study the mathematics of vector analysis, which we shall utilize in developing and applying the differential forms of Maxwell's equations and the equation of continuity.

REFERENCES

Booker, H. B., *An Approach to Electrical Science*, McGraw-Hill Book Co., New York, 1959, Chaps. 3, 4 of Part 3.

Hayt, W. H., Jr., *Engineering Electromagnetics*, McGraw-Hill Book Co., New York, 1958, Chaps. 2, 3.

Kraus, J. D., *Electromagnetics*, McGraw-Hill Book Co., New York, 1953, Chap. 7.

PROBLEMS

Sections 9-1 and 9-2

9-1. If the current in a lightning stroke is 100,000 amperes from the earth to a cloud, what is the displacement current from the cloud to ground at this instant?

9-2. In the circuit of Fig. 9-10 all displacement currents, except that between the plates of the capacitor, are negligible. Deduce that the sum of the currents i_1,

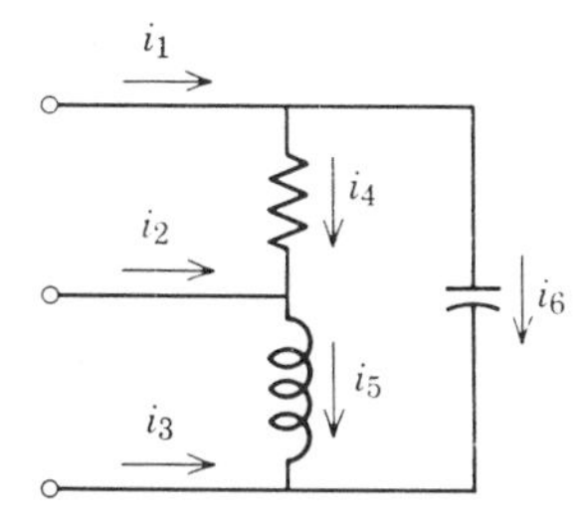

FIG. 9-10. Electric circuit.

i_2, and i_3 is zero. Determine each of these line currents if $i_4 = -3$, $i_5 = 5$, and $i_6 = 1$.

9-3. A fluid has mass density m, and the particles have velocity $\mathbf{v}$, with both m and $\mathbf{v}$ being functions of the space coordinates and time. Write the integral form of the equation of continuity for fluid flow, which expresses mathematically the conservation of fluid mass.

9-4. An antenna, consisting of a vertical wire whose base is close to the ground, is fed with a base current of $5 \sin 10^8 t$ amperes, upward. Determine the displacement current leaving the antenna, and from this displacement current find the outward electric flux ψ. Also, use the equation of continuity to find the charge q stored on the antenna, and compare this charge with the outward flux. All quantities vary sinusoidally with time.

9-5. The charging current i of a certain capacitor is $1 \cos 100t$, and the *leakage current* between the plates, due to a poor dielectric, is $0.2 \sin 100t$. The positive directions of the given currents are identical. From the equation of continuity determine, at time $t = 0.02$, the stored charge q of a plate, and from the displacement current find the flux ψ leaving this plate at this instant. Compare ψ and q. All quantities vary sinusoidally with time.

Sections 9-3 and 9-4

9-6. Derive the equation of continuity from the Maxwell-Ampère law and Gauss's law.

9-7. The Maxwell-Ampère law is often erroneously written with the omission of displacement current density. Show that this erroneous equation, when applied to a region with time-varying charge densities, leads to the conclusion that charge is not conserved.

9-8. Three point charges of 20 μc, 30 μc, and -40 μc are located at the points (0, 0, 0), (1, 1, 0), and (1, -1, 1), respectively, in a medium having a relative permittivity of 1.5. Find the Coulomb force on the -40-μc charge.

9-9. A copper ball of radius a, located in a dielectric of permittivity ϵ, has a net charge q. Find the voltage drop v along a path from the ball to infinity, and determine the ratio q/v. This is the *capacitance* of the ball. Calculate this capacitance if the radius is one meter and the dielectric is free space.

9-10. What is the maximum charge that can be placed on an isolated copper ball of radius 5 cm without exceeding the *dielectric strength* of air, which is about 30,000 volts/cm? With this maximum charge on the ball, what is the voltage drop from the ball to a point at infinity?

9-11. A dielectric ball of radius 10 cm and relative permittivity 4 is located in free space. If a charge of 5 μc is uniformly distributed throughout the volume of the ball, find the electric field intensity as a function of the distance r from the center. What is the maximum value of this field?

9-12. At time zero a charged conductor is connected to a good ground in earth, and the discharging current to ground is e^{-1000t} ampere. Find as a function of time the displacement current and the electric flux leaving the conductor. Also, determine the initial charge of the conductor and the rate with which this charge is decreasing immediately after the connection is made.

9-13. The inner conductor of a coaxial transmission line has a radius a and a charge per unit length of q coulombs per meter. The outer conductor has an inner radius b and a charge per unit length of $-q$. The permittivity of the dielectric between the conductors is ϵ. Using Gauss's law, find the electric field as a function of the distance r from the axis. Determine the voltage v between the conductors, and find the ratio q/v in terms of a, b, and ϵ. This is the *capacitance C per unit length* of the cable, in farads per meter. Calculate C for $a = 0.5$ cm and $b = 1.5$ cm. The dielectric is free space.

9-14. Two large parallel plates A and B are separated a small distance d by a perfect dielectric of permittivity ϵ. The area of each plate is S. If plates A and B have charges q and $-q$, respectively, find the electric field intensity in the dielectric between the plates, assuming a uniform field in this region. Determine the capacitance C in terms of d, S, and ϵ, and calculate C for $d = 0.5$ cm, $S = 400$ cm^2, and $\epsilon_r = 4$.

9-15. A current generator supplies a current i to a capacitance C. What is the resulting voltage drop across the capacitor (a) in the direction of the positive current, and (b) in the direction opposite the positive current? If $i = I_m \sin(\omega t + \theta)$, determine these drops as sinusoidal time functions.

9-16. A voltage generator supplies a voltage v to a capacitance C. What is the resulting current (a) in the direction of the voltage drop v across C, and (b) in the direction of the voltage rise v? If $v = V_m \sin(\omega t + \theta)$, determine these drops as sinusoidal time functions.

9-17. The displacement current between the plates of a 10-μf capacitor is $5 \sin 1000t$ amperes. Find the sinusoidal voltage drop across the capacitor, in the direction opposite the positive current.

9-18. The voltage drop across a 50-$\mu\mu$f capacitor is $50 \cos 10^7 t$. Find the sinusoidal current in the direction of the voltage drop.

9-19. Shown in Fig. 9-11 is a rod with a steady current I. A magnetic field directed into the paper exerts transverse forces on the drifting charge carriers, causing a *slightly* nonuniform current distribution over a cross section. The resulting separation of charge produces an electric field transverse to the rod. This phenomenon is known as the *Hall effect*. If I is positive, determine whether the charge carriers are electrons or holes for a voltmeter reading that is (a) positive, and (b) negative.

9-20. Two large parallel metallic plates are a centimeter apart in free space, and an impressed voltage produces equal and opposite charges on the plates. The surface charge densities, uniformly distributed over the surfaces that face one another, are ± 0.5 μc/m^2. At time zero an electron is released with zero velocity at the negative plate, and this electron moves toward the positive plate. Determine the current in the external electric circuit as a function of time.

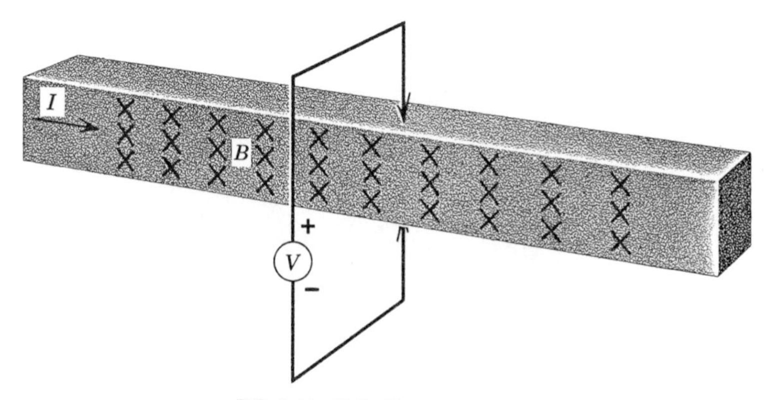

FIG. 9-11. Hall-effect experiment.

9-21. Both the electric and magnetic fields are solenoidal in a region devoid of electric charges. Deduce that these fields are tangential to the moving surface of the wavefront of an electromagnetic wave, provided the medium is a perfect dielectric. Also, show that the electric field may have a component normal to the wavefront if the medium has conductivity.

Section 9-5

9-22. In Fig. 9-12, $\mathbf{E}_1$ and $\mathbf{E}_2$ are the electric field intensities on the two sides of the surface, and θ_1 and θ_2 are the respective angles with the normal, as illustrated.

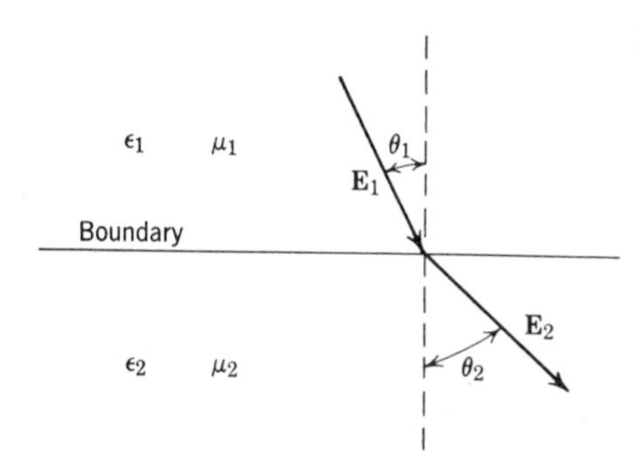

FIG. 9-12. Refraction of electric field at a boundary between two different media.

There are no charges at the boundary. Use Eqs. (9-11) and (9-14) to show that $(\tan \theta_1)/\tan \theta_2 = \epsilon_1/\epsilon_2$. This is the law of refraction of the electric field at a boundary free of charge.

9-23. Let $\mathbf{H}_1$ and $\mathbf{H}_2$ denote the magnetic field intensities on the two sides of a boundary between two different physical media, and let θ_1 and θ_2 denote the respective angles between the field vectors and the normal to the surface. This is illustrated in Fig. 9-12 with $\mathbf{H}$ replacing $\mathbf{E}$. There are no surface currents. Use Eqs. (9-12) and (9-13) to show that $(\tan \theta_1)/\tan \theta_2 = \mu_1/\mu_2$. This is the law of refraction of the magnetic field at a boundary free of surface current.

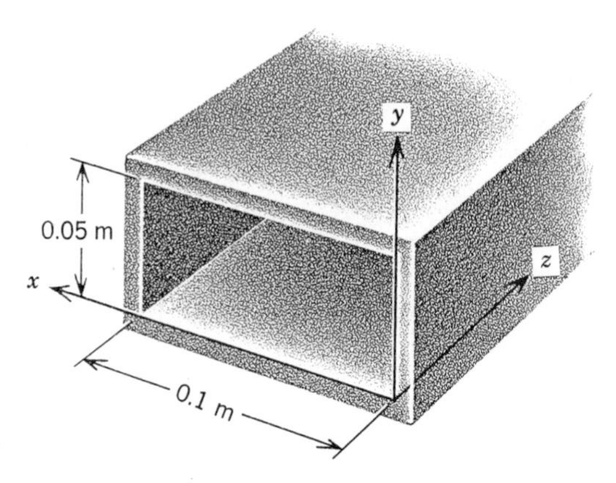

FIG. 9-13. Rectangular waveguide.

9-24. The fields in the free-space dielectric of the rectangular waveguide of Fig. 9-13 are

$$H_x = -7 \sin 10\pi x \sin (\omega t - \beta z)$$

$$H_z = 8 \cos 10\pi x \cos (\omega t - \beta z)$$

$$E_y = 4000 \sin 10\pi x \sin (\omega t - \beta z)$$

Assuming perfect conductors, find the surface current density $\mathbf{J}_s$ and the surface charge density ρ_s, as functions of time, at the point (0.01, 0, 0) on the surface. Repeat for the point (0, 0.01, 0).

Vector Analysis

CHAPTER 10

When two or three space dimensions are involved in equations, the branch of mathematics known as *vector analysis* is often utilized. As electromagnetic field theory involves spatial relationships, vector analysis can be employed to express the field equations in compact and meaningful form. Furthermore, solutions of the equations, when specific problems are encountered, are often expedited by the application of the principles of vector analysis.

An introduction to vector analysis has already been presented. The scalar and vector products, derivatives of vectors, and line and surface integrals have been used in many of our equations. In this chapter some of the differential operations in vector analysis, particularly the *gradient*, the *divergence*, and the *curl*, are considered. In addition, several important theorems are discussed, and the most common coordinate systems are examined.

10-1. THE GRADIENT OF A SCALAR FIELD

A scalar is a quantity that has magnitude but no direction. Examples of scalars are temperature, energy, current, and electric charge density. A scalar point function, or field, is present in a region having a scalar quantity associated with each of its points. Examples of scalar fields are the temperature distribution throughout a solid and the pressure distribution throughout the earth's atmosphere.

Let us consider a scalar point function $\phi(x, y, z)$ that is continuous and differentiable at all points of a region. The specific value of ϕ at a certain point P is ϕ_P. Suppose a straight line is drawn from P in an arbitrary manner. The function ϕ, in general, varies along this line. At the point P, in the direction of the line, ϕ has a certain rate of change with respect to distance; in some particular direction this space rate of change of ϕ is a *positive maximum*. Let a unit vector $\mathbf{n}$ at P be oriented in this direction, and let Δn denote an elemental length at P in the direction of this unit vector $\mathbf{n}$. Along the elemental length Δn the function ϕ changes an incremental amount $\Delta\phi$, and the limit of the ratio $\Delta\phi/\Delta n$, as Δn approaches zero, is the space rate of change of ϕ at P in the direction of $\mathbf{n}$. This is, of course, the partial derivative of ϕ with respect to n. Multiplying $\partial\phi/\partial n$ by the unit vector $\mathbf{n}$ gives a vector at P that points in the direction of the *maximum space rate of change of* ϕ, and this vector has a magnitude equal to this maximum change of ϕ with distance. Such a vector is called the *gradient* of the scalar ϕ, usually abbreviated **grad** ϕ. Hence by definition we have

$$\textbf{grad}\ \phi = \frac{\partial\phi}{\partial n}\,\mathbf{n} \tag{10-1}$$

It is understood that the unit vector $\mathbf{n}$ is oriented so that $\partial\phi/\partial n$ is a positive maximum at the point P.

Although ϕ is a scalar, **grad** ϕ is a vector. At each point of the scalar field ϕ there is the vector **grad** ϕ. *The magnitude of* **grad** ϕ *equals the maximum value of the space derivative of* ϕ *at the point. The direction of* **grad** ϕ *is that direction in which* ϕ *increases most rapidly with respect to distance.* If ϕ varies with time, *the partial derivative of Eq.* (10-1) *signifies that time is treated as a constant in evaluating the gradient*, and the vector **grad** ϕ is also a function of time.

Several examples should serve to clarify the meaning of the gradient of a scalar point function. Let us consider the region near the surface of a large flat metal surface that is uniformly heated. The temperature T in this region is a scalar field. At a point just off the surface, the gradient of the temperature T is a vector directed toward the heated surface, having a magnitude that is equal to the rate of change of T with respect to distance in this direction. The pressure of the earth's atmosphere is another scalar which has a gradient. If the variation of the pressure with respect to geographical position is negligible throughout a certain region, then the rate of change of pressure with respect to distance is a maximum in the downward direction. Therefore, at any arbitrary point in the region the gradient of the pressure p is a vector directed toward the earth's center, having a magnitude equal to the space derivative of the pressure p in this direction. Next, suppose a lighted bulb is placed in a closed room with black walls. The light intensity is, of course, a scalar point function. At any point P in the room the light intensity has its maximum rate of change with respect to distance in the direction toward the bulb. This is the direction of the gradient of the light intensity at P, and the magnitude of this vector equals this maximum space derivative.

10-2. THE GRADIENT IN RECTANGULAR COORDINATES

We shall now develop the rectangular form of the gradient of a scalar. To simplify the geometry of the problem we shall first consider a scalar ϕ that is a function of x and y only, and independent of z.

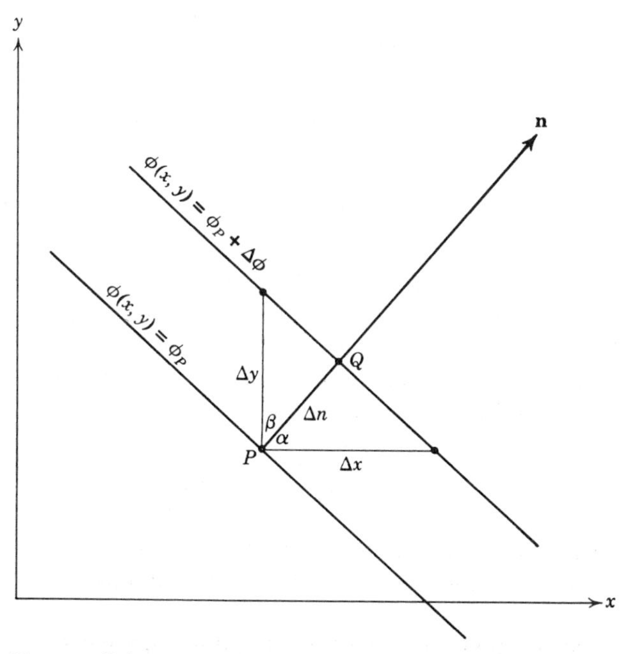

FIG. 10-1. Two parallel curves with constant values of the scalar point function ϕ.

Shown in Fig. 10-1 are small parallel sections of two curves in the xy-plane in the close vicinity of the point P. The region under examination is so small that the curves approximate straight lines. The curve through P is the locus of points satisfying the equation $\phi(x, y) = \phi_P$, with the constant ϕ_P denoting the value of ϕ at P. The other curve is a plot of the equation $\phi(x, y) = \phi_P + \Delta\phi$, with $\Delta\phi$ denoting a constant that is very small compared with ϕ_P. At all points on this curve the function ϕ equals the constant $\phi_P + \Delta\phi$. It is evident that the space derivative of ϕ along either of the curves is zero.

From the point P to any point of the curve that passes through the point Q the function ϕ changes by $\Delta\phi$. Consequently, the space rate of change of ϕ is a maximum along the *shortest* path between the curves. This is the path that follows the illustrated unit vector **n** directed normal to the curves. Along this path from P to Q the average space rate of change of ϕ is $\Delta\phi/\Delta n$. If these incremental quantities are allowed to approach zero, the vector $(\Delta\phi/\Delta n)\mathbf{n}$ obviously is the gradient of ϕ at P. The x and y components of this vector equal the magnitude of the vector multiplied by the respective direction cosines, and we have

$$\frac{\Delta\phi}{\Delta n}\,\mathbf{n} = \frac{\Delta\phi}{\Delta n}\cos\alpha\,\mathbf{i} + \frac{\Delta\phi}{\Delta n}\cos\beta\,\mathbf{j}$$

with α and β denoting the direction angles, as illustrated. As $\cos\alpha$ equals $\Delta n/\Delta x$ and $\cos\beta$ equals $\Delta n/\Delta y$, which is evident from the geometry of Fig. 10-1, the equation becomes

$$\frac{\Delta\phi}{\Delta n}\,\mathbf{n} = \frac{\Delta\phi}{\Delta x}\,\mathbf{i} + \frac{\Delta\phi}{\Delta y}\,\mathbf{j}$$

Examination of Fig. 10-1 shows that $\Delta\phi$ may be regarded as the increase in ϕ as x increases by Δx, with y constant, or it may be regarded as the increase in ϕ as y increases by Δy, with x constant. All the incremental quantities become differentials as the distance between the curves approaches zero, and the resulting equation is

$$\frac{\partial\phi}{\partial n}\,\mathbf{n} = \frac{\partial\phi}{\partial x}\,\mathbf{i} + \frac{\partial\phi}{\partial y}\,\mathbf{j} \qquad (10\text{-}2)$$

Partial derivatives are utilized, for each term of Eq. (10-2) denotes a rate of change with respect to the indicated variable with other variables held constant.

If the scalar function ϕ is a function of all three space coordinates, the three-dimensional illustration corresponding to Fig. 10-1 will show parallel planes in the vicinity of the point P, and the unit vector **n** at P will be normal to these surfaces. Similar reasoning leads to the rectangular form of **grad** ϕ in three dimensions. The result is

$$\mathbf{grad}\ \phi = \frac{\partial\phi}{\partial x}\,\mathbf{i} + \frac{\partial\phi}{\partial y}\,\mathbf{j} + \frac{\partial\phi}{\partial z}\,\mathbf{k} \qquad (10\text{-}3)$$

It is convenient to define a *del* operator ∇ by

$$\nabla = \frac{\partial}{\partial x}\,\mathbf{i} + \frac{\partial}{\partial y}\,\mathbf{j} + \frac{\partial}{\partial z}\,\mathbf{k} \qquad (10\text{-}4)$$

Alone, del has no meaning. *It is an operator treated mathematically as a vector.* If we let del operate on the scalar ϕ, we obtain

$$\nabla\phi = \left(\frac{\partial}{\partial x}\mathbf{i} + \frac{\partial}{\partial y}\mathbf{j} + \frac{\partial}{\partial z}\mathbf{k}\right)\phi = \frac{\partial\phi}{\partial x}\mathbf{i} + \frac{\partial\phi}{\partial y}\mathbf{j} + \frac{\partial\phi}{\partial z}\mathbf{k} \tag{10-5}$$

Therefore, the gradient of ϕ in rectangular form is $\nabla\phi$.

The x component of the gradient of ϕ is the rate of change of ϕ with respect to x. This is called the *directional derivative of ϕ in the x-direction*. The y and z components of the gradient are the directional derivatives in the y- and z-directions, respectively. In general, the directional derivative of ϕ in the direction of a unit vector $\mathbf{a}$ is $(\mathbf{grad}\ \phi) \cdot \mathbf{a}$. The magnitude of $\mathbf{grad}\ \phi$ at a point is the maximum value of the directional derivative of ϕ at the point.

In evaluating the line integral of $\mathbf{grad}\ \phi$ we encounter the product $(\mathbf{grad}\ \phi) \cdot d\mathbf{l}$, which can be written $(\mathbf{grad}\ \phi) \cdot \mathbf{n}\, dl$. The scalar product of $\mathbf{grad}\ \phi$ and the unit vector $\mathbf{n}$ is, of course, the directional derivative $\partial\phi/\partial l$, and $(\mathbf{grad}\ \phi) \cdot d\mathbf{l}$ becomes $(\partial\phi/\partial l)\, dl$. This is simply the differential increase $d\phi$ in the distance dl. It is evident that

$$\int_C (\mathbf{grad}\ \phi) \cdot d\mathbf{l} = \int_{\phi_1}^{\phi_2} d\phi = \phi_2 - \phi_1 \tag{10-6}$$

with ϕ_1 and ϕ_2 denoting the values of the scalar point function at the end points of the path C. Clearly, the line integral of $\mathbf{grad}\ \phi$ is independent of the actual path that connects the end points, and $\mathbf{grad}\ \phi$ *is a conservative vector*. If the path closes on itself, $\phi_1 = \phi_2$ and the integral of Eq. (10-6) is zero, a deduction that applies to any conservative vector.

In conclusion, if $\phi(x, y, z)$ is a continuous and differentiable scalar function, then $\mathbf{grad}\ \phi$ is the vector $(\partial\phi/\partial n)\mathbf{n}$, with $\mathbf{n}$ representing a unit vector directed so that $\partial\phi/\partial n$ is a maximum. In rectangular coordinates $\mathbf{grad}\ \phi$ equals $\nabla\phi$, with the del operator defined by Eq. (10-4). At a point P the gradient of ϕ is directed normal to the surface $\phi(x, y, z) = \phi_P$. The component of $\nabla\phi$ in any direction is the space rate of increase, or directional derivative, of ϕ in that direction, and $\nabla\phi$ is a conservative vector.

Let us consider an example of the gradient operation. In Sec. 7-3 it was stated that the diffusion current density at a point in a medium is proportional to the gradient of the charge density ρ at the point. This can be expressed mathematically as

$$\mathbf{J}_{\text{diffusion}} = -D\ \mathbf{grad}\ \rho \tag{10-7}$$

with D denoting the *diffusion constant*. The negative sign is the result of the diffusion of the charge carriers *away from* the concentration, and consequently, diffusion current density and $\mathbf{grad}\ \rho$ have opposite directions.

In semiconductors diffusion currents are due to concentrations of both holes and free electrons. Suppose there are p holes per cubic meter and n free electrons per cubic meter at a point in a medium. The charge density of the holes is pe, and the charge density of the electrons is $-ne$, with $e = 1.602 \times 10^{-19}$ c. It follows that the diffusion current densities $\mathbf{J}_p$ and $\mathbf{J}_n$ due to the holes and electrons, respectively, are

$$\mathbf{J}_p = -eD_p \nabla p \tag{10-8}$$

$$\mathbf{J}_n = eD_n \nabla n \tag{10-9}$$

with D_p and D_n denoting the hole and electron diffusion constants. For germanium, typical values of D_p and D_n are 0.0045 and 0.0095 m^2/sec, and for silicon, typical values are 0.0013 and 0.0033 m^2/sec, respectively. The total diffusion current density at a point is, of course, the sum of $\mathbf{J}_p$ and $\mathbf{J}_n$.

EXAMPLE. The hole density p is $10^{16} \exp(-20\sqrt{x^2 + y^2 + z^2})$ holes/cm³ in a region of a certain germanium semiconductor, with the space coordinates in centimeters. Find the hole current density due to diffusion at the point (0.03, 0.04, 0), these coordinates also given in centimeters. The hole diffusion constant is 45 cm^2/sec.

Solution. For convenience we shall use the centimeter as the unit of length in this problem. From Eq. (10-8) we determine the hole current density $\mathbf{J}_p$ to be $-72.1 \times 10^{-19} \nabla p$ ampere/cm². The hole density p is known as a function of the space coordinates. Using Eq. (10-3) to find the gradient of p as a function of the space coordinates and then substituting the coordinates of the specified point give

$$\nabla p = -4.42 \times 10^{16}\mathbf{i} - 5.89 \times 10^{16}\mathbf{j}$$

We deduce that the diffusion current density J_p is $0.318\mathbf{i} + 0.424\mathbf{j}$ ampere/cm².

10-3. THE DIVERGENCE OF A VECTOR

The flux of a vector $\mathbf{A}$ over some specified surface S has been defined as the surface integral of $\mathbf{A}$ over S. In previous chapters we have many times been interested in fluxes over closed surfaces. For example, Gauss's law specifies that the electric flux over a closed surface equals the enclosed charge. The total electric current over a closed surface is zero, and this current is the flux of the current density. The magnetic flux over a closed surface is likewise zero. The flux of the convection current density leaving a closed surface equals the time rate of decrease of the charge enclosed, by the equation of continuity. These as well as many other important relations can be applied to *points* in space by means of the *divergence* operation of vector analysis. If the vector $\mathbf{A}$ is differentiable at each point of a region of space, *the divergence of the vector* $\mathbf{A}$ *at a point* P *in the region is the net outward flux of* $\mathbf{A}$ *per unit volume at* P. The divergence of $\mathbf{A}$, usually abbreviated *div* **A**, is a scalar quantity, although **A** is a vector. We shall now proceed to express div **A** in mathematical form.

Let ΔV denote an elemental volume with elemental dimensions, with the point P located within ΔV. The net flux of **A** leaving ΔV is given by the integral $\oint \mathbf{A} \cdot d\mathbf{S}$ over the closed surface S around ΔV. The outward flux *per unit volume* is $(\oint \mathbf{A} \cdot d\mathbf{S})/\Delta V$, and this is the outward flux per unit volume *at the point* P, provided the elemental volume is reduced to an infinitesimal volume with differential dimensions. Of course, as ΔV approaches zero, the surface integral of **A** also approaches zero, and both ΔV and the surface integral become differential quantities. Their ratio, however, may be positive, negative, or zero, depending on the field of **A**. As div **A** is the outward flux per unit volume, the equation defining the divergence operation is

$$\text{div}\,\mathbf{A} = \lim_{\Delta V \to 0} \frac{\oint_S \mathbf{A} \cdot d\mathbf{S}}{\Delta V} \tag{10-10}$$

The surface integral of **A** in Eq. (10-10) equals the source strength of **A** in the elemental volume ΔV. Therefore, the divergence of **A** at a point P is *the source strength per unit volume* at P. A positive source represents an origin of the field, whereas a negative source, or sink, represents a termination of the field. Let us consider several applications that illustrate the physical significance of divergence.

When the valve on an automobile tire is opened, the pressure inside the tire drops as air escapes. In this example it is not necessary to consider the discrete nature of the molecules or their random thermal motion. Therefore, we shall understand that a *point* denotes a volume that is very small but still large enough to contain a great many molecules. At any point P inside the tire the air has mass density w kg/m^3 and velocity $\mathbf{v}$, and these quantities are functions of the space coordinates and time. Let dV denote a differential volume at P, and let S denote the closed surface around this volume. The divergence of $w\mathbf{v}$ at P is $(\oint w\mathbf{v} \cdot d\mathbf{S})/dV$. The product $w\mathbf{v}$, with units of kilograms per second per square meter, represents the mass flow per unit area in the direction of $\mathbf{v}$. Obviously, the scalar product $w\mathbf{v} \cdot d\mathbf{S}$, in kilograms per second, is the mass flow through the differential surface $d\mathbf{S}$. It follows that the integral of $w\mathbf{v}$ over the closed surface S equals the flow of mass, in kilograms per second, out of the differential volume. The outward flow of mass is a differential quantity, because the surface surrounds a differential volume. Dividing the surface integral by dV gives the outward flow of mass *per unit volume*, in kilograms per second per cubic meter, and this is the divergence of $w\mathbf{v}$. As mass is conserved, this must equal the time rate of decrease of the mass density at the point.

Therefore

$$\operatorname{div} w\mathbf{v} = -\frac{\partial w}{\partial t} \tag{10-11}$$

The mass density w at P decreases as air escapes from the valve, and we deduce from Eq. (10-11) that div $w\mathbf{v}$ is positive. However, if air is being pumped into the tire, the mass density at P increases, and the divergence is negative. Negative divergence is sometimes referred to as *convergence*. Expanding gas has positive divergence, and contracting gas has negative divergence.

Equation (10-11) states mathematically the conservation of fluid mass. It is called the *equation of continuity* applied to a fluid, including both gases and liquids. For an incompressible fluid the mass density w cannot vary, and div $w\mathbf{v}$ is zero. As electric charge is also conserved, it is evident that Eq. (10-11) applies to electric charge density ρ as well as to mass density w, with $\mathbf{v}$ denoting the drift velocity of the charge carriers. Thus

$$\operatorname{div} \rho\mathbf{v} = -\frac{\partial \rho}{\partial t} \tag{10-12}$$

This is the equation of continuity, in differential form, applied to electric charge. The integral form of this equation was presented earlier as Eq. (9-3). The differential form can be derived directly from the integral form by applying the latter to a volume that approaches zero as a limit. It can also be derived from the integral form by utilization of the divergence theorem of Sec. 10-5, and this is done in the next chapter.

It has been shown that the total electric flux ψ leaving an electric charge q is equal to q. If q is positive, it is a source of electric flux; if q is negative, the flux lines enter the charge, and the charge is a sink. As charge density ρ is the charge per unit volume at a point, clearly ρ is the *source strength per unit volume* of the electric flux density $\mathbf{D}$ at the point, and div $\mathbf{D}$ equals ρ. This is proved mathematically by the equation

$$\operatorname{div} \mathbf{D} = \lim_{\Delta V \to 0} \frac{\oint_S \mathbf{D} \cdot d\mathbf{S}}{\Delta V} = \frac{d\psi}{dV} = \frac{dq}{dV} = \rho \tag{10-13}$$

with $d\psi$ denoting the net outward electric flux from the differential volume dV, and dq denoting the charge in dV. Certainly $d\psi = dq$. The equation

$$\operatorname{div} \mathbf{D} = \rho \tag{10-14}$$

is Gauss's law applied to a point. As charge density may be either positive or negative, the divergence of $\mathbf{D}$ may be either positive or negative. In a region devoid of electric charge, the divergence of $\mathbf{D}$ is zero at all points.

The differential form of Gauss's law was presented here to illustrate the meaning of divergence.

If a vector field **A** has no sources or sinks, the flux of **A** is zero over every closed surface, and the field is solenoidal. All solenoidal fields have zero divergence everywhere. In fact, a solenoidal field can be defined as one without divergence. As the magnetic flux density **B** is solenoidal, the

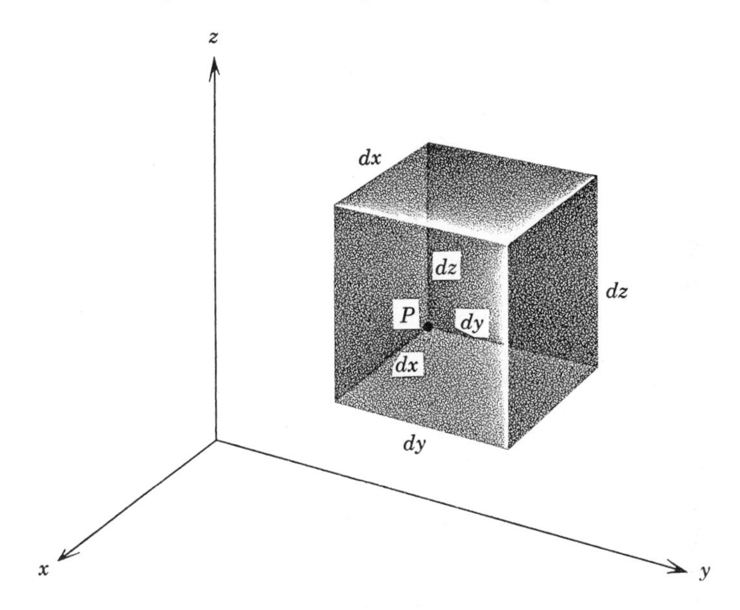

FIG. 10-2. A differential cube greatly enlarged.

divergence of **B** is always zero at all points. The magnetic equivalent of Gauss's law, in differential form, is the equation

$$\operatorname{div} \mathbf{B} = 0 \tag{10-15}$$

With the definition and meaning of divergence understood, we are now ready to develop the expression for divergence in terms of the rectangular coordinates.

10-4. THE DIVERGENCE IN RECTANGULAR COORDINATES

The first step in determining the divergence in rectangular coordinates is to find the outward flux of **A** over the closed surface S of the cubical box shown in Fig. 10-2. One vertex is at $P(x, y, z)$, and the sides of the cube are of differential lengths dx, dy, and dz. In determining the surface integral of **A** over S, the sides of the box will be considered separately.

Let A_y denote the component of **A** in the y-direction at points on the left-hand face of the box. The rate of change of A_y with respect to y is $\partial A_y/\partial y$, and the increase in the y component of **A** through the differential length dy is $\partial A_y/\partial y\, dy$. Therefore, the y component of **A** at corresponding points of the right-hand face of the box is $A_y + \partial A_y/\partial y\, dy$. The flux of **A** over the left-hand face is $-A_y\, dx\, dz$, the negative sign resulting from the selection of the outside surface as the positive side. Over the right-hand face the flux of **A** is $(A_y + \partial A_y/\partial y\, dy)\, dx\, dz$. The sum of these two fluxes is $\partial A_y/\partial y\, dx\, dy\, dz$, and this is the net flux out of the left-hand and right-hand faces. As $dx\, dy\, dz$ is the volume of the box, this outward flux *per unit volume* is $\partial A_y/\partial y$. Similarly, the outward fluxes per unit volume over the other two pairs of parallel faces are found to be $\partial A_x/\partial x$ and $\partial A_z/\partial z$. It follows that the total outward flux per unit volume, which is the divergence of **A**, is

$$\text{div}\,\mathbf{A} = \partial A_x/\partial x + \partial A_y/\partial y + \partial A_z/\partial z \qquad (10\text{-}16)$$

Although the derivation lacks mathematical rigor, the result is correct.

The scalar product of the del operator and the vector **A** can be found by a term-by-term expansion. The result is

$$\nabla \cdot \mathbf{A} = \partial A_x/\partial x + \partial A_y/\partial y + \partial A_z/\partial z \qquad (10\text{-}17)$$

We note that div $\mathbf{A} = \nabla \cdot \mathbf{A}$. The divergence of **A** at a point is the net outward flux of **A** per unit volume. **A** is a vector, but its divergence is a scalar.

10-5. THE DIVERGENCE THEOREM

According to the *divergence theorem*, the volume integral of div **A** throughout a volume V equals the surface integral of **A** over the surface S that encloses V, provided the vector **A** has continuous derivatives. In mathematical language the theorem states that

$$\int_V \nabla \cdot \mathbf{A}\, dV = \oint_S \mathbf{A} \cdot d\mathbf{S} \qquad (10\text{-}18)$$

The proof of the theorem is simple. Consider the finite volume V to be subdivided into differential volumes, with each dV having differential dimensions. The net outward flux of **A** from a differential volume dV is $\nabla \cdot \mathbf{A}\, dV$. Let us consider two adjacent volume elements having a common surface between them. The flux *out* of one volume element through the common surface is a flux *into* the adjacent element. When the contributions of the net outward fluxes of all the volume elements are added in the integration of $\nabla \cdot \mathbf{A}\, dV$, the fluxes over all the common surfaces cancel one another. All that remains is the flux over the outside surface, and this is the surface integral of **A**.

With the aid of the divergence theorem it is sometimes possible to convert a volume integral, which is a triple integral, into a surface integral, which is a double integral. Often it is convenient to convert a surface integral into a volume integral, and the divergence theorem can be employed for this purpose also.

10-6. THE CURL OF A VECTOR

We have examined the gradient of a scalar and the divergence of a vector. A third differential operation of vector analysis, which we shall use extensively in our study of electromagnetism, is the *curl* of a vector, which will now be defined.

Let us consider an elemental surface ΔS with elemental dimensions, and let C denote the closed contour of this surface. We select one side of the surface as the positive side and construct a unit vector **n** normal to the surface out of the positive side. The circulation of the vector **A** around the contour C is the line integral of **A** around this closed path. The direction of integration is understood to abide by the right-hand integration rule, this direction being counterclockwise when viewed from the tip of the unit vector **n**. On a per-unit-area basis the circulation of **A** is

$$\frac{1}{\Delta S} \oint_C \mathbf{A} \cdot d\mathbf{l}$$

If we let ΔS approach zero in a manner that makes the total length of the path C also approach zero, the expression gives the circulation per unit area at a point P. In general, the circulation per unit area at P depends upon the orientation of the elemental surface.

Now suppose the elemental area is oriented so that the circulation per unit area is a positive maximum. *The vector whose magnitude equals this maximum circulation per unit area and whose direction is that of* **n** *is called the curl of the vector* **A**, *or* **curl A**. Thus

$$\mathbf{curl\,A} = \lim_{\Delta S \to 0} \frac{1}{\Delta S} \oint_C \mathbf{A} \cdot d\mathbf{l}\,\mathbf{n} \tag{10-19}$$

Of course, the unit vector **n** out of the positive side of ΔS is understood to be oriented so as to make the magnitude of the vector of Eq. (10-19) a positive maximum. At any point P the vector **curl A** has a magnitude equal to the maximum circulation of **A** per unit area at P and the direction of the unit vector **n**. This unit vector is oriented normal to the differential area enclosed by the path C, pointing in the direction that makes the counterclockwise circulation positive when viewed from the tip of $\mathbf{n}$. The vector **curl A** denotes *the intensity of the circulation of* $\mathbf{A}$ at the point P.

The curl operation is immensely important in electromagnetic field theory. The fundamental equations have been expressed in terms of line integrals. In order to obtain the differential forms of these equations, we shall apply the line integrals to an infinitesimal closed path in space, and the resulting equations involve the curl. The two fundamental electromagnetic laws in differential form are often called *Maxwell's curl equations.*

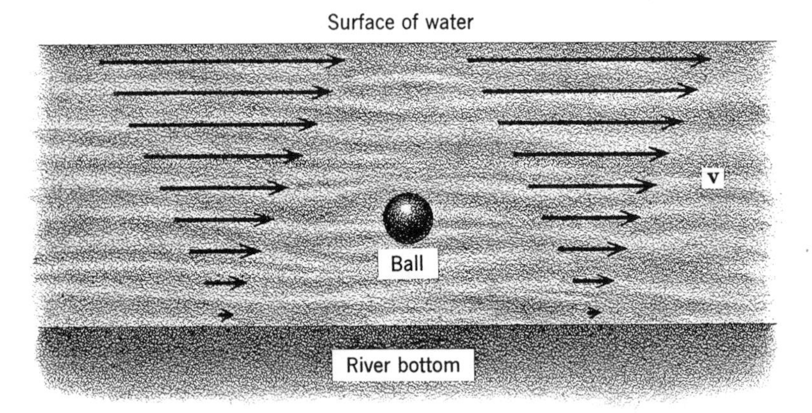

FIG. 10-3. Side view of a submerged ball that is drifting downstream. The arrows denote the velocity vectors of the water.

The concept of the curl of a vector is usually difficult for the beginning student to grasp, but the importance of the curl operation in electromagnetism cannot be overemphasized. The student should study the definition of the curl of a vector carefully. He should work problems involving its use and, in doing so, he should try to understand the physical significance of the curl of a vector.

10-7. SOME EXAMPLES OF THE CURL

The first example to be considered is the case of smooth water flow in a river. Shown in Fig. 10-3 is a cross-sectional view of the stream with velocity vectors that represent the velocities of the stream at different points. Turbulence is assumed to be negligible, and the velocity of the water at the bottom of the river is zero due to friction.

Suppose we release in the water a very small ball with a mass density such that the ball submerges to the depth shown. As the ball drifts downstream, it also rotates about its axis normal to the paper, and this rotation is clockwise. The rotation is the result of the difference in the velocities of the water particles over the top and bottom surfaces of the ball. At the instant the ball is at a certain point P in the stream, the angular velocity of the ball is a measure of the curl of the velocity vector $\mathbf{v}$ at P. In the illustration the curl of $\mathbf{v}$ is a vector directed into the paper, for the maximum circulation per unit area of $\mathbf{v}$ is positive in the clockwise direction.

Next, let us consider a thin solid disk rotating clockwise as shown in Fig. 10-4. The clockwise circulation of the velocity vector $\mathbf{v}$ around path

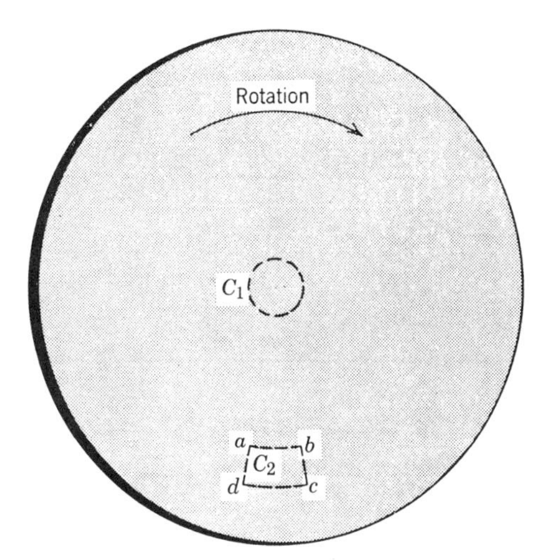

FIG. 10-4. Thin rotating disk.

C_1 is positive, because $\mathbf{v}$ and $d\mathbf{l}$ have the same direction at each point of the path. As C_1 shrinks to a circular path of infinitesimal length, both the circulation and the area enclosed by C_1 approach zero. However, the circulation per unit area is finite and positive. In this case the magnitude of **curl** $\mathbf{v}$ equals twice the angular velocity of the disk, and this should be verified by the student. The direction of the vector is into the paper.

The path C_2 will now be considered, with the circulation of $\mathbf{v}$ taken clockwise. The paths *ab* and *cd* are along circular arcs, and the paths *bc* and *da* are along radii. The line integrals along *bc* and *da* are zero. From a to b the integral is negative, because $\mathbf{v} \cdot d\mathbf{l}$ equals $-v\,dl$ at points on this path. From c to d the line integral is positive. Clearly, the total line integral around the closed path is positive, for the magnitude of v at points along *cd* is greater than at points along *ab*, and furthermore, the path *cd* is longer. As C_2 shrinks to infinitesimal length, both the circulation and the area enclosed by the path approach zero, but the circulation per unit area is finite and positive. As the circulation is positive in the clockwise direction, the unit vector **n** is directed into the paper, and this is the direction of **curl v**. The determination of the magnitude of **curl v** in terms of the angular velocity ω is left as an exercise.

An example that involves no motion of a physical quantity is the curl of an electric field **E**. Shown in Fig. 10-5 are the flux lines of an electric field at a certain instant of time. The field does not vary in the direction into the paper, but it is nonuniform in the plane of the paper. The intensity of the field is proportional to the spacing of the lines.

Consider the path *abcda*. Let the positive side of the plane surface bounded by the path be the side facing the reader. Then the unit vector **n**

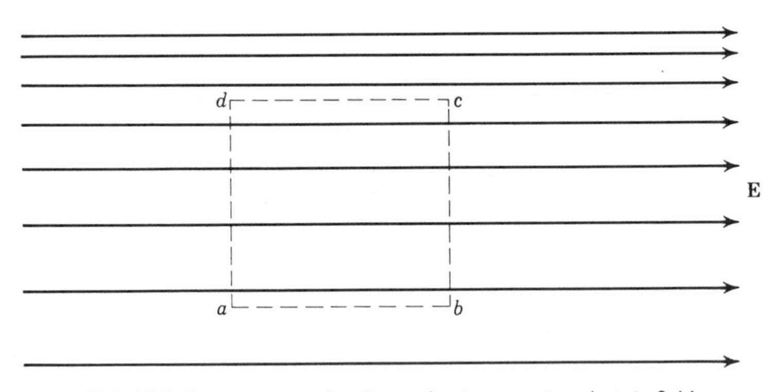

FIG. 10-5. Instantaneous flux lines of a time-varying electric field.

is directed out of the paper, and the line integral is taken counterclockwise by the right-hand rule. As the field intensity along *cd* has greater magnitude than that along *ab*, the circulation of **E** is negative. If the path is reduced to a square path of infinitesimal length, the circulation of **E** per unit area is negative. This negative circulation per unit area signifies that the vectors **curl E** and **n** have opposite directions. As **n** is directed out of the paper, **curl E** is directed into the paper. The negative sign resulting from the circulation per unit area, combined with the vector **n**, gives a vector $-\mathbf{n}$ in the direction of **curl E**. This shows that the selection of the positive side of the surface is arbitrary, but the surface must be oriented, of course, so that the circulation intensity is a maximum. Although not shown in Fig. 10-5, the electric field must have a time-varying magnetic field associated with it, for otherwise the circulation of **E** would be zero.

The Maxwell-Faraday law states that the circulation of **E** equals the surface integral of $-\dot{\mathbf{B}}$ over a surface S bounded by the path. When this law is applied to a path of infinitesimal length, enclosing a plane *differential* surface, the equation becomes

$$\oint_C \mathbf{E} \cdot d\mathbf{l} = -\dot{\mathbf{B}} \cdot \mathbf{n}\, dS \tag{10-20}$$

with $\mathbf{n}$ denoting a unit vector out of the designated positive side of dS. Both sides of Eq. (10-20) are maximized by orienting the differential surface so that the directions of the vectors $-\dot{\mathbf{B}}$ and $\mathbf{n}$ are the same. With this orientation the scalar product $-\dot{\mathbf{B}} \cdot \mathbf{n} = |-\dot{\mathbf{B}}|$. If this is substituted into Eq. (10-20) and if both sides of the equation are multiplied by $\mathbf{n}$ and divided by dS, we obtain

$$\frac{1}{dS} \oint_C \mathbf{E} \cdot d\mathbf{l}\, \mathbf{n} = |-\dot{\mathbf{B}}|\, \mathbf{n} \tag{10-21}$$

The term on the left is obviously the vector **curl E**. The term on the right is the vector $-\dot{\mathbf{B}}$, because $\mathbf{n} = -\dot{\mathbf{B}}/|-\dot{\mathbf{B}}|$. Therefore,

$$\mathbf{curl\, E} = -\dot{\mathbf{B}} \tag{10-22}$$

The maximum circulation of $\mathbf{E}$ per unit area equals the magnitude of the vector $-\dot{\mathbf{B}}$. This circulation per unit area is positive if the surface is oriented so that the unit vector $\mathbf{n}$ is in the direction of the vector $-\dot{\mathbf{B}}$. Equation (10-22) is Maxwell's first curl equation.

The Maxwell-Ampère law states that the circulation of $\mathbf{H}$ equals the surface integral of the vector $\rho\mathbf{v} + \dot{\mathbf{D}}$ over a surface S bounded by the path. This law is similar in form to the Maxwell-Faraday law, the difference being that $\mathbf{H}$ replaces $\mathbf{E}$ and $\rho\mathbf{v} + \dot{\mathbf{D}}$ replaces $-\dot{\mathbf{B}}$. Making these substitutions into Eq. (10-22), we obtain

$$\mathbf{curl\, H} = \rho\mathbf{v} + \dot{\mathbf{D}} \tag{10-23}$$

This is Maxwell's second curl equation.

10-8. THE CURL IN RECTANGULAR COORDINATES

The curl of a vector is itself a vector. Therefore, it can be resolved into space components. Let $\mathbf{m}$ denote a unit vector drawn from a point P in an arbitrary direction, and let the component of **curl A** at P, in the direction of $\mathbf{m}$, be designated $\text{curl}_m\, \mathbf{A}$. Then

$$\text{curl}_m\, \mathbf{A} = (\mathbf{curl\, A}) \cdot \mathbf{m} \tag{10-24}$$

The right side of Eq. (10-24) equals the component of the vector **curl A** in the direction of **m** multiplied by the magnitude of **m**, which is unity. It should be noted that $\text{curl}_m\, \mathbf{A}$ is a scalar whose value may be positive, negative, or zero. If an elemental surface at P is oriented normal to **m** and if the circulation around the contour C is taken counterclockwise when viewed from the tip of **m**, the circulation per unit area equals the scalar $\text{curl}_m\, \mathbf{A}$. The truth of this statement is not evident, but for simplicity the proof is omitted.*

In rectangular form the curl of the vector **A** is

$$\mathbf{curl\,A} = (\text{curl}_x\, \mathbf{A})\mathbf{i} + (\text{curl}_y\, \mathbf{A})\mathbf{j} + (\text{curl}_z\, \mathbf{A})\mathbf{k} \tag{10-25}$$

$\text{Curl}_x\, \mathbf{A}$ is the circulation per unit area at a point P, with the elemental

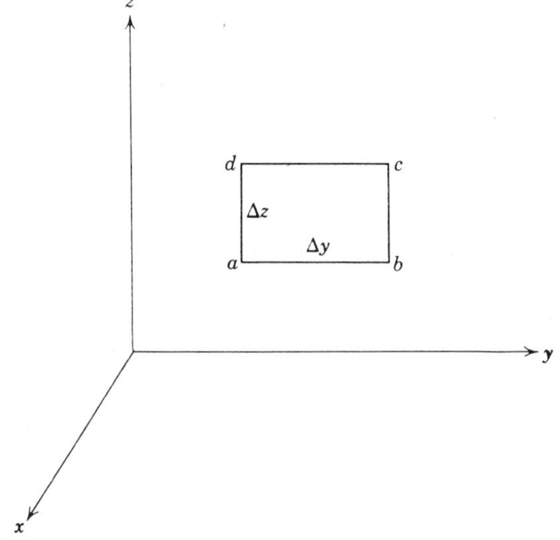

FIG. 10-6. Rectangle.

surface at P parallel to the yz-plane and with the circulation taken counterclockwise when viewed from the tip of the unit vector **i**. The scalars $\text{curl}_y\, \mathbf{A}$ and $\text{curl}_z\, \mathbf{A}$ are defined similarly. We are now ready to determine the mathematical expression for **curl A** in rectangular coordinates.

The x component of **curl A** is $\text{curl}_x\, \mathbf{A}$. To determine $\text{curl}_x\, \mathbf{A}$, let us consider an elemental rectangle parallel to the yz-plane, as shown in Fig. 10-6. The rectangular shape is convenient, and it can be shown* that the circulation per unit area is independent of the shape of the elemental

* See H. E. Newell, Jr., *Vector Analysis*, McGraw-Hill Book Co., New York, 1955, Chap. 4.

surface. With C denoting the closed path *abcda*, the scalar $\text{curl}_x\,\mathbf{A}$ is the limit, as Δy and Δz approach zero, of the ratio

$$\frac{1}{\Delta y\,\Delta z}\oint_C \mathbf{A}\cdot d\mathbf{l} \tag{10-26}$$

Let us examine the line integral of (10-26). Around the closed path C the circulation of $\mathbf{A}$ is

$$\int_a^b \mathbf{A}\cdot d\mathbf{l} + \int_b^c \mathbf{A}\cdot d\mathbf{l} + \int_c^d \mathbf{A}\cdot d\mathbf{l} + \int_d^a \mathbf{A}\cdot d\mathbf{l}$$

Rearranging terms and changing the signs before the integrals with the limits interchanged, we obtain

$$\left[\int_a^b \mathbf{A}\cdot d\mathbf{l} - \int_d^c \mathbf{A}\cdot d\mathbf{l}\right] - \left[\int_a^d \mathbf{A}\cdot d\mathbf{l} - \int_b^c \mathbf{A}\cdot d\mathbf{l}\right] \tag{10-27}$$

The left-hand expression in brackets in (10-27) contains the line integrals along the paths *ab* and *dc*. From a to b the scalar product $\mathbf{A}\cdot d\mathbf{l} = A_y\,dy$. From d to c this scalar product is approximately $(A_y + \partial A_y/\partial z\,\Delta z)\,dy$, with $\partial A_y/\partial z\,\Delta z$ denoting the *increase* in A_y from a point on the path *ab* to a point directly above it on path *dc*. This increase is only approximated by the given expression, but the error introduced by this approximation approaches zero as Δz approaches zero. Therefore, the left-hand expression of (10-27) becomes

$$\int_a^b A_y\,dy - \int_d^c (A_y + \partial A_y/\partial z\,\Delta z)\,dy \tag{10-28}$$

The integrals involving A_y cancel, their y limits being the same. This leaves in (10-28) the integral

$$-\int_d^c (\partial A_y/\partial z\,\Delta z)\,dy \tag{10-29}$$

As Δy and Δz approach the limit zero, the term in parentheses becomes a constant along the path, equal to $\partial A_y/\partial z\,dz$, and the expression of (10-29) equals the negative of this constant multiplied by the differential path length dy. This gives

$$-\partial A_y/\partial z\,dz\,dy \tag{10-30}$$

The right-hand expression in brackets in (10-27) can be treated in a similar manner. From a to d the scalar product $\mathbf{A}\cdot d\mathbf{l} = A_z\,dz$, and from b to c this scalar product is $(A_z + \partial A_z/\partial y\,\Delta y)\,dz$. When the integrals of these quantities are subtracted, the A_z terms cancel. Letting Δy and Δz approach zero, we obtain

$$-\partial A_z/\partial y\,dy\,dz \tag{10-31}$$

Replacing the bracketed terms of (10-27) with the expressions of (10-30) and (10-31) gives the circulation of **A** in rectangular coordinates. The result is

$$\oint_C \mathbf{A} \cdot d\mathbf{l} = \left(\frac{\partial A_z}{\partial y} - \frac{\partial A_y}{\partial z}\right) dy\, dz \tag{10-32}$$

The differential area of the rectangle is $dy\, dz$. Therefore, the circulation per unit area, with the differential surface parallel to the yz-plane, is

$$\text{curl}_x\, \mathbf{A} = \partial A_z/\partial y - \partial A_y/\partial z \tag{10-33}$$

The y and z components of **curl A** can be determined in a similar manner. A more direct way, however, is to rotate the subscripts. For example, to find $\text{curl}_y\, \mathbf{A}$ from the expression for $\text{curl}_x\, \mathbf{A}$ we can replace x with y, y with z, and z with x. This procedure is justified by changing the designation of the axes of Fig. 10-6 while maintaining their orientations with respect to one another. The resulting expression for **curl A** is

$$\textbf{curl A} = \left(\frac{\partial A_z}{\partial y} - \frac{\partial A_y}{\partial z}\right)\mathbf{i} + \left(\frac{\partial A_x}{\partial z} - \frac{\partial A_z}{\partial x}\right)\mathbf{j} + \left(\frac{\partial A_y}{\partial x} - \frac{\partial A_x}{\partial y}\right)\mathbf{k} \tag{10-34}$$

Curl A can be expressed in terms of the del operator. Del is treated mathematically as though it is a vector. The vector product of two vectors can be expressed as a determinant that contains the unit vectors **i**, **j**, and **k** and the rectangular components of the two vectors. It follows that

$$\nabla \times \mathbf{A} = \begin{vmatrix} \mathbf{i} & \mathbf{j} & \mathbf{k} \\ \dfrac{\partial}{\partial x} & \dfrac{\partial}{\partial y} & \dfrac{\partial}{\partial z} \\ A_x & A_y & A_z \end{vmatrix} \tag{10-35}$$

The expansion of the determinant gives the correct expression for **curl A** in rectangular coordinates.

We have found that the gradient, the divergence, and the curl can be expressed in terms of the del operator. The relations are

$$\textbf{grad}\, \phi = \nabla \phi \tag{10-36}$$

$$\text{div}\, \mathbf{A} = \nabla \cdot \mathbf{A} \tag{10-37}$$

$$\textbf{curl A} = \nabla \times \mathbf{A} \tag{10-38}$$

The gradient, the divergence, and the curl were initially defined without reference to any particular coordinate system. We then developed expressions for these differential operations in rectangular coordinates. In

Sec. 10-14 the corresponding expressions in cylindrical and spherical coordinates are presented. *Although the operator* ∇ *cannot be given an explicit form for coordinate systems other than rectangular, the del notation is used regardless of the coordinate system employed.* For example, $\nabla \times \mathbf{A}$ represents **curl A** in any coordinate system, but it can be treated as the cross product of a vector operator ∇ and a vector **A** *only in the rectangular system.*

A conservative field has been defined as one in which the circulation of **A** is zero, regardless of the path of integration. It is clear that, if a vector field **A** is conservative in a region, then **curl A** is zero at all points of the region. A vector field with zero curl and also zero divergence is both conservative and solenoidal.

Some of the advantages of using the notation of vector analysis in electromagnetic field theory should be apparent. For example, Maxwell's first equation in differential form is quite simply expressed as **curl E** $= -\dot{\mathbf{B}}$. This equation is a natural description of a physical situation that avoids reference to an extraneous coordinate system. In rectangular coordinates, without the use of vector notation, this equation is written as three partial differential equations, which are

$$\partial E_z/\partial y - \partial E_y/\partial z = -\partial B_x/\partial t \tag{10-39}$$

$$\partial E_x/\partial z - \partial E_z/\partial x = -\partial B_y/\partial t \tag{10-40}$$

$$\partial E_y/\partial x - \partial E_x/\partial y = -\partial B_z/\partial t \tag{10-41}$$

The first of these is the result of equating the x components of the vectors **curl E** and $-\dot{\mathbf{B}}$, and the second and third equations were obtained by equating the y components and the z components, respectively.

Not only is the vector form easier to write, but it also helps us to understand the meaning of the equation, provided we understand the significance of the differential operators. Perhaps it should be mentioned that engineers and scientists, and also most textbooks on electromagnetism, commonly use the language of vector analysis. The engineer who is not thoroughly familiar with this language will have difficult communication problems.

10-9. STOKES'S THEOREM

We shall now examine a theorem of special importance in electromagnetic theory. Suppose **A** denotes a vector function with continuous derivatives at each point of a two-sided surface S bounded by the closed contour C. The surface is in three-dimensional space and is not necessarily planar. *Stokes's theorem* states that the circulation of **A** around the path C equals the flux of **curl A** over the surface S. The positive side of S is arbitrarily selected, and the right-hand integration rule applies. Mathematically, we have

$$\oint_C \mathbf{A} \cdot d\mathbf{l} = \int_S (\mathbf{curl\ A}) \cdot d\mathbf{S} \tag{10-42}$$

To prove the theorem, consider the surface S shown in Fig. 10-7, with the contour C. Let S be subdivided into a very large number of differential areas with each being approximately planar even though the surface S may be curved. In Fig. 10-7 the differential areas are shown greatly

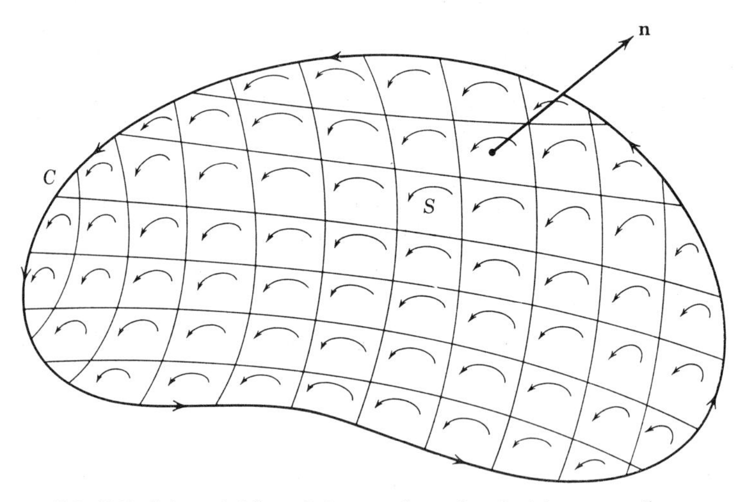

FIG. 10-7. Enlarged differential areas of a surface S with contour C.

enlarged. Now consider the sum of the line integrals of **A**, in a counterclockwise direction, around the individual differential areas of the surface S. Each part of a path that is common to two areas is traversed twice and in opposite directions. Therefore, only the differential lengths of the outer boundary contribute to the summation, and the summation becomes the circulation of **A** around the closed path C.

Next, consider a single element dS with a unit vector **n** normal to its plane and directed away from the positive side. The circulation per unit area is $\text{curl}_n\ \mathbf{A}$, and this equals $(\mathbf{curl\ A}) \cdot \mathbf{n}$ by Eq. (10-24). Therefore, the circulation around the contour of dS is $(\mathbf{curl\ A}) \cdot \mathbf{n}\, dS$, or $(\mathbf{curl\ A}) \cdot d\mathbf{S}$. The summation over the surface S is the surface integral of **curl A**.

Thus it has been shown that the summation over S of the circulation of **A** around the contour of each dS equals the circulation of **A** around the boundary C; this summation also equals the surface integral of **curl A** over S. Equation (10-42) follows.

Stokes's theorem enables us to convert a line integral into a surface integral. Often it provides a way to convert a surface integral into a line integral. An important deduction from Stokes's theorem is the vector identity div **curl A** = 0. To show this, let a surface S in a region be nearly closed, with its contour C having a length that is very small. For example, the surface could be spherical with a small hole, and the contour C is the closed path around the small hole. In the limit as the path C shrinks to a point, causing S to approach a closed surface, the circulation of **A** around C approaches zero. As S is a closed surface, Eq. (10-42) becomes

$$\oint_S (\mathbf{curl\ A}) \cdot d\mathbf{S} = 0$$

Thus the surface integral of **curl A** is zero over any closed surface. Such a vector field is solenoidal and, therefore, the divergence of **curl A** is zero. This useful vector identity can be verified also by expanding div **curl A** in rectangular coordinates, and this is suggested as an exercise.

10-10. THE LAPLACIAN OPERATOR

A differential operation that is frequently encountered is the divergence of the gradient of a scalar point function ϕ. This can be expressed as div **grad** ϕ, or $\nabla \cdot (\nabla\phi)$, and it is called the *scalar Laplacian of* ϕ. Expansion in rectangular coordinates gives

$$\nabla \cdot (\nabla\phi) = \frac{\partial^2\phi}{\partial x^2} + \frac{\partial^2\phi}{\partial y^2} + \frac{\partial^2\phi}{\partial z^2} \tag{10-43}$$

Let us consider the operator $\nabla \cdot \nabla$. As $\mathbf{A} \cdot \mathbf{A} = A^2$, we can write $\nabla \cdot \nabla = \nabla^2$, and from the scalar product we obtain

$$\nabla^2 = \nabla \cdot \nabla = \left(\frac{\partial}{\partial x}\right)^2 + \left(\frac{\partial}{\partial y}\right)^2 + \left(\frac{\partial}{\partial z}\right)^2$$

Each of the terms in parentheses is an operator. The square of an operator means that the operation is performed twice. Therefore,

$$\nabla^2 = \nabla \cdot \nabla = \frac{\partial^2}{\partial x^2} + \frac{\partial^2}{\partial y^2} + \frac{\partial^2}{\partial z^2} \tag{10-44}$$

Comparison of Eqs. (10-43) and (10-44) reveals that

$$\nabla^2\phi = (\nabla \cdot \nabla)\phi = \nabla \cdot \nabla\phi \tag{10-45}$$

The operator *div grad*, usually denoted by the symbol ∇^2, is called the *Laplacian operator*. The Laplacian of the scalar point function ϕ is given in rectangular coordinates by Eq. (10-43), and expressions for $\nabla^2\phi$ in other coordinate systems are given in Sec. 10-14.

The Laplacian of a vector **A** is defined as the vector whose *rectangular* components are the scalar Laplacians of the *rectangular* components of **A**. Therefore,

$$\mathbf{\nabla}^2\mathbf{A} = \nabla^2 A_x\,\mathbf{i} + \nabla^2 A_y\,\mathbf{j} + \nabla^2 A_z\,\mathbf{k} \tag{10-46}$$

The scalar Laplacian ∇^2 denotes the operator *div grad.* However, as can be seen from the vector identity of Eq. (10-57), the vector Laplacian $\mathbf{\nabla}^2$ denotes the operator *grad div* — *curl curl.* In rectangular coordinates the components of the vector Laplacian resemble the form of the scalar

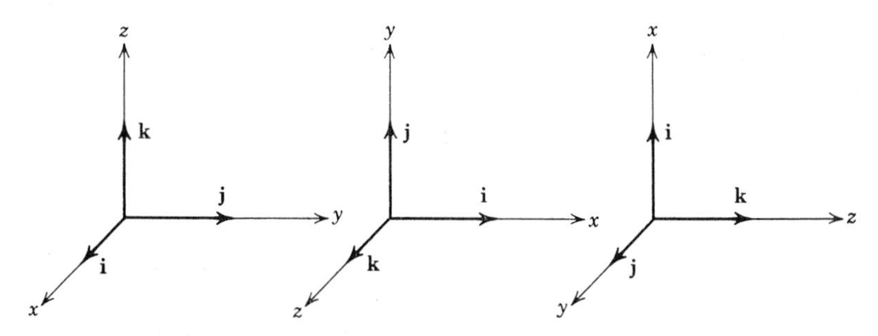

FIG. 10-8. Rectangular coordinates and the unit vectors.

Laplacian, but *there is no such similarity in the other common coordinate systems.* The use of similar symbols to denote these different operators should not be confusing, for the scalar Laplacian always operates on a scalar and the vector Laplacian always operates on a vector.

10-11. THE RECTANGULAR COORDINATE SYSTEM

The right-hand rectangular coordinate system has been utilized extensively in the preceding sections. Such a coordinate system is illustrated in Fig. 10-8 with three different orientations. It should be noted that

$$\mathbf{i} \times \mathbf{j} = \mathbf{k} \qquad \mathbf{j} \times \mathbf{k} = \mathbf{i} \qquad \mathbf{k} \times \mathbf{i} = \mathbf{j} \tag{10-47}$$

A point (x_1, y_1, z_1) in rectangular coordinates can be regarded as the intersection of the planes $x = x_1$, $y = y_1$, and $z = z_1$. As the differential lengths in the three coordinate directions are dx, dy, and dz, the vector length $d\mathbf{l}$ is

$$d\mathbf{l} = dx\,\mathbf{i} + dy\,\mathbf{j} + dz\,\mathbf{k} \tag{10-48}$$

A differential area can be regarded as a vector with magnitude dS and with direction normal to the surface. The differential areas in the x-, y-, and z-directions are $dy\,dz$, $dz\,dx$, and $dx\,dy$, respectively, Therefore,

$$d\mathbf{S} = dy\,dz\,\mathbf{i} + dz\,dx\,\mathbf{j} + dx\,dy\,\mathbf{k} \tag{10-49}$$

A differential volume is $dx\,dy\,dz$.

10-12. THE CYLINDRICAL COORDINATE SYSTEM

The physical boundaries of many problems dictate the use of the cylindrical coordinate system. The cylindrical coordinates r, φ, and z are shown in Fig. 10-9. A point (r_1, φ_1, z_1) can be regarded as the intersection

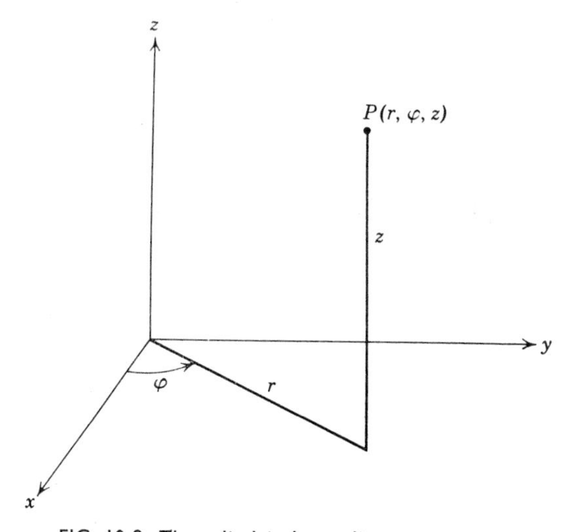

FIG. 10-9. The cylindrical coordinate system.

of the surfaces $r = r_1$, $\varphi = \varphi_1$, and $z = z_1$. The surface $r = r_1$ is a circular cylinder; the surface $\varphi = \varphi_1$ is a plane containing the axis of the circular cylinder; and the surface $z = z_1$ is a plane normal to this axis.

The unit vectors in cylindrical coordinates are designated $\mathbf{a}_r$, $\mathbf{a}_\varphi$, and $\mathbf{a}_z$, and these are shown in Fig. 10-10. The unit vector $\mathbf{a}_\varphi$ is tangential to the surface of the cylinder, and the three unit vectors are normal to each other. Also shown in Fig. 10-10 are the differential lengths dr, $r\,d\varphi$, and dz. Clearly

$$d\mathbf{l} = dr\,\mathbf{a}_r + r\,d\varphi\,\mathbf{a}_\varphi + dz\,\mathbf{a}_z \tag{10-50}$$

The respective differential surface areas in the $\mathbf{a}_r$-, $\mathbf{a}_\varphi$-, and $\mathbf{a}_z$-directions are $r\,d\varphi\,dz$, $dr\,dz$, and $r\,dr\,d\varphi$, and the vector $d\mathbf{S}$ is

$$d\mathbf{S} = r\,d\varphi\,dz\,\mathbf{a}_r + dr\,dz\,\mathbf{a}_\varphi + r\,dr\,d\varphi\,\mathbf{a}_z \tag{10-51}$$

The differential volume, illustrated in Fig. 10-10, is $r\,dr\,d\varphi\,dz$.

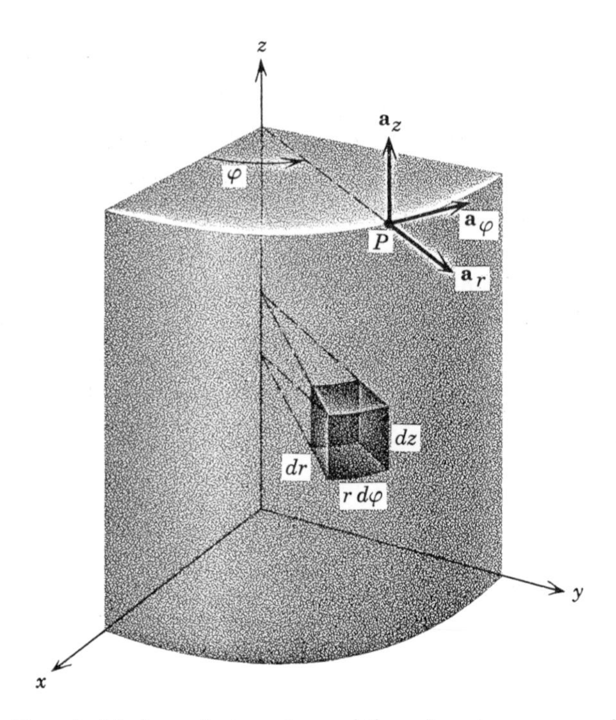

FIG. 10-10. The cylindrical coordinate system and the unit vectors $\mathbf{a}_r$, $\mathbf{a}_\varphi$, and $\mathbf{a}_z$ at the point P.

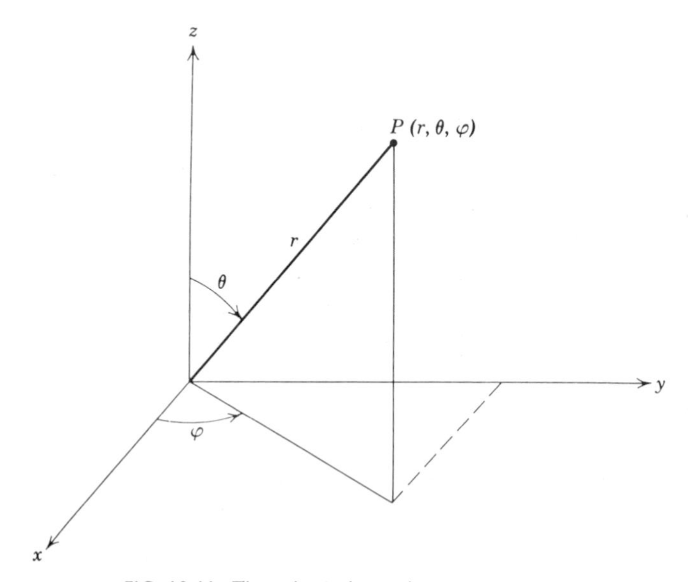

FIG. 10-11. The spherical coordinate system.

10-13. THE SPHERICAL COORDINATE SYSTEM

The spherical coordinates r, θ, and φ are shown in Fig. 10-11. Note that r represents the distance from the origin, whereas in cylindrical coordinates r is the distance of the point from the z-axis. The angle θ is that formed by the z-axis and the line connecting the origin to the point P. The angle φ is precisely the same as the angle φ in cylindrical coordinates. A point $(r_1, \theta_1, \varphi_1)$ in spherical coordinates can be regarded

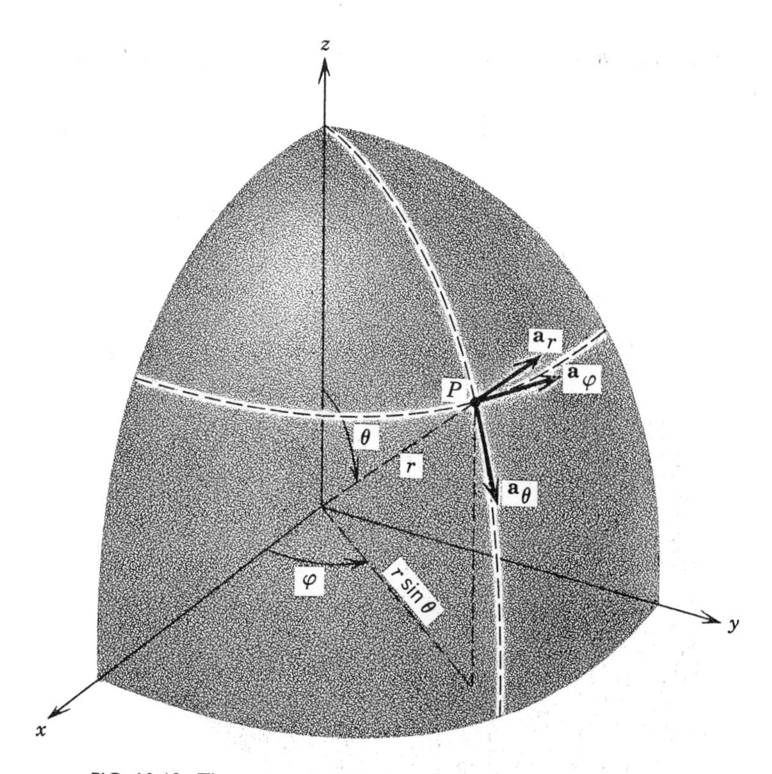

FIG. 10-12. The unit vectors in the spherical coordinate system.

as the intersection of the surfaces $r = r_1$, $\theta = \theta_1$, and $\varphi = \varphi_1$. The surface $r = r_1$ is a sphere; the surface $\theta = \theta_1$ is a cone about the z-axis; and the surface $\varphi = \varphi_1$ is a plane containing the z-axis.

The unit vectors in spherical coordinates are designated $\mathbf{a}_r$, $\mathbf{a}_\theta$, and $\mathbf{a}_\varphi$. Figure 10-12 shows these unit vectors at a point P on a section of a spherical surface. The unit vector $\mathbf{a}_r$ is along the radius r; $\mathbf{a}_\theta$ is tangent to the circle centered at the origin; and $\mathbf{a}_\varphi$ is tangent to the circle around the

z-axis, the radius of this circle being $r \sin\theta$. The differential lengths in the directions of the unit vectors are dr, $r\,d\theta$, and $r \sin\theta\, d\varphi$, giving

$$d\mathbf{l} = dr\,\mathbf{a}_r + r\,d\theta\,\mathbf{a}_\theta + r\sin\theta\,d\varphi\,\mathbf{a}_\varphi \tag{10-52}$$

The differential surface areas in the $\mathbf{a}_r$-, $\mathbf{a}_\theta$-, and $\mathbf{a}_\varphi$-directions are $r^2 \sin\theta\, d\theta\, d\varphi$, $r\sin\theta\, dr\, d\varphi$, and $r\,dr\,d\theta$. Hence the vector $d\mathbf{S}$ is

$$d\mathbf{S} = r^2\sin\theta\,d\theta\,d\varphi\,\mathbf{a}_r + r\sin\theta\,dr\,d\varphi\,\mathbf{a}_\theta + r\,dr\,d\theta\,\mathbf{a}_\varphi \tag{10-53}$$

The differential volume, which is shown in Fig. 10-13, is $r^2 \sin\theta\, dr\, d\theta\, d\varphi$.

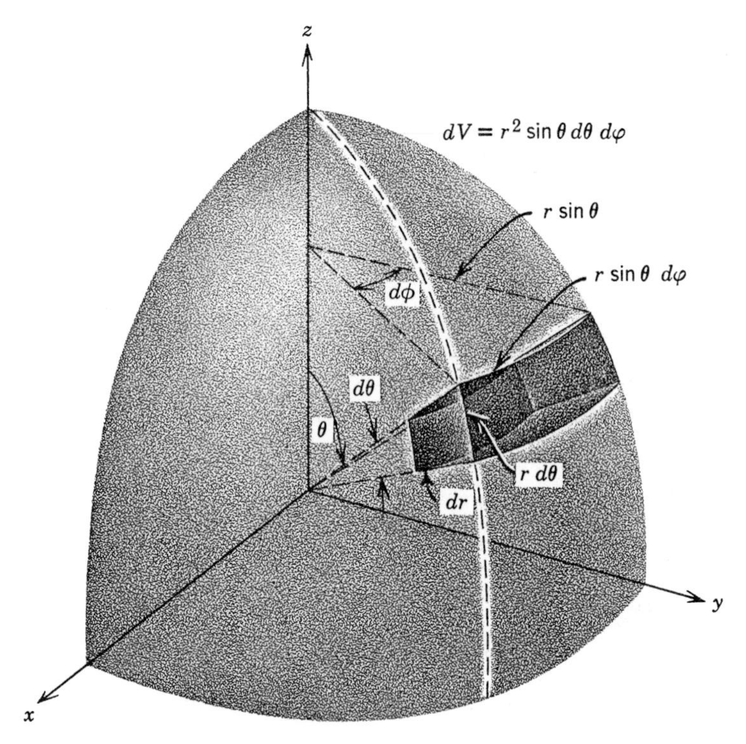

FIG. 10-13. An enlarged differential volume in spherical coordinates.

10-14. DIFFERENTIAL OPERATIONS IN THE COMMON COORDINATE SYSTEMS

The gradient, divergence, curl, and Laplacian have been developed in rectangular coordinates. The differential expressions in cylindrical and spherical coordinates can be developed in a similar manner, and the interested student is referred to the end-of-chapter references. The results are as follows:

Rectangular Coordinates (x, y, z)

$$\nabla\phi = \frac{\partial\phi}{\partial x}\,\mathbf{i} + \frac{\partial\phi}{\partial y}\,\mathbf{j} + \frac{\partial\phi}{\partial z}\,\mathbf{k}$$

$$\nabla\cdot\mathbf{A} = \frac{\partial A_x}{\partial x} + \frac{\partial A_y}{\partial y} + \frac{\partial A_z}{\partial z}$$

$$\nabla\times\mathbf{A} = \left(\frac{\partial A_z}{\partial y} - \frac{\partial A_y}{\partial z}\right)\mathbf{i} + \left(\frac{\partial A_x}{\partial z} - \frac{\partial A_z}{\partial x}\right)\mathbf{j} + \left(\frac{\partial A_y}{\partial x} - \frac{\partial A_x}{\partial y}\right)\mathbf{k}$$

$$\nabla^2\phi = \frac{\partial^2\phi}{\partial x^2} + \frac{\partial^2\phi}{\partial y^2} + \frac{\partial^2\phi}{\partial z^2}$$

Cylindrical Coordinates (r, φ, z)

$$\nabla\phi = \frac{\partial\phi}{\partial r}\,\mathbf{a}_r + \frac{1}{r}\frac{\partial\phi}{\partial\varphi}\,\mathbf{a}_\varphi + \frac{\partial\phi}{\partial z}\,\mathbf{a}_z$$

$$\nabla\cdot\mathbf{A} = \frac{1}{r}\frac{\partial}{\partial r}(rA_r) + \frac{1}{r}\frac{\partial A_\varphi}{\partial\varphi} + \frac{\partial A_z}{\partial z}$$

$$\nabla\times\mathbf{A} = \left(\frac{1}{r}\frac{\partial A_z}{\partial\varphi} - \frac{\partial A_\varphi}{\partial z}\right)\mathbf{a}_r + \left(\frac{\partial A_r}{\partial z} - \frac{\partial A_z}{\partial r}\right)\mathbf{a}_\varphi + \frac{1}{r}\left(\frac{\partial}{\partial r}(rA_\varphi) - \frac{\partial A_r}{\partial\varphi}\right)\mathbf{a}_z$$

$$\nabla^2\phi = \frac{1}{r}\frac{\partial}{\partial r}\left(r\frac{\partial\phi}{\partial r}\right) + \frac{1}{r^2}\frac{\partial^2\phi}{\partial\varphi^2} + \frac{\partial^2\phi}{\partial z^2}$$

Spherical Coordinates (r, θ, φ)

$$\nabla\phi = \frac{\partial\phi}{\partial r}\,\mathbf{a}_r + \frac{1}{r}\frac{\partial\phi}{\partial\theta}\,\mathbf{a}_\theta + \frac{1}{r\sin\theta}\frac{\partial\phi}{\partial\varphi}\,\mathbf{a}_\varphi$$

$$\nabla\cdot\mathbf{A} = \frac{1}{r^2}\frac{\partial}{\partial r}(r^2A_r) + \frac{1}{r\sin\theta}\frac{\partial}{\partial\theta}(\sin\theta\,A_\theta) + \frac{1}{r\sin\theta}\frac{\partial A_\varphi}{\partial\varphi}$$

$$\nabla\times\mathbf{A} = \frac{1}{r\sin\theta}\left[\frac{\partial}{\partial\theta}(A_\varphi\sin\theta) - \frac{\partial A_\theta}{\partial\varphi}\right]\mathbf{a}_r + \frac{1}{r}\left[\frac{1}{\sin\theta}\frac{\partial A_r}{\partial\varphi} - \frac{\partial}{\partial r}(rA_\varphi)\right]\mathbf{a}_\theta + \frac{1}{r}\left[\frac{\partial}{\partial r}(rA_\theta) - \frac{\partial A_r}{\partial\theta}\right]\mathbf{a}_\varphi$$

$$\nabla^2\phi = \frac{1}{r^2}\frac{\partial}{\partial r}\left(r^2\frac{\partial\phi}{\partial r}\right) + \frac{1}{r^2\sin\theta}\frac{\partial}{\partial\theta}\left(\sin\theta\frac{\partial\phi}{\partial\theta}\right) + \frac{1}{r^2\sin^2\theta}\frac{\partial^2\phi}{\partial\varphi^2}$$

10-15. VECTOR IDENTITIES

The following vector identities are readily verified by expanding in rectangular coordinates. They will be utilized frequently.

$$\nabla \times (\nabla\phi) = 0 \tag{10-54}$$

$$\nabla \cdot (\nabla \times \mathbf{A}) = 0 \tag{10-55}$$

$$\nabla \times (\phi\mathbf{A}) = \nabla\phi \times \mathbf{A} + \phi(\nabla \times \mathbf{A}) \tag{10-56}$$

$$\nabla^2\mathbf{A} = \nabla(\nabla \cdot \mathbf{A}) - \nabla \times (\nabla \times \mathbf{A}) \tag{10-57}$$

$$\nabla \cdot (\mathbf{A} \times \mathbf{B}) = \mathbf{B} \cdot (\nabla \times \mathbf{A}) - \mathbf{A} \cdot (\nabla \times \mathbf{B}) \tag{10-58}$$

EXAMPLE. Verify the identity of Eq. (10-54).

Solution. From Eqs. (10-3) and (10-35) we deduce that the curl of the gradient of the scalar point function ϕ, in rectangular coordinates, is

$$\nabla \times (\nabla\phi) = \begin{vmatrix} \mathbf{i} & \mathbf{j} & \mathbf{k} \\ \dfrac{\partial}{\partial x} & \dfrac{\partial}{\partial y} & \dfrac{\partial}{\partial z} \\ \dfrac{\partial\phi}{\partial x} & \dfrac{\partial\phi}{\partial y} & \dfrac{\partial\phi}{\partial z} \end{vmatrix}$$

The x component of the resulting vector is

$$\frac{\partial^2\phi}{\partial y\,\partial z} - \frac{\partial^2\phi}{\partial z\,\partial y}$$

This is zero, because the order in which the partial derivatives are taken is not important. By inspection of the determinant we note that the y and z components are also zero, and the identity is verified.

REFERENCES

Bronwell, A., *Advanced Mathematics in Physics and Engineering* McGraw-Hill Book Co., New York, 1953, Chap. 10.

Hildebrand, F. B., *Advanced Calculus for Engineers*, Prentice-Hall, Englewood Cliffs, N.J., 1949, Chap. 10.

Lass, H., *Vector and Tensor Analysis*, McGraw-Hill Book Co., New York, 1950.

Newell, H. E., Jr., *Vector Analysis*, McGraw-Hill Book Co., New York, 1955.

Phillips, H. B., *Vector Analysis*, John Wiley and Sons, New York, 1933.

Plonsey, R., and R. E. Collin, *Principles and Applications of Electromagnetic Fields*, McGraw-Hill Book Co., New York, 1961, Chap. 1.

Spiegel, M. R., *Vector Analysis*, Schaum Publishing Co., New York, 1959.

Walsh, J. B., *Electromagnetic Theory and Engineering Applications*, The Ronald Press Co., New York, 1960, Chap. 2 and Appendix A.

PROBLEMS

Section 10-2

10-1. An *electric dipole*, consisting of two equal and opposite charges separated a small distance, is located at the origin of a rectangular system and produces an *electric potential* ϕ of $z(x^2 + y^2 + z^2)^{-1.5}$ volts in the region around the dipole. The electric field intensity $\mathbf{E}$ equals $-\nabla\phi$. Find $\mathbf{E}$ as a function of the space coordinates and evaluate both ϕ and $\mathbf{E}$ at the points (1, 1, 1) and (1, −2, 0).

10-2. For the dipole of Prob. 10-1, find $\mathbf{E}$ as a function of y and z in the plane $x = 0$. Determine the slope dz/dy, which equals E_z/E_y, of the field lines in the yz-plane, and sketch the approximate field pattern.

10-3. If the electric field intensity $\mathbf{E}$ equals $-\nabla\phi$, with $\phi = (x^2 + y^2 + z^2)^{-1/2}$ volts, find $\mathbf{E}$ at the points (1, 0, 0) and (1, 1, 0). If this field is produced by a point charge q at the origin, in free space, what is this charge?

10-4. If u and v are scalar functions of the space coordinates, show that

$$\nabla(uv) = u\,\nabla v + v\,\nabla u$$

Also, verify that $\nabla(au) = a\,\nabla u$ if a is constant.

10-5. (*a*) Assume that $\mathbf{E} = -\nabla\phi$, with ϕ denoting a scalar point function called electric potential. If $\mathbf{E} = x\mathbf{i}$, determine ϕ. Show that the addition of a constant to the potential ϕ does not change $\mathbf{E}$. (*b*) If $\mathbf{E} = \sin(\omega t - \beta z)\,\mathbf{j}$, with ω and β denoting constants, show that $\mathbf{E}$ cannot possibly equal $-\nabla\phi$, regardless of the function ϕ.

10-6. Find the space rate of change of ρ at the point (1, −4, 3) in the direction of the vector $\mathbf{A} = 2\mathbf{i} - 4\mathbf{j} + 4\mathbf{k}$, if $\rho = xyz + 4x^2 - 2\sin z$.

10-7. Find the directional derivative of ϕ at the point (1, 1, 2) in the direction of the vector $\mathbf{A} = 2\mathbf{i} - \mathbf{j} - 2\mathbf{k}$, if $\phi = e^{2x}\sin xyz$.

10-8. The base region of a certain PNP junction transistor extends from $x = 0$ to $x = 0.0025$ cm. If the hole density p in this region is $10^{13}[1.65\exp(-100x) - \exp 100x]$ holes per cm³, with x expressed in centimeters, determine the hole density and the hole diffusion current density at the midpoint and at each end of the base. The diffusion constant is 45 cm²/sec.

Sections 10-3, 10-4, and 10-5

10-9. The holes of a semiconductor are thermally generated at a rate equal to p_e/τ_p holes per second per unit volume, with p_e denoting the hole density under equilibrium conditions and τ_p denoting a constant called the *hole lifetime*. Because of recombination with electrons, holes disappear at a rate p/τ_p holes per second per unit volume, with p representing the actual hole density. If $\mathbf{v}$ denotes the drift velocity of the holes, deduce that

$$\partial p/\partial t = -\operatorname{div} p\mathbf{v} + p_e/\tau_p - p/\tau_p$$

10-10. If the current density in the base of a transistor is due to diffusion of holes through the region, use Eq. (10-8) and the result of Prob. 10-9 and derive the important *diffusion equation*

$$\nabla \cdot \nabla p = (1/D_p)(\partial p/\partial t) + (p - p_e)/L_p^2$$

with the *diffusion length* $L_p = (D_p\tau_p)^{1/2}$. Write this equation in terms of x, assuming p is independent of y and z.

10-11. In a certain PNP transistor holes are injected from the P-type emitter into the N-type base at a steady rate. In terms of the distance x in centimeters from the emitter-base junction, the hole density p in holes/cm³ in the base region is

$$p = (0.01 + 2.53e^{-100x} - 1.54e^{100x}) \times 10^{12}$$

(*a*) Using the diffusion equation of Prob. 10-10 and assuming a hole diffusion constant of 50 cm²/sec, find the hole lifetime τ_p and the equilibrium hole density p_e. (*b*) Plot the hole diffusion current density J_p and the hole density p as functions of x in the base region. The base extends from $x = 0$ to $x = 0.0025$ cm.

10-12. If $\mathbf{A} = x^2yz\,\mathbf{i} + 5y \sin 2x\,\mathbf{j} + yze^z\,\mathbf{k}$, find div **A** at the point (1, 2, 3). Also, determine $\nabla(\nabla \cdot \mathbf{A})$ at the same point.

10-13. By expansion in rectangular coordinates verify the identity

$$\nabla \cdot (\phi\mathbf{A}) = \mathbf{A} \cdot \nabla\phi + \phi\,\nabla \cdot \mathbf{A}$$

10-14. Verify that the magnetic field of the rectangular waveguide of Prob. 8-37 is solenoidal.

10-15. Deduce that the divergence of the *total* electric current density at any point is always zero.

10-16. By integrating Eq. (10-11) over a volume V and applying the divergence theorem, derive the integral form of the equation of continuity applied to fluid mass.

10-17. Deduce the differential form of Gauss's law by applying the divergence theorem to the integral form.

10-18. $\mathbf{A} = y^3\,\mathbf{j} + \sin z\,\mathbf{k}$ and $\mathbf{B} = x \cos z\,\mathbf{i} + 3y^2z\,\mathbf{k}$. Show that **A** and **B**, although different vector fields, have the same divergence. What is the source strength per unit volume of the fields of **A** and **B** at the origin?

10-19. At a point P the vector **r** is $r\mathbf{a}_r$, with r denoting the distance from the origin to P and with $\mathbf{a}_r$ denoting a unit vector directed radially outward. (*a*) Express **r**, r, and $\mathbf{a}_r$ in terms of rectangular coordinates. (*b*) Determine $\nabla \cdot \mathbf{r}$. (*c*) Find the source strength of **r** in a spherical volume of radius 1 meter. (*d*) Show that $\nabla r = \mathbf{a}_r$ and explain the physical significance of this equation.

10-20. If the electromagnetic fields in a region are static, the electric field intensity **E** equals $-\nabla\phi$, with ϕ denoting the *electric potential.* From this and Eq. (10-14) show that $\nabla \cdot (\nabla\phi) = -\rho/\epsilon$. This is *Poisson's equation.* If ϕ varies only with respect to x in a limited homogeneous region with the charge density ρ numerically equal to ϵ, find ϕ and **E**, assuming both are zero at $x = 0$. Determine the potential drop from $x = 0$ to $x = 1$.

Sections 10-7, 10-8, *and* 10-9

10-21. At any point on the rotating disk of Fig. 10-4 the curl of the velocity **v** has magnitude equal to twice the angular velocity ω of the disk. Verify this at the origin, using path C_1. Also, verify the statement using path C_2. Recall that $v = r\omega$ and $l = r\varphi$, with l denoting the length of the arc subtended by the angle φ.

10-22. Equation (10-22) is developed in Sec. 10-7 from its integral form. In the same manner derive Eq. (10-23) from its integral form.

10-23. A very small plane surface S at P is oriented normal to the vector $4\mathbf{i} + 4\mathbf{j} - 2\mathbf{k}$, with the positive side of S facing in the direction of this vector. If **curl A** at P equals $\mathbf{i} - 8\mathbf{j} + 2\mathbf{k}$, find the circulation of **A** per unit area around the path C of S.

10-24. Determine **curl A** and **curl B**, with **A** and **B** given in Prob. 10-18. Also, evaluate $\nabla \times (\mathbf{A} \times \mathbf{B})$ at the point $(1, 1, -1)$.

10-25. If $\mathbf{A} = xyz\,\mathbf{i} + y \sin x\,\mathbf{j} + (x^2 + y^2)\mathbf{k}$, find **curl A** and **curl curl A** at the point (1, 1, 1).

10-26. Find the curl of the electric field intensity of Prob. 10-5(*b*), and utilize Eq. (10-22) to determine the magnetic field intensity **H**. Show that the fields satisfy Eq. (10-23), with $\beta = \omega(\mu\epsilon)^{1/2}$, assuming no convection currents in the region.

10-27. Find the curl of the magnetic field intensity of the rectangular waveguide of Prob. 8-37. Utilizing Eq. (10-23) with $\rho = 0$, determine the electric field intensity **E**. Show that the fields satisfy Eq. (10-22).

10-28. The fields of a certain rectangular waveguide are given in Prob. 9-24. By substitution into Eq. (10-22), determine the angular frequency ω and the phase constant β. The dielectric is free space. Verify that the fields satisfy Eq. (10-23). (Ans.: $\omega = 1.25 \times 10^{10}$, $\beta = 27.5$.)

10-29. Verify Eq. (10-55) by expansion in rectangular coordinates.

10-30. Verify Eq. (10-56) by expansion in rectangular coordinates.

10-31. Verify Eq. (10-58) by expansion in rectangular coordinates.

10-32. If $\mathbf{E} = -\nabla\phi$, with ϕ denoting the electric potential, deduce from Eq. (10-22) that the magnetic flux density is a static field. Then reason from Eq. (10-23) that the electric field is also static.

10-33. Write the Maxwell-Ampère law in the form of Eqs. (10-39), (10-40), and (10-41).

10-34. Deduce the differential form of the Maxwell-Ampère law by applying Stokes's theorem to the integral form.

Section 10-10

10-35. Evaluate $\nabla^2\phi$ at the point (1, 1, 1) for the scalar point function ϕ of (*a*) Prob. 10-1; (*b*) Prob. 10-7.

10-36. Show that the electric field **E** of Prob. 10-5(*b*) satisfies the wave equation, $\nabla^2\mathbf{E} = \mu\epsilon\ddot{\mathbf{E}}$, provided $\beta = \omega(\mu\epsilon)^{1/2}$.

10-37. Verify that the magnetic field **H** of the rectangular waveguide of Prob. 8-37 satisfies the wave equation $\nabla^2\mathbf{H} = \mu\epsilon\ddot{\mathbf{H}}$.

Sections 10-12, 10-13, 10-14, *and* 10-15

10-38. The *magnetic vector potential* **A** in the region around a long straight wire carrying a steady current I in the positive z direction is $-(\frac{1}{2}\mu I/\pi) \ln r\,\mathbf{k}$, with r denoting the distance from the axis of the wire. The magnetic flux density $\mathbf{B} = \mathbf{curl}\,\mathbf{A}$. Find **B** as a function of r.

10-39. In spherical coordinates the potential ϕ of Prob. 10-1 is $(\cos\theta)/r^2$ volts. Find the electric field intensity **E** in spherical coordinates, and evaluate **E** at $(r, \theta, \varphi) = (1.2, \pi/4, \pi/4)$.

10-40. In spherical coordinates the magnetic vector potential **A** of a small current loop at the origin, with the plane of the loop normal to the z-axis, is $C/r^2 \sin\theta\,\mathbf{a}_\varphi$, with C denoting a constant. The magnetic flux density **B** equals **curl A**. Find **B**.

10-41. If $\mathbf{A} = 6\mathbf{a}_r + 5\mathbf{a}_\theta - 3\mathbf{a}_\varphi$ and $\mathbf{B} = 2\mathbf{a}_r - 4\mathbf{a}_\theta + 3\mathbf{a}_\varphi$, determine $\mathbf{A} \cdot \mathbf{B}$ and $\mathbf{A} \times \mathbf{B}$.

10-42. The magnetic vector potential **A** of the current element $I_m \sin \omega t \, dz \, \mathbf{k}$ in free space is

$$\mathbf{A} = \frac{C}{r}\left[\cos\theta \, \mathbf{a}_r - \sin\theta \, \mathbf{a}_\theta\right]\left[\sin(\omega t - \beta r)\right]$$

with C denoting the constant $\mu_0 I_m \, dz/4\pi$ and with $\beta = \omega\sqrt{\mu_0\epsilon_0}$. The magnetic flux density $\mathbf{B} = \nabla \times \mathbf{A}$. Find the magnetic field intensity **H**.

10-43. Verify that the field **A** of Prob. 10-42 satisfies the wave equation $\nabla^2\mathbf{A} = \mu_0\epsilon_0\ddot{\mathbf{A}}$. Utilize Eq. (10-57).

10-44. In free space the electric scalar potential ϕ and the magnetic vector potential **A** are related by the equation $\nabla \cdot \mathbf{A} = -\mu_0\epsilon_0\dot{\phi}$. Find the electric scalar potential ϕ of the current element of Prob. 10-42. Also, determine the electric field intensity **E** from the relation $\mathbf{E} = -\nabla\phi - \dot{\mathbf{A}}$.

10-45. Show that the electric and magnetic fields of the current element of Probs. 10-42 and 10-44 satisfy the Maxwell-Ampère curl equation.

10-46. Verify Eqs. (10-54) and (10-55) by expansion in cylindrical coordinates.

10-47. Verify Eqs. (10-54) and (10-55) by expansion in spherical coordinates.

10-48. Using spherical coordinates, determine the vector Laplacian of **A** and the scalar Laplacian of A_r, if $\mathbf{A} = (1/r)\mathbf{a}_r$. Utilize Eq. (10-57).

Maxwell's Equations and Electromagnetic Energy

CHAPTER 11

Many problems of electromagnetism are readily handled with the integral field equations. The equivalent differential point relations are more flexible mathematically, however, and their applications are therefore far more numerous. We shall utilize them in our studies of electromagnetic energy, wave propagation, skin effect, circuit concepts, magnetostatics, electrostatics, waveguides, and antennas. Indeed, it is hardly possible to treat these subjects more than superficially without the use of these point relations. In applying the differential forms of the field laws to these areas, we shall, of course, acquire a deeper understanding of electromagnetism.

The objective of this chapter is to examine the differential field laws, the wave equations, and the storage, dissipation, and propagation of electromagnetic energy. The mathematical expressions developed are the basis of much of the investigation of the remainder of this book.

11-1. MAXWELL'S EQUATIONS

By utilizing the integral field equations and the definitions of the curl and divergence operations, we deduced in Chapter 10 the differential point relations, commonly referred to as Maxwell's equations. These are

$$\mathbf{curl}\ \mathbf{E} = -\dot{\mathbf{B}} \tag{11-1}$$

$$\textbf{curl H} = \rho\mathbf{v} + \dot{\mathbf{D}} = \mathbf{J}_t \tag{11-2}$$

$$\text{div } \mathbf{B} = 0 \tag{11-3}$$

$$\text{div } \mathbf{D} = \rho \tag{11-4}$$

Maxwell's two curl equations are the Maxwell-Faraday and Maxwell-Ampère laws in differential form. The Maxwell-Faraday curl equation states that *the maximum circulation per unit area of the electric field intensity* **E** *equals the time rate of change of the magnetic flux density* **B** *at the point.* If the extended thumb of the right hand is pointed in the direction of the vector $-\dot{\mathbf{B}}$, the curled fingers indicate the direction of the maximum circulation of **E** per unit area. The Maxwell-Ampère curl equation states that *the maximum circulation per unit area of the magnetic field intensity* **H** *equals the total electric current density* $\mathbf{J}_t$ *at the point.* If the extended thumb of the right hand is pointed in the direction of $\mathbf{J}_t$, the curled fingers indicate the direction of the maximum circulation of **H** per unit area. Each curl equation represents *three* partial differential equations involving the space coordinates and time, for the corresponding vector components on both sides of each equation must be equal.

The curl equations are easily derived from the integral field laws by utilizing Stokes's theorem. The integral form of the Maxwell-Faraday law is

$$\oint_C \mathbf{E} \cdot d\mathbf{l} = -\int_S \dot{\mathbf{B}} \cdot d\mathbf{S}$$

By Stokes's theorem the circulation of **E** around C equals the surface integral of **curl E** over the surface S. Therefore,

$$\int_S (\textbf{curl E}) \cdot d\mathbf{S} = -\int_S \dot{\mathbf{B}} \cdot d\mathbf{S}$$

This equation applies to *any* surface S, regardless of size or shape. It follows that the integrands **curl E** and $-\dot{\mathbf{B}}$ must be equal at each point of space. In a similar manner the Maxwell-Ampère curl equation can be derived from its integral form. As the derivations can be reversed, with the integral equations deduced from the curl equations, it is evident that the integral and differential forms contain precisely the same basic information.

Maxwell's two divergence equations give information about the sources of the fields. *The magnetic flux density* **B**, *having zero divergence, is a solenoidal field without sources.* The second divergence equation is Gauss's law, which states that *the net outward flux of* **D** *per unit volume at a point equals the charge per unit volume, or charge density, at the point.* The divergence equations are partial differential equations involving the space coordinates. They are easily derived from the corresponding integral equations by utilizing the divergence theorem. The integral form of Gauss's law is

$$\oint_S \mathbf{D} \cdot d\mathbf{S} = \int_V \rho \, dV$$

By the divergence theorem the surface integral of **D** over the closed surface S equals the volume integral of div **D** over the volume V enclosed by the surface, and we obtain

$$\int_V \text{div } \mathbf{D} \, dV = \int_V \rho \, dV$$

As this applies to *any* volume, large or small, the divergence of **D** must equal ρ at each point of space. Similarly, we can show that the divergence of **B** is zero. As the derivations can be reversed, with the integral equations deduced from the divergence equations, it is clear that the integral and differential forms contain precisely the same basic information.

The point form of the equation of continuity is readily deduced from its integral form just as Maxwell's divergence equations were deduced from their integral forms. We have

$$\oint_S \mathbf{J} \cdot d\mathbf{S} = -\frac{\partial}{\partial t} \int_V \rho \, dV \tag{11-5}$$

By the divergence theorem the surface integral of **J** over the closed surface S equals the volume integral of div **J** over the volume V enclosed by the surface. As this equals the volume integral of $-\dot{\rho}$ by Eq. (11-5), it follows that

$$\text{div } \mathbf{J} = -\dot{\rho} \tag{11-6}$$

with $\mathbf{J} = \rho\mathbf{v}$. The left side of this equation is *the outward flow of charge at a point, on a per-unit-volume basis*, and the right side is *the time rate of decrease of the charge per unit volume at the point.* Both sides have units of coulombs per second per cubic meter.

Maxwell's divergence equations can be derived directly from the curl equations. The divergence of the curl of any vector is zero, by Eq. (10-55). Taking the divergence of both sides of the Maxwell-Faraday curl equation gives div $\dot{\mathbf{B}} = 0$, or $\partial(\text{div } \mathbf{B})/\partial t = 0$. Therefore, div $\mathbf{B} = C_1$, with C_1 denoting a constant *independent of time.* As immobile, invariant magnetic point sources appear illogical and, in fact, have never been observed, we postulated their nonexistence in Sec. 8-4, and in accordance with this postulate, C_1 is zero.

Now let us take the divergence of both sides of the Maxwell-Ampère curl equation, obtaining $\text{div}\,(\rho\mathbf{v} + \dot{\mathbf{D}}) = 0$, or $\text{div}\,\dot{\mathbf{D}} = -\text{div}\,\rho\mathbf{v}$. By the equation of continuity the divergence of $\rho\mathbf{v}$ equals $-\dot{\rho}$, and therefore, $\text{div}\,\dot{\mathbf{D}} = \dot{\rho}$. Integrating with respect to time gives $\text{div}\,\mathbf{D} = \rho + C_1$, with C_1 denoting a constant *independent of time*. The constant is everywhere zero, because immobile, invariant electric point sources do not exist; this was postulated in Sec. 9-3.

Maxwell's equations require the conservation of electric charge. By taking the divergence of both sides of Eq. (11-2) and replacing the divergence of $\mathbf{D}$ with ρ, by Gauss's law, one obtains the equation of continuity. Thus *if Maxwell's four equations were selected as postulates, the conservation of charge would be a logical deduction.*

For time-changing fields the electromagnetic equations are helpful in determining the electric field from a known magnetic field, or vice versa. The following example illustrates the procedure.

EXAMPLE. If $\mathbf{E} = 1000 \sin x \cos 3 \times 10^8 t\, \mathbf{k}$ in a region of free space, find the time-varying magnetic field $\mathbf{H}$.

Solution. From the Maxwell-Faraday law we obtain

$$\mathbf{H} = -\frac{1}{\mu_0}\int \nabla \times \mathbf{E}\, dt$$

As $\nabla \times \mathbf{E} = -1000 \cos x \cos 3 \times 10^8 t\, \mathbf{j}$, the magnetic field becomes

$$\mathbf{H} = 2.65 \cos x \sin 3 \times 10^8 t\, \mathbf{j}$$

The $\mathbf{E}$ and $\mathbf{H}$ fields also satisfy, of course, the Maxwell-Ampère law, and this is easily verified.

11-2. ELECTRIC POWER SUPPLIED TO MOVING CHARGES

The electromagnetic field is a concept used to describe the forces between stationary and moving charges. As a matter of fact, the presence of a field is evident only through the forces exerted on the charged particles of matter. However, the electromagnetic field is also an important physical concept that is capable of storing, propagating, and dissipating energy. We shall begin our investigation of electromagnetic power and energy by discussing the power supplied by an electric field to moving electric charges. In the next section we shall, with the help of Maxwell's equations, develop mathematical expressions for the storage and flow of electromagnetic energy.

When electric charges move in response to the force of an electric field, work is done by the field on the charge carriers. If the charges move in opposition to the force of the field, work is done by some force that drives the charges against the field force, and the work done on the charge carriers by the field is negative. In any event, only the component of the electric field in the direction of the motion contributes to this work.

Let us consider a charge q moving with velocity $\mathbf{v}$ in an electric field $\mathbf{E}$. The electric force $\mathbf{F}$ on the charge is $q\mathbf{E}$. The power p supplied by the field is $\mathbf{F} \cdot \mathbf{v}$, because

$$\mathbf{F} \cdot \mathbf{v} = \mathbf{F} \cdot \frac{d\mathbf{l}}{dt} = \frac{dW}{dt} = p$$

Clearly $p = q\mathbf{E} \cdot \mathbf{v}$. The differential power dp to the charge $\rho\, dV$ in the differential volume dV is $(\rho\, dV)\mathbf{E} \cdot \mathbf{v}$; the *power density*, obtained by dividing by dV, is

$$\mathbf{E} \cdot \rho\mathbf{v} = \mathbf{E} \cdot \mathbf{J} \text{ watts/m}^3 \tag{11-7}$$

The scalar product $\mathbf{E} \cdot \mathbf{J}$ *is the power density supplied to* $\mathbf{J}$ *by* $\mathbf{E}$. A negative value signifies that the current density is supplying power to the electric field, because of some force that moves the charge carriers in opposition to the field force. The total power supplied by the electric field to the charge carriers throughout a volume V is

$$p = \int_V \mathbf{E} \cdot \mathbf{J}\, dV \text{ watts} \tag{11-8}$$

Usually the power supplied to charge carriers by an electric field is converted into heat. In the region between the plates of a vacuum tube the power acts to increase the kinetic energy of the electrons. However, this energy is dissipated as heat when the high-velocity electrons strike the metallic anode. In conductors the kinetic energy acquired by the charge carriers during the time intervals between collisions with the atoms is imparted to the atoms during collisions and appears as heat. If the current density $\mathbf{J}$ in a conductor is a drift current density $\sigma\mathbf{E}$, the scalar product $\mathbf{E} \cdot \mathbf{J}$ becomes σE^2, and *the power dissipated as heat in the volume* V *is*

$$p = \int_V \sigma E^2\, dV = \int_V \frac{J^2}{\sigma}\, dV \tag{11-9}$$

Frequently, the current density $\mathbf{J}$ is confined to a *filamentary* wire, defined as one whose cross section is so small that the current is uniformly distributed over its area. In this case, $\mathbf{J}\, dV$ in Eq. (11-8) can be replaced with $i\, d\mathbf{l}$, giving

$$p = i \int_C \mathbf{E} \cdot d\mathbf{l}$$

provided i is the same at all points of the path C. The power p is the power supplied by the field $\mathbf{E}$ to the *charge carriers comprising the current* i, and this is not necessarily the total power delivered to the circuit. The line integral of **E** is the voltage drop *along the wire*, provided there is no motional emf. This is not necessarily the same as the voltage drop across the terminals of the path of the circuit. For example, the voltage along the metallic wire of a coil carrying a time-varying current is often very small compared with the voltage across its terminals, because the time-varying magnetic flux has considerable effect on the terminal voltage. If v denotes the terminal voltage, the product vi is the total power to the circuit. However, *if v denotes the voltage drop along the filamentary conducting path, the product vi is only that power delivered to the charge carriers.* A negative power p signifies that the charge carriers that constitute the current i are moving in opposition to the force of the field, thereby increasing the stored energy of the field.

EXAMPLE. A brass rod with a circular cross section of radius 2.1 cm carries a sinusoidal current at a frequency of 1590 cycles per second. The axial drift current density J is approximately

$$J = 0.001e^{\pi r} \sin(\omega t + \pi r) \text{ ampere/cm}^2$$

with $\omega = 10^4$ and r representing the distance in centimeters from the center of the wire. Find the dissipated power per centimeter of length. The conductivity of brass is 1.57×10^5 mhos/cm.

Solution. The dissipated power p in *watts per centimeter* is, from Eq. (11-9), equal to

$$p = \int_S (J^2/\sigma)\, dS = \int_0^{2.1} (J^2/\sigma) 2\pi r\, dr$$

with S denoting the cross-sectional area and with all lengths expressed in centimeters. The current density squared can be written as

$$J^2 = 10^{-6} e^{2\pi r}[\tfrac{1}{2} - \tfrac{1}{2}\cos(2\omega t + 2\pi r)]$$

Substitution for J^2 and σ in the expression for p gives

$$p = 31.8 \times 10^{-13} \int_0^{2.1} e^{2\pi r}[1 - \cos(2\omega t + 2\pi r)] 2\pi r\, dr$$

It is convenient to change the variable of integration from r to x, with $x = 2\pi r$. The dissipated power per centimeter becomes

$$p = 5.06 \times 10^{-13} \int_0^{4.2\pi} x e^x [1 - \cos(2\omega t + x)]\, dx$$

The integral of xe^x is readily evaluated by integration by parts. Equation (7-15), with ωt replaced with $2\omega t + 90^\circ$, can be utilized to evaluate the integral of $xe^x \cos(2\omega t + x)$. The resulting power is

$$p = [3.31 - 2.44 \sin(2\omega t + 83.3^\circ)] \times 10^{-6} \text{ watt/cm}$$

The time-average dissipated power is obviously 3.31 μw/cm, for the time average of the sinusoidal term is zero.

Later it will be shown that the *resistance* of a wire equals twice the time-average dissipated power divided by the maximum value of the current squared. In Example 1 of Sec. 7-5 the current i of this rod was shown to be

$$i = 2.024 \sin (\omega t - 22.3°)$$

It follows that the resistance of the rod per centimeter of length is $6.62 \times 10^{-6}/(2.024)^2$, or 1.62×10^{-6} ohm/cm, at a frequency of 1590 cycles per second. This is more than three times the d-c resistance of the rod.

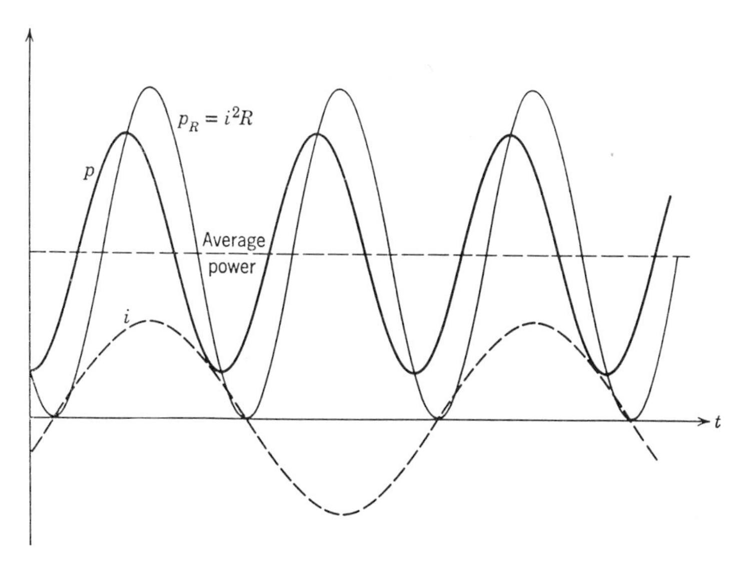

FIG. 11-1. A plot of the waveforms of the instantaneous dissipated power p, the instantaneous power p_R to the resistance, and the current i, for a unit length of the brass rod. Note that the instantaneous power p is never zero.

The product of the current i and the resistive voltage drop iR gives the power i^2R supplied to the resistance of the rod. Utilizing the current i and the resistance per centimeter, we readily obtain

$$p_R = [3.31 - 3.31 \sin (2\omega t + 45.4°)] \times 10^{-6} \text{ watt/cm}$$

It should be noted that the instantaneous power supplied to the resistance of the rod is *not* equal to the instantaneous dissipated power, although the time-average values are equal. The relationships between these quantities are illustrated in Fig. 11-1.

11-3. POYNTING'S THEOREM

We shall begin our investigation of energy storage with a study of the parallel-plate capacitor C of Fig. 11-2. The power supplied to C is vi, or $v\, dq/dt$, and the differential energy dW_E supplied in the time dt is $v\, dq$.

The charge dq is the differential increase in the charge q of the capacitor.

The parallel plates are assumed to be perfect conductors that are so closely spaced that the field lines in the nonconducting dielectric region are straight lines directed from the positive to the negative plate, with negligible fringing at the edges. The line integral of $\mathbf{E}$ along a field line from one plate to the other is Ed, and this equals the applied voltage v. At each point of the dielectric the field E has the value v/d; as this is independent

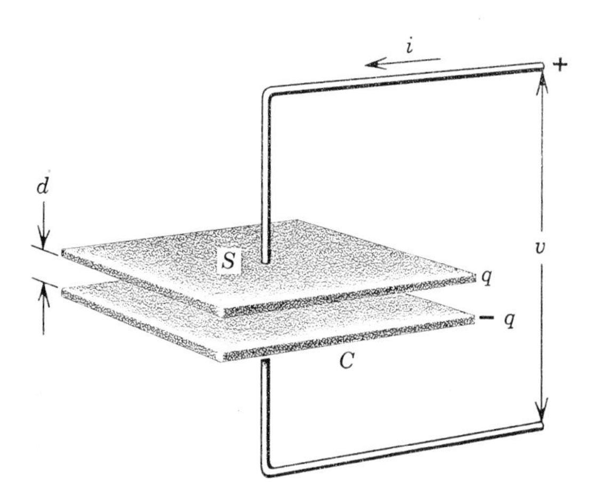

FIG. 11-2. Parallel-plate capacitor.

of the space coordinates, the field in the dielectric is uniform. The surface charge density $\rho_s = D$, according to Eq. (9-16), and therefore ρ_s is likewise uniform over the area S of a plate. Thus $q = \rho_s S = DS$. Replacing q with DS and v with Ed in the expression for dW_E gives $ESd\,dD$. As Sd is the volume of the dielectric, the differential energy dw_E *per unit volume* is $E\,dD$. Integration gives

$$w_E = \int_0^D E\,dD \text{ joules/m}^3 \tag{11-10}$$

The energy w_E is that supplied to the capacitor, per unit volume of dielectric, when the field increases from 0 to D. It does not include losses in the conducting plates, for we assumed perfect conductors. However, it does include dielectric hysteresis losses, if any. The additional energy is stored in the region between the plates. The equation applies to dielectrics that are either linear or nonlinear, but for the usual case of linear dielectrics, E in Eq. (11-10) can be replaced with D/ϵ, with ϵ constant. Evaluation of the integral then gives $\frac{1}{2}D^2/\epsilon$, and in terms of E we have

$$w_E = \tfrac{1}{2}\epsilon E^2 \text{ joules/m}^3 \tag{11-11}$$

We interpret the expression $\frac{1}{2}\epsilon E^2$ as representing the energy density of the energy stored in the electric field of a linear medium.

We shall now investigate the energy stored in the magnetic field of the toroid of Fig. 11-3. Let us assume that the coil of wire has negligible resistance and has many closely spaced turns that approximate a uniform current sheet. Furthermore, the dimensions of the cross section are

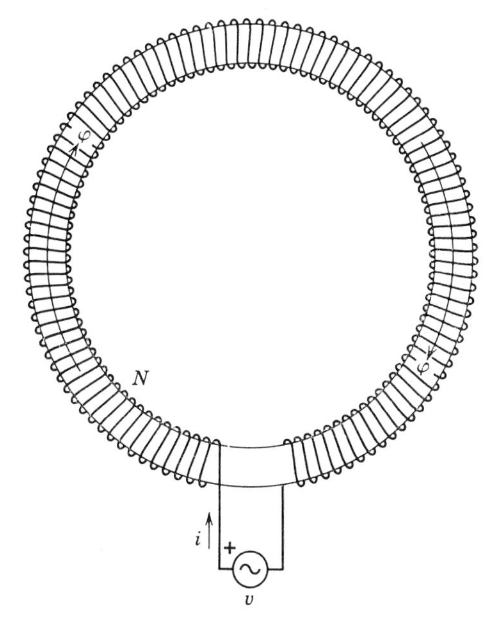

FIG. 11-3. Toroid with N closely spaced turns.

assumed to be very small compared with the radius of the toroid; consequently, all flux lines have approximately the same length l. The mmf along the path of a circular flux line is Hl, and this equals Ni by the Maxwell-Ampère law. Therefore, $i = Hl/N$.

The voltage drop around the closed path of the winding and directly across the terminals of the generator, in the direction of the reference current i, is $-v$; this is a consequence of the assumption that the wire is without resistance. By the Maxwell-Faraday law this voltage equals $-N\, d\varphi/dt$, with φ denoting the core flux, and $v = N\, d\varphi/dt$. As $H = Ni/l$, with all lines having approximately the same length l, the magnetic field is approximately uniform over a cross-sectional area S of the toroid. Thus $\varphi = BS$, and the voltage v becomes $NS\, dB/dt$.

We have found expressions for v and i in terms of the fields. The power vi becomes $HSl\, dB/dt$, and the differential energy supplied in the time

dt is $HSl\,dB$. As Sl is the volume of the core, the differential energy dw_H per unit volume is $H\,dB$. Integration gives

$$w_H = \int_0^B H\,dB \text{ joules/m}^3 \tag{11-12}$$

The energy w_H is that supplied to a unit volume of the core when the field increases from 0 to B. It includes any core losses present, and the additional energy is regarded as stored in the magnetic field of the core. The equation applies to magnetic materials that are either linear or nonlinear. For linear materials we can substitute B/μ for H, with μ constant, and evaluation of the integral gives $\frac{1}{2}B^2/\mu$. In terms of H we have

$$w_H = \tfrac{1}{2}\mu H^2 \text{ joules/m}^3 \tag{11-13}$$

We interpret the expression $\frac{1}{2}\mu H^2$ as representing the energy density of the energy stored in the magnetic field of a linear medium.

We are now ready to examine the energy relations in electromagnetic fields from a broader viewpoint. In the preceding section it was shown that the power per unit volume supplied by the electric field to the charge carriers at a point is $\mathbf{E} \cdot \mathbf{J}$ watts/m³. As the current density $\mathbf{J}$ equals $\mathbf{curl\,H} - \dot{\mathbf{D}}$, by the Maxwell-Ampère law, we have

$$\mathbf{E} \cdot \mathbf{J} = \mathbf{E} \cdot \mathbf{curl\,H} - \mathbf{E} \cdot \dot{\mathbf{D}}$$

From the vector identity of Eq. (10-58) we note that

$$\mathbf{E} \cdot \mathbf{curl\,H} = \mathbf{H} \cdot \mathbf{curl\,E} - \operatorname{div} \mathbf{E} \times \mathbf{H}$$

Using this, with $\mathbf{curl\,E}$ replaced with $-\dot{\mathbf{B}}$, and rearranging terms, we obtain

$$-\operatorname{div} \mathbf{E} \times \mathbf{H} = \mathbf{E} \cdot \mathbf{J} + \mathbf{E} \cdot \dot{\mathbf{D}} + \mathbf{H} \cdot \dot{\mathbf{B}} \tag{11-14}$$

The electromagnetic power *per unit volume* supplied to a point of a region is the sum of that supplied to the charge carriers and that supplied to the electric and magnetic fields. This is precisely the interpretation of Eq. (11-14). The term $\mathbf{E} \cdot \mathbf{J}$ is that supplied to the charge carriers; from the previous discussion of the energy densities of the electric and magnetic fields, the terms $\mathbf{E} \cdot \dot{\mathbf{D}}$ and $\mathbf{H} \cdot \dot{\mathbf{D}}$ can logically be interpreted to represent the power per unit volume to the electric and magnetic fields, respectively. We deduce that the expression $-\operatorname{div} \mathbf{E} \times \mathbf{H}$ represents the total power supplied per unit volume, or the flow of electromagnetic energy per unit volume per unit time into the point.

Let us multiply each term of Eq. (11-14) by the differential volume dV and then integrate both sides of the equation over a volume V. By the divergence theorem the volume integral of the divergence of $\mathbf{E} \times \mathbf{H}$

over V can be replaced with the surface integral of $\mathbf{E} \times \mathbf{H}$ over the closed surface S around the volume V. The result, known as *Poynting's theorem*, is

$$-\oint_S (\mathbf{E} \times \mathbf{H}) \cdot d\mathbf{S} = \int_V \mathbf{E} \cdot \mathbf{J}\, dV + \int_V (\mathbf{E} \cdot \dot{\mathbf{D}} + \mathbf{H} \cdot \dot{\mathbf{B}})\, dV \tag{11-15}$$

For linear media ϵ and μ are independent of the fields and hence are independent of time. The scalar product $\mathbf{E} \cdot \dot{\mathbf{D}}$ can be written $\epsilon \mathbf{E} \cdot \dot{\mathbf{E}}$. By the vector identity of Eq. (2-19) this is $\epsilon E\dot{E}$, which obviously equals $\partial(\frac{1}{2}\epsilon E^2)/\partial t$. Similarly, $\mathbf{H} \cdot \dot{\mathbf{B}} = \partial(\frac{1}{2}\mu H^2)/\partial t$. Equation (11-15) applied to *linear* media becomes

$$-\oint_S (\mathbf{E} \times \mathbf{H}) \cdot d\mathbf{S} = \int_V \mathbf{E} \cdot \mathbf{J}\, dV + \frac{\partial}{\partial t} \int_V (\tfrac{1}{2}\epsilon E^2 + \tfrac{1}{2}\mu H^2)\, dV$$

Clearly, this expresses the conservation of energy in a fixed volume V.

The left side of Eq. (11-15) is the total power supplied to the volume V, and this power is the net flow of energy in joules per second into V through the closed surface S around it. It follows that the net flow of energy in joules per second, or watts, *out of the closed surface S is*

$$p = \oint_S (\mathbf{E} \times \mathbf{H}) \cdot d\mathbf{S} \text{ watts} \tag{11-16}$$

Thus *the surface integral of* $\mathbf{E} \times \mathbf{H}$ *over any closed surface S gives the electromagnetic power out of the volume V enclosed by S.* Let us consider an example illustrating the use of this important relation.

EXAMPLE. The approximate radiation fields of a certain antenna are $H_\varphi = (1/r) \sin\theta \cos(\omega t - \beta r)$ and $E_\theta = 377 H_\varphi$. Determine the energy flow in watts out of the volume surrounded by the spherical surface S of radius r, with center at the origin.

Solution. $\mathbf{E} \times \mathbf{H} = E_\theta H_\varphi \mathbf{a}_r$, because $\mathbf{a}_\theta \times \mathbf{a}_\varphi = \mathbf{a}_r$. Therefore,

$$\mathbf{E} \times \mathbf{H} = (377/r^2) \sin^2\theta \cos^2(\omega t - \beta r)\, \mathbf{a}_r$$

Equation (11-16) gives the power out of the surface S. A differential vector surface area $d\mathbf{S}$ of this spherical surface is $r^2 \sin\theta\, d\theta\, d\varphi\, \mathbf{a}_r$, by Eq. (10-53). Substitution for $\mathbf{E} \times \mathbf{H}$ and $d\mathbf{S}$ into Eq. (11-16), with the limits of θ being 0 and π and the limits of φ being 0 and 2π, yields

$$p = 377 \cos^2(\omega t - \beta r) \int_0^{2\pi} \int_0^{\pi} \sin^3\theta\, d\theta\, d\varphi$$

Evaluation of the integrals gives $p = 3160 \cos^2(\omega t - \beta r)$ watts. As time varies, the cosine squared function varies between zero and unity, with an average value of one-half. Therefore, the time-average power is 1580 watts, and this is the radiated power.

11-4. THE POYNTING VECTOR

The electromagnetic energy flow per unit time out of a volume equals the surface integral of $\mathbf{E} \times \mathbf{H}$ over the closed surface around the volume. The vector $\mathbf{E} \times \mathbf{H}$ is called the *Poynting vector* $\mathbf{S}$. Its mks unit is the watt per square meter, and $\mathbf{S}$ can be interpreted to represent the energy flow per unit time per unit area at a point. Thus

$$\mathbf{S} = \mathbf{E} \times \mathbf{H} \text{ watts/m}^2 \tag{11-17}$$

The vectors $\mathbf{S}$, $\mathbf{E}$, and $\mathbf{H}$ are, of course, instantaneous functions of time.

The interpretation of the Poynting vector $\mathbf{S}$ as the energy density flow at a point does not necessarily follow from Eq. (11-16). In fact, if the curl of an arbitrary function is added to $\mathbf{S}$, the value of the integral of Eq. (11-16) is unchanged, because the integral of the curl of a vector over a closed surface is zero. Nevertheless, *it is usually attractive to regard the Poynting vector as representing the magnitude and direction of the energy flow per unit area at a point.* Of course, the surface integral of the Poynting vector *over a closed surface* always gives the correct power through this surface.

Let us consider the flow of electromagnetic energy in an electric circuit that consists of a generator connected by means of wires to a resistive load. The terminal voltage of the generator is assumed to vary sinusoidally with time. If the wires are regarded as perfect conductors, there are no fields within these conductors, and the Poynting vector is zero. Certainly no energy flows inside the conducting region. In the dielectric around the circuit there are electric and magnetic fields. At a point on the surface of a wire the electric field is normal to the surface, and the magnetic field is tangential, being directed around the wire in accordance with the boundary relation $\mathbf{n} \times \mathbf{H} = \mathbf{J}_s$. Thus the Poynting vector $\mathbf{E} \times \mathbf{H}$, at points just outside the surface, is directed parallel to the wire. The flow of energy from the generator to the load occurs in the dielectric. The wires guide the electromagnetic energy of the fields of the dielectric to the load.

If the wires are not perfect conductors, the electric field at the surface has a small component in the direction of the current density. This tangential component of the electric field combined with the magnetic field directed around the wire gives a component of the Poynting vector $\mathbf{S}$ directed radially into the wire. This component of $\mathbf{S}$ represents an energy flow per unit area per unit time into the wire. The energy is dissipated as heat. At the resistive load the tangential component of the electric field is large, and considerable energy flows from the dielectric into the load.

EXAMPLE. A straight cylindrical wire of length l has a steady current I that is uniformly distributed over the cross section of radius a. The conductivity is σ. Using the Poynting vector, find the power dissipated.

Solution. At the surface the electric field intensity has a component along the wire with magnitude E equal to J/σ, or $I/(\pi a^2\sigma)$. The magnetic field intensity is directed around the wire with magnitude H equal to $I/(2\pi a)$, by the Maxwell-Ampère law. The product EH equals $I^2/(2\pi^2 a^3 \sigma)$, and this is the inward component of the Poynting vector at the surface. Multiplication by the surface area $2\pi a l$ of the wire gives $I^2 l/(\pi a^2 \sigma)$, which is the dissipated power in watts. This can be written as $I^2 R$, with R equal to the length l divided by the product of the conductivity σ and the cross-sectional area S. The expression $l/(\sigma S)$ represents the d-c resistance of the wire.

11-5. THE WAVE EQUATIONS

For the usual case of an uncharged medium with ϵ, μ, and σ constant and with no convection currents other than drift currents, the Maxwell equations reduce to

$$\nabla \times \mathbf{E} = -\mu \dot{\mathbf{H}} \tag{11-18}$$

$$\nabla \times \mathbf{H} = \sigma \mathbf{E} + \epsilon \dot{\mathbf{E}} \tag{11-19}$$

$$\nabla \cdot \mathbf{H} = 0 \tag{11-20}$$

$$\nabla \cdot \mathbf{E} = 0 \tag{11-21}$$

Taking the curl of both sides of the first equation and substituting the second, we obtain

$$\nabla \times \nabla \times \mathbf{E} = -\mu \frac{\partial}{\partial t}(\nabla \times \mathbf{H}) = -\mu\sigma\dot{\mathbf{E}} - \mu\epsilon\ddot{\mathbf{E}}$$

Since $\nabla \cdot \mathbf{E} = 0$, the left side of this equation is equal to the negative of the vector Laplacian of $\mathbf{E}$, by Eq. (10-57), and therefore

$$\nabla^2 \mathbf{E} = \mu\sigma\dot{\mathbf{E}} + \mu\epsilon\ddot{\mathbf{E}} \tag{11-22}$$

This is the *propagation equation* for the electric field intensity $\mathbf{E}$. It involves partial space derivatives and partial time derivatives of $\mathbf{E}$, and it is a vector equation that represents three partial differential scalar equations. The equation relating the x components of the vectors is

$$\frac{\partial^2 E_x}{\partial x^2} + \frac{\partial^2 E_x}{\partial y^2} + \frac{\partial^2 E_x}{\partial z^2} = \mu\sigma \frac{\partial E_x}{\partial t} + \mu\epsilon \frac{\partial^2 E_x}{\partial t^2} \tag{11-23}$$

Similar equations apply to the y and z components. However, it should be noted that in other coordinate systems the components of the vector $\mathbf{E}$

are not separated in the three scalar equations represented by Eq. (11-22). For example, in spherical coordinates the radial component of the vector Laplacian $\nabla^2\mathbf{E}$ involves not only the radial component of $\mathbf{E}$ but also its azimuthal and meridional components. The scalar partial differential equations become three simultaneous equations involving the three components of $\mathbf{E}$. Similar statements apply to the cylindrical system except that E_z is separated; this cylindrical component is, of course, also the rectangular component E_z, which satisfies Eq. (11-23).

The propagation equation for the magnetic field intensity $\mathbf{H}$ is developed similarly. We take the curl of both sides of Eq. (11-19) and substitute Eq. (11-18) into the result. Since $\nabla \cdot \mathbf{H} = 0$, the curl of the curl of $\mathbf{H}$ is equal to the negative of the vector Laplacian of $\mathbf{H}$, by Eq. (10-57), and the resulting equation is

$$\nabla^2\mathbf{H} = \mu\sigma\dot{\mathbf{H}} + \mu\epsilon\ddot{\mathbf{H}} \tag{11-24}$$

As will be seen later, the general solutions of the propagation equations for $\mathbf{E}$ and $\mathbf{H}$ are damped traveling waves.

In a nonconducting medium the equations reduce to the ordinary *wave equations*:

$$\nabla^2\mathbf{E} = \mu\epsilon\ddot{\mathbf{E}} \tag{11-25}$$

$$\nabla^2\mathbf{H} = \mu\epsilon\ddot{\mathbf{H}} \tag{11-26}$$

The solutions represent waves that propagate without attenuation due to the physical medium. Energy is not dissipated in the medium, for the conductivity is zero. An example of an electromagnetic wave governed by these equations is a radio wave in free space.

In good conductors the conductivity is so large that the damped propagation equations reduce to the *diffusion equations*:

$$\nabla^2\mathbf{E} = \mu\sigma\dot{\mathbf{E}} \tag{11-27}$$

$$\nabla^2\mathbf{H} = \mu\sigma\dot{\mathbf{H}} \tag{11-28}$$

These can be derived directly from Maxwell's equations by neglecting the term $\epsilon\dot{\mathbf{E}}$ of Eq. (11-19). Inspection of (11-19) indicates that this is reasonable, *provided the displacement current density* $\epsilon\dot{\mathbf{E}}$ *is negligible compared with the drift current density* $\sigma\mathbf{E}$ *at all points of the region under consideration.* It is easily shown that the approximation is valid for the common metallic conductors at frequencies below the optical range. As $\mathbf{J} = \sigma\mathbf{E}$, Eq. (11-27) can be written in terms of $\mathbf{J}$, giving

$$\nabla^2\mathbf{J} = \mu\sigma\dot{\mathbf{J}} \tag{11-29}$$

This is often called the *skin-effect equation*, and it is used to determine the current distribution in good conductors.

The solutions of the wave equations are subject to the boundary conditions imposed by the shape, size, and electrical properties of the media present and by the sources that excite the fields. In the next section the wave equations are applied to a uniform plane electromagnetic wave in a lossless medium. Chapter 12 is devoted to a general discussion of waves and wave equations. The potential functions are employed in Chapter 13 as aids in solving the wave equations and these potential functions are later employed to determine the electric and magnetic fields produced by a current element. A number of practical applications are considered in several of the remaining chapters.

11-6. PLANE ELECTROMAGNETIC WAVES

In order to illustrate an application of a wave equation, let us consider a uniform plane wave traveling in the z-direction in a lossless dielectric. It is assumed that only one component of **E** exists, with $\mathbf{E} = E_x\mathbf{i}$. For a uniform plane wave the fields do not vary with respect to the space coordinates in the plane transverse to the direction of propagation. Therefore, partial derivatives with respect to x and y are zero.

As the dielectric is nonconducting and as the partial derivatives of **E** with respect to x and y are zero, the wave equation for **E** is

$$\frac{\partial^2 E_x}{\partial z^2} = \mu\epsilon \frac{\partial^2 E_x}{\partial t^2} \qquad (11\text{-}30)$$

This is a one-dimensional wave equation. It has many solutions. In fact, *any function of the variable* $t - z/v$, with $v = 1/\sqrt{\mu\epsilon}$, is a solution. Thus $E_x = F(t - z/v)$. This solution can be verified by substitution into Eq. (11-30), noting that $\partial^2 E_x/\partial z^2 = F''/v^2$ and $\partial^2 E_x/\partial t^2 = F''$, with the primes denoting derivatives with respect to the entire variable $t - z/v$. A second solution of Eq. (11-30) is any function of the variable $t + z/v$, and this is also readily verified by substitution. Hence,

$$E_x = F_1(t - z/v) + F_2(t + z/v) \qquad (11\text{-}31)$$

F_1 and F_2 are *any* functions, and v equals $1/\sqrt{\mu\epsilon}$.

We have found that Eq. (11-30) is satisfied by innumerable different functions. Field theory deals with partial differential equations, such as (11-30), and these have an infinity of solutions. A particular physical problem, however, has only a single solution, which must satisfy Maxwell's equations and the boundary conditions. *These boundary conditions determine which of the infinite set of solutions to the field equations is the actual one*. For example, suppose a perfectly conducting metal pipe, to be used as an antenna, has an axial slot cut in its side with a given time-varying electric field impressed across the slot at its midpoint. The fields that satisfy Maxwell's equations must also satisfy a number of boundary conditions. At all points on the surface of the perfect conductor, both inside the pipe and outside, the electric field must be normal and the magnetic field must be tangential, by Eqs. (9-15) and (9-16). The fields inside the pipe and those outside must match where they meet at points in the slot. The electric field must equal the given impressed field at the middle of the slot, and both **E** and **H** must be zero at infinity. In addition, the fields at the surfaces of different physical media in the region must satisfy the boundary relations of Sec. 9-5. The geometrical complexity of many practical problems often makes exact solutions all but impossible, and approximate methods are frequently utilized. Let us now examine the solutions of the one-dimensional wave equation.

The function F_1 represents a wave traveling in the positive z-direction with velocity v. If we wish to observe a constant value of the function F_1 as time varies, we must move along the z-axis so as to keep the argument $t - z/v$ constant; that is, $t - z/v = C$. Therefore, the position of the observer along the axis is

$$z = vt - vC$$

The velocity of the observer is dz/dt, and this obviously equals v, or $1/\sqrt{\mu\epsilon}$. The velocity v is called the *velocity of the wave*. In a similar manner the function F_2 can be shown to represent a wave traveling in the negative z-direction with velocity v. An observer moving in the negative z-direction with velocity v observes a constant value for F_2.

In many practical cases the time variations are approximately sinusoidal. For waves that vary sinusoidally with time a possible solution of Eq. (11-30) is

$$E_x = A \sin \omega(t - z/v) + B \sin \omega(t + z/v) \tag{11-32}$$

Letting E^+ and E^- denote the component waves traveling in the positive and negative z-directions, respectively, gives $E_x = E^+ + E^-$.

The magnetic field intensity can be determined by substituting Eq. (11-32) into the Maxwell-Ampère curl equation. The curl of **E** is $\partial E_x/\partial z\,\mathbf{j}$, and this equals $-\mu\dot{\mathbf{H}}$. Therefore, the magnetic field has a y component only, which can be found from the relation

$$H_y = -\frac{1}{\mu}\int \frac{\partial E_x}{\partial z}\,dt$$

Substitution for E_x, using Eq. (11-32), gives H_y. It is readily shown that

$$H_y = \sqrt{\epsilon/\mu}\,(E^+ - E^-) = H^+ + H^- \tag{11-33}$$

with H^+ and H^- denoting the component waves traveling in the positive and negative z-directions, respectively. The expressions for the electric and magnetic fields are the solutions of the wave equation for this special case. The solutions contain two arbitrary constants A and B whose values depend on the boundary conditions of the particular physical problem. The constant ω is determined by the frequency of the sinusoidal time variations.

It should be noted that each component wave travels at a velocity equal to $1/\sqrt{\mu\epsilon}$. In free space this velocity is approximately 3×10^8 meters per second. The ratio of the electric and magnetic field intensities of the component waves is

$$\frac{E^+}{H^+} = -\frac{E^-}{H^-} = \sqrt{\frac{\mu}{\epsilon}} = \eta \tag{11-34}$$

with η denoting the *intrinsic impedance* of the dielectric in ohms.

The Poynting vector $\mathbf{S}$ is $E_x\mathbf{i} \times H_y\mathbf{j}$, or $E_xH_y\mathbf{k}$. For the wave component that propagates in the positive z-direction, this becomes

$$\mathbf{S} = \sqrt{\epsilon/\mu}\, A^2 \sin^2 \omega(t - z/v)\, \mathbf{k} \text{ watts/m}^2$$

The energy flow in the positive z-direction is positive at every instant of time. Application of the Poynting vector to the wave component traveling in the negative z-direction shows an energy flow in this direction. The electric and magnetic fields are perpendicular to one another, and the energy flow is normal to the plane of $\mathbf{E}$ and $\mathbf{H}$.

Also of interest is the energy density of the plane electromagnetic wave. For the wave component propagating in the positive z-direction the energy per unit volume stored in the electric field at a point is

$$w_E = \tfrac{1}{2}\epsilon E^2 = \tfrac{1}{2}\epsilon A^2 \sin^2 \omega(t - z/v) \text{ joules/m}^3$$

For this same wave component the energy density w_H stored in the magnetic field is $\frac{1}{2}\mu H^2$, which is exactly equal to the energy density of the electric field at every instant of time. However, the energy densities of the electric and magnetic fields of the total wave, consisting of both wave components, are not equal.

The uniform plane wave has been examined here primarily to show that the solution of a wave equation represents a traveling wave. The electromagnetic wave propagates energy, and the velocity of propagation depends on the physical constants of the medium. The wave which has been discussed is called a *plane* wave because the electric field intensities, and also the magnetic field intensities, are in time phase at all points in a plane normal to the direction of propagation. A plane wave is *uniform* if the field intensities are independent of the coordinates in each such plane.

The plane electromagnetic wave is a very important and practical case. The wave in a limited region of free space a large distance away from its source approximates a uniform plane wave. If the electric and magnetic field vectors of a wave lie completely in planes *transverse* to the direction of propagation, the wave is called a *transverse electromagnetic wave*, or *TEM wave*. It is easily shown that a uniform plane wave is an example of a TEM wave (see Prob. 11-31).

The principal wave associated with a transmission line, such as an open-wire telephone line, is a TEM wave. The line guides a wave component from the source to the load. This component is the *incident wave*, and it propagates energy from the source to the load. If the load is not properly matched to the transmission line, a *reflected wave* results, and this wave transfers some of the energy back to the source. These wave components correspond to the two components of Eqs. (11-32) and (11-33). The TEM wave as well as other types are discussed in later chapters.

11-7. IMPOSSIBLE FIELDS

As electric and magnetic fields must satisfy Maxwell's equations, they must also satisfy the wave equations derived from Maxwell's equations. At each point of an uncharged medium with no convection current density other than a drift current density, the electric field intensity must satisfy the wave equation

$$\nabla^2\mathbf{E} = \mu\sigma\dot{\mathbf{E}} + \mu\epsilon\ddot{\mathbf{E}}$$

The magnetic field intensity must satisfy an identical equation. The left side of the equation involves space derivatives and the right side involves time derivatives. It is evident that *the spatial distributions and the time variations are interdependent.* If the spatial distribution and the time variation are each specified arbitrarily, the result is likely to be absurd. Let us consider several examples.

We wish to find the voltage around a circular conducting loop enclosing a unit area that is normal to a time-varying magnetic field. The magnetic flux density is assumed to be 0.001 sin 10,000t at all points. The magnetic current $\dot{\Phi}$ over the unit area is 10 cos 10,000t volts, and this is the voltage around the loop, according to the Maxwell-Faraday law. However, the magnetic field has zero curl, and by the Maxwell-Ampère curl equation there is no time-varying electric field. Therefore, the voltage around the loop is zero. The conflicting results are the consequence of assuming a magnetic field that does not satisfy the wave equation. Such a field cannot exist.

Two large parallel plates, separated by a dielectric of permittivity ϵ, have charges of q and $-q$ coulombs per square meter, with $q = q_0 \sin \omega t$.

Assuming a uniform charge distribution, we shall attempt to find the magnetic field in the dielectric between the plates.

The electric flux density in the dielectric equals the charge q per unit area and is directed from the positive to the negative plate. It follows that the electric field intensity E is q/ϵ, or $(q_0/\epsilon)\sin\omega t$. Being independent of the space coordinates, E is a uniform field with zero curl. By the Maxwell-Faraday law the magnetic field must be static. However, according to the Maxwell-Ampère law, the curl of $\mathbf{H}$ has magnitude equal to $\epsilon\dot{E}$, or $q_0\omega\cos\omega t$, and $\mathbf{H}$ varies with time. This discrepancy is the result of the impossible electric field deduced from the assumed charge distribution. *Uniform time-varying fields do not satisfy the wave equations and, therefore, do not exist.*

Suppose we wish to find the magnetic field intensity in a region of free space in which the electric field intensity is assumed to be $\sin x \sin 10^5 t\,\mathbf{j}$. By the Maxwell-Faraday law

$$\mathbf{H} = -\frac{1}{\mu_0}\int \nabla \times \mathbf{E}\,dt$$

Evaluation gives $\mathbf{H} = 7.96\cos x\cos 10^5 t\,\mathbf{k}$. On the other hand, if the Maxwell-Ampère law is used, a different result is obtained. According to this law, $\nabla \times \mathbf{H} = \epsilon_0\dot{\mathbf{E}}$. As the fields are independent of y and z and as the given electric field has only a y component, this equation becomes

$$-\partial H_z/\partial x\,\mathbf{j} = 8.85 \times 10^{-7}\sin x\cos 10^5 t\,\mathbf{j}$$

Integration gives $H_z = 8.85 \times 10^{-7}\cos x\cos 10^5 t$, which disagrees with the previous result. Obviously, the specified electric field violates the wave equation and is impossible.

It is evident that mathematical expressions that satisfy one of Maxwell's curl equations may fail to satisfy the other. The spatial and time variations are related by the wave equations, and this interdependence must be observed when specifying fields. It should be mentioned that approximate solutions of field problems are frequently obtained by utilizing approximate spatial distributions that may not satisfy Maxwell's equations. In such cases, however, the generality suffers.

REFERENCES

Booker, H. G., *An Approach to Electrical Science*, McGraw-Hill Book Co., New York, 1959, Chap. 1 of Part 4.

Carter, G. W., *The Electromagnetic Field in Its Engineering Aspects*, Longmans, Green and Co., London, 1954, Chap. 13.

Frank, N. H., *Introduction to Electricity and Optics*, McGraw-Hill Book Co., New York, 2nd ed., 1950, Chap. 10.

Jordan, E. C., *Electromagnetic Fields and Radiating Systems*, Prentice-Hall, Englewood Cliffs, N. J., 1950, Chap. 6.

PROBLEMS

Section 11-1

11-1. Derive the Maxwell-Ampère curl equation from its integral form, the Maxwell-Faraday integral equation from its curl form, and the integral form of the equation of continuity from its point form.

11-2. Derive the integral form of the equation of continuity directly from Maxwell's equations in integral form, and derive the differential form of this equation directly from Maxwell's equations in differential form.

11-3. Write the Maxwell-Ampère law as three partial differential equations, using (*a*) rectangular coordinates, (*b*) cylindrical coordinates, and (*c*) spherical coordinates.

11-4. Using divergence, write the equation specifying that the total electric current density is solenoidal. Compare this with the equation of continuity and with Gauss's law, and show that each of these equations can be derived from the other two.

11-5. Deduce from the field equations that the displacement current leaving a volume V through its surrounding surface S equals the time rate of increase of the charge within V.

11-6. If $\mathbf{E} = 1000 \sin(10^6 t - 0.01z)\,\mathbf{i}$ in a nonconducting dielectric, find $\mathbf{H}$. What is the dielectric constant?

11-7. The magnetic flux density $\mathbf{B} = 10^{-7} \cos 0.1y \cos \omega t\,\mathbf{i}$, with $\omega = 3 \times 10^7$, in a region of free space. (*a*) Find $\mathbf{E}$. (*b*) Determine the magnetic flux out of the square area, of unit side length, of Fig. 11-4. (*c*) Calculate the voltage drop counterclockwise around the square path by evaluating $-\dot{\Phi}$ and also by evaluating the line integral of $\mathbf{E}$.

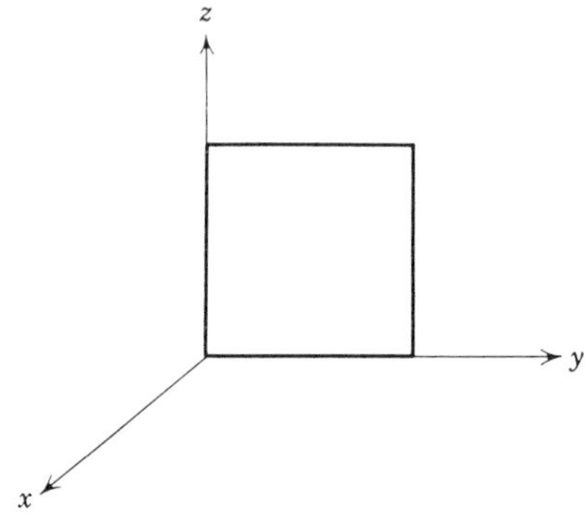

FIG. 11-4.

11-8. In cylindrical coordinates the approximate magnetic flux density in a region of free space within a meter of the z-axis is

$$\mathbf{B} = 10^{-8}(1 - r^2/4 + r^4/64) \sin 3 \times 10^8 t\,\mathbf{k}$$

Find the electric field intensity in this region, and use this field to find the voltage drop in the φ direction around a circular path whose points are a meter from the z axis. Compare your answer with that given in Example 1 of Sec. 8-2.

11-9. In a nonferromagnetic conductor the electric field is

$$\mathbf{E} = 0.0001e^{-1000x}\sin(10^5 t - 1000x)\,\mathbf{k}$$

Find the magnetic field **H**, the current density **J**, and the conductivity σ.

(*Ans*: $\sigma = 1.59 \times 10^7$).

Section 11-2

11-10. In the conductor of Prob. 11-9, find the power dissipated as a function of time in the unit cube occupying unit area in the yz-plane and extending from $x = 0$ to $x = 1$. Also, determine the time-average dissipated power.

11-11. In a region with an electric field $\mathbf{E} = 10{,}000\mathbf{i}$, a hydrogen ion with a mass of 1.67×10^{-27} kg and a charge of 1.6×10^{-19} coulomb is released at the origin of a coordinate system at time zero with zero initial velocity. Assuming the ion moves freely under the influence of the field to the point $x = 0.5$, determine the power supplied to the ion, as a function of time. What is the total energy supplied by the field?

11-12. The electric field intensity in a certain parallel-plate diode is $-500{,}000x^{1/3}\,\mathbf{i}$, with x denoting the distance from the cathode. The plate is located at $x = 0.005$ m. If the convection current density **J** is equal to $-500\mathbf{i}$, find the power per unit volume supplied to the electrons at $x = 0.001$ and also at $x = 0.004$. What is the total power to the electrons if the plate area is 0.001?

11-13. A 1-volt, 60-cps generator is connected across the terminals of an inductor consisting of a coil of copper wire on a ferromagnetic core, and the current of the coil is $0.001 \sin 377t$ ampere. The wire has a radius of 0.0001 m, a length of 30 m, and a conductivity of 5.8×10^7 mhos/m. Assuming a uniform current distribution over the cross section of the wire, find the instantaneous power dissipated, the time-average power dissipated, and the voltage drop *along the path of the wire*.

11-14. (*a*) In the Example of Sec. 11-2, what is the power supplied to the resistance R of the rod at the instant of time when i is zero? What is the power dissipated as heat at this same instant? (*b*) If the radius of the rod is changed to 2.3 cm, with the expression for J unchanged, what is the instantaneous power and the average power dissipated in one centimeter of length?

11-15. In the Example of Sec. 11-2, calculate the resistance of the rod at the given frequency, if the radius of the rod is changed to 2.3 cm.

Sections 11-3 and 11-4

11-16. Verify that $\epsilon\mathbf{E}\cdot\dot{\mathbf{E}} = \partial(\frac{1}{2}\epsilon E^2)/\partial t$, by substitution of the rectangular form of **E**.

11-17. For the fields of Prob. 11-8, find the instantaneous and time-average Poynting vectors at $r = 0.5$.

11-18. In spherical coordinates, the electric field in the free space around a *biconical waveguide*, consisting of two coaxial conducting cones with a source between their apices at the origin, is

$$\mathbf{E} = \frac{1000\sin(\omega t - \beta r)}{r \sin\theta}\,\mathbf{a}_\theta$$

with $\omega = 3 \times 10^9$ and $\beta = \omega(\mu_0\epsilon_0)^{1/2}$. Find (*a*) the magnetic field intensity **H**, (*b*) the ratio E/H, (*c*) the Poynting vector **S**, (*d*) the energy densities of the electric and magnetic fields. (*e*) Also, evaluate **E**, **H**, **S**, and the energy densities at the point $(r, \theta, \varphi) = (0.1, \frac{1}{2}\pi, 2)$, at time zero.

11-19. For the biconical waveguide of Prob. 11-18, find the time-average power radiated if the fields occupy the region from $\theta = 30°$ to $\theta = 150°$. The remainder of the space is occupied by the conducting cones.

11-20. Find the time-average power flow, in watts, along the waveguide of Prob. 9-24.

11-21. A parallel-plate capacitor, consisting of two metallic plates of area S and separation d, stores a charge q due to a voltage v impressed between the plates. Using Eq. (11-11), find the energy stored in the electric field between the plates, and show that this equals $\frac{1}{2}qv$. Assume the charge distribution of each plate is uniform.

Section 11-5

11-22. The wave equation for the electric field intensity in an uncharged medium is given by Eq. (11-22). For a charged medium, show that the term $\nabla(\rho/\epsilon)$ must be added to the right side of this equation.

11-23. Derive Eq. (11-24). What would this wave equation be for a region containing a convection current density $\mathbf{J}_1$ in addition to a drift current density $\sigma\mathbf{E}$?

11-24. Verify that the wave equation is satisfied for (*a*) the electric field of Prob. 11-6 and (*b*) the magnetic field of Prob. 11-7.

11-25. Show that the electric field of Prob. 11-9 satisfies the wave equation for a good conductor.

11-26. Show that the electric field of Prob. 11-18 satisfies the wave equation. Use the vector identity of Eq. (10-57) to find the vector Laplacian of $\mathbf{E}$ in spherical coordinates.

11-27. Utilize the wave equation to determine the angular frequency ω, if the x component of the magnetic field intensity in the free-space dielectric of a waveguide is

$$\sin 10x \cos 20y \cos (\omega t - 20z)$$

11-28. Utilizing the wave equation, determine the phase constant β and calculate the wave velocity ω/β of the electromagnetic wave of Prob. 9-24. The angular frequency ω is $4\pi \times 10^9$. Note that the wave velocity exceeds the free-space velocity of light.

Section 11-6

11-29. By direct substitution, show that Eq. (11-32) is a solution of Eq. (11-30).

11-30. If $E_x = \sin(\omega t - \beta z) + \sin(\omega t + \beta z)$, with $\omega = 10^6$ and $\beta = 0.005$, (*a*) find the wave velocities, expressed as vectors, of the incident and reflected waves, and (*b*) calculate the maximum values of E_x, as time varies, at distances such that βz equals 0, $\pi/4$, $\frac{1}{2}\pi$, $3\pi/4$, and π.

11-31. The fields of a uniform plane wave propagating in free space in the z-direction are independent of the x- and y-coordinates. From this and Maxwell's curl equations deduce that time-varying z components of $\mathbf{E}$ and $\mathbf{H}$ cannot exist.

11-32. A TEM wave propagating in free space in the z-direction has $E_z = H_z = 0$. From this and Maxwell's curl and divergence equations deduce that each field component satisfies an equation of the form

$$\frac{\partial^2 \phi}{\partial x^2} + \frac{\partial^2 \phi}{\partial y^2} = 0$$

Section 11-7

11-33. Show that the magnetic field of Prob. 11-8 approximately satisfies the wave equation for the region of space within a meter of the z-axis.

11-34. In the Example of Sec. 11-2, the given current density does not satisfy the wave equation and is, therefore, only an approximation. Show that the wave equation is approximately satisfied for large values of r.

11-35. Show that the expression $\cos r \sin \omega t \, \mathbf{a}_z$, in cylindrical coordinates, cannot possibly represent a valid magnetic field in a region in which the only convection current densities are drift current densities.

11-36. Deduce that the expression $\sin (\omega t - \beta x) \, \mathbf{i}$ cannot possibly represent a valid magnetic field. Also, show that $\sin y \, \mathbf{i}$ cannot possibly represent a valid static electric field.

Waves

CHAPTER 12

A wave is a function of both time and space. *If a disturbance that occurs at a particular point in space at a particular time is related in a definite manner to what occurs at distant points at later times, then there is wave motion.* In general, the equation of wave motion contains second partial space derivatives and both first and second partial time derivatives. Thus it is a second-order partial differential equation involving space and time variables.

The wave equation is encountered in all branches of time-varying electromagnetism. For example, it is inevitably utilized in the study of radio waves, transmission lines, waveguides, antennas, and high-frequency electronic tubes. Then there are related equations, such as the *diffusion equations* that govern the behavior of transistors and describe the current distribution in conductors. These do not have second partial time derivatives, and as a consequence, their solutions represent heavily damped waves. Even the Poisson and Laplace equations of electrostatics can be viewed as very special and restricted cases of the general wave equation, although their solutions are certainly not waves. Also, of course, there are many important nonelectrical partial differential equations with both space and time variables, such as the quantum-mechanical, the heat-flow, and the chemical-diffusion equations.

The objective of this chapter is to become acquainted with some of the properties of waves and their equations. The method of separation of variables, which enables us to reduce a partial differential equation to several ordinary differential equations, is discussed. Applications to specific problems in electromagnetism are considered in later chapters.

12-1. THE SINUSOIDAL TIME FUNCTION

In the mathematical analysis of waves, by far the most important time-varying case is that in which the quantities vary sinusoidally with time. This is so because of the *Fourier series* and the *Fourier integral*, which show that both periodic and transient time-functions can be

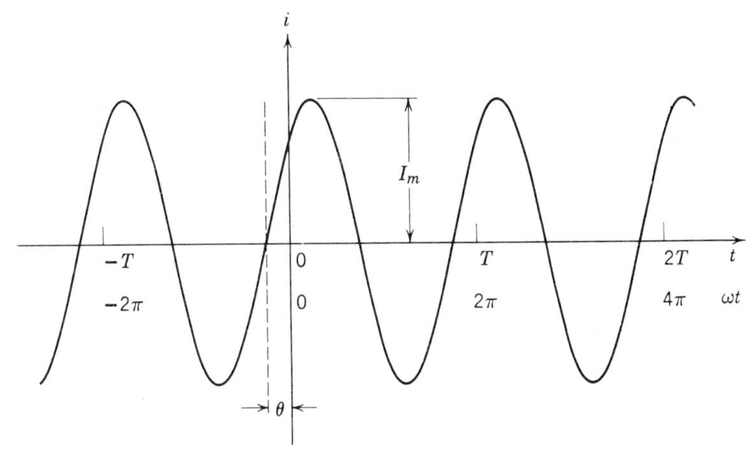

FIG. 12-1. The sinusoidal time-function $i = I_m \sin(\omega t + \theta)$. Both the time t and the angle ωt scales are shown.

expressed in terms of sinusoidal functions of different frequencies and amplitudes, each of which is known as a single-frequency component. The linearity of the wave equation justifies our treating a transient wave as the sum of many noninteracting sinusoidal waves, each traveling *independently* of every other component wave of different frequency. Thus sinusoidal waves are extremely important, even though actual waves are, in general, nonsinusoidal.

The mathematical expression for a quantity i that varies sinusoidally with time t is

$$i = I_m \sin(\omega t + \theta) \tag{12-1}$$

with I_m, ω, and θ denoting constants independent of time. In Fig. 12-1 the instantaneous quantity i is plotted as a function of time. Below the time scale is shown the scale for the angle ωt. Although time zero is arbitrarily selected, it should be clearly understood that a pure sine function is without beginning or end.

As time varies, $\sin(\omega t + \theta)$ varies between the limits $+1$ and -1.

Therefore, the maximum value of i is I_m, called the *amplitude* of the sine function. The *angle* $(\omega t + \theta)$ is dimensionless, and its mks unit, the *radian*, is a dimensionless unit. Tables of the trigonometric functions usually give the angle in degrees. One degree corresponds to $\pi/180$ radian, with $360°$ corresponding to 2π radians. If the angle of the sine function is changed by 2π radians, the value of the function is unchanged, and the function is said to be *periodic*. Throughout a time interval of one period of T seconds, the sine function passes through a *cycle*, and the number of cycles in one second is the *frequency* f. Obviously, $f = 1/T$ cycles per second (cps). For example, if one cycle takes 0.01 second, the frequency is 100 cps.

At time zero the sine function becomes $I_m \sin \theta$. When t equals the time T of a period, the function is $I_m \sin (\omega T + \theta)$, and the angle has increased by 2π radians. Therefore, $\omega T = 2\pi$, and $\omega = 2\pi/T$, or

$$\omega = 2\pi f \text{ radians/sec} \tag{12-2}$$

The constant ω, with dimensions of reciprocal time, is referred to as the *angular frequency*. The angle θ is called the *phase angle*. Its unit is the dimensionless radian, but θ is often expressed in degrees. As i is $I_m \sin \theta$ at time zero, it is clear that the phase angle θ depends on the arbitrary selection of this zero time.

A sinusoidal current is an *alternating current*. In general, any electrical quantity that varies with time, having an average value of zero, is referred to as an *a-c* quantity. If a current does not vary with time, it is a *steady*, or *direct*, current. The abbreviation *d-c* is used to denote a direct current. It is also employed to denote any electrical quantity that is steady with time. A quantity that varies with time, having an average value that is not zero, is said to consist of both a-c and d-c components.

As the frequency of a sinusoidal quantity i approaches the limit zero, the angle ωt becomes infinitesimal for any finite time, and $i = I_m \sin \theta$, a quantity independent of time. Clearly *d-c* can be regarded as a limiting case of *a-c*. In both fields and circuits, *equations written in terms of sinusoidal time functions can be applied to d-c quantities by letting the frequency approach zero*. The d-c component of a time-varying quantity can be regarded as the zero-frequency component.

The sine function is broadly interpreted to include the cosine function, which is a sine function whose angle is displaced by $\frac{1}{2}\pi$ radians, or $90°$. For example, the sinusoid of Fig. 12-1 can be expressed as $i = I_m \cos (\omega t + \theta')$, with $\theta' = \theta - \frac{1}{2}\pi$. A sinusoid is often referred to as a *sine wave*, and its plot, as shown in Fig. 12-1, is called the *waveform*. Actually, a wave is a function of both time and space, and the sinusoid, if a function of time only, is not a true wave.

When two sinusoids of the same frequency are added or subtracted, the result is sinusoidal, with only the amplitude and phase angle affected. Time derivatives and integrals of sinusoids are likewise sinusoidal. These mathematical operations appear in the equations of linear field and circuit theory. It follows that *a sinusoidal excitation in an electrical system governed by these linear equations produces sinusoidal fields, currents, and voltages in all parts of the system, and only a single frequency is involved.* Along with the Fourier theorem, this explains the extensive use of the sinusoid in field and circuit analysis. In the generation and transmission of electrical energy supplied to the home and factory, the sinusoidal time function is widely utilized. If some other time function were used, the waveform would vary from point to point in the system and the result would be quite impractical.

The elementary trigonometric and exponential functions are discussed in considerable detail in Chapter 19. In field theory, as in circuit theory, it is customary and convenient to express sinusoids in terms of *complex exponentials.* As will be shown later, this readily leads to the elimination of the time variable from the equations. However, for students not thoroughly familiar with this mathematics, it seems desirable to show the sinusoidal time function explicitly in the expressions and equations dealing with wave propagation, for otherwise the physical significance may be somewhat obscured. Consequently, the presentation and utilization of the mathematics of complex exponentials are deferred to the latter part of this text, beginning with Chapter 19.

12-2. WAVES IN GENERAL

When a pebble is dropped into a body of water, the water particles in the vicinity of the pebble are immediately displaced from their equilibrium position. The motion of these particles disturbs adjacent particles, causing them to move, and the process continues, creating a wave. Because of the finite velocity of the wave, a finite time elapses before the disturbance causes the water particles at a distant point to move. Thus the initial disturbance produces, at distant points, effects that are *retarded* in time. All wave motion is characterized by *retardation.* The water wave consists of ripples that move along the surface away from the disturbance. Although the motion of any particular water particle is essentially a small up-and-down movement, the cumulative effects of all the particles produce the wave. As the wave propagates away from its source, the water crests become smaller and smaller. This *attenuation* is due to the expanding region of the wave and also to the dissipation of energy as heat because of frictional effects. The water wave is both retarded and attenuated.

Another excellent example of wave propagation is the motion of sound in a medium. In air this motion occurs through the to-and-fro movement of the air molecules, but these molecules do not actually move along with the wave. Both attenuation and retardation are present.

Electromagnetic waves consist of time-varying electric and magnetic fields. Suppose an electrical disturbance, such as a change in the current of a conductor, occurs at a point in a region. The time-changing electric field resulting from the disturbance generates, according to the Maxwell-Ampère law, a time-changing magnetic field with flux lines that encircle those of the electric field. The time-changing magnetic field, in turn, produces an electric field according to the Maxwell-Faraday law. These time-changing fields continue to generate one another in an ever-expanding region, and the resulting wave, with electric and magnetic field lines encircling one another, propagates away from its source. Although there is no vibration of physical particles, as in water and sound waves, there is both retardation and attenuation. The retardation is the result of the finite wave velocity, and the attenuation is due to the expanding region of the wave and also to the ohmic losses, if any, that dissipate energy as heat.

Let us consider the expression $A \sin (\omega t - \beta x)$, which denotes a sine wave traveling in the positive x-direction. The *phase of the wave* is $\omega t - \beta x$, and the amplitude of the wave is A, which is, in general, a function of the space coordinates. If the phase is equated to the constant C_1 and the resulting equation is solved for x, we obtain $x = (\omega/\beta)t - C_1/\beta$. This is the x-coordinate, as a function of time, of the constant phase C_1, and this coordinate progresses along the x-axis at a velocity dx/dt that obviously equals ω/β. At all points of a surface normal to the x-axis, and moving with a velocity dx/dt equal to ω/β, the wave function is independent of time; if the phase of this surface is C_1, the wave function is $A \sin C_1$. It should not be inferred that the equiphase surface is always planar. An example of a nonplanar wave is one propagating radially outward from a point source. The preceding discussion is applicable to this case if the rectangular coordinate x is replaced with the spherical coordinate r, and the equiphase surface is spherical. In any event, the velocity ω/β of a point of constant phase is called the *wave velocity*, or the *phase velocity*. It is usually denoted by the symbol v_p.

The constant β is called the *phase constant*. It is expressed in radians per meter, and it represents the phase shift per unit length. The distance between two points that differ in phase by 2π radians is called the *wavelength* λ. It follows that $\beta\lambda = 2\pi$, or $\lambda = 2\pi/\beta$. Obviously, the velocity ω/β equals $f\lambda$, and we have

$$v_p = \omega/\beta = f\lambda \tag{12-3}$$

When the source that produces the wave passes through one cycle, the wave advances a distance in space equal to one wavelength. The number of cycles per second multiplied by the wavelength in meters gives the phase velocity in meters per second. The time required for the wave to propagate through a distance x is x/v_p seconds. This is called the *phase delay* τ_p for the specified distance.

In Fig. 12-2 a sine wave traveling in the positive x-direction is plotted as a function of x at a particular time. As time varies, the wave progresses

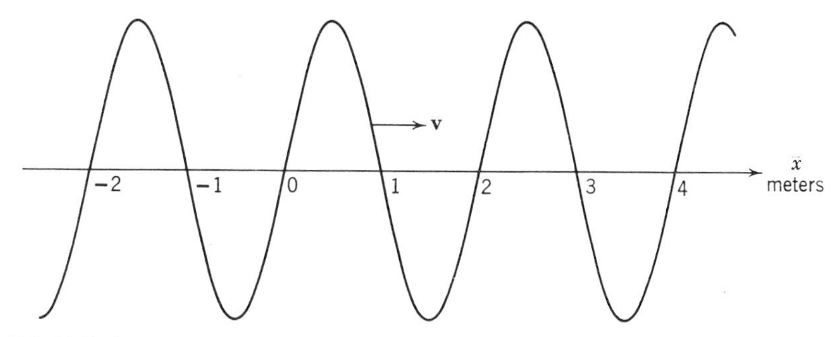

FIG. 12-2. An unattenuated wave traveling in the positive x-direction with velocity **v**. The sine curve represents the magnitude of the wave at points along the x-axis at the instant of time under consideration.

in the positive x-direction. It should be noted that the time variation at a fixed point is sinusoidal, and the wave is periodic in both time and space. In this illustration the wavelength λ, which is a "spatial period," is two meters; the phase constant β, which is a "spatial frequency," is π radians per meter.

The expressions *phase velocity* and *phase delay* are often applied to a network or to a number of networks in cascade. Actually, we do not have true wave motion in a network, for space coordinates are not involved. However, we can consider β as representing the phase shift per section and x as representing the number of sections. For one section $x = 1$, and the "wave" becomes $A \sin(\omega t - \beta)$. The phase velocity is ω/β sections per second, and the phase delay τ_p for the section is $1/v_p$, or β/ω seconds. As β may be positive or negative, the phase velocity and the phase delay may also be positive or negative, and neither has real physical significance.

The phase velocity of a wave is a function of the direction under consideration. To illustrate this let us examine Fig. 12-3, which shows a two-dimensional view of a wave. The sketch can be regarded as representing the overhead view of water waves, with the equiphase lines indicating crests of the wave moving in direction *oa* with velocity v_{pa}. An observer at *o* looking in the direction *ob* sees a wave velocity v_{pb} that is greater than

v_{pa}. Clearly the wavelength λ_b in direction *ob* is greater than λ_a in direction *oa*, and certainly the time required for a crest to propagate through a wavelength is the same for both directions. From Eq. (12-3) we deduce that $v_{pb}/v_{pa} = \lambda_b/\lambda_a$. From the sketch it is evident that $\lambda_b = \lambda_a/\cos\theta$ and, consequently,

$$v_{pb} = v_{pa}/\cos\theta$$

It is interesting to note that the phase velocity v_{pb} approaches infinity as θ approaches 90°. In a hollow-pipe waveguide at the lowest usable

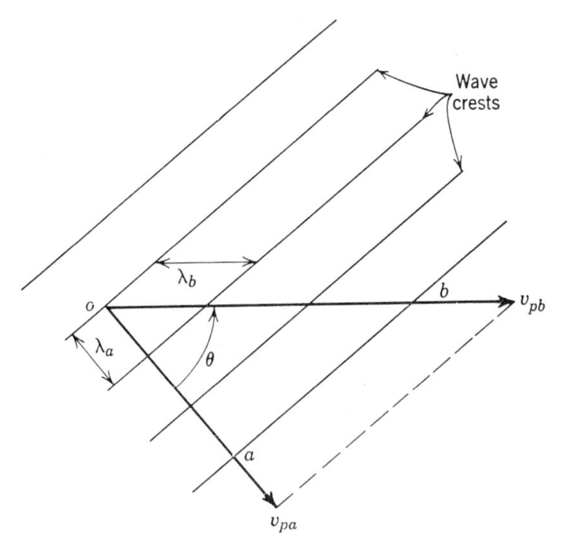

FIG. 12-3. Crests of a wave.

frequencies the equiphase surfaces travel almost at right angles to the axis of the guide and the phase velocity in the direction of energy flow along the guide may be very much greater than the velocity of light.

Periodic waves exhibit *interference* effects. Suppose two point sources of waves have the same amplitude and frequency and are in time phase. If the sources are separated a distance equal to a half wavelength, the waves cancel one another in the direction along the straight line passing through the two sources. However, the waves strengthen one another along the path normal to this straight line at the point midway between the sources. Interference effects can be observed with a single wave. For example, suppose a monochromatic light wave strikes a plate having two small holes. If a second plate is located behind the first plate, the light intensity on the second plate is strong in regions where the waves from the two holes reinforce one another, but weak where the waves from the two holes destructively interfere. The interference is destructive when the distances of travel differ by a half wavelength.

Waves can be *reflected* and *refracted.* When waves travel from one medium into another, there may be both reflection and refraction at the boundary, as shown in Fig. 12-4. That part of the wave reflected back into the first medium is the reflected wave, and that part passing into the second medium is the refracted wave. It can be shown that the angle of reflection B equals the angle of incidence A, but the angle of refraction C differs from the angle of incidence by an amount that depends on the

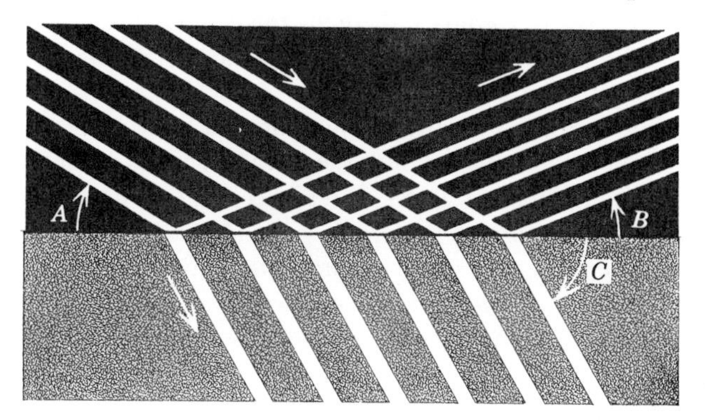

FIG. 12-4. Reflection and refraction of a wave.

properties of the media. In general, a wave is bent, or its direction of propagation is changed, when passing from one medium into another. This is what is meant by refraction.

Waves can be *diffracted.* This is the bending of the waves around the edges of an object. Examples of diffraction are the bending of electromagnetic waves around the curvature of the earth and the bending of light waves passing through a narrow slit.

A wave has stored energy. The energy density of any wave can be expressed as the sum of the squares of two quantities whose magnitudes define the state of the wave. For elastic waves these quantities are the displacement and the velocity of the medium. For the electromagnetic wave they are E and H, and the energy density is $\frac{1}{2}\epsilon E^2 + \frac{1}{2}\mu H^2$ joules/m^3. At each point of a region with an electromagnetic wave there is a continual interchange of energy between the electric and magnetic fields. In general, the energy density decreases as a wave propagates, and this is due to both the expanding region of the wave and to the dissipation of energy as heat.

Two waves of the same frequency, traveling in opposite directions, produce *standing waves.* At certain points in the medium the two waves strengthen each other, and at other points they destructively interfere.

Standing waves occur when a wave is reflected. For example, suppose the two waves can be represented by the expressions $\sin(\omega t - \beta x)$ and $\sin(\omega t + \beta x)$. These represent waves of equal amplitude traveling in opposite directions. It is easily shown that their sum is $2 \cos \beta x \sin \omega t$. Therefore, at points where βx is 0, π, 2π, etc., the resultant wave has an amplitude of 2, but at points where βx is $\frac{1}{2}\pi$, $3\pi/2$, etc., the resultant wave is zero at every instant. At any point the time variations are sinusoidal, with an amplitude between 0 and 2.

Suppose a source that produces a wave varies nonsinusoidally with respect to time. By the Fourier theorem this source can be regarded as composed of a number of sinusoidal time functions of different amplitudes and frequencies. The resulting wave has many frequency components, and each component has its own attenuation and phase velocity. A wave is said to travel without distortion if the disturbances at distant points are the same as the disturbances at the source, except for changes in magnitude and delay in time. It follows that, *if the nonsinusoidal wave is to propagate without distortion, the different frequency components must be attenuated the same amount, and they must travel with the same velocity.* If the different frequency components are attenuated different amounts, the waveform changes as it propagates, and the resulting distortion is called *frequency distortion.* If the different frequency components travel with different phase velocities, the summation of the components yields a waveform that changes as it propagates. In this case the distortion is referred to as *phase distortion*, or *delay distortion.* As phase velocity equals ω/β, the phase constant β must be directly proportional to the frequency if there is to be no phase distortion. Media in which the phase velocity depends on the frequency are said to be *dispersive*; such media, of course, introduce phase distortion. In *nondispersive* media the phase velocity is independent of frequency, and there is no phase distortion. Fortunately, free space is nondispersive for the electromagnetic wave.

12-3. WAVE EQUATIONS

The equations of wave motion have far-reaching applications in engineering and science. Wave equations for the electric and magnetic fields and also the skin-effect equation for the current distribution in a conductor have already been encountered. In later chapters we employ wave equations to solve many different problems. The objective here is to become acquainted with the form of such equations and the separation-of-variables method so helpful in obtaining solutions.

A general form of a vector wave equation is

$$\nabla^2 \mathbf{A} = C_1 \mathbf{A} + C_2 \dot{\mathbf{A}} + C_3 \ddot{\mathbf{A}} + \mathbf{G}(x, y, z, t) \tag{12-4}$$

The function **G** is a forcing function, or energy source, of the wave. In general, it is a function of the space coordinates and time. For the electromagnetic wave this function might be an impressed current or a specified charge distribution, serving as the source of the wave. The vector Laplacian $\mathbf{\nabla}^2$ denotes the operator *grad div — curl curl.*

Each of the rectangular components of **A** satisfies the scalar wave equation

$$\nabla^2\phi = C_1\phi + C_2\dot{\phi} + C_3\ddot{\phi} + g(x, y, z, t) \tag{12-5}$$

The scalar Laplacian ∇^2 denotes the operator *div grad.* An excellent example of a scalar that satisfies Eq. (12-5) is the current along a transmission line. Although only one space dimension is involved, all the terms on the right side of Eq. (12-5) have value, with the forcing function being the current impressed on the line at the sending end.

A special case occurs when the wave equation is applied to a region with no energy sources. Along a transmission line the forcing function is normally zero everywhere except for the generator at the sending end. In the region of free space around a transmitting antenna the forcing function is zero, for the source of the radiated wave is the current of the antenna. A region without sources of energy is said to be *passive*; otherwise, it is *active.* The scalar wave equation applied to a passive region is

$$\nabla^2\phi = C_1\phi + C_2\dot{\phi} + C_3\ddot{\phi} \tag{12-6}$$

Special cases of this equation occur if C_1, C_2, or C_3 is zero. For C_1 zero we have

$$\nabla^2\phi = C_2\dot{\phi} + C_3\ddot{\phi} \tag{12-7}$$

Solutions of this equation represent *damped* waves. On the other hand, if C_2 is also zero, we have the *undamped* wave equation

$$\nabla^2\phi = C_3\ddot{\phi} \tag{12-8}$$

Its solutions are waves that propagate without attenuation other than that due to the spreading of the waves, if this occurs. The equation applies to lossless passive nondispersive regions. If C_3 is zero, Eq. (12-8) becomes the Laplace equation $\nabla^2\phi = 0$. Although the Laplace equation is a special case of the wave equation, its solutions do not represent waves.

A wave equation is a partial differential equation involving the space and time variables. It can frequently be solved by the method of separation of variables, which reduces the equation to several separate and distinct ordinary differential equations. The product of the solutions of the ordinary differential equations gives the solution of the partial differential equation.

Let us apply the method to the scalar wave equation for a passive region. To separate the time variable from the space variables, we let ϕ be the product of two functions

$$\phi(x, y, z, t) = F(x, y, z)T(t) \tag{12-9}$$

with F a function of the space coordinates only and T a function of time only. Substitution into Eq. (12-6) gives

$$T\,\nabla^2 F = C_1 FT + C_2 F\dot{T} + C_3 F\ddot{T}$$

Division by the product FT yields

$$\frac{\nabla^2 F}{F} = C_1 + C_2\frac{\dot{T}}{T} + C_3\frac{\ddot{T}}{T} \tag{12-10}$$

The left side of Eq. (12-10) is a function of the space coordinates only, and the right side is a function of time only. Now consider a fixed point in space. As time varies, the left side of Eq. (12-10) does not change, for it depends only on the space coordinates of the point. Consequently, the right side of Eq. (12-10) must also be constant as time varies. Next, suppose the variables x, y, and z change, with time constant. The right side of Eq. (12-10) certainly does not change, for it is a function of time only. Therefore, the left side of Eq. (12-10) stays constant as x, y, and z vary. Thus both sides of (12-10) remain constant, regardless of the manner in which the variables x, y, z, and t change. Accordingly, we can equate both sides to a constant that is independent of the variables. Designating this constant by $-k^2$, we obtain

$$\frac{\nabla^2 F}{F} = C_1 + C_2\frac{\dot{T}}{T} + C_3\frac{\ddot{T}}{T} = -k^2$$

It is obvious that

$$C_3\ddot{T} + C_2\dot{T} + (C_1 + k^2)T = 0 \tag{12-11}$$

and

$$\nabla^2 F = -k^2 F \tag{12-12}$$

Equation (12-11) is an ordinary differential equation, with the single variable time. In many applications our interest is only in the sinusoidal, or steady-state, behavior. For such cases T is a sinusoidal function of time, whose frequency is that of the forcing function. Equation (12-12) is a partial differential equation involving the space coordinates only. It is often referred to as the *time-independent wave equation*, or the *scalar Helmholtz equation*. The solution of this equation, when multiplied by the time function, gives the solution for the wave function ϕ.

The method of separation of variables can be applied to Eq. (12-12). Let $F(x, y, z) = X(x)Y(y)Z(z)$, with X a function of x, Y a function of y, and Z a function of z. Substitution into Eq. (12-12) and division by XYZ give

$$\frac{1}{X}\frac{d^2X}{dx^2} + \frac{1}{Y}\frac{d^2Y}{dy^2} + \frac{1}{Z}\frac{d^2Z}{dz^2} = -k^2 \tag{12-13}$$

Each term on the left side of the equation has a single independent variable. Therefore, each of these terms must be independent of the space coordinates. Denoting the constants as $-k_x^2$, $-k_y^2$, and $-k_z^2$, we obtain

$$\frac{1}{X}\frac{d^2X}{dx^2} = -k_x^2 \qquad \frac{1}{Y}\frac{d^2Y}{dy^2} = -k_y^2 \qquad \frac{1}{Z}\frac{d^2Z}{dz^2} = -k_z^2 \tag{12-14}$$

These are ordinary differential equations, whose solutions are easily obtained. It is evident that the constants of Eqs. (12-13) and (12-14) are related by the equation

$$k_x^2 + k_y^2 + k_z^2 = k^2 \tag{12-15}$$

The determination of these constants depends on the boundary conditions of the particular problem.

The function F is found by multiplying together the solutions of the equations of (12-14), and the wave function ϕ is

$$\phi(x, y, z, t) = X(x)Y(y)Z(z)T(t) \tag{12-16}$$

Although rectangular coordinates have been employed, the method applies equally well to other coordinate systems, provided the partial differential equation is separable in the selected system. For example, in spherical coordinates Eq. (12-16) would be

$$\phi(r, \theta, \varphi, t) = R(r)\Theta(\theta)\Phi(\varphi)T(t) \tag{12-17}$$

We shall find the separation-of-variables method helpful in solving partial differential equations that will be encountered later in the text. To illustrate the application of the method, an elementary example is treated in the next section.

12-4. THE VIBRATING STRING

The natural vibration of a uniform elastic string is an excellent example of a one-dimensional wave. Shown in Fig. 12-5 is the string, with the x-axis oriented along its equilibrium position. The ends are fastened at $x = 0$ and at $x = l$. The deflection Ψ of the string from its equilibrium position is a function of the variables x and t. Small-amplitude vibrations are assumed, and damping is neglected.

Assume the string is in the position illustrated in Fig. 12-5. Examination shows that the *net upward* force that acts on the elemental section Δl at the point P is $F \sin \theta' - F \sin \theta$, with F denoting the tensile force of the string. The difference between the sine functions is the rate of change of $\sin \theta$ with respect to the distance l, at the point P, multiplied by the elemental length Δl. Therefore, the net upward force on Δl is $F\,\Delta l\, d(\sin \theta)/dl$. As $\sin \theta$ equals $d\Psi/dl$ and as dl is approximately equal to dx, for small-amplitude vibrations, this upward force at a fixed time becomes

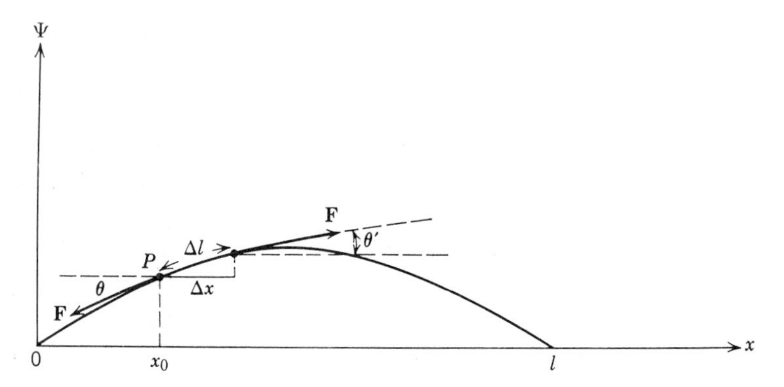

FIG. 12-5. A vibrating string fastened at $x = 0$ and at $x = l$. Small-amplitude vibrations are assumed. **F** represents the tensile force.

$F\,\Delta l\, d^2\Psi/dx^2$. The mass of the elemental length is $m\,\Delta l$, with m denoting the mass per unit length of the string. Equating the force on Δl to the product of mass and acceleration gives

$$F\,\Delta l\,\frac{\partial^2 \Psi}{\partial x^2} = m\,\Delta l\,\frac{\partial^2 \Psi}{\partial t^2}$$

If we let $v^2 = F/m$, the equation becomes

$$\frac{\partial^2 \Psi}{\partial x^2} = \frac{1}{v^2}\frac{\partial^2 \Psi}{\partial t^2} \qquad (12\text{-}18)$$

This is a one-dimensional wave equation with no damping term.

Utilizing the method of separation of variables, we let $\Psi = X(x)\,T(t)$. If we substitute for Ψ and divide by XT, we obtain

$$\frac{1}{X}\frac{d^2X}{dx^2} = \frac{1}{v^2T}\frac{d^2T}{dt^2}$$

Each term contains a separate independent variable. Therefore, we can equate both sides to the constant $-k^2$, with the negative sign selected in anticipation of a negative constant, and we have

$$\frac{d^2X}{dx^2} = -k^2X \qquad \frac{d^2T}{dt^2} = -k^2v^2T \tag{12-19}$$

These are ordinary differential equations whose solutions are

$$X = C_1 \sin kx + C_2 \cos kx$$

$$T = C_3 \sin \omega t + C_4 \cos \omega t$$

with $\omega = kv$. The frequency f of the vibrations is, of course, $\omega/2\pi$.

The displacement Ψ, which equals the product XT, is zero at $x = 0$ and also at $x = l$ at every instant. For $x = 0$, $X = C_2 = 0$. For $x = l$, $X = C_1 \sin kl = 0$. If there is any displacement of the string, C_1 is not zero and, therefore, $kl = n\pi$ with n denoting *any integer*. Thus $k = n\pi/l$, and X becomes $C_1 \sin n\pi x/l$. Consequently, the displacement Ψ is

$$\Psi = \sin n\pi x/l \,(A \sin \omega t + B \cos \omega t) \tag{12-20}$$

The constants A and B replace the products C_1C_3 and C_1C_4, respectively. This can be written

$$\Psi = C \sin n\pi x/l \sin (\omega t + \theta) \tag{12-21}$$

by utilization of the trigonometric identity

$$A \sin \omega t + B \cos \omega t = C \sin (\omega t + \theta) \tag{12-22}$$

with $C = \sqrt{A^2 + B^2}$ and $\theta = \arctan B/A$.

The expression for the displacement Ψ contains two arbitrary constants. These are determined from the starting conditions. As the amplitude of Ψ is a sinusoidal function of x, the displacement is a *standing wave*. The angular frequency ω of vibration equals kv, with $k = n\pi/l$ and $v = (F/m)^{1/2}$ Therefore,

$$\omega = (n\pi/l)\sqrt{F/m} \tag{12-23}$$

The angular frequency depends on n. Although n has an infinite number of possible values, it must be an integer, and this restricts ω to certain discrete values. The string can vibrate *only at certain discrete frequencies.* Normally a partial differential equation has continuous solutions rather than discrete solutions. The boundary conditions in this problem restrict the vibrations to certain discrete frequencies. The lowest frequency is called the *fundamental*, or *first harmonic*; the higher frequencies are *harmonics*, or *overtones*. In general, the allowed frequencies are referred to as *modes*, and the string may vibrate in a single mode or in a combination of modes, depending on the starting conditions. The natural frequencies of the vibrating string are harmonically related, for each allowed frequency is a multiple of the fundamental.

By means of a trigonometric identity we can express the displacement Ψ of Eq. (12-21) as

$$\Psi = \tfrac{1}{2}C\cos(\omega t - kx + \theta) - \tfrac{1}{2}C\cos(\omega t + kx + \theta) \qquad (12\text{-}24)$$

This shows that Ψ is the sum of two waves traveling in opposite directions. Thus the standing wave of a single mode can be represented as the sum of two waves, one traveling in the positive x-direction and the other traveling in the negative x-direction. Each of these waves has a phase velocity of ω/k, which equals v, or $(F/m)^{1/2}$. Therefore, the constant v of Eq. (12-18) is the phase velocity of a mode, and this phase velocity is determined by the tension and the mass per unit length of the string.

In terms of the frequency f of oscillation, the phase velocity is $2\pi f/k$, and this equals the product of the frequency and the wavelength. Therefore, $k = 2\pi/\lambda$. As k also equals $n\pi/l$, it follows that the length l of the wire is $n(\frac{1}{2}\lambda)$. For the first, or lowest, mode the length is $\frac{1}{2}\lambda$, and for the next mode, $l = \lambda$. Because the ends of the string are fixed, the wavelength must be such that an integral number of half-wavelengths exist between these fixed ends. This explains physically why only certain discrete frequencies are allowed.

In terms of all possible modes the displacement is

$$\Psi = \sum_{n=1}^{\infty} C_n \sin k_n x \sin(\omega_n t + \theta_n) \qquad (12\text{-}25)$$

As $\omega = kv$, $\omega_n = (n\pi/l)(F/m)^{1/2}$. The solution is expressed in terms of the length l of the string, the tension F, the mass m per unit length, and the mode constants C_n and θ_n that depend on the starting conditions. If a particular mode is not excited, the constant C_n for that mode is zero.

The wave equation of the vibrating string is one-dimensional, and its general solution, subject to the specified boundary conditions, consists of an infinite set of modes that represent standing waves of discrete frequencies. Each allowed frequency is characterized by an integer n. The general solution of a two-dimensional wave equation, whose wave function is fixed at the boundaries of the two-dimensional region, consists of a doubly infinite set of modes that represent standing waves; associated with these are certain discrete frequencies. Each mode has two integers, usually designated m and n, and each of these can have integral values from zero to infinity. Two examples of such two-dimensional problems are the vibrating membrane of a drum, such as that discussed in Prob. 12-12, and the electromagnetic fields of a rectangular waveguide, discussed in Chap. 22.

A very important three-dimensional wave equation is the quantum-mechanical wave equation. When this is applied to an electron of an atom, the imposed boundary conditions lead to a solution that allows the electron to occupy only certain discrete energy levels. Each energy level is characterized by three integers, called *quantum numbers*. A fourth quantum number is introduced to account for the spin orientation of the electron. There are certain restrictions on the values of the quantum numbers, these restrictions resulting from the boundary conditions applied to the solution of the wave equation.

The electromagnetic wave is, in general, a three-dimensional wave. The wave equations for the electromagnetic wave in an infinite medium are considered in the next chapter. If the wave is confined to a hollow cavity in a conductor, standing waves of discrete frequencies result. The solution consists of a triply infinite set of modes, each characterized by three integers. Such resonant cavities are not analyzed in this text.

REFERENCES

Bronwell, A., *Advanced Mathematics in Physics and Engineering*, McGraw-Hill Book Co., New York, 1953, Chaps. 8, 11.

Frank, N. H., *Introduction to Electricity and Optics*, McGraw-Hill Book Co., New York, 2nd ed., 1950, Chap. 15.

Kraus, J. D., *Electromagnetics*, McGraw-Hill Book Co., New York, 1953, Chap. 9.

Plonsey, R., and R. E. Collin, *Principles and Applications of Electromagnetic Fields*, McGraw-Hill Book Co., New York, 1961, Chap. 4.

PROBLEMS

Section 12-1

12-1. If $i_1 = 8 \sin 5000t$ and $i_2 = 10 \sin (5000t - 1.2)$, determine the angular frequency, the frequency, and the period. Also, find the amplitudes and phase angles of $i_1 + i_2$, di_1/dt, and $\int i_2\, dt$. What is i_2 at time $t = 0.001$?

Section 12-2

12-2. A crest of the wave $10 \cos (5000t - 0.0001x)$ is located at $x = 0$ at time zero. Where is this crest a microsecond later and also a second later? What is the velocity of the wave? Calculate the distance between successive crests.

12-3. A crest of the wave $5 \sin (8000t + 0.02x + 90^\circ)$ is located at $x = 0$ at time zero. Where is this crest a microsecond later and also a second later? Find the phase delay in a distance of 60 meters, expressed as a percentage of the period. In addition, calculate the value of the wave at $x = -100$ at time zero.

12-4. The refraction of an electromagnetic wave is due to the change in its velocity as it passes from one medium to another. In an unbounded medium the velocity of an electromagnetic wave is $(\mu\epsilon)^{-1/2}$. Deduce that this velocity is $c\epsilon_r^{-1/2}$ in a nonferromagnetic medium, with c denoting the free-space velocity of light, and calculate the change in the velocity when the wave passes from free space into a medium with a dielectric constant of 9.

12-5. A sinusoidal wave, with a constant amplitude of 5 and a frequency of 1000 kilocycles, propagates in the positive x-direction with a velocity that is twice the free-space velocity of light. Calculate the wavelength and the phase constant, and write the equation of this wave.

12-6. If $i_1 = 2 \sin(\omega t - \pi x)$ and $i_2 = \sin(\omega t + \pi x)$, determine the amplitude and phase angle of the sum $i_1 + i_2$ of the waves at each of the points $x = 0, 1, 2,$ and 3. Calculate the distance in meters from a point of maximum amplitude to the next point of maximum amplitude, and express this distance as a percentage of the wavelength.

12-7. The voltage v along a certain transmission line is

$$v = 3e^{-\alpha_1 x} \sin(3000t - \beta_1 x) + e^{-\alpha_2 x} \cos(3900t - \beta_2 x)$$

If the voltage wave travels without distortion, determine α_2 and β_2 in terms of α_1 and β_1.

Section 12-3

12-8. Show that the expression $\phi = e^{-\alpha z} \sin(\omega t - \beta z)$ is a solution of Eq. (12-6), provided $\beta^2 - \alpha^2 = \omega^2 C_3 - C_1$ and $2\alpha\beta = \omega C_2$.

12-9. In spherical coordinates show that the wave $(1/r) \sin(\omega t - \beta r)$, traveling radially outward from the origin, is a solution of Eq. (12-8), provided C_3 equals the reciprocal of the wave velocity squared.

Section 12-4

12-10. A violin string of length 0.4 m and of mass 0.0008 kg has its ends fixed. If the tensile force is 250 newtons, calculate the natural frequencies of vibration.

12-11. A lossless transmission line consisting of two long parallel wires is fed at the sending end with a current of $5 \sin 3 \times 10^6 t$ amperes. As the receiving end, 400 meters away, is open, the current at this end is zero. The line current is governed by Eq. 12-8, with the wave function ϕ representing the current i and with $C_3 = 10^{-16}/9$. Using the method of separation of variables, find i as a function of time t and distance x from the sending end. Also, calculate the amplitude and phase angle of the current at $x = 200$.

12-12. Shown in Fig. 12-6 is an elastic membrane that is rectangular in shape and bound at its edges. For natural small-amplitude vibrations, with damping neglected, the displacement Ψ in the z-direction is governed by the wave equation

$$\frac{\partial^2 \Psi}{\partial x^2} + \frac{\partial^2 \Psi}{\partial y^2} = \frac{1}{v^2} \frac{\partial^2 \Psi}{\partial t^2}$$

with the constant v^2 depending on the tension and mass of the membrane. Let $\Psi = XYT$, and show that

$$\frac{d^2 X}{dx^2} = -k_x^2 X \qquad \frac{d^2 Y}{dy^2} = -k_y^2 Y \qquad \frac{d^2 T}{dt^2} = -k^2 v^2 T$$

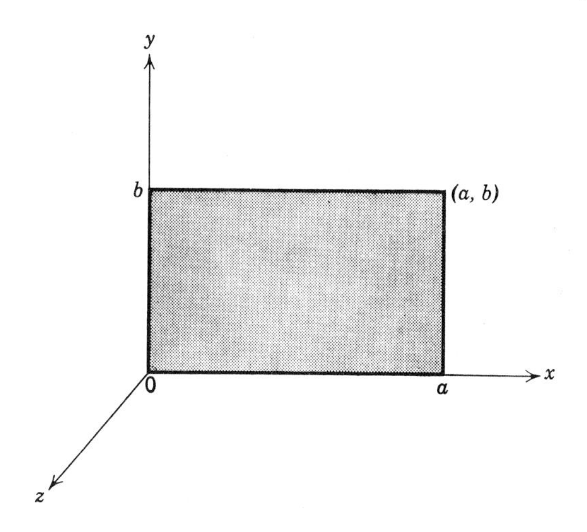

FIG. 12-6. A vibrating membrane. The rectangular membrane is bound at the edges of the rectangle, and small-amplitude vibrations in the z-direction are assumed.

with $k_x^2 + k_y^2 = k^2$. From these equations and the boundary conditions, deduce that

$$\Psi = A \sin m\pi x/a \sin n\pi y/b \sin (\omega t + \theta)$$

with A and θ constants depending on the starting conditions, with m and n any integers, and with $\omega = kv$. Also, show that the allowed frequencies of vibration are $\frac{1}{2}v(m^2/a^2 + n^2/b^2)^{\frac{1}{2}}$. Note that these frequencies are inharmonic, accounting for the nonmusical sound of the drum.

Potential Functions and Electromagnetic Fields

CHAPTER 13

In theory, any electromagnetic field problem can be solved by finding a solution to Maxwell's equations that also satisfies the appropriate boundary conditions. Unfortunately, the mathematical difficulties are often insurmountable, and exact solutions are not always possible. The use of potential functions frequently simplifies the mathematics.

In electrical theory, *a potential function is a scalar or vector point function from which electric or magnetic fields are obtainable by processes of differentiation.* Such functions are mathematical tools that may appreciably help us solve important field problems. It is never necessary to give these tools physical significance. In many cases it is easier to determine the potentials, with the fields found by appropriate differentiation, than it is to determine the fields directly from Maxwell's equations.

There are many useful potential functions in electromagnetic field theory. However, we shall consider only two, the electric scalar and magnetic vector potentials. It is shown that they satisfy wave equations, and solutions of these equations give the potentials directly in terms of the currents and charges that produce them. The electric and magnetic fields of a current element are obtained from the potentials; application of the Poynting vector to these fields reveals that an alternating current radiates energy, this energy being propagated by the electromagnetic wave. Radio communication is based on this phenomenon.

13-1. THE POTENTIAL FUNCTIONS

By far the most common and useful potential functions in electromagnetism are the *electric scalar potential*, or simply *electric potential*, and the *magnetic vector potential*. As the purpose of a potential function is to provide a convenient way to find the electric and magnetic fields produced by a system of charges and currents, we must express the field quantities in terms of the potential functions, and we must define the potentials so that they are useful. Furthermore, we must be careful that our definitions do not violate Maxwell's equations.

The magnetic flux density **B** is solenoidal. This means that it has no sources or sinks and has zero divergence at every point of space at every instant of time. Now the curl of any vector **A** is a vector with zero divergence. From the Maxwell equation div **B** = 0 and from the vector identity div(**curl A**) = 0, it follows that we might let **B** equal the curl of some vector **A**. Thus

$$\mathbf{B} = \mathbf{curl\ A} \tag{13-1}$$

The vector **A** is a potential function, although not yet completely defined. However, if **A** were known, we could determine the magnetic flux density by taking the curl of **A**. By definition, the curl of **A** must equal **B**.

Although the curl of **A** has been defined, **A** is not completely specified, for there are any number of vector functions having the same curl. To show this, let us examine the relation **R** = **A** + **grad** a, with a denoting any scalar point function. As the curl of the gradient of a is zero by a vector identity, the functions **A** and **R** have the same curl. It is evident that an infinite number of different vector fields can have the same curl. For a given magnetic field **B**, there are an infinite number of vector fields **A** that satisfy Eq. (13-1). In order to define **A** uniquely, we must specify additional information about this field, and this must be done intelligently if **A** is to be a useful function.

Next, let us investigate what might be done to express the electric field **E** in terms of potential functions. Maxwell's first curl equation states that **curl E** = $-\dot{\mathbf{B}}$. As **B** = **curl A**, we have

$$\mathbf{curl\ E} = -\frac{\partial}{\partial t}(\mathbf{curl\ A}) = \mathbf{curl}\,(-\dot{\mathbf{A}}) \tag{13-2}$$

From this result we might be tempted to write **E** = −**A**. However, this would imply that, in the absence of time-varying conditions, the electric field is zero. Of course this is absurd, and consequently, we must examine Eq. (13-2) more closely. Recalling that the curl of the gradient of any scalar point function ϕ is zero, we might let **E** equal $-(\mathbf{grad}\ \phi + \dot{\mathbf{A}})$. This expression satisfies Eq. (13-2) and also allows for the existence of a static electric field. Thus

$$\mathbf{E} = -\mathbf{grad}\,\phi - \dot{\mathbf{A}} \tag{13-3}$$

Equations (13-1) and (13-3) give the magnetic field **B** and the electric field **E** in terms of the two potential functions **A** and ϕ. Neither of these potentials is uniquely defined. As **A** is not completely defined by Eq. (13-1), then we should certainly not expect Eq. (13-3) to define completely either **A** or ϕ. We can rather arbitrarily impose a relationship between **A** and ϕ. To do this intelligently, let us examine Maxwell's equations. The equation requiring **B** to have zero divergence and the Maxwell-Faraday equation are obviously satisfied by Eqs. (13-1) and (13-3). We need to examine the other two Maxwell equations.

The analysis is restricted to media that are linear, isotropic, and homogeneous. For such media the permittivity ϵ and the permeability μ are constants independent of the space coordinates and time, even though the fields are functions of these variables. The Maxwell-Ampère law and Gauss's law, in terms of **B** and **E**, are

$$\nabla \times \mathbf{B} = \mu\epsilon\dot{\mathbf{E}} + \mu\mathbf{J} \tag{13-4}$$

$$\nabla \cdot \mathbf{E} = \rho/\epsilon \tag{13-5}$$

These can be expressed in terms of the potential functions by utilizing Eqs. (13-1) and (13-3), giving

$$\nabla \times (\nabla \times \mathbf{A}) = \mu\epsilon(-\nabla\dot{\phi} - \ddot{\mathbf{A}}) + \mu\mathbf{J} \tag{13-6}$$

$$\nabla \cdot (-\nabla\phi - \dot{\mathbf{A}}) = \rho/\epsilon \tag{13-7}$$

By replacing the left side of Eq. (13-6) with $\nabla(\nabla \cdot \mathbf{A}) - \nabla^2\mathbf{A}$, this being justified by a vector identity, and by rearranging terms and combining those terms involving the gradient, we obtain

$$\nabla^2\mathbf{A} = \mu\epsilon\ddot{\mathbf{A}} - \mu\mathbf{J} + \nabla(\nabla \cdot \mathbf{A} + \mu\epsilon\dot{\phi}) \tag{13-8}$$

$$\nabla^2\phi = -\nabla \cdot \dot{\mathbf{A}} - \rho/\epsilon \tag{13-9}$$

Equations (13-8) and (13-9) are quite involved. Each contains both **A** and ϕ. The problem that we are confronted with is to determine a relationship between **A** and ϕ that gives useful potential functions. Examination of Eqs. (13-8) and (13-9) reveals that ϕ is eliminated from (13-8) and **A** is eliminated from (13-9) if we let

$$\nabla \cdot \mathbf{A} = -\mu\epsilon\dot{\phi} \tag{13-10}$$

This particular choice is known as the Lorentz condition. Earlier it was mentioned that the definitions of **A** and ϕ would be completed by specifying a relationship between them, and this relationship is that of Eq. (13-10). Equations (13-8) and (13-9) become

$$\nabla^2 \mathbf{A} = \mu\epsilon\ddot{\mathbf{A}} - \mu\mathbf{J} \tag{13-11}$$

$$\nabla^2 \phi = \mu\epsilon\ddot{\phi} - \rho/\epsilon \tag{13-12}$$

These are the wave equations for the potentials **A** and ϕ. The vector **A** is called the *magnetic vector potential*, and its mks unit is the *weber per meter*. The scalar ϕ is the *electric scalar potential*, or simply *electric potential*, with the mks unit of *volt*. Both **A** and ϕ are immensely important in electromagnetism.

The potential functions **A** and ϕ are defined by Eqs (13-1), (13-3), and (13-10). These three equations and the two wave equations (13-11) and (13-12) are Maxwell's equations in potential form. This form is frequently more useful than the integral and differential forms previously encountered. The forcing functions $\mu\mathbf{J}$ and ρ/ϵ of the wave equations act as sources that produce the waves of the potential functions **A** and ϕ, respectively. It is possible and desirable to solve these wave equations, obtaining **A** and ϕ directly in terms of the current and charge densities of a region. After an illustrative example, we shall proceed with the problem of finding these solutions, with the electric scalar potential being considered first.

EXAMPLE. If $\mathbf{A} = 10^{-7} \cos 6x \cos 8z \cos \omega t\, \mathbf{k}$, determine the electric scalar potential ϕ and the electric and magnetic field intensities. The medium is free space.

Solution. The angular frequency ω can be found by substituting the expression for the magnetic vector potential into the wave equation. As the current density is zero in free space, the wave equation becomes $\nabla^2 A_z = \mu_0\epsilon_0\ddot{A}_z$. The second partial derivative of A_z with respect to x is $-36A_z$, and the second partial derivative with respect to z is $-64A_z$. Therefore, $\nabla^2 A_z = -100A_z$. As this equals $\mu_0\epsilon_0\ddot{A}_z$, or $-\omega^2\mu_0\epsilon_0 A_z$, it follows that $\omega^2\mu_0\epsilon_0 = 100$, and ω becomes 3×10^9 radians per second.

From Eq. (13-10) the electric scalar potential is

$$\phi = -\frac{1}{\mu\epsilon}\int \nabla \cdot \mathbf{A}\, dt \tag{13-13}$$

As $\nabla \cdot \mathbf{A} = -8 \times 10^{-7} \cos 6x \sin 8z \cos \omega t$, the electric scalar potential is determined to be

$$\phi = 24 \cos 6x \sin 8z \sin \omega t$$

The magnetic flux density $\mathbf{B} = \nabla \times \mathbf{A}$, or $-\partial A_z/\partial x\, \mathbf{j}$. Performing this differentiation and dividing by the permeability give the magnetic field intensity **H**, which is

$$\mathbf{H} = 0.477 \sin 6x \cos 8z \cos \omega t\, \mathbf{j}$$

The electric field intensity can be found from the Maxwell-Ampère curl equation, using the magnetic field intensity **H**, or it can be found directly from the potential functions, by means of Eq. (13-3). The result is

$$\mathbf{E} = 144 \sin 6x \sin 8z \sin \omega t\, \mathbf{i} + 108 \cos 6x \cos 8z \sin \omega t\, \mathbf{k}$$

13-2. THE ELECTRIC SCALAR POTENTIAL

The wave equation for the electric scalar potential ϕ contains the forcing function ρ/ϵ. The charge density ρ of a region is, in general, a function of the space coordinates and time. Each differential volume that contains a time-varying charge acts as a point source of a wave, and the potential ϕ at a point P is the superposition of the individual waves of the point sources. In this section we shall solve the wave equation, obtaining the potential ϕ at a point P directly in terms of an arbitrary distribution of electric charges. The discussion is restricted to the very important case of a single dielectric region extending to infinity, and the medium is assumed to be linear, isotropic, and homogeneous.

Suppose the charge densities at points of the medium vary sinusoidally with time with angular frequency ω. Then

$$\rho = \rho_m \sin (\omega t + \Theta) \tag{13-14}$$

with ρ_m and Θ denoting the amplitude and phase angle, respectively, of ρ. Both the amplitude and phase angle are functions of the space coordinates. If each side of Eq. (13-14) is multiplied by a small elemental volume, we obtain

$$q = q_m \sin (\omega t + \Theta) \tag{13-15}$$

with q denoting the charge in the elemental volume. Each such point charge of a region acts as a source of a wave.

At points of the medium not occupied by electric charge, ρ is zero, and the wave equation for ϕ becomes

$$\nabla^2\phi = \mu\epsilon\ddot{\phi} \tag{13-16}$$

It should be noted that this is a *linear* partial differential equation. If ϕ_1 and ϕ_2 are both solutions of this equation, it is easily shown by substitution that the sum $\phi_1 + \phi_2$ is also a solution. Consequently, the superposition principle can be employed. We shall first determine the potential ϕ due to a single point charge q that varies sinusoidally with time according to Eq. (13-15). Then we shall use the superposition principle to find the potential due to a distribution of such charges. This is done by adding together the contributions to ϕ of all the point charges that are present in the region. As each point charge can be regarded as the product

$\rho\, dV$, with dV denoting a differential volume of the region, the addition of the contributions of all the charges becomes an integration over the entire volume of all space. Of course, only those differential volumes containing electric charge contribute to the result.

Let us locate the origin of a spherical coordinate system at the point charge q that varies sinusoidally with time according to Eq. (13-15). *All other charges are eliminated from consideration by the superposition principle.* Later, of course, their effects will be considered. At points excluding the origin the wave equation for ϕ is Eq. (13-16). From symmetry considerations the only variation in ϕ, due to the point charge q at the origin, is in the radial direction. Therefore, $\partial\phi/\partial\theta = \partial\phi/\partial\varphi = 0$, and the wave equation for ϕ becomes

$$\frac{\partial^2\phi}{\partial r^2} + \frac{2}{r}\frac{\partial\phi}{\partial r} = \mu\epsilon\ddot{\phi} \tag{13-17}$$

Utilizing the method of separation of variables, let $\phi(r, t) = R(r)T(t)$. Replacing ϕ in Eq. (13-17) with RT and dividing both sides of the equation by the product RT give

$$\frac{1}{R}\frac{d^2R}{dr^2} + \frac{2}{rR}\frac{dR}{dr} = \mu\epsilon\frac{\ddot{T}}{T} \tag{13-18}$$

The left side of this equation is a function of r, and the right side is a function of t. As r and t may vary independently of each other, we can equate both sides to a constant. Selecting $-\beta^2$ for this constant, we obtain the two ordinary differential equations

$$\frac{d^2R}{dr^2} + \frac{2}{r}\frac{dR}{dr} + \beta^2R = 0 \tag{13-19}$$

$$\mu\epsilon\ddot{T} + \beta^2T = 0 \tag{13-20}$$

An easy way to solve Eq. (13-19) is indicated in Prob. 13-8, and the solution of Eq. (13-20) is obvious. The solutions, each of which can be verified by direct substitution, are

$$R = C_1\frac{\sin\beta r}{r} + C_2\frac{\cos\beta r}{r} \tag{13-21}$$

$$T = C_3\sin\omega t + C_4\cos\omega t \tag{13-22}$$

with $\omega = \beta/(\mu\epsilon)^{1/2}$. It is evident that ω is the angular frequency of the point charge q, and the constant β is $\omega(\mu\epsilon)^{1/2}$.

The electric potential ϕ equals the product RT. By multiplying the expressions for R and T, by utilizing trigonometric identities involving the product of sine and cosine terms, and by employing the trigonometric identity of Eq. (12-22), the potential ϕ can be written

$$\phi = \frac{C_1}{r} \sin (\omega t - \beta r + \Theta) + \frac{C_2}{r} \sin (\omega t + \beta r + \alpha) \qquad (13\text{-}23)$$

with C_1, C_2, Θ, and α denoting new constants. The first expression on the right is an outward traveling wave, and the second expression is an inward traveling wave. As the medium is infinite, there is no reflection, and the inward traveling wave is zero. Thus $C_2 = 0$, and the electric potential is

$$\phi = \frac{C_1}{r} \sin (\omega t - \beta r + \Theta) \qquad (13\text{-}24)$$

The constant Θ in Eq. (13-24) is obviously the phase angle of the point charge q, because at $r = 0$ the potential must be in time phase with the charge q. We now need to determine C_1.

The constant C_1 is readily evaluated by letting the frequency approach zero, finding the electric field from the electric potential, and comparing the result with Coulomb's law. As the frequency approaches zero, both ω and β in Eq. (13-24) approach zero, and ϕ becomes $(C_1 \sin \Theta)/r$. At zero frequency $\dot{\mathbf{A}}$ is zero, and the electric field $\mathbf{E} = -\nabla\phi$ by Eq. (13-3). Evaluation of the gradient gives

$$\mathbf{E} = \frac{C_1 \sin \Theta}{r^2} \mathbf{a}_r \qquad (13\text{-}25)$$

At zero frequency the point charge q is $q_m \sin \Theta$, by Eq. (13-15). It follows from Coulomb's law that

$$\mathbf{E} = \frac{q_m \sin \Theta}{4\pi\epsilon r^2} \mathbf{a}_r \qquad (13\text{-}26)$$

Comparison of Eqs. (13-25) and (13-26) shows that $C_1 = q_m/(4\pi\epsilon)$. Therefore,

$$\phi = \frac{q_m}{4\pi\epsilon r} \sin (\omega t - \beta r + \Theta) \qquad (13\text{-}27)$$

This is the electric potential a distance r from the point charge $q_m \sin (\omega t + \Theta)$ in a perfect dielectric. The phase constant $\beta = \omega(\mu\epsilon)^{1/2}$, with μ and ϵ denoting the permeability and permittivity, respectively, of the medium.

The expression for ϕ represents a wave traveling away from its source at a velocity v equal to ω/β. From this we determine that the phase velocity of the wave is $1/(\mu\epsilon)^{1/2}$, and for free space this becomes approximately 3×10^8 meters per second. The amplitude of the wave decreases as the distance r from the source increases. The phase angle of ϕ lags the phase of the source by βr radians. This lag in phase, or retardation, is due to the finite wave velocity.

The electric scalar potential of Eq. (13-27) can be written

$$\phi = \frac{q_m}{4\pi\epsilon r} \sin (\omega t' + \Theta) \tag{13-28}$$

with $t' = t - (\beta/\omega)r = t - r/v$. *The time t' is earlier than t by r/v seconds, which is the finite time required for the wave to propagate from its source through the distance r.* If we let

$$[q] = q_m \sin (\omega t' + \Theta) \tag{13-29}$$

then the potential becomes

$$\phi = \frac{[q]}{4\pi\epsilon r} \tag{13-30}$$

The brackets signify that the charge q is evaluated at a time earlier than t by the time of propagation, which is r/v seconds. Thus the electric potential at a point P at time t depends on the charge that existed at the earlier time $t' = t - r/v$.

Suppose the time variations of the point charge q are nonsinusoidal. In such a case the point charge can be regarded as having a number of different frequency components. The sum of the sinusoidal components of different frequencies gives the nonsinusoidal variations in q. In the perfect dielectric each frequency component travels with a velocity v equal to $1/(\mu\epsilon)^{1/2}$. As each component travels with the same velocity, there is no phase distortion. Also, there is no frequency distortion, for the amplitude of each component-wave varies inversely with distance r, regardless of the frequency. Thus the wave propagates with unchanging waveform. A change in q produces an effect at the point P located a distance r from q, but the effect is delayed by the time r/v seconds, this being the time required for propagation. Clearly, Eq. (13-30) applies *regardless of the manner in which the charge varies with time.* As the effect of a change in q is delayed at distant points because of the time of propagation, the potential ϕ is frequently referred to as a *retarded potential.*

We have found the electric scalar potential at a point P in a perfect dielectric, due to a point charge q. To obtain the potential due to a volume distribution of charges, we shall apply the superposition principle. The differential contribution to ϕ of the differential point charge $\rho\, dV$ in the differential volume dV is found from the preceding expressions for ϕ with q replaced with $\rho\, dV$. The total potential is found by integrating over the volume of all space occupied by electric charges. Equations (13-27) and (13-30) become

$$\phi = \frac{1}{4\pi\epsilon} \int_V \frac{\rho_m}{r} \sin(\omega t - \beta r + \Theta)\, dV \tag{13-31}$$

$$\phi = \frac{1}{4\pi\epsilon} \int_V \frac{[\rho]}{r}\, dV \tag{13-32}$$

The charge density ρ is, in general, a function of the space coordinates and time, and its amplitude ρ_m and its phase angle Θ are functions of the space coordinates. The retarded form of ρ is

$$[\rho] = \rho_m \sin(\omega t' + \Theta) \tag{13-33}$$

with $t' = t - r/v$. The distance r is the distance from the differential volume dV with the charge density ρ to the point P.

The electric scalar potential is frequently used in problems involving static charges. At zero frequency the time derivative of ϕ is zero, and the wave equation for ϕ reduces to

$$\nabla^2\phi = -\rho/\epsilon \tag{13-34}$$

This is known as *Poisson's equation.* As ω and β are zero, the *electrostatic potential* is

$$\phi = \frac{1}{4\pi\epsilon} \int_V \frac{\rho}{r}\, dV \tag{13-35}$$

This is the solution of Poisson's equation applied to an infinite dielectric with a charge distribution ρ. If the charges are point charges, the potential becomes

$$\phi = \frac{1}{4\pi\epsilon}\left(\frac{q_1}{r_1} + \frac{q_2}{r_2} + \cdots\right) \tag{13-36}$$

There is, of course, no retardation at zero frequency, because there are no time-varying charges. For static fields the time derivative of the magnetic vector potential is zero, and the electric field $\mathbf{E}$ is $-\nabla\phi$. Thus the electrostatic field is readily determined from a known electrostatic potential function. More will be said of this later. Let us now consider an important problem involving the retarded electric potential.

EXAMPLE. Shown in Fig. 13-1 is a short length of wire located at the origin of a spherical coordinate system and carrying a current $i = I_m \sin \omega t$. Present at the ends of the wire are charges $+q$ and $-q$, with $q = \int i\, dt = -(I_m/\omega)\cos \omega t$.

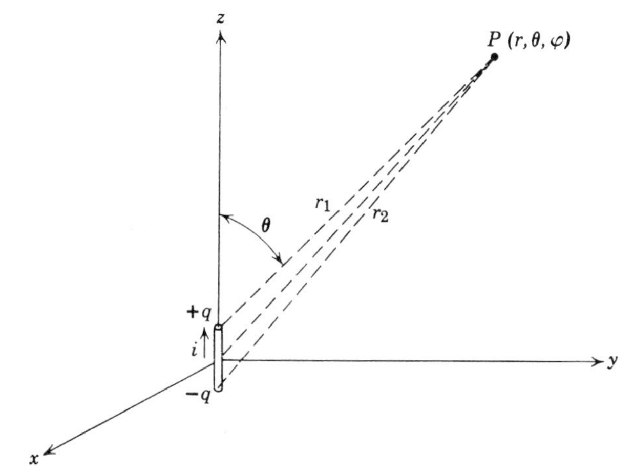

FIG. 13-1. A short wire with an alternating current i.

Determine the electric scalar potential ϕ at the point $P(r, \theta, \varphi)$ in the dielectric of permittivity ϵ and permeability μ. Assume that the length l of the wire is very small in comparison with both the wavelength λ and the distance r.

Solution. From Eq. (13-30) it follows that the potential ϕ_1 at P due to the point charge $+q$ is

$$\phi_1 = -\frac{q_m}{4\pi\epsilon r_1}\cos(\omega t - \beta r_1)$$

with $q_m = I_m/\omega$, and with $\beta = \omega(\mu\epsilon)^{1/2} = \omega/v = 2\pi/\lambda$. The term βr_1 accounts for the finite time of propagation. The potential ϕ_2 due to the point charge $-q$ is

$$\phi_2 = \frac{q_m}{4\pi\epsilon r_2}\cos(\omega t - \beta r_2)$$

By superposition, the total electric scalar potential at P is the sum of ϕ_1 and ϕ_2, which can be expressed as

$$\phi = \frac{q_m}{4\pi\epsilon r_1 r_2}[r_1\cos(\omega t - \beta r_2) - r_2\cos(\omega t - \beta r_1)]$$

The distances r_1 and r_2 are approximately equal to $r - \frac{1}{2}l\cos\theta$ and $r + \frac{1}{2}l\cos\theta$, respectively, for $r \gg l$. Also, $r_1 r_2 \approx r^2$. By substituting for r_1 and r_2, by grouping together the resulting terms in the brackets multiplied by r and also grouping those terms multiplied by $\frac{1}{2}l\cos\theta$, and by utilizing a common trigonometric identity, the potential becomes

$$\phi = \frac{q_m}{4\pi\epsilon r^2}[2r\sin(\tfrac{1}{2}\beta l\cos\theta)\sin(\omega t - \beta r) - l\cos\theta\cos(\tfrac{1}{2}\beta l\cos\theta)\cos(\omega t - \beta r)]$$

The angle $\frac{1}{2}\beta l\cos\theta$ is very small, for $\beta l = 2\pi l/\lambda$ and $l \ll \lambda$. Therefore, the sine of this angle equals $\frac{1}{2}\beta l\cos\theta$, and the cosine is unity. Consequently, the expression for ϕ can be written

$$\phi = \frac{I_m l\cos\theta}{4\pi\omega\epsilon}\left[\frac{\beta}{r}\sin(\omega t - \beta r) - \frac{1}{r^2}\cos(\omega t - \beta r)\right] \qquad (13\text{-}37)$$

with I_m/ω substituted for q_m. This is the retarded electric scalar potential at the point P. It should be noted that $-\nabla\phi$ does not give the electric field, because the fields are changing with time and **A** has value. The electric and magnetic fields of this current element are found in Sec. 13-4.

13-3. THE MAGNETIC VECTOR POTENTIAL

We shall now examine the wave equation for the magnetic vector potential **A** applied to the important case of a single dielectric region extending to infinity. The medium is assumed to be linear, isotropic, and homogeneous. The vector wave equation, given as Eq. (13-11), actually represents three scalar equations. In terms of the rectangular component A_x of **A**, we have

$$\nabla^2 A_x = \mu\epsilon \ddot{A}_x - \mu J_x \tag{13-38}$$

In the preceding section we learned that the equation

$$\nabla^2 \phi = \mu\epsilon\ddot{\phi} - \rho/\epsilon \tag{13-39}$$

yielded the solution

$$\phi = \frac{1}{4\pi\epsilon}\int_V \frac{[\rho]}{r}\,dV \tag{13-40}$$

Equation (13-38) is similar to (13-39), with A_x in place of ϕ and μJ_x in place of ρ/ϵ. By analogy, we deduce that the equation for A_x has a solution of the form of (13-40), with A_x substituted for ϕ, μ for $1/\epsilon$, and J_x for ρ. The result is

$$A_x = \frac{\mu}{4\pi}\int_V \frac{[J_x]}{r}\,dV \tag{13-41}$$

This gives the x component of **A** at a point P at time t in terms of the x components of the convection current densities that act as sources of the wave. The volume integral must include all volumes with convection currents. The retarded current density $[J_x]$ is the x component of **J** in the differential volume dV at a time earlier than t by r/v seconds. Of course, r is the distance from dV to P, and v is the wave velocity $1/(\mu\epsilon)^{1/2}$.

For sinusoidal time variations $J_x = (J_x)_m \sin(\omega t + \Theta_x)$, and $[J_x]$ equals J_x with t replaced with $t - r/v$. This can be written

$$[J_x] = (J_x)_m \sin(\omega t - \beta r + \Theta_x) \tag{13-42}$$

with $\beta = \omega/v = \omega(\mu\epsilon)^{1/2} = 2\pi/\lambda$. In general, the amplitude $(J_x)_m$ and the phase angle Θ_x of J_x are functions of the space coordinates.

The expressions for the y and z components of **A** are similar to the one for A_x. Obviously, the scalar expressions for these components can be compounded into a single vector equation, which is

$$\mathbf{A} = \frac{\mu}{4\pi} \int_V \frac{[\mathbf{J}]}{r}\, dV \tag{13-43}$$

The retarded vector current density [**J**], in terms of its rectangular components, is $[J_x]\mathbf{i} + [J_y]\mathbf{j} + [J_z]\mathbf{k}$, and for sinusoidal time variations each component has the form of Eq. (13-42). The magnetic vector potential **A** is often called a retarded potential.

If the convection current densities are surface current densities, we must replace $[\mathbf{J}]\, dV$ in Eq. (13-43) with $[\mathbf{J}_s]\, dS$, and the integration becomes a surface integral. If the current densities are confined to filamentary paths, we must replace $[\mathbf{J}]\, dV$ with $[i]\, d\mathbf{l}$ and integrate along the paths of the currents. For this latter case the expression for the magnetic vector potential becomes

$$\mathbf{A} = \frac{\mu}{4\pi} \int_C \frac{[i]}{r}\, d\mathbf{l} \tag{13-44}$$

For sinusoidal time variations, $i = I_m \sin(\omega t + \Theta)$, and the retarded form of i is

$$[i] = I_m \sin(\omega t - \beta r + \Theta) \tag{13-45}$$

In general, a region may have volume current densities, surface current densities, and currents along filamentary paths. All currents must be included in the determination of **A**. Although the determination of the potential functions has been restricted to a lossless medium, the results are easily extended to a dissipative medium by applying the method of Prob. 19-40 to the potential functions in complex-exponential form, given in Sec. 19-11.

An important special case is that involving direct currents. For currents steady with time, both ω and β are zero, there is no retardation, and Eqs. (13-43) and (13-44) become

$$\mathbf{A} = \frac{\mu}{4\pi} \int_V \frac{\mathbf{J}}{r}\, dV \tag{13-46}$$

$$\mathbf{A} = \frac{\mu}{4\pi} \int_C \frac{I}{r}\, d\mathbf{l} \tag{13-47}$$

Direct currents act as sources of the *magnetostatic* vector potential.

If a known system of currents is present in a medium, the expressions for **A** can be utilized to advantage in many types of problems. In the usual case the medium is free space, and the currents that produce the fields are conduction currents in metals. Once the magnetic vector potential is determined as a function of the space coordinates and time, the electric and magnetic fields are readily found. The magnetic flux density **B** equals the curl of **A**, and the electric field intensity **E** can be found from the magnetic field by employing the Maxwell-Ampère curl equation. An alternate way to determine the electric field is to find both ϕ and **A**, and then employ Eq. (13-3). The electric potential ϕ is easily obtained from **A** by means of Eq. (13-13), or ϕ can be found directly from the charges present. After the example, we shall investigate the electric and magnetic fields of a current element, utilizing the retarded potentials to find these fields.

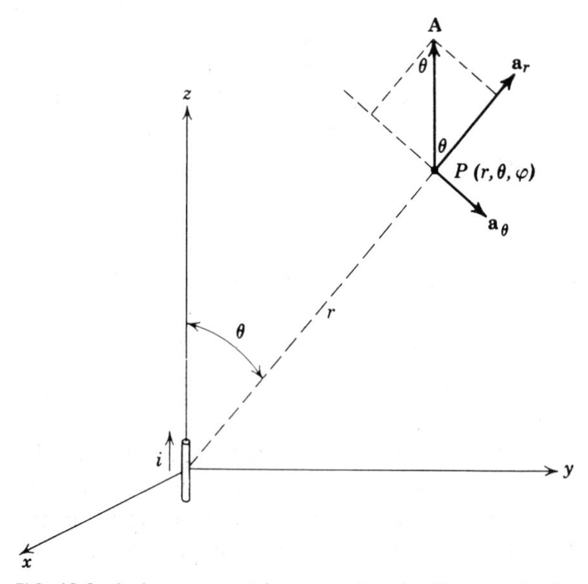

FIG. 13-2. A short wire with current i, and a distant point P.

EXAMPLE. In the example of the preceding section we found the *electric* potential of a short length l of wire carrying a current $i = I_m \sin \omega t$. Our problem now is to determine the spherical components of the *magnetic vector* potential at the point $P(r, \theta, \varphi)$, shown in Fig. 13-2. As before, the length l is very small in comparison with both the wavelength λ and the distance r.

Solution. Each differential length of the wire has the same current i and, as $l \ll r$, is approximately the same distance r from the point P. Therefore, the integrand $[i]/r$ of Eq. (13-44) can be taken outside the integral sign, leaving the integral of $d\mathbf{l}$ over the length l of the wire. This integral equals $l\mathbf{k}$, and the magnetic vector potential becomes $\mu[i]l\mathbf{k}/(4\pi r)$. The retarded current $[i]$ is given by Eq. (13-45) with the phase angle equal to zero. Consequently,

$$A_z = \frac{\mu I_m l}{4\pi r} \sin(\omega t - \beta r) \tag{13-48}$$

with $\beta = \omega(\mu\epsilon)^{1/2} = \omega/v = 2\pi/\lambda$. It should be noted that **A** at P is parallel to the wire.

With reference to Fig. 13-2, we note that there are spherical components of **A** in the directions of the unit vectors $\mathbf{a}_r$ and $\mathbf{a}_\theta$. The radial component A_r is $A_z \cos\theta$, and the component A_θ is $-A_z \sin\theta$. Obviously, A_φ is zero. Therefore the magnetic vector potential is

$$\mathbf{A} = A_z \cos\theta\, \mathbf{a}_r - A_z \sin\theta\, \mathbf{a}_\theta \tag{13-49}$$

with A_z given by Eq. (13-48).

13-4. FIELDS OF A CURRENT ELEMENT

The electric and magnetic fields of a system of currents can be found by superimposing the differential fields of all the differential current elements of the system. Thus the fields of a single isolated current element in a dielectric extending to infinity are of considerable engineering importance. Let us consider the current element $i\, d\mathbf{l}$, also often called a *current moment*, a *differential dipole*, or a *Hertzian dipole*. Assuming sinusoidal time variations, we can represent i by $I_m \sin(\omega t + \Theta)$. With $i\, d\mathbf{l}$ located at the origin of a coordinate system that is oriented so that $d\mathbf{l} = dz\, \mathbf{k}$, the current element becomes

$$i\, d\mathbf{l} = I_m\, dz \sin(\omega t + \Theta)\, \mathbf{k} \tag{13-50}$$

In the examples of Secs. 13-2 and 13-3 we found the potential functions of a short wire similarly located and carrying a sinusoidal current. The assumption was made that the length l of the wire was very small compared with both the wavelength and the distance to the arbitrary point P. This assumption is satisfied perfectly by the current element of differential length dz. Therefore, if we substitute dz for l in the expressions for ϕ and **A**, and also add the phase angle Θ of i to the phases of these wave functions, we obtain the electric scalar and magnetic vector potentials of our current element. Specifically, ϕ is given by Eq. (13-37), and **A** is given by Eqs. (13-48) and (13-49), with dz substituted for l and with $(\omega t - \beta r + \Theta)$ substituted for $(\omega t - \beta r)$.

The electric and magnetic fields are readily obtained from the potential functions. The magnetic flux density $\mathbf{B} = \nabla \times \mathbf{A}$. As A_φ is zero and as A_r and A_θ are independent of the variable φ, the curl of **A** in spherical coordinates becomes

$$\nabla \times \mathbf{A} = \frac{1}{r}\left[\frac{\partial}{\partial r}(rA_\theta) - \frac{\partial A_r}{\partial \theta}\right] \mathbf{a}_\varphi \tag{13-51}$$

If we substitute for A_r and A_θ and perform the indicated operations, we obtain **B**. Division of the result by μ gives the magnetic field intensity **H**.

The component H_φ is

$$H_\varphi = \frac{I_m\,dz \sin\theta}{4\pi}\left[\frac{\beta}{r}\cos(\omega t - \beta r + \Theta) + \frac{1}{r^2}\sin(\omega t - \beta r + \Theta)\right] \tag{13-52}$$

The components H_r and H_θ are zero. An important conclusion is that the magnetic field of a current element has field lines that are circular about the element, with the planes of these circles normal to the direction of the current element. There is no component of **H** in the direction of the current element, and there is no radial component.

The electric field **E** can be determined directly from the potential functions, using Eq. (13-3), or it can be found from the Maxwell-Ampère curl equation and the known magnetic field. The resulting spherical components of **E** are

$$E_r = \frac{I_m\,dz \cos\theta}{2\pi\omega\epsilon}\left[\frac{\beta}{r^2}\sin(\omega t - \beta r + \Theta) - \frac{1}{r^3}\cos(\omega t - \beta r + \Theta)\right] \tag{13-53}$$

$$E_\theta = \frac{I_m\,dz \sin\theta}{4\pi\omega\epsilon}\left[\frac{\beta^2}{r}\cos(\omega t - \beta r + \Theta) + \frac{\beta}{r^2}\sin(\omega t - \beta r + \Theta) - \frac{1}{r^3}\cos(\omega t - \beta r + \Theta)\right] \tag{13-54}$$

The component $E_\varphi = 0$. It should be noted that the electric and magnetic fields are normal to one another at each point of the dielectric.

13-5. RADIATION FROM A CURRENT ELEMENT

The phase constant β in the expressions for the fields of a current element equals $2\pi/\lambda$. At a distance r that is very large compared with the wavelength λ, it is evident that $\beta/r \gg 1/r^2$, and the magnetic field of Eq. (13-52) becomes

$$H_\varphi = \frac{I_m\,dz\,\beta \sin\theta}{4\pi r}\cos(\omega t - \beta r + \Theta) \tag{13-55}$$

Also, for $r \gg \lambda$ it is evident that $\beta^2/r \gg \beta/r^2 \gg 1/r^3$, and the electric field of Eq. (13-54) becomes

$$E_\theta = \frac{I_m\,dz\,\beta^2 \sin\theta}{4\pi\omega\epsilon r}\cos(\omega t - \beta r + \Theta) \tag{13-56}$$

The radial component E_r of Eq. (13-53) is negligible in comparison, and the component E_φ is zero. H_φ and E_θ of Eqs. (13-55) and (13-56) are the distant, or *radiation*, fields.

The ratio of E to H is the intrinsic impedance η of the medium in ohms. From Eqs. (13-55) and (13-56) this ratio is found to be $\beta/(\omega\epsilon)$. As $\beta = \omega(\mu\epsilon)^{1/2}$, it is evident that

$$\eta = E_\theta/H_\varphi = (\mu/\epsilon)^{1/2} \tag{13-57}$$

In free space η is 377 ohms, and the electric field intensity is 377 times the magnetic field intensity at every point at every instant, provided $r \gg \lambda$.

Electromagnetic energy flow is determined from the Poynting vector $\mathbf{S}$. As $\mathbf{E} = E_\theta \mathbf{a}_\theta$ and $\mathbf{H} = H_\varphi \mathbf{a}_\varphi$, and as $\mathbf{a}_\theta \times \mathbf{a}_\varphi = \mathbf{a}_r$, the Poynting vector becomes

$$\mathbf{S} = \mathbf{E} \times \mathbf{H} = E_\theta H_\varphi \mathbf{a}_r \text{ watts/m}^2 \tag{13-58}$$

Performing this multiplication and replacing $\beta^3/(\omega\epsilon)$ with $(2\pi/\lambda)^2(\mu/\epsilon)^{1/2}$, we obtain

$$\mathbf{S} = \frac{I_m^{\ 2}}{4}\sqrt{\frac{\mu}{\epsilon}}\left(\frac{dz}{\lambda}\right)^2 \frac{\sin^2\theta}{r^2}\cos^2(\omega t - \beta r + \Theta)\,\mathbf{a}_r \tag{13-59}$$

The flow of energy at every point is *radially outward at every instant.* At each point the energy flow per unit area per unit time varies with time, but the flow is always outward. Clearly, *a time-varying electric current radiates energy.* As time varies, the cosine squared term of Eq. (13-59) varies between zero and one, with a time average of one-half. Therefore, the time-average power per unit area, in watts/m², is

$$\mathbf{S}_{\text{ave}} = \frac{I_m^{\ 2}}{8}\sqrt{\frac{\mu}{\epsilon}}\left(\frac{dz}{\lambda}\right)^2 \frac{\sin^2\theta}{r^2}\,\mathbf{a}_r \tag{13-60}$$

The total power radiated by the current element can be found by evaluating the surface integral of $\mathbf{S}_{\text{ave}}$ over a surface that encloses the origin. Selecting for convenience a spherical surface of radius r, having a differential vector surface area of $r^2 \sin\theta\, d\theta\, d\varphi\, \mathbf{a}_r$, with limits of 0 and π for θ and 0 and 2π for φ, we find the time-average radiated power P to be

$$P = \frac{\pi I_m^{\ 2}}{3}\sqrt{\frac{\mu}{\epsilon}}\left(\frac{dz}{\lambda}\right)^2 \text{ watts} \tag{13-61}$$

For free space this is approximately $395 I_m^{\ 2}(dz/\lambda)^2$ watts. If the wavelength is not infinite, there is energy radiated. A direct current has an infinite wavelength and does not radiate. However, a time-varying current radiates energy that propagates in the electromagnetic wave at a finite velocity determined by the electrical properties of the medium.

The phase $(\omega t - \beta r + \Theta)$ of the electromagnetic wave of a current element is the same at all points of a spherical surface of radius r. As the *equiphase surfaces* are spheres, the wave is a *spherical* wave. A small portion of an equiphase surface a large distance from the current element approximates a plane and, therefore, the radiated wave in a limited region approximates a *plane* wave. Furthermore, the wave in this limited region is nearly *uniform*, for the components do not vary appreciably from point to point in any equiphase surface of this limited region. Thus the radiation wave of a current element approximates a uniform plane wave in any region sufficiently limited. The electric and magnetic fields of the radiated wave are perpendicular to one another, and the energy flow at a point is normal to the plane of **E** and **H**.

The convection current density **J** at a point P is defined as the product $\rho\mathbf{v}$. If the charge carriers at P are accelerating, the velocity **v** and the current density **J** vary with time. As **J** varies with time, there is energy radiated. Therefore, *an accelerating charge radiates energy*. Thus we have deduced from Maxwell's equations the fact that time-varying currents and accelerating charges radiate energy. It was this deduction that led to the development of radio.

Electric circuit theory deals with circuits having dimensions that are very small compared with the wavelength. Radiation from such circuits is usually negligible. The current i is approximately the same in all parts of a series circuit that is physically small compared with the wavelength, and the summation of all the current elements of such a circuit is $i \oint d\mathbf{l} = 0$. The fields produced by the closely spaced current elements, whose vector sum is zero, tend to cancel. However, at sufficiently high frequencies the circuit dimensions are no longer very small compared with the wavelength, and the currents in the different parts of the circuit have different values. In certain directions the fields of the individual current elements may reinforce one another, and radiation may be appreciable.

The conductors of electric transmission lines are separated a distance that is very small compared with the wavelength of the exciting source. Each current element of each conductor has an equal but oppositely directed current element nearby. Consequently, the radiation fields are very small, for the fields of the equal and opposite current elements tend to cancel. The radiated power is often inconsequential.

In antennas the conductors are arranged so that the fields of the individual current elements reinforce one another in the directions in which it is desired to radiate energy. Each current element is a source of electromagnetic radiation. However, if an antenna system is to be an efficient radiator, the radiated power must be large compared with the power dissipated as heat in the antenna. This requires antenna dimensions not too small compared with the wavelength. Consequently, efficient low-frequency antennas are large, and efficient high-frequency antennas are relatively small. The expressions for the fields of a current element are the basic equations of antenna theory.

13-6. THE BIOT-SAVART LAW

Having examined the distant fields, let us now consider the magnetic field in the immediate vicinity of a current element. As $\beta/r = 2\pi/(\lambda r)$, it follows that $\beta/r \ll 1/r^2$ for $r \ll \lambda$. Therefore, the only important term in the expression for H_φ in Eq. (13-52), at distances very small compared with

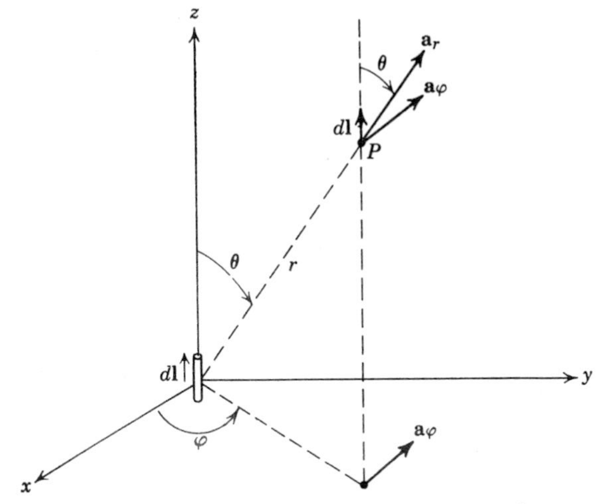

FIG. 13-3. Sketch showing that $d\mathbf{l} \times \mathbf{a}_r = dz \sin\theta\, \mathbf{a}_\varphi$.

the wavelength, is the one that varies as $1/r^2$. The phase of the wave contains the angle βr, which is negligibly small for $r \ll \lambda$, and the differential magnetic field near the current element becomes

$$d\mathbf{H} = \frac{i\, dz \sin\theta}{4\pi r^2}\, \mathbf{a}_\varphi \tag{13-62}$$

This is the *Biot-Savart law*. It gives the magnetic field of a current element *at distances very small compared with the wavelength*. The field at time t is proportional to the value of the current i at this same instant, because retardation is negligible at these small distances. The expression is exact only if the current is steady, for in this case the wavelength is infinite and all distances are small in comparison. Of course the dielectric must be linear, isotropic, and homogeneous.

A common vector form of the Biot-Savart law is

$$d\mathbf{H} = \frac{i\, d\mathbf{l} \times \mathbf{a}_r}{4\pi r^2} \tag{13-63}$$

The equivalence of Eqs. (13-62) and (13-63) is evident from a study of Fig. 13-3. The cross product $d\mathbf{l} \times \mathbf{a}_r$ obviously equals $dz \sin\theta\, \mathbf{a}_\varphi$. It should be noted that r is the distance from the current element to the point P, and $\mathbf{a}_r$ is a unit vector at P directed radially away from the element. If $\mathbf{r}$ denotes the vector distance from the element to P, then $\mathbf{a}_r = \mathbf{r}/r$.

Let us examine the accuracy of the Biot-Savart law at a distance of 0.01λ. In the general expression for the magnetic field of a current element, given as Eq. (13-52), the amplitude of the neglected term is βr times the amplitude of the retained term, and the neglected phase lag is βr radians. For $r = 0.01\lambda$, βr is 0.02π, or 0.063. Therefore, the amplitude of the neglected term is 6.3% of that of the retained term, and the neglected phase angle is 0.063 radian, or 3.6°. Thus the Biot-Savart law is only a rough approximation at a distance of 0.01λ. Its accuracy increases, of course, at shorter distances. At 60 cycles, 0.01λ is about 31 miles, and the Biot-Savart law can be safely applied to 60-cycle laboratory circuits. On the other hand, at 3 mc a distance of 0.01λ is one meter, and at 300 mc it is only a centimeter.

EXAMPLE. Shown in Fig. 13-4 is a section of an infinitely long straight wire carrying a steady current I. Using the Biot-Savart law, find the magnetic field at the point P a distance r_1 from the wire.

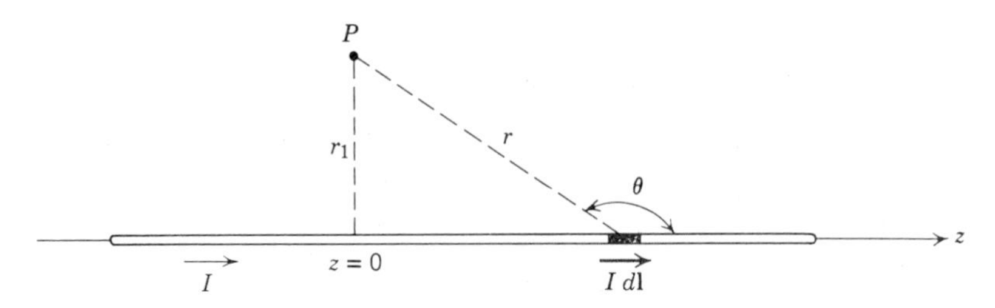

FIG. 13-4. A long straight wire with a steady current I.

Solution. The differential magnetic field of a single current element is given by Eq. (13-62), with the unit vector $\mathbf{a}_\varphi$ at P directed out of the paper. Therefore, the total magnetic field at P is

$$\mathbf{H} = \int_{-\infty}^{\infty} \frac{I \sin \theta}{4\pi r^2} \, dz \, \mathbf{a}_\varphi$$

From the illustration it is evident that $\sin \theta = r_1/r$ and $r = (z^2 + r_1{}^2)^{1/2}$. Using these relations to eliminate the variables $\sin \theta$ and r gives the integral in terms of the single variable z. Evaluation reveals that the magnetic field $\mathbf{H}$ is $I/(2\pi r_1)\,\mathbf{a}_\varphi$. This same result was obtained in Sec. 8-5 by applying the integral form of the Maxwell-Ampère law to a circular path around the wire. There is no restriction on the distance r_1, for the current is steady, with zero frequency and an infinite wavelength.

13-7. VOLTAGE AND ELECTRIC POTENTIAL

Now that both voltage and electric potential have been defined, it would be improper to neglect consideration of their similarities and differences, which are frequently misunderstood. Both quantities have the same dimensions and are measured in volts. When the electromagnetic fields are static, as we shall see, the voltage drop along a path equals the potential drop between the end points of the path. Furthermore, these quantities are also equal in *idealized* electric circuit diagrams, and they are approximately equal in physical circuits, provided voltmeter leads do not encircle appreciable time-changing magnetic flux. This is discussed in the next chapter.

The electromotive force, or voltage drop, along a path C has been defined as the work per unit charge done by the electromagnetic fields on a test charge moved along C. In terms of the fields the voltage drop is the line integral of the vector $\mathbf{E} + \mathbf{v} \times \mathbf{B}$, and for stationary paths this becomes simply the line integral of the electric field intensity. In accordance with Eq. (13-3), the electric field consists of the components $-\nabla\phi$ and $-\dot{\mathbf{A}}$ Therefore, the voltage drop v along a stationary path C, in terms of the potential functions, is

$$v = -\int_C \nabla\phi \cdot d\mathbf{l} - \int_C \dot{\mathbf{A}} \cdot d\mathbf{l} \tag{13-64}$$

The scalar product of $\nabla\phi$ and $d\mathbf{l}$ is $d\phi$, which denotes the differential increase in the electric potential ϕ in the length $d\mathbf{l}$. This is evident from the discussion of Sec. 10-2, and also from the expansion of the product in rectangular coordinates, which gives

$$\nabla\phi \cdot d\mathbf{l} = \frac{\partial\phi}{\partial x}\,dx + \frac{\partial\phi}{\partial y}\,dy + \frac{\partial\phi}{\partial z}\,dz = d\phi \tag{13-65}$$

The integral of this scalar product along the path C is, of course, the potential rise along the path, and the negative of this integral is the potential drop. Therefore, the voltage drop becomes

$$v = \phi_1 - \phi_2 - \int_C \dot{\mathbf{A}} \cdot d\mathbf{l} \tag{13-66}$$

with ϕ_1 and ϕ_2 denoting the electric potentials of the starting and end points, respectively, of the path C. Thus the voltage drop v equals the potential drop $\phi_1 - \phi_2$ less the line integral of $\dot{\mathbf{A}}$.

The line integral of $\dot{\mathbf{A}}$ depends on the actual path C between the end points, because the vector $\mathbf{A}$ is, in general, nonconservative. The electric potential drop depends only on the end points, however; the vector $\nabla\phi$ is conservative. Each point of space at any given instant has one, and only one, electric scalar potential, and the potential drop between any two points is the difference between their potentials, with no path involved in this calculation. For the special case of static fields, the time derivative of **A** is zero, and the voltage drop along a stationary path equals the potential drop between the end points of the path. For time-varying fields, v depends on the actual path of integration. As there are an infinite number of possible paths between any two points, the voltage drop between the points may have an infinite number of possible values. The potential drop, however, is single-valued.

EXAMPLE 1. A static charge q is located in an infinite dielectric of permittivity ϵ. The point P_1 is r_1 meters from q, and the point P_2 is r_2 meters from q. Find the voltage drop v from P_1 to P_2.

Solution. As the fields are static, the voltage drop v equals the potential drop. The potential of P_1 is $q/(4\pi\epsilon r_1)$, and the potential of P_2 is $q/(4\pi\epsilon r_2)$, retardation being nonexistent. Therefore, $v = (q/4\pi\epsilon)(1/r_1 - 1/r_2)$. This is the voltage drop along any path from P_1 to P_2.

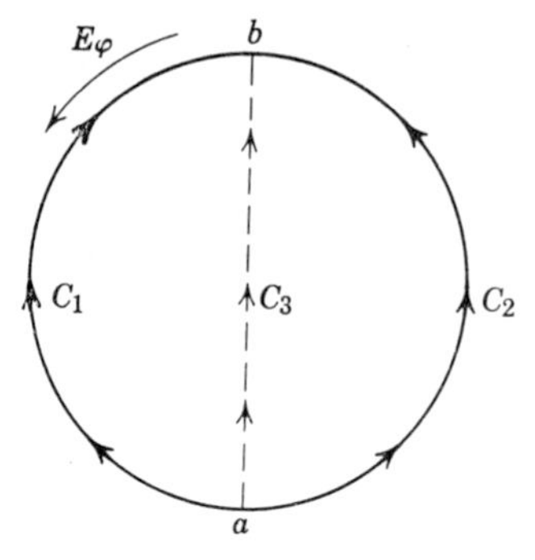

FIG. 13-5. A loop of unit radius in electromagnetic fields.

EXAMPLE 2. Shown in Fig. 13-5 is a loop of unit radius, centered at the origin of a cylindrical coordinate system with the unit vector $\mathbf{a}_z$ directed out of the paper. For $r \leq 1$, the approximate **E** and **B** fields are

$$\mathbf{E} \approx -3(r/2 - r^3/16 + r^5/384) \cos \omega t \, \mathbf{a}_\varphi$$
$$\mathbf{B} \approx 10^{-8}(1 - r^2/4 + r^4/64) \sin \omega t \, \mathbf{a}_z$$

with $\omega = 3 \times 10^8$. Find the potentials ϕ and **A**, and calculate the voltage drop along each of the paths C_1, C_2, and C_3. This example is quite similar to one discussed in Example 1 of Sec. 8-2.

Solution. As the fields are independent of the cylindrical coordinates φ and z, so are the potential functions. Consequently, $\nabla\phi = \partial\phi/\partial r \, \mathbf{a}_r$. However, this must be zero, because E_r is zero. Therefore, the electric potential ϕ is independent of the space coordinates, and the electric potential difference between any two points is zero. It follows that $\mathbf{E} = -\dot{\mathbf{A}}$. From this we readily determine the magnetic vector potential **A** to be

$$\mathbf{A} \approx 10^{-8}(r/2 - r^3/16 + r^5/384) \sin \omega t \, \mathbf{a}_\varphi$$

for $r \leq 1$.

At $r = 1$, $E_\varphi = -1.32 \cos \omega t$. The voltage drop along C_1 is $-E_\varphi$ multiplied by the path length π, or 4.15 cos ωt volts. Along C_3, the electric field lines are normal to the path, and the voltage is zero. The voltage drop along C_2 is the negative of that along C_1. Between the points a and b the voltage drop depends on the path, but the electric potential drop is, of course, zero.

13-8. SUMMARY

A potential function in electrical theory is a scalar or vector point function from which electric or magnetic fields are obtainable by processes of differentiation. In terms of the electric scalar potential ϕ and the magnetic vector potential **A**, Maxwell's equations applied to media that are linear, isotropic, and homogeneous are

$$\mathbf{B} = \nabla \times \mathbf{A} \tag{13-67}$$

$$\mathbf{E} = -\nabla\phi - \dot{\mathbf{A}} \tag{13-68}$$

$$\nabla \cdot \mathbf{A} = -\mu\epsilon\dot{\phi} \tag{13-69}$$

$$\nabla^2\phi = \mu\epsilon\ddot{\phi} - \rho/\epsilon \tag{13-70}$$

$$\nabla^2\mathbf{A} = \mu\epsilon\ddot{\mathbf{A}} - \mu\mathbf{J} \tag{13-71}$$

The first two of these equations give the fields in terms of the potential functions, and the last three equations fix the relationships between the potentials and the charge and current densities that produce the fields.

Application of the wave equations for ϕ and **A** to a linear, isotropic, and homogeneous dielectric, extending to infinity and containing an arbitrary distribution of charges and currents, revealed that

$$\phi = \frac{1}{4\pi\epsilon}\int_V \frac{[\rho]}{r}\,dV \tag{13-72}$$

$$\mathbf{A} = \frac{\mu}{4\pi}\int_V \frac{[\mathbf{J}]}{r}\,dV \tag{13-73}$$

with the brackets around ρ and **J** signifying that these are the charge and current densities present at time $t - r/v$, t being the time under consideration and v denoting the wave velocity $1/(\mu\epsilon)^{1/2}$. For filamentary conductors Eq. (13-73) becomes

$$\mathbf{A} = \frac{\mu}{4\pi}\int_C \frac{[i]}{r}\,d\mathbf{l} \tag{13-74}$$

The potential functions were utilized to determine the fields of a current element. By means of the Poynting vector, applied to the distant fields, we deduced that alternating currents and accelerating charges radiate energy in the electromagnetic wave. At distances from the current element very small compared with the wavelength, the approximate magnetic field is

$$d\mathbf{H} = \frac{i\,d\mathbf{l} \times \mathbf{a}_r}{4\pi r^2} \tag{13-75}$$

This is known as the Biot-Savart law. It applies to perfect dielectrics that are linear, isotropic, and homogeneous.

We also found that the voltage drop along a stationary path equals the electric potential drop between the end points of the path less the line integral of $\dot{\mathbf{A}}$. For static fields the voltage and potential drops are equal.

REFERENCES

Cullwick, E. G., *The Fundamentals of Electromagnetism*, Cambridge University Press, London, 2nd ed., 1949, Chap. 5.

Moon, P., and D. E. Spencer, *Foundations of Electrodynamics*, D. Van Nostrand Co., Princeton, N.J., 1960, Chaps. 1, 2, 3.

Moullin, E. B., *The Principles of Electromagnetism*, Oxford University Press, London, 2nd ed., 1950, Chap. 5.

Phillips, H. B., *Vector Analysis*, John Wiley and Sons, New York, 1933.

Ramo, S., and J. R. Whinnery, *Fields and Waves in Modern Radio*, John Wiley and Sons, New York, 2nd ed., 1953, Chap. 4.

PROBLEMS

Section 13-1

13-1. If $\mathbf{A} = x(1 + 2y)\mathbf{j}$ and $\mathbf{B} = -y^2\mathbf{i} + x\mathbf{j}$, find the curls of the vectors $\mathbf{A}$ and $\mathbf{B}$. Deduce that $\mathbf{A}$ can be equated to $\mathbf{B} + \nabla w$, and determine the scalar point function w.

13-2. For any given distribution of charges and currents the electric scalar potential ϕ and the magnetic vector potential $\mathbf{A}$ are zero an infinite distance away, for the fields are zero at such a distance from their sources. Show that the fields determined from the potential functions are unchanged if the electric potential is changed to $\phi + C_1$, with C_1 denoting any constant independent of the space coordinates but not necessarily independent of time. From this result deduce that the point of zero electric potential can be selected arbitrarily insofar as the direct determination of the fields is concerned.

13-3. Determine the quantity that must be added to the expression for the electric scalar potential ϕ of the Example of Sec. 13-1 if the point (0.1, 0.1, 0.1) is to be at zero potential. Does the resulting expression for ϕ satisfy Eq. (13-3)? Does it satisfy Eq. (13-12)?

13-4. Deduce that the magnetic field determined from the magnetic vector potential is unchanged if the vector potential is changed to $\mathbf{A} + \mathbf{C}$, with $\mathbf{C}$ denoting any vector independent of the space coordinates but not necessarily independent of time. However, show that the electric field determined from ϕ and $\mathbf{A}$ is changed if $\mathbf{C}$ varies with time. From these results deduce that the point of zero magnetic vector potential can be selected arbitrarily for static fields, and also for time-varying fields if $\mathbf{A}$ is used *only* to find $\mathbf{B}$.

13-5. If the expression for $\mathbf{A}$ in the Example of Sec. 13-1 is modified so as to make the origin a point of zero magnetic potential, show that the result can be employed to determine the magnetic field but *not* the electric field.

13-6. By direct substitution show that the electric and magnetic fields of Eqs. (13-1) and (13-3) satisfy Maxwell's equations, provided the potential functions are related to the charge and current densities according to Eqs. (13-10), (13-11), and (13-12).

13-7. If $\mathbf{A} = 10^{-7} \sin 3x \sin 4y \sin \omega t\, \mathbf{k}$ in free space, find ω and the electric scalar potential ϕ, and determine the electric and magnetic field intensities directly from the potential functions. By direct substitution verify that the resulting fields satisfy the four Maxwell equations.

Section 13-2

13-8. Replace R in Eq. (13-19) with y/r, and solve for y. Divide this solution by r to obtain the function R of Eq. (13-21).

13-9. By direct substitution verify that Eqs. (13-21) and (13-22) are solutions of Eqs. (13-19) and (13-20). Also, deduce Eq. (13-23) from the product RT.

13-10. A generator connected between two small conducting balls 8 m apart in free space produces charges of $+q$ and $-q$ on the balls, with $q = 10^{-8} \sin 3 \times 10^7 t$ coulomb. If the charge $+q$ is at the origin of a rectangular coordinate system and the charge $-q$ is on the x-axis at $x = 8$, find the amplitude and phase angle of the electric potential at $y = 6$ on the y-axis. Also, what is the potential if the charges are static, with $q = 10^{-8}$?

Section 13-4

13-11. From the magnetic vector potential of a current element, derive the expression for the magnetic field intensity.

13-12. From the electric scalar and magnetic vector potentials of a current element, derive the expression for the electric field intensity.

13-13. Determine the electric field intensity of a current element directly from the magnetic field intensity of Eq. (13-52).

13-14. Derive the expression for the electric scalar potential of a current element directly from the magnetic vector potential of Eqs. (13-48) and (13-49).

Section 13-6

13-15. At a frequency of 1 mc, at what distance from a current element is the amplitude of the radiation magnetic field equal to 10 times the amplitude of the near magnetic field? At what distance is the amplitude of the radiation magnetic field equal to 0.1 the amplitude of the near magnetic field, and what is the phase retardation in degrees at this distance? The medium is free space.

13-16. The *magnetostatic* vector potential of a current element, in spherical coordinates, can be found from Eqs. (13-47) and (13-49). For the case of static fields, derive the Biot-Savart law from the magnetostatic vector potential.

13-17. The current element $10 \sin 10^5 t\, dz\, \mathbf{k}$ ampere-meters is located at the point $(-3, 4, 6)$ in rectangular coordinates. From the Biot-Savart law find the differential magnetic field intensity, due to this current element, at the point $(3, -2, 9)$. Express the magnetic field in terms of dz and the unit vectors. Also, justify the use of the approximate Biot-Savart law.

General

13-18. The electric field intensity between the plates of a certain vacuum diode is $-500{,}000x^{1/3}\mathbf{i}$ volts/meter. Find the electric scalar potential ϕ in the region, with zero potential taken at $x = 0$. What is the potential at $x = 0.005$?

13-19. The electric field in a nonferromagnetic conductor is

$$\mathbf{E} = 0.0001 e^{-1000x} \sin (10^5 t - 1000x)\, \mathbf{k}$$

Find the potential functions ϕ and $\mathbf{A}$ directly from $\mathbf{E}$, recalling that the potentials are zero at infinity. From $\mathbf{A}$ determine the magnetic field $\mathbf{H}$. Also, find the drift current density $\mathbf{J}$ and the conductivity σ.

13-20. Find the potential functions ϕ and $\mathbf{A}$ for the fields of Prob. 11-7.

13-21. For the fields of Prob. 13-19, calculate the voltage drop v along the path that extends directly from the origin O to the point P on the z-axis at $z = 10$. Also, find v from O to P along the path from O to the point $(0.001, 0, 0)$ to $(0.001, 0, 10)$ to P. What is the potential drop from O to P?

13-22. A small conducting loop of area S, carrying a steady current I, is located at the origin of a spherical coordinate system with the plane of the loop in the plane $\theta = \frac{1}{2}\pi$. The magnetic vector potential at a distant point $P(r, \theta, \varphi)$ in a dielectric of permeability μ is

$$\mathbf{A} = \frac{\mu IS \sin\theta}{4\pi r^2}\,\mathbf{a}_\varphi$$

Find the magnetic flux density $\mathbf{B}$.

13-23. If we let the magnetic vector potential $\mathbf{A} = \mu\epsilon\dot{\mathbf{Z}}$, determine the electric potential ϕ and the field intensities $\mathbf{E}$ and $\mathbf{H}$ in terms of $\mathbf{Z}$. Also, show that the wave equations for $\mathbf{A}$ and ϕ each become

$$\nabla^2\mathbf{Z} = \mu\epsilon\ddot{\mathbf{Z}} - \mathbf{G}/\epsilon$$

with the vector point function $\mathbf{G}$ defined in terms of the charge and convection current densities by the equations

$$\nabla\cdot\mathbf{G} = -\rho \qquad \dot{\mathbf{G}} = \mathbf{J}$$

Neglect all time-independent constants of integration. The point function $\mathbf{Z}$ is the *Hertz vector potential.*

13-24. From the wave equation for the vector potential $\mathbf{A}$ deduce the integral expression for A_z corresponding to Eq. (13-41). Follow closely the procedure of Sec. 13-2, evaluating the constant of proportionality with the aid of the Biot-Savart law. (For a steady current element the Biot-Savart law is derived in Sec. 17-1 without utilizing potential functions.)

Circuit Concepts I

CHAPTER 14

Many important problems in electrical engineering involve linear circuits. Usually a circuit consists of power sources, resistors that dissipate energy, and capacitors and inductors that store energy in their electric and magnetic fields, respectively. The foundation of circuit theory is classical electromagnetic field theory. Application of the fundamental laws of electromagnetism to circuits with dimensions suitably restricted leads to the circuit concepts of Kirchhoff and Ohm.

The engineer who is to understand and utilize circuit theory properly should be familiar with its electromagnetic basis. Field theory is employed to calculate values of resistance, inductance, and capacitance. Frequently, circuit concepts are applied to problems that involve conductors with one or several unrestricted dimensions. For example, the analysis and design of antennas, waveguides, and transmission lines usually make use of some circuit concepts. In such cases a knowledge of the relationship between fields and circuits is essential.

In this chapter the integro-differential equation of a series *RLC* circuit is developed, with resistance, inductance, and capacitance precisely defined. Kirchhoff's laws are applied to a lumped circuit, and power and energy relations are examined. Finally, *skin effect* is discussed at the beginning of the chapter and again at the end.

The analysis is based on the sinusoidal time function. Because resistance and inductance are, in general, *functions of frequency*, a careful analysis *requires* the assumption of sinusoidal time variations. However, this is not restrictive; the Fourier integral and the principle of superposition justify the application of the results to nonsinusoidal waveforms, provided the circuit elements have approximately the same values for all important frequency components of the excitation. In the next chapter the low-frequency expressions for resistance and inductance are derived, and the important concept of mutual inductance is introduced.

14-1. SKIN EFFECT

Introductory presentations of electric circuit theory often treat the current of a circuit as though it is uniformly distributed over the cross-sectional area, and this sometimes leads to definitions of the circuit parameters inconsistent with their use. Consequently, the student may erroneously deduce that the circuit parameters are independent of frequency, that the instantaneous power dissipated in heating a circuit is i^2R, that inductance equals the flux linkages per unit current, and others. Although these statements are valid for direct currents, they are certainly not exact for alternating currents and, in fact, they are not always good approximations. Avoidance of the restriction of a uniform distribution of current over the cross-sectional area requires a knowledge of the actual distribution. Therefore, we shall investigate this briefly.

Time-varying currents in conductors tend to concentrate in the surface region of the surfaces *nearest the external fields*. This phenomenon is known as *skin effect*. For example, the fields of a hollow-pipe waveguide are confined to the interior region, and the currents concentrate on the inner surface of the pipe. For a round wire the external fields cause a concentration of current near the outer surface. In any good conductor the current distribution is governed by the diffusion equation

$$\nabla^2 \mathbf{J} = \mu\sigma\dot{\mathbf{J}} \tag{14-1}$$

This was developed in Sec. 11-5 by assuming negligible displacement currents. We shall now apply Eq. (14-1) to an important theoretical situation.

Suppose that all space on the positive x-side of the yz-plane of Fig. 14-1 is occupied by a metal of conductivity σ, carrying a current density J_z that varies sinusoidally with time with angular frequency ω. J_z is assumed to vary with distance x into the conductor, but it is independent of y and z. Equation (14-1) becomes

$$\frac{\partial^2 J_z}{\partial x^2} = \mu\sigma \frac{\partial J_z}{\partial t} \tag{14-2}$$

As might be expected, the general solution has the mathematical form of two waves, one traveling in the positive x-direction and the other traveling in the negative x-direction. However, in this problem the conductor extends an infinite distance in the x-direction, and there can be no reflection. Therefore, the solution consists of a single wave that propagates in the positive x-direction. Because of heat losses in the conductor, the amplitude of J_z decreases with distance x, and this decrease is exponential. With the phase angle of J_z taken as zero at $x = 0$, the solution is

$$J_z = J_0 e^{-x/\delta} \sin (\omega t - x/\delta) \tag{14-3}$$

with the *skin depth* δ, or *depth of penetration*, equal to

$$\delta = \frac{1}{\sqrt{\pi f \mu \sigma}} \tag{14-4}$$

Obviously, J_0 is the amplitude of J_z at $x = 0$.

The expression for J_z represents a wave traveling in the positive x-direction with velocity $\omega\delta$ and with amplitude that decreases exponentially with distance x. The formal solution of Eq. (14-2) is readily accomplished

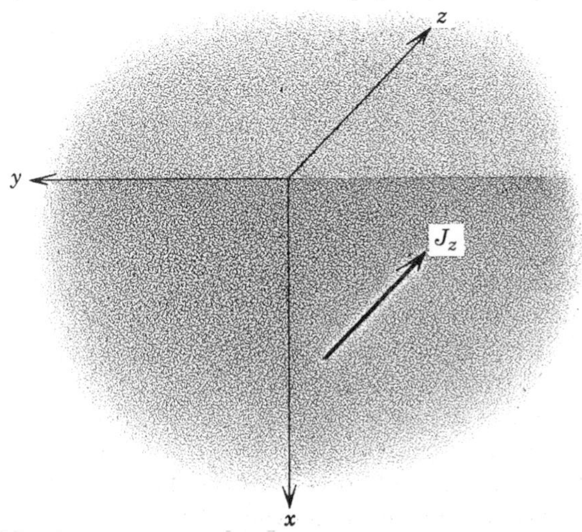

FIG. 14-1. Semi-infinite planar conductor occupying the region of positive x.

with the aid of the mathematics of complex exponentials, discussed in Chapter 19 (see Prob. 19-33). Of course, the given solution can be verified by direct substitution. We note that J_z, at a distance x equal to the skin depth δ, has an amplitude equal to $1/e$, or 36.8%, of the amplitude of J_z at the surface. Also, the phase angle at a distance of one skin depth lags the phase angle at the surface by one radian, or 57.3°. The attenuation is the result of ohmic losses, and the retardation is due to the finite velocity of propagation. Although the mathematical expression for J_z is that of a wave, there is not true electromagnetic wave propagation in the usual way, for there are no appreciable displacement currents. The propagation of the fields into the conductor should be regarded as a diffusion phenomenon quite similar to the propagation of heat through a solid. We note from Eq. (14-3) that the phase constant β is $1/\delta$, and thus the wavelength is $2\pi\delta$. At a distance into the conductor of only one wavelength the amplitude of the current density is less than 0.2% of its value at the surface.

The infinite conductor with a planar surface may appear to be of little practical importance. Such is not the case, however. The results can be applied to a cylindrical wire with only a small error provided the radius of the wire is considerably larger than the skin depth. If this condition is satisfied, the current density is attenuated to a negligible value after penetration through a thin surface layer, and the actual size and shape of the wire become rather unimportant. In fact, the results can be applied to a conductor of any size or shape provided the frequency is sufficiently high to make the skin depth δ very small. Thus the solution of our theoretical problem has practical aspects.

Let us examine the skin depth of a copper conductor having a conductivity of 5.8×10^7 mhos per meter. As copper is nonferromagnetic, its relative permeability is unity. The skin depth becomes

$$\delta = \frac{6.6}{\sqrt{f}} \text{ cm} \tag{14-5}$$

At the power frequency of 60 cps, the skin depth is 0.85 cm. At 1000 cps it is 0.21 cm, or about one-twelfth of an inch. At 1000 kc δ is 0.0066 cm, and at 1000 mc it is 0.00021 cm. Skin effect is quite pronounced at high frequencies. On the other hand, a direct current exhibits no skin effect, for the skin depth is infinite at zero frequency. It should be noted that δ is zero for a perfect conductor, which has an infinite conductivity, provided the frequency is not zero. Time-varying currents reside on the surfaces of perfect conductors, occupying a layer of zero thickness.

At sufficiently low frequencies skin effect is negligible, and the current i over a cross-sectional area S of a homogeneous conductor equals the product JS. However, if skin effect is appreciable, the current is determined from the current density by evaluation of the surface integral of $\mathbf{J}$. For sinusoidal time variations the phase angle of $\mathbf{J}$ varies with respect to the distance into the conductor. It is clear that the current i of a conductor and the current density $\mathbf{J}$ at a point of the cross section are not, in general, in time phase. At an instant of time when the sinusoidal current i is zero, the current densities have values. At some points of S the current densities are in one direction, and at other points they are in the opposite direction. However, the surface integral of $\mathbf{J}$ is zero at the instant of zero current.

The current densities in a metallic conductor produce heat, with the dissipated power per unit volume equal to J^2/σ watts/m^3. Therefore, power is consumed in heating the metal even at the instant of time when the current i is zero. In fact, if the current varies sinusoidally with time, this power is never zero, because the current densities do not have zero values at the same instant. The instantaneous power that is dissipated as heat is proportional to the current squared *only if the current is steady with respect to time.*

The skin-effect equation (14-1) can be applied to conductors of any size or shape. The mathematics is somewhat involved even for conductors of rather simple geometry, such as a cylindrical wire. We learned from the analysis of the semi-infinite planar conductor that the current density tends to concentrate at the surface near the external fields. These external fields are produced by an exciting source, such as a generator, and they propagate into the conductors with a phase velocity $\omega\delta$ that is very small compared with the free-space velocity. Because of this finite velocity, there is phase retardation. There is also attenuation, for energy is absorbed and converted into heat. As the fields are attenuated, the current density **J**, being proportional to **E** by Ohm's law, is likewise attenuated. In general, if the transverse dimensions of the conductors are very small compared with δ, there is no appreciable skin effect. On the other hand, if the transverse dimensions are not small compared with δ, the current distribution is nonuniform because of skin effect. It should be clearly understood that the physical interpretation given to δ in this section applies to the semi-infinite planar conductor and also to practical conductors *at sufficiently high frequencies.*

EXAMPLE. A brass rod of conductivity 1.57×10^5 mhos/cm has a radius of 2.1 cm. A cylindrical coordinate system is located so that the z-axis is along the axis of the rod. If the rod carries a current of $2.024 \sin 10^4 t$ amperes in the positive z-direction, determine the current density J_z as a function of the radial distance r in centimeters.

Solution. At the given frequency the skin depth δ of brass is found from Eq. (14-4) to be 0.318 cm, or approximately $1/\pi$ cm. The radius is about seven skin depths and, therefore, the *approximate* current density can be found by treating the rod as a semi-infinite solid. As the distance into the conductor is $2.1 - r$ cm, this should be substituted for x in Eq. (14-3). Also, a constant should be added to the phase of J_z, because the current i, which equals the surface integral of J_z, has a phase angle of zero. It follows that

$$J_z = J_1 e^{r/\delta} \sin(\omega t + r/\delta + \theta) \text{ amperes/cm}^2$$

with J_1 and θ to be determined.

The current i is $\int J_z 2\pi r\, dr$ with the limits of zero and 2.1 cm. This can be evaluated by the method of Example 1 of Sec. 7-5, giving

$$i = 2024 J_1 \sin(\omega t + \theta - 22.3^\circ)$$

Comparison with the given current shows that $J_1 = 0.001$ and $\theta = 22.3°$. Substitution for J_1, θ, ω, and δ into the expression for J_z gives

$$J_z = 0.001e^{\pi r} \sin (10^4 t + \pi r + 22.3°) \text{ amperes/cm}^2$$

Note that the sign of J_z at any fixed instant depends on the distance r.

14-2. THE APPROXIMATIONS OF LINEAR LUMPED-CONSTANT CIRCUIT THEORY

Many electrical circuits have dimensions that are quite small compared with the wavelength of a sinusoidal exciting source. For such cases the time required for an electrical effect to be transmitted from one part to another is but a minute fraction of the period of oscillation, and retardation is of no consequence. The phase delay βr, or $2\pi r/\lambda$, is practically zero at points in the close vicinity of the circuit, except inside the actual conducting medium. Circuit theory is based on the assumption that retardation in the dielectric between any two current elements is negligible. Therefore, the theory is applicable, in general, *only to those circuits whose dimensions are very small compared with the wavelength of the excitation.* Changes in the applied voltage are assumed to be felt instantaneously in all parts of the region occupied by the circuit, other than the interior of the conductors. If the voltage is a nonsinusoidal function of time, the physical dimensions must be small compared with the wavelengths of all the important sinusoidal components. As a consequence of this restriction, the potential functions in the vicinity of the circuit are not retarded, and the Biot-Savart law applies, provided the dielectric is linear, isotropic, and homogeneous.

In addition, we shall assume that *the only displacement currents of importance in the circuit are those across discontinuities, or gaps, referred to as capacitors.* This assumption implies that time-varying charge densities at points along the conducting wire are negligible. Consequently, the current of a series circuit is the same at all points along the path of the circuit at each instant. Of course, there may be time-varying charges on the plates of a capacitor of the series circuit, producing a displacement current between the plates equal to the conduction current.

Electric circuit theory is based on the assumptions which we have considered. Physical circuits satisfy these requirements *provided they have dimensions small compared with the wavelength and provided that current elements are located so as to minimize displacement currents between them.* Wires at different potentials must not be so close together that appreciable displacement current flows through the dielectric separating them. If such is unavoidable, it is possible to employ circuit theory by imagining the existence of lumped capacitors between certain selected points. This is often done when analyzing a high-frequency circuit containing a coil of wire, because the displacement currents between the turns may be appreciable. However, the use of the lumped capacitors in the analysis is an approximation.

Radiation from a circuit that is small compared with the wavelength is usually negligible. The vector summation of all the current elements is zero, and the distances between them are but small fractions of the wavelength. Thus their radiation fields nearly cancel. Most of the power supplied to a circuit is dissipated as heat, although some may be lost through radiation.

As the excitation frequency of a circuit is increased, the wavelength decreases. Eventually frequencies are reached at which the circuit dimensions are no longer small compared with the wavelength. At such frequencies there is appreciable retardation and radiation. The current of a series circuit is no longer the same over all cross sections, and displacement currents flow from the individual current elements. Circuit theory becomes invalid, and analysis must be based on the field equations. Later, we shall learn how to extend circuit theory to the very special but important case of a transmission line that is electrically long. Also, we shall utilize some circuit concepts in our studies of waveguides and antennas. In this chapter, however, our attention is confined to electrically small circuits. The dielectric around the conductors is assumed to be linear, isotropic, and homogeneous. We begin the development of circuit theory with the study of a series circuit with no capacitance and, therefore, with negligible displacement currents.

14-3. RESISTANCE AND INDUCTANCE

Shown in Fig. 14-2 is a series circuit with a generator that produces small equal-and-opposite charges on its terminals a and b. These charges vary sinusoidally with time. An electric field $\mathbf{E}$ is produced by the charges, and the line integral of $\mathbf{E}$ along the direct path from b to a is the voltage drop v, which also varies sinusoidally with time. Connected between the terminals a and b of the generator is a wire of conductivity σ. A section of this wire is looped into several turns in order to increase the flux linkages. The current is the same over each cross section, for displacement currents and retardation are assumed to be negligible. Skin effect is present.

An important property of the sinusoidal time-function is that its waveform is unchanged by processes of differentiation or integration with respect to time. Also, addition and subtraction of sine functions having the same frequency do not change the waveform. Maxwell's equations involve time derivatives. Wave reflections due to boundaries between physical media result in addition of sine functions of the same frequency. Clearly, if the excitation is sinusoidal and if the media are linear, isotropic, and homogeneous, the electric and magnetic fields at every point also vary sinusoidally with time. The current density **J** in the conducting material, being proportional to **E** by Ohm's law, is sinusoidal, and so is the current i, which equals the surface integral of **J**. If we select the zero of time so that $i = I_m \sin \omega t$, the voltage v can be expressed as

$$v = V_m \sin(\omega t + \theta) \tag{14-6}$$

In the circuit of Fig. 14-2, let C denote a closed path that proceeds directly from a to b and then returns to a along some arbitrarily selected

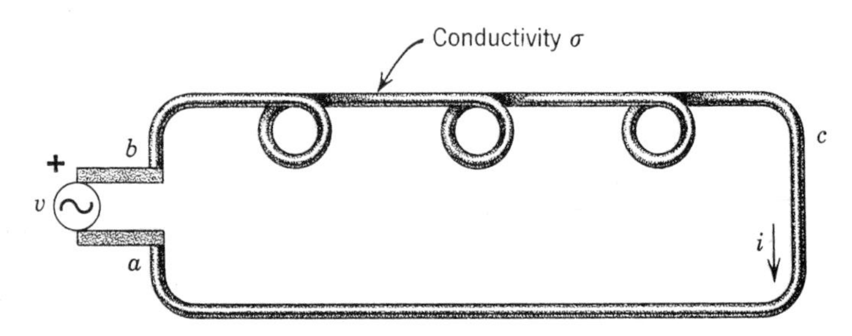

FIG. 14-2. A series electric circuit.

path *within* the copper wire. Let S represent a surface with the contour C. In accordance with the right-hand rule the positive side of S faces into the paper. With v_{bca} denoting the line integral of $\mathbf{J}/\sigma$ along the conducting portion of C, the voltage drop around the closed path is $-v + v_{bca}$, and this equals $-\dot{\Phi}$ by the Maxwell-Faraday law. Thus we obtain

$$v = \int_{bca} (\mathbf{J}/\sigma) \cdot d\mathbf{l} + \dot{\Phi} \tag{14-7}$$

The voltage of the generator is the sum of the drop along the copper wire and the emf of self-induction. At very low frequencies $\dot{\Phi}$ is negligible, there is no skin effect, and the voltage v of Eq. (14-7) is clearly proportional to the current i. For this case the angle θ of Eq. (14-6) is zero. On the other hand, at very high frequencies the term $\dot{\Phi}$ is the dominant term. Skin effect is considerable, and the current flows in a thin surface layer. By the Biot-Savart law the magnetic flux is proportional to this current, and the constant of proportionality is positive. Therefore, the voltage is proportional to the time derivative of i, which is $\omega I_m \sin(\omega t + 90°)$. It follows that the angle θ of Eq. (14-6) is 90° at high frequencies. *At intermediate frequencies this angle is between the low and high frequency limits of zero and 90°.*

The voltage v is said to *lead* the current i by the angle θ. We could also say the current *lags* the voltage by the angle θ. Equation (14-6) can be written

$$v = V_m \cos\theta \sin\omega t + V_m \sin\theta \sin(\omega t + 90°) \tag{14-8}$$

As $\cos\theta$ is positive, the first component of v on the right side of this equation is in time phase with the current i and is called the *resistive voltage drop* v_R. As $\sin\theta$ is also positive, the second component leads the current i by 90° and is called the *inductive voltage drop* v_L. Thus $v = v_R + v_L$. The resistive voltage drop is directly proportional to the current i, and the inductive voltage drop is directly proportional to the time derivative of i, because $di/dt = \omega I_m \sin(\omega t + 90°)$. The positive constants of proportionality are called the *resistance* R and the *inductance* L, respectively. Therefore, by definition we have

$$R = \frac{v_R}{i} \text{ ohms} \tag{14-9}$$

$$L = \frac{v_L}{di/dt} \text{ henrys} \tag{14-10}$$

In terms of R and L, Eq. (14-8) becomes

$$v = iR + L\frac{di}{dt} \tag{14-11}$$

This is the equation of a series circuit that has no capacitors. The resistance R and the inductance L depend, in general, upon *the dimensions of the circuit, the properties of the physical media, and the frequency. If these quantities are invariant with time, R and L are time-independent constants.* This is evident from the defining equations (14-9) and (14-10), because v_R and i are in time phase and v_L and di/dt are likewise in time phase. Thus the circuit equation is a linear differential equation, and the superposition principle applies. If the voltage and current are nonsinusoidal functions of time, the equation can be applied to each frequency component of the nonsinusoidal waveforms. In many practical cases the important frequency components are in a band sufficiently limited to justify treating R and L as though they were independent of frequency.

It should be noted that the volt-ampere relationship of a *filamentary* circuit can be deduced directly from Eq. (14-7). As there is no skin effect in such a circuit, the line integral of $\mathbf{J}/\sigma$ is proportional to the current i. Also, Φ is proportional to i, and $\dot{\Phi}$ can be replaced with $L\,di/dt$. Equation (14-11) follows. In this derivation it was not necessary to assume sinusoidal time variations. The resistance and inductance of linear circuits vary with frequency only because of skin effect, which is negligible in filamentary circuits.

EXAMPLE. If $i = 2 \sin 377t$ and $v = 10 \sin (377t + 30°)$ in the circuit of Fig. 14-2, find the parameters R and L.

Solution. From Eqs. (14-8) and (14-9) we deduce that

$$R = (V_m \cos \theta)/I_m = (10 \cos 30°)/2 = 4.33 \text{ ohms}$$

Likewise, we deduce from Eqs. (14-8) and (14-10) that

$$L = (V_m \sin \theta)/\omega I_m = (10 \sin 30°)/754 = 6.63 \text{ mh}$$

The angle θ is the angle by which the current lags the voltage. If the phase angle of the current had been given as $-30°$, with the voltage taken as the reference quantity with zero phase angle, θ in the expressions for R and L would still be $+30°$, because this is the angle by which the current lags the voltage.

14-4. CAPACITANCE

Let us now introduce a small gap, or capacitor, into the series circuit. The current i equals dq/dt, with dq denoting the differential charge passing through a cross section of the conductor in the differential time dt. As

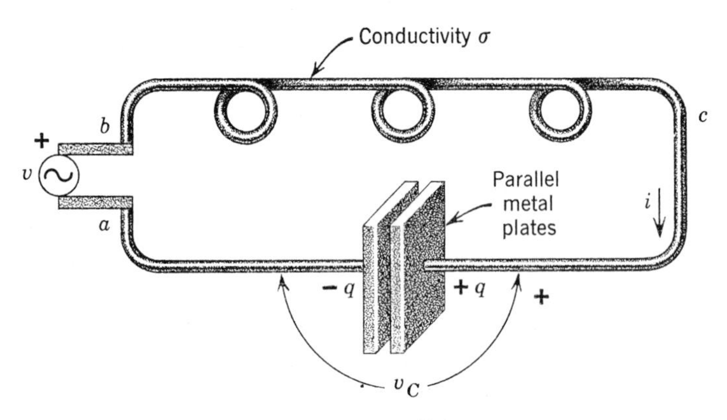

FIG. 14-3. A series *RLC* circuit.

charge will not flow through the dielectric of the gap, the differential charge dq, which equals $i\,dt$, flows out of one terminal of the capacitor and into the other in the time dt. Consequently, equal and opposite charges $+q$ and $-q$ appear across the terminals, with

$$q = \int i\,dt \tag{14-12}$$

If $i = I_m \sin \omega t$, $q = -(I_m/\omega) \cos \omega t$, with the constant of integration neglected for assumed sinusoidal time variations.

Shown in Fig. 14-3 is the series *RLC* circuit with two closely spaced parallel plates placed at the gap in order to increase the stored charge q.

At a point P in the close vicinity of the capacitor the electric scalar potential is determined by the charges stored on the plates, because there are no appreciable net charges anywhere else in the circuit. Furthermore, as P is near the charges, this potential is not appreciably retarded. We deduce that the electric potential at P is directly proportional to the charge q. This should be evident from the expression for the unretarded potential, given as Eq. (13-35). Obviously, the *potential difference* between the plates of the capacitor is also proportional to q. The voltage drop along a path directly across the terminals of the capacitor equals the potential drop less the line integral of $\dot{\mathbf{A}}$. The magnetic vector potential $\mathbf{A}$ in this region is small, for there is no appreciable concentration of current as there is in the vicinity of an inductance coil. Even more important is the fact that the length of the path of integration is quite small. Consequently, the line integral of $\dot{\mathbf{A}}$ is negligible compared with the potential drop, and the voltage and potential drops are equal. Therefore, the voltage drop v_C across the capacitor is proportional to q.

The ratio of the stored charge q to the voltage v_C is the *capacitance* C of the capacitor, and the mks unit of capacitance is, of course, the *farad*. Thus

$$C = q/v_C \text{ farads} \tag{14-13}$$

C is a function of the dimensions of the capacitor and the permittivity of the dielectric, but if these quantities do not vary with time, the capacitance C is a time-independent constant. It should be noted that a large capacitance stores a large electric charge per applied volt, whereas a small capacitance stores only a small charge per volt. From Eqs. (14-12) and (14-13) we find the capacitive voltage drop to be

$$v_C = \frac{q}{C} = \frac{1}{C}\int i\,dt \tag{14-14}$$

If $i = I_m \sin \omega t$, this becomes

$$v_C = \frac{I_m}{\omega C} \sin(\omega t - 90°) \tag{14-15}$$

The result shows that the voltage drop across C, in the direction of the positive current i, lags i by 90°, and the amplitude of v_C equals $1/(\omega C)$ times the amplitude of i. Between the plates of the capacitor there is, of course, a displacement current equal to the charging current i.

As in the previous section, the voltage v applied to the series circuit can be written as $V_m \sin(\omega t + \theta)$, with the current i equal to $I_m \sin \omega t$. The component $V_m \cos\theta \sin \omega t$, being in time phase with i, is the resistive voltage drop. However, the out-of-phase component $V_m \sin\theta \cos\omega t$ now equals the *sum* of the inductive and capacitive voltage drops and is referred to as the *reactive voltage.* Equating this to the sum of v_L, which equals $\omega L I_m \cos \omega t$, and v_C, which equals $-I_m/(\omega C) \cos \omega t$, gives

$$V_m \sin \theta = \left(\omega L - \frac{1}{\omega C}\right) I_m \tag{14-16}$$

We note that the angle θ is positive if ωL is greater than $1/(\omega C)$, and it is negative if ωL is less than $1/(\omega C)$. Thus the reactive voltage drop, *in the direction of the positive current*, leads the current if the amplitude of the inductive voltage is greater than that of the capacitive voltage. It lags the current if the inductive voltage has a smaller amplitude than the capacitive voltage. If both amplitudes are equal, the reactive voltage is zero, the input voltage and current are in time phase, and the circuit is said to be *resonant.*

The total applied voltage v is the sum of the resistive and reactive voltages. In terms of the current i the voltage v is

$$v = iR + L\frac{di}{dt} + \frac{1}{C}\int i\,dt \tag{14-17}$$

This is the basic integro-differential equation of electric circuit theory. The parameters R, L, and C depend on the circuit dimensions and the properties of the physical media. In addition, R and L depend on the phenomenon of skin effect and are, therefore, functions of frequency. This is discussed in the latter part of this chapter. If the dimensions of the circuit, the properties of the media, and the frequency do not vary with time, the circuit parameters are time-independent constants. This is, of course, the usual case.

EXAMPLE. If $i = 2 \sin 377t$ and $v = 17.32 \sin (377t - 60°)$ in the circuit of Fig. 14-3, and if the voltage across the capacitor has an amplitude of 20 volts, calculate the circuit parameters R, L, and C.

Solution. The resistive voltage drop has an amplitude of $17.32 \cos(-60°)$, or 8.66 volts. Division by the amplitude of i gives a resistance R of 4.33 ohms.

The capacitive voltage drop in the direction of the positive current lags the current by 90° and has an amplitude of 20. Therefore, $v_C = -20 \cos 377t$. The stored charge q is the time integral of the current i, which becomes $-0.00531 \cos 377t$. Evaluation of the ratio q/v_C gives a capacitance C of 265.5 μf.

The reactive voltage drop is $17.32 \sin(-60°) \cos 377t$, or $-15 \cos 377t$. As this equals the sum of v_L and v_C, it follows that $v_L = 5 \cos 377t$. Therefore $\omega L I_m = 5$, and the inductance L is 6.63 mh.

14-5. LUMPED CIRCUIT ELEMENTS AND KIRCHHOFF'S LAWS

The series circuit with resistance, inductance, and capacitance is shown in Fig. 14-4 as a lumped circuit. The entire resistance is lumped into a single resistor R; the inductance is represented as a lumped inductance

L, and the capacitance of the discontinuity is represented by the capacitor C. Although the illustrated circuit contains idealized elements, it accurately relates the voltage v and the current i. In the actual physical circuit the resistance and the inductance are not separable, of course, for the turns of wire that constitute the inductor contain resistance. Furthermore, the inductance is to some extent distributed throughout the actual circuit.

The resistive, inductive, and capacitive voltages are indicated by their respective symbols, with double-headed arrows denoting the paths to which these voltages refer and with plus signs used to show the selected reference directions. In the previous section it was shown that the applied voltage v equals the sum of the resistive, inductive, and capacitive voltage drops in the direction of the positive current, giving

$$v - v_R - v_L - v_C = 0 \quad (14\text{-}18)$$

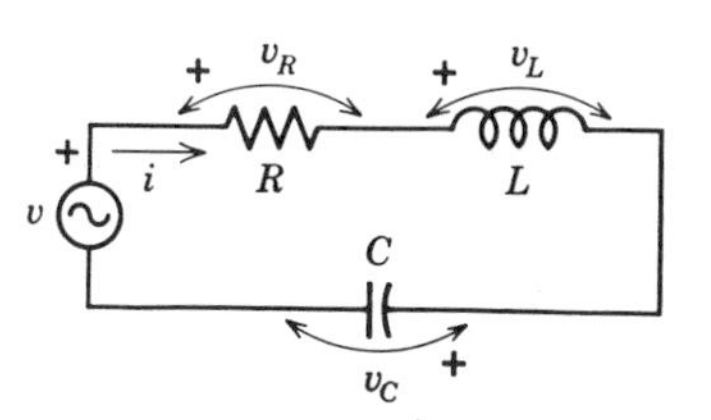

FIG. 14-4. A lumped *RLC* series circuit.

With reference to Fig. 14-4 we note that the left side of Eq. (14-18) is the sum of the voltage rises around the circuit in a clockwise direction, and this sum is equal to zero at each instant of time. Obviously, the sum of the voltage drops around the closed circuit is also zero, this being another way to state Kirchhoff's voltage law. It should be clearly understood that the effect of the time-changing magnetic flux that links the actual physical circuit is accounted for by the inductive term v_L. In the physical circuit this magnetic flux is not completely confined to a lumped inductor, and the sum of the voltage rises around a closed loop is not zero if appreciable time-varying magnetic flux links the loop.

Actually, many practical circuits approximate the lumped circuit of Fig. 14-4. There are noninductive resistors that are nearly pure resistances over wide frequency bands. There are inductors having resistive voltage drops that are very much smaller than their inductive voltage drops. Capacitors generally have negligible resistive and inductive voltage drops. However, regardless of whether or not the actual series circuit is approximately a lumped circuit, *the representation of Fig.* 14-4 *can be utilized to analyze the circuit.*

The analysis of electric networks containing a number of interconnected loops is based on Kirchhoff's voltage and current laws and on the differential equation of a series circuit. Each branch of such a network is a series circuit, although one or two of the parameters R, L, and C may be zero for any given branch. The currents of the branches that join at a junction are related by Kirchhoff's current law, and the voltages around a closed loop are related by the voltage law. For sinusoidal time variations the mathematics is greatly simplified by the use of complex exponentials, investigated in Chapter 19. Although it is not our purpose to discuss circuit analysis, let us consider an elementary example that illustrates the use of the differential circuit equation.

EXAMPLE. If the generator in the circuit of Fig. 14-4 supplies a current of 2 amperes maximum value at an angular frequency of 1000 radians per second, find the voltages of the circuit, assuming $R = 3$ ohms, $L = 16$ mh, and $C = 50\ \mu$f.

Solution. Selecting zero time so that the phase angle of i is zero gives a current of $2 \sin 1000t$. The resistive voltage drop v_R in the direction of the positive current is iR, and therefore

$$v_R = 6 \sin 1000t$$

The inductive voltage drop in the direction of the positive current is $L\,di/dt$. Multiplying the time derivative of i by 0.016 henry gives

$$v_L = 32 \cos 1000t$$

This voltage leads the current by 90°.

The capacitive voltage drop in the direction of the positive current is $(1/C)\int i\,dt$. The constant $1/C$ equals 20,000, and the time integral of i is $-0.002 \cos 1000t$. Therefore

$$v_C = -40 \cos 1000t$$

This voltage lags the current by 90°.

The net reactive voltage drop, $v_L + v_C$, is $-8 \cos 1000t$. Thus the voltage v of the generator is

$$v = 6 \sin 1000t - 8 \cos 1000t$$

The amplitude of this voltage is the square root of the sum of the squares of 6 and 8, which becomes 10; the phase angle of v is the arctangent of $-8/6$, or $-53.1°$. Therefore

$$v = 10 \sin (1000t - 53.1°)$$

The applied voltage lags the current by 53.1°.

14-6. POWER AND ENERGY IN THE ELECTRIC CIRCUIT

If v represents the instantaneous voltage drop across a circuit element in the direction of the positive current i, the power supplied is

$$p = vi \text{ watts} \tag{14-19}$$

For a resistance R this becomes

$$p = i^2 R \tag{14-20}$$

Regardless of the time variations the power varies between the values of zero and $I_m{}^2 R$, but it is never negative.

The power to an inductance L is $v_L i$, or

$$p = Li\frac{di}{dt} = \frac{d}{dt}(\tfrac{1}{2}Li^2) \tag{14-21}$$

For sinusoidal time variations this is alternately positive and negative, because the quantities i and di/dt are 90° out of time phase. Integration of Eq. (14-21) shows that the energy stored in an inductance L is

$$W_L = \tfrac{1}{2}Li^2 \text{ joules} \tag{14-22}$$

The constant of integration is dropped, for W_L is certainly zero when there is no current.

The power to a capacitor C is $v_C i$. As $v_C = q/C$, the supplied power can be expresed as

$$p = \frac{qi}{C} = \frac{q}{C}\frac{dq}{dt} = \frac{d}{dt}\left(\frac{1}{2}\frac{q^2}{C}\right) \tag{14-23}$$

For sinusoidal time variations this power is alternately positive and negative, because q and i are 90° out of time phase. Integration of Eq. (14-23) shows that the energy stored in the capacitor is

$$W_C = \frac{1}{2}\frac{q^2}{C} = \tfrac{1}{2}Cv_C^2 = \tfrac{1}{2}qv_C \tag{14-24}$$

The constant of integration is zero, for there can be no stored energy when v_C is zero. As W_C equals the energy W_E stored in the electric field between the plates of the capacitor, it is evident that the capacitance C is

$$C = 2W_E/v_C^2 \tag{14-25}$$

This is often used to define capacitance.

The total instantaneous power supplied to a series RLC circuit by a generator that delivers a voltage v and a current i is vi. As this must equal the total power to R, L, and C, we have

$$vi = i^2R + \frac{d}{dt}(\tfrac{1}{2}Li^2) + \frac{d}{dt}(\tfrac{1}{2}Cv_C^2) \tag{14-26}$$

The capacitive term is the power supplied to the electric field between the plates of the capacitor. Displacement currents outside the dielectric of the capacitor are assumed negligible. Therefore, the external electric fields are small compared with that inside the dielectric, and the energy stored in these external electric fields is negligible. It follows that the sum of the resistive and inductive terms of Eq. (14-26) represents the sum of the power dissipated in the conducting material and the power delivered to the magnetic field in and around the circuit. There is no appreciable radiation of energy. Although i^2R gives the instantaneous power delivered to the resistance, it is not correct to regard this as the instantaneous power dissipated in the conducting material of the circuit. Because of skin effect, the current densities at points inside the conductor are not zero when the sinusoidal current i is instantaneously zero. In the next chapter it is shown that the product i^2R does, however, represent the instantaneous power dissipated at frequencies so low that skin effect is negligible.

EXAMPLE. A current $i = 2 \sin 1000t$ is supplied to a series LC circuit with $L = 15$ mh and $C = 50\ \mu$f. The conductors are assumed to be perfect, and therefore, the resistance is zero. Find the voltages of the circuit, the energies stored in L and C, the power to each of these parameters, and the input power.

Solution. In the direction of the positive current, the voltage drop across L is $L\, di/dt$, or $30 \cos 1000t$, and that across C is q/C, or $-40 \cos 1000t$. The applied voltage v is the sum of these, or $-10 \cos 1000t$.

The stored energy $\frac{1}{2}Li^2$ is $0.03 \sin^2 1000t$, and $\frac{1}{2}Cv_C{}^2$ is $0.04 \cos^2 1000t$. Differentiating these energies with respect to time gives an inductive power of $30 \sin 2000t$ watts and a capacitive power of $-40 \sin 2000t$ watts. The sum of these is $-10 \sin 2000t$, and this is the input power. The input power can also be found from the product vi. It should be noted this power has a time average of zero.

14-7. TIME-AVERAGE POWER AND ENERGY

Usually, average power is of more interest than instantaneous power. To determine the time-average value of a quantity over a time interval from t_1 to t_2, we integrate the quantity with respect to time from t_1 to t_2, and divide the result by the interval $t_2 - t_1$. If the time interval is from 0 to T, the average power P is

$$P = \frac{1}{T}\int_0^T p\, dt \tag{14-27}$$

Our interest is in the average power over innumerable cycles. Therefore, we can let T in Eq. (14-27) approach infinity, or we can let T be a period of the periodic function. Obviously, the average power over a single period is the same as the average power over a time interval that includes a great many periods. For sinusoids the period T equals $1/f$.

Let us now consider the average power to the inductance L of the series circuit. The instantaneous power to L can be expressed as $Li\, di/dt$, and if i is $I_m \sin \omega t$, this becomes

$$p = \omega L I_m{}^2 \sin \omega t \cos \omega t = \tfrac{1}{2}\omega L I_m{}^2 \sin 2\omega t$$

As this power is a sinusoidal function of time, with angular frequency 2ω, its average value is zero. Similarly, it can be shown that the average power supplied to the capacitor C is zero. At any instant of time there may be an energy flow into or out of L and C, but *the average power over a complete cycle is zero.* Any energy supplied to the inductance or the capacitance during a portion of a period is returned to the circuit during another portion of the period.

The average power P to the resistance R of the series circuit is the time average value of i^2R. As R is a constant, this becomes

$$P = \left[\frac{1}{T}\int_0^T i^2\,dt\right] R \tag{14-28}$$

The expression in the brackets is the average value of i^2. The square root of the average value of i^2 is a quantity known as the *root-mean-square current*, or *effective current*, and is designed by the symbol I. Mathematically, the rms current I is

$$I = \sqrt{\frac{1}{T}\int_0^T i^2\,dt} \tag{14-29}$$

with T equal to a period, or with T approaching infinity. This current is, of course, a constant independent of time. In terms of I, the average power to R, as given by Eq. (14-28), is

$$P = I^2R \tag{14-30}$$

The definition of rms current applies regardless of the waveform. For sinusoidal time variations, however, the current I is found from Eq. (14-29) to be $I_m/\sqrt{2}$. Most ammeters are designed to read rms current. It should be noted that the rms value of a direct current I equals I. The instantaneous power i^2R can be expressed as v_R^2/R, and the average power is V_R^2/R, with V_R denoting the *rms voltage* across the resistor.

Let us now consider the average power P supplied to the series circuit by the generator. With the phase angles of the current and voltage taken as θ_1 and θ_2, respectively, the average value of the product vi becomes

$$P = \frac{1}{T}\int_0^T V_m I_m \sin(\omega t + \theta_1)\sin(\omega t + \theta_2)\,dt$$

Evaluation gives

$$P = \tfrac{1}{2}V_m I_m \cos\theta = VI\cos\theta \tag{14-31}$$

with θ denoting the *difference* between the phase angles θ_1 and θ_2. Of course, V and I are the rms voltage and current. The product VI is called the *volt-amperes* of the circuit, and the term $\cos\theta$ is the circuit *power factor*.

We have deduced that the average power supplied to the RLC circuit is

$$P = VI\cos\theta = I^2R = V_R^2/R \tag{14-32}$$

The inductance and the capacitance absorb no average power. Although the product i^2R does not give the *instantaneous* power dissipated as heat, the product I^2R certainly gives the average power dissipated. Also, the time integral of i^2R *over a complete period* yields the energy dissipated in this period. The energy $\frac{1}{2}Li^2$ stored in the inductance L varies with time, but it is always positive. The average value of this energy over a period is the average energy stored in the magnetic field of the circuit. This follows from the fact that the energy dissipated in a period is entirely accounted for by the resistance; also, there is no appreciable energy stored in the electric field of the circuit, except that between the plates of the capacitor. Thus the time average of $\frac{1}{2}Li^2$, which equals $\frac{1}{2}LI^2$, gives the average energy stored in the magnetic field. Consequently, inductance L can be expressed as

$$L = \frac{2(W_H)_{\text{ave}}}{I^2} \tag{14-33}$$

with $(W_H)_{\text{ave}}$ denoting the time-average energy stored in the magnetic field and with I denoting the rms current. It is not permissible, in general, to write Eq. (14-33) in terms of the instantaneous energy W_H and the instantaneous current i. These quantities are not in time phase unless skin effect is negligible. Equation (14-33) is often used to define inductance and it is valuable in the analytical determination of the inductance of a circuit. Furthermore, *it enables us to attach physical significance to this important circuit parameter.*

14-8. RESISTANCE AT HIGH FREQUENCIES

The analysis of the semi-infinite planar conductor, with the conducting material occupying all of space on the positive x side of the yz-plane, showed that the current density J_z varies with x according to the relation

$$J_z = J_0 e^{-x/\delta} \sin(\omega t - x/\delta) \tag{14-34}$$

J_0 is the amplitude of J_z at the surface, and the skin depth δ is $1/\sqrt{\pi f \mu \sigma}$.

Let us consider a region of this conductor that occupies unit area in the yz-plane and extends to infinity in the x-direction. The width in the y-direction and the length in the z-direction are each unity. This parallelepiped, with one dimension infinite, is shown in Fig. 14-5.

The current i of the parallelepiped is the surface integral of J_z over the cross section, and a cross-sectional differential area is $dx\,dy$. As J_z is independent of y and as the y limits are zero and unity, the current is

$$i = J_0 \int_0^\infty e^{-x/\delta} \sin(\omega t - x/\delta)\, dx \tag{14-35}$$

By expanding the sine function, we obtain i in terms of definite integrals whose values are given in common integral tables. The result can be expressed as

$$i = (J_0\,\delta/\sqrt{2}) \sin(\omega t - \pi/4) \tag{14-36}$$

The current lags the current density at the surface by 45°, and the rms current I is $\frac{1}{2}J_0\,\delta$.

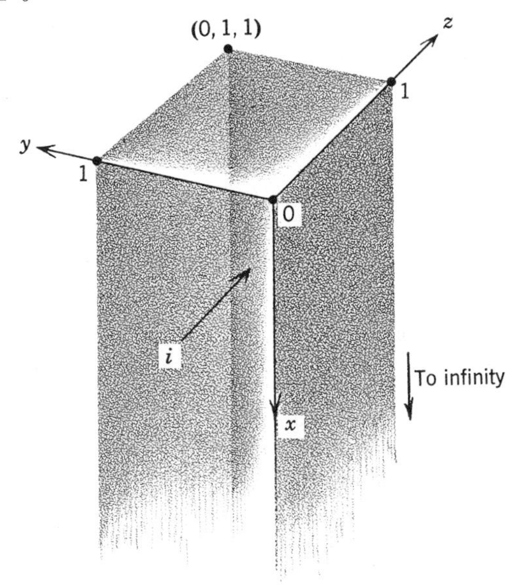

FIG. 14-5. Parallelepiped extending to infinity in direction of positive x.

Let us now determine the power p dissipated in the parallelepiped. This power is found by evaluating the volume integral of J_z^2/σ, with a differential volume being $dx\,dy\,dz$. As J_z is independent of y and z and as the dimensions in these directions are unity, the power equals the integral of J_z^2/σ with respect to x, from zero to infinity. Utilizing Eq. (14-34) gives

$$p = \frac{J_0^2}{\sigma} \int_0^\infty e^{-2x/\delta} \sin^2(\omega t - x/\delta)\,dx \tag{14-37}$$

This can be evaluated by replacing the sine squared function with $\frac{1}{2} - \frac{1}{2}\cos(2\omega t - 2x/\delta)$, thereby obtaining two definite integrals. One of these is readily integrated, and the other can be evaluated by the method suggested for Eq. (14-35) or by utilizing complex exponentials. The result is

$$p = \frac{J_0^2\,\delta}{4\sigma}\left[1 - \frac{1}{\sqrt{2}} \sin\left(2\omega t + \frac{\pi}{4}\right)\right] \tag{14-38}$$

It should be noted that the instantaneous power dissipated in the parallelepiped is not proportional to the instantaneous current squared. The power p is never zero, whereas i^2 is zero at certain instants. The time-average power P is simply the constant term of Eq. (14-38), or $P = J_0^2\, \delta/(4\sigma)$. Dividing this by the rms current squared gives the resistance R_s to be

$$R_s = P/I^2 = \frac{1}{\delta\sigma} = \sqrt{\frac{\pi f \mu}{\sigma}} \text{ ohms} \tag{14-39}$$

If the length of the parallelepiped is l, instead of unity, the power dissipated is multiplied by l, but the current is unchanged. Therefore, R_s is multiplied by l. On the other hand, if the width of the parallelepiped is w, both the power and the current are multiplied by w, and consequently, the resistance is divided by w. Thus the resistance *per unit square* is given by Eq. (14-39), and this must be multiplied by the length l and divided by the width w if these are not unity. The resistance of Eq. (14-39) is called the *surface resistivity*. For copper the surface resistivity is $2.61 \times 10^{-7}\sqrt{f}$ ohm.

An important deduction from the preceding discussion is the variation of resistance with frequency. The surface resistivity is proportional to the square root of the frequency. At high frequencies the radii of curvature and the dimensions of conductors are much greater than δ, and the theory of the semi-infinite conductor applies. Therefore, if the external fields are uniform over the surface of the conductor and if dielectric losses are negligible, the resistance at sufficiently high frequencies is proportional to the square root of the frequency.

The d-c resistance of a unit length of a conductor of cross-sectional area S is $1/(\sigma S)$ ohms. The a-c resistance of the parallelepiped of unit width and length is $1/(\sigma\delta)$ ohms, and *this is exactly the d-c resistance of the surface layer of thickness* δ. Consequently, a steady current of one ampere, existing only throughout a skin depth δ, produces in the semi-infinite conductor a power dissipation equal to that dissipated by an alternating current of one ampere rms, with the a-c distributed according to Eq. (14-34).

The results of the analysis of the semi-infinite conductor can be applied to practical conductors. At high frequencies the current is crowded into the surface regions *nearest the more intense external fields*. Very little current exists in the region of the conductor located more than several skin depths from the surface, for the free electrons of this region are acted upon by the *very weak* electric field present. This field is weak because of the considerable attenuation that takes place as it propagates into the conductor from the external dielectric. Thus the effective cross-sectional area is reduced, and the a-c resistance is greater than the d-c resistance. It should be noted that the current density is not, in general, uniform over the surface of a conductor. For example, at high frequencies the equal-and-opposite currents of a parallel-wire transmission line tend to concentrate on the surfaces of the wires that are nearest to one another, for the fields are more intense in the region between the wires. Although this phenomenon is due to skin effect, it is often referred to as *proximity effect*, because the high-frequency resistance of each wire is increased on account of the proximity of the other wire. Thus proximity effect is skin effect that is nonuniform due to the presence of nearby conductors. Another important example of proximity effect is the high-frequency current distribution of a single-layer solenoidal coil with closely spaced turns. In this case the current tends to concentrate in the surface region on the inside of the coil, where the fields are most intense, and this concentration may appreciably increase the a-c resistance of the solenoid.

As skin effect is absent when currents are steady, proximity effect is, of course, also absent. Direct currents are uniformly distributed over the cross sections of conductors with constant conductivities. The electric field does not vary with distance into the conductor, for there is no attenuation at zero frequency. Furthermore, the distribution of the free electrons is not appreciably affected by applied electric or magnetic forces. Any slight change in this distribution would disturb the electrical neutrality of the medium, resulting in intense electrostatic forces opposing the change.

The inductance of a circuit depends on the current distribution, which is a function of frequency because of skin effect. Therefore, inductance varies with frequency. This is discussed in the next section and the next chapter.

EXAMPLE. A length l of wire of radius a has a d-c resistance of 1 ohm. Determine the resistance R at a frequency such that the skin depth δ is $0.05a$.

Solution. As the skin depth is only 5% of the radius a, the surface resistivity can be utilized. The resistance R is $R_s l/w$, with the width w being the circumference $2\pi a$ of the wire. Therefore, $R = R_s l/(2\pi a)$.

The d-c resistance R_{dc} is $l/\sigma S$, or $l/(\sigma\pi a^2)$. It follows that $R/R_{dc} = \frac{1}{2}R_s a\sigma$. Substituting $1/(\sigma\delta)$ for R_s gives $R/R_{dc} = \frac{1}{2}a/\delta$, which equals 10. As R_{dc} is 1, $R = 10$ ohms. This method gives the a-c resistance of a round wire, with an error of not more than 10% provided $a/\delta > 5.5$, and the actual resistance is greater than that calculated.

14-9. INTERNAL INDUCTANCE AT HIGH FREQUENCIES

It has been shown that the inductance L of a circuit equals $2/I^2$ times the average energy stored in the magnetic field. That part of L due to the magnetic energy stored *inside* the metallic conductor is called the *internal inductance* L_i, and that due to the magnetic energy stored in the dielectric around the circuit is the *external inductance* L_e. Thus

$$L = L_i + L_e \tag{14-40}$$

We shall now confine our attention to the internal inductance at high frequencies.

From the expression for the current density of the semi-infinite planar conductor, given by Eq. (14-34), the electric field intensity can be found by utilizing Ohm's law, and the magnetic field intensity can then be determined by employing the Maxwell-Faraday curl equation. The resulting magnetic field is

$$H_y = \frac{J_0 \delta}{\sqrt{2}} e^{-x/\delta} \sin(\omega t - x/\delta + 135°) \tag{14-41}$$

The energy density $\frac{1}{2}\mu H_y^2$ of the magnetic field has a time-average value of $(\mu J_0^2 \delta^2/8)e^{-2x/\delta}$, for the average value of the sine squared term is $\frac{1}{2}$. We deduce that the time-average energy stored in the parallelepiped of Fig. 14-5 is

$$(W_H)_{\text{ave}} = \frac{\mu J_0^2 \delta^2}{8} \int_0^\infty e^{-2x/\delta}\, dx = \frac{\mu J_0^2 \delta^3}{16}$$

It is evident from Eq. (14-36) that the rms current I is $\frac{1}{2}J_0 \delta$. Therefore, the internal inductance L_i becomes $\frac{1}{2}\mu \delta$, and as the skin depth δ varies inversely as the square root of the frequency, so does L_i. It is easily shown that

$$\omega L_i = \sqrt{\frac{\pi f \mu}{\sigma}} = R_s \tag{14-42}$$

Thus the internal inductive *reactance* ωL_i equals the surface resistivity R_s in ohms. If the parallelepiped has length l in the direction of current flow and width w, the internal inductance should be multiplied by l and divided by w, because the stored energy is proportional to the product wl, and I^2 is proportional to w^2.

At sufficiently high frequencies the results of the preceding discussion can be applied to practical conductors with but small errors. For example, the internal inductive reactance per unit length of a round wire of radius a is obtained by dividing the surface resistivity R_s by the width w, which is for this case the circumference $2\pi a$. This is also the resistance per unit length at high frequencies. Thus for a round wire of radius a, we have

$$R = \omega L_i = \frac{R_s}{2\pi a} \text{ ohms/m} \tag{14-43}$$

The error is less than 10% provided the radius a is greater than 5.5δ and provided the current distribution is not appreciably affected by the proximity of other conductors. It should be noted that both the resistance and the internal inductive reactance vary as the square root of the frequency at high frequencies.

The internal inductance of a wire of radius a is easily determined at very low frequencies. In terms of a steady current I the magnetic field intensity H_φ inside the wire is $Ir/(2\pi a^2)$, a result readily verified by application of the Maxwell-Ampère integral equation. The magnetic energy per unit length stored in the region between cylinders of radii r and $r + dr$ is $(\frac{1}{2}\mu H_\varphi^2)(2\pi r\, dr)$. Integration between the limits of zero and a gives a stored energy of $\mu I^2/(16\pi)$ joules per meter, and multiplication of this result by $2/I^2$ gives

$$L_i = \frac{\mu}{8\pi} \text{ henry/m} \tag{14-44}$$

At very low frequencies the internal inductance per unit length is independent of the radius of the wire. If the metal is nonferromagnetic, the inductance per unit length is 0.05 μh/m.

We have obtained expressions for the resistance and the internal inductance of a cylindrical wire for both very low and very high frequencies. At intermediate frequencies the mathematics is rather involved, and the values of R and L_i are somewhere between their values at low and high frequencies. Although the primary purpose of the development of the expressions for R and L was to show their dependence on skin effect and frequency, the results are of practical importance. We have not yet considered external inductance, which is usually of greater importance than internal inductance, but we shall do so in the next chapter. In general, external inductance is also a function of frequency because of the phenomenon of skin effect.

REFERENCES

Carter, G. W., *The Electromagnetic Field in Its Engineering Aspects*, Longmans, Green and Co., London, 1954, Chap. 11.

Kraus, J. D., *Electromagnetics*, McGraw-Hill Book Co., New York, 1953, Chap. 10.

Ramo, S., and J. R. Whinnery, *Fields and Waves in Modern Radio*, John Wiley and Sons, New York, 2nd ed., 1953, Chaps. 5, 6.

Walsh, J. B., *Electromagnetic Theory and Engineering Applications*, The Ronald Press Co., New York, 1960, Chap. 8.

PROBLEMS

Section 14-1

14-1. By direct substitution show that the current density of Eq. (14-3) satisfies the skin-effect equation (14-1).

14-2. For a semi-infinite planar conductor, determine the amplitude of the current density, expressed as a percentage of the amplitude at the surface, at a distance of 8 skin depths from the surface. Also, what is the phase retardation in degrees?

14-3. For a semi-infinite planar conductor made of copper with a conductivity of 5.8×10^7, calculate the velocities with which the fields propagate at frequencies of 60, 10^4, and 10^8 cps.

14-4. Using cylindrical coordinates write the skin-effect equation (14-1) for a cylindrical wire. The current density J_z is a function of time t and the distance r from the axis of the wire. By direct substitution, show that a valid approximate expression for J_z, for a region of the wire in which $r \gg \delta$, is $e^{r/\delta} \sin(\omega t + r/\delta)$.

14-5. For the brass rod of the Example of Sec. 14-1 calculate J_z at radial distances of 1.0, 1.6, and 2.1 centimeters at the instants when (a) the current i is zero (b) i is a maximum, and (c) $\omega t = -40.3°$.

14-6. A copper wire with a radius of 0.4 cm has a current of $5 \sin 10^5 t$ amperes in the positive z-direction, with the z-axis of a cylindrical coordinate system oriented along the axis of the rod. Find J_z as a function of the radial distance r in centimeters.

Section 14-3

14-7. If $i = 10 \sin 1000t$ and $v = 50 \sin(1000t + 60°)$ in the series RL circuit of Fig. 14-2, determine the resistive and inductive voltage drops in the direction of the positive current, and calculate the values of R and L.

14-8. If $i = 4 \sin(5000t + 50°)$ in a series RL circuit, with $R = 15$ ohms and $L = 2$ mh, find as functions of time the resistive and inductive voltage drops in the direction opposite to the positive current, and calculate the sum of these voltages at time $t = 0$.

14-9. A voltage $v = 25 \sin 1000t$ is impressed across a series RL circuit, with $R = 10$ ohms and $L = 20$ mh. Find the amplitude and phase angle of the current $I_m \sin(1000t + \theta)$.

Section 14-4

14-10. A 60-cps current of 3 amperes maximum value is supplied to a capacitor, and the amplitude of the resulting voltage is 150 volts. Calculate the capacitance in microfarads.

14-11. If the voltage drop v across a capacitor of 100 $\mu\mu$f is $50 \sin 10^6 t$, determine the stored charge q and the current i in the direction of the voltage drop v.

14-12. For a series RLC circuit deduce that $V_m \cos\theta = I_m R$, with V_m denoting the amplitude of the applied voltage and θ denoting the angle by which the voltage leads the current. Use this result and Eq. (14-16) to show that $V_m/I_m = \sqrt{R^2 + X^2}$ and $\theta = \tan^{-1} X/R$, with the *reactance* $X = \omega L - 1/\omega C$. If $R = 10$, $L = 25$ mh, $C = 20$ μf, and $i = 5 \sin 1000t$, find the voltage v.

Section 14-5

14-13. A series RLC circuit has a current of $2 \sin 377t$ amperes. If $R = 5$, $L = 40$ mh, and $C = 100$ μf, find the resistive, inductive, and capacitive voltage rises in the direction of the positive current, and determine the amplitude and phase angle of the sum of these voltages.

14-14. At resonance the current and voltage of a series RLC circuit are in time phase. Determine the resonant frequency in terms of the circuit parameters. If $R = 0.5$ ohm, $L = 10$ mh, and $C = 1$ μf, find at resonance the resistive, inductive, and capacitive voltage drops in the direction of the positive current $i = 2 \sin \omega t$. Also, find the total voltage across the input.

Section 14-6

14-15. If $i = 5 \sin 1000t$ in a series resonant circuit with $R = 1$ ohm, $L = 5$ mh, and $C = 200\ \mu$f, find the instantaneous power to each of the parameters R, L, and C. Also, show that the total energy stored in L and C is independent of time, and calculate this energy.

14-16. If $i = 2 \sin 4000t$ in a series RLC circuit with $R = 6$ ohms, $L = 2$ mh, and $C = 25\ \mu$f, determine the instantaneous power supplied to each of the parameters R, L, and C. Also, find the energy stored in the inductance and that stored in the capacitance.

Section 14-7

14-17. In the series circuit of Prob. 14-16 determine the rms current, the rms voltages across each of the circuit parameters, and the rms voltage across the entire circuit. Calculate the average power dissipated by the circuit.

14-18. From the expression for the energy density of the electric field, show that the total energy stored between the plates of a parallel-plate capacitor is $\frac{1}{2}qv_C$. Assume a uniform charge distribution on the plates.

14-19. If $i = I_1\sqrt{2} \sin \omega_1 t + I_2\sqrt{2} \sin \omega_2 t$, show from Eq. (14-29) that the rms current $I = \sqrt{I_1^2 + I_2^2}$, provided ω_1 and ω_2 are not equal. Let T in (14-29) approach infinity.

14-20. A generator supplies a voltage of $100 \sin (500t + 30°)$ and a current of $4 \sin (500t - 20°)$ to an electric circuit. Determine the instantaneous power, the volt-amperes, and the average power supplied by the generator, and calculate the circuit power factor.

14-21. A charging current $i = 2 + \sin 377t$ flows into the positive terminal of a 6-volt battery of negligible internal resistance. Find the instantaneous power and the average power supplied to the battery. If the battery has an internal resistance of 0.1 ohm, determine the instantaneous power and the average power dissipated in this resistance. What is the rms current?

14-22. The rms voltage and current of a series RC circuit are 100 volts and 5 amperes at 60 cycles. If $R = 16$ ohms, find the angle θ by which the current leads the applied voltage, and calculate the capacitance C.

Section 14-8

14-23. (*a*) Derive Eq. (14-36) from (14-35). (*b*) Derive Eq. (14-38) from (14-37).

14-24. At the instant that makes $\omega t = 3\pi/4$, the current of Eq. (14-36) is a maximum. At this instant show that the power p dissipated as heat in the parallelepiped is 75% of the power i^2R supplied to the resistance.

14-25. The *quality factor* Q of a coil of wire of resistance R and inductance L is $\omega L/R$. At frequencies such that the radius of the wire is at least several times the skin depth δ, determine the manner in which Q varies with frequency, provided proximity effect is negligible, dielectric losses are negligible, and L is independent of frequency. In general, what is the effect on Q of proximity effect and dielectric losses?

14-26. In what manner does the resistance of a round wire depend on the radius at very low frequencies and also at very high frequencies?

14-27. Calculate the approximate per-unit-length resistances of a copper wire, of radius 10^{-4} m, at frequencies of 60 cps, 16 mc, and 400 mc. Estimate the percentage of error at each frequency.

14-28. Calculate the approximate per-unit-length resistance of a brass rod of radius 0.021 m at a frequency of 1590 cps. The conductivity of brass is 1.57×10^7 mhos/meter.

Section 14-9

14-29. Derive Eq. (14-41).

14-30. Determine the instantaneous energy stored in the magnetic field of the parallelepiped of Fig. 14-5, and show that this energy is not proportional to i^2. Use Eq. (14-41).

14-31. The conductors of a coaxial transmission line have permeability μ and conductivity σ and are separated by a dielectric of permeability μ_0. The radius of the inner conductor is a, and the inner and outer radii of the outer conductor are b and c, respectively. Find the high-frequency resistance and internal inductance per unit length, including both conductors. Also, use Eq. (14-33) and determine the external inductance per unit length.

14-32. For the coaxial line of Prob. 14-31 find the d-c resistance per unit length. Also, show that the low-frequency inductance per unit length is

$$L = \frac{\mu_0}{2\pi} \ln \frac{b}{a} + \frac{\mu c^4}{2\pi(c^2 - b^2)^2} \ln \frac{c}{b} - \frac{\mu c^2}{4\pi(c^2 - b^2)}$$

14-33. The approximate magnetic field in the brass rod of the Example of Sec. 14-1 is

$$H_\varphi = 0.000225 e^{\pi r} \sin(\omega t + \pi r - 45^\circ) \text{ ampere/cm}$$

with r in centimeters. Find directly from H_φ the time-average energy per unit length stored in the magnetic field of the rod, and use this result to determine the internal inductive reactance per unit length. Check your answer by employing Eq. (14-42). Also, compare with the resistance calculated in the Example of Sec. 11-2. Use centimeter units.

Circuit Concepts II

CHAPTER 15

At sufficiently low frequencies there is no appreciable skin effect in an electric circuit. Neglecting skin effect enables us to develop, in this chapter, several useful and common interpretations of the meaning of resistance and inductance. The results are quite important, for a great many practical circuits operate at frequencies such that the values of these parameters are approximately equal to their d-c values. This is especially so for the inductance parameter. Of course, the capacitance of a lumped capacitor does not depend at all on the phenomenon of skin effect.

If a large sinusoidal voltage is impressed across the input of a vacuum-tube or transistor amplifier, the output voltage is nonsinusoidal, and the circuit is said to be nonlinear. However, most nonlinear electronic circuits have very small a-c voltages and currents superimposed on much larger d-c quantities. Such circuits are linear insofar as the a-c components are concerned. The analyses of these circuits utilize *incremental* circuit parameters, defined in terms of the a-c components of the currents and voltages. In fact, these incremental parameters are employed whenever small-signal quantities are superimposed on larger d-c quantities in nonlinear circuits. We shall examine incremental resistance, inductance, and capacitance.

We shall also examine mutual inductance, a circuit concept of primary importance. According to the Maxwell-Ampère law, a time-changing current in a circuit produces a time-changing magnetic flux. If part of this flux links a second circuit, a voltage is induced in accordance with the Maxwell-Faraday law, and this voltage is proportional to the time rate of change of the current of the first circuit. The constant of proportionality is the mutual inductance. Expressions useful in calculating mutual inductance are developed, followed by a discussion of inductively coupled circuits.

15-1. THE CIRCUIT PARAMETERS AT LOW FREQUENCIES

Suppose a power source supplies a voltage v and a current i to an electric circuit. The instantaneous power p delivered to the circuit is the product vi, and p may have positive and negative values as time varies. At any instant the power p equals the sum of the power p_d dissipated in heating the conducting material, the power p_H supplied to the magnetic field, and the power p_E supplied to the electric field. Thus

$$vi = p_d + p_H + p_E \tag{15-1}$$

The instantaneous power dissipated as heat is the volume integral of σE^2, or J^2/σ, with all regions having a drift current density J included. For linear media the energy densities of the electric and magnetic fields are $\frac{1}{2}\epsilon E^2$ and $\frac{1}{2}\mu H^2$, respectively, and integration of these energy densities over all space in and around the circuit gives the total energy stored in the fields. The power supplied to the fields is the time derivative of this stored energy. Consequently, Eq. (15-1) can be written

$$vi = \int_V J^2/\sigma \, dV + \frac{d}{dt}\int_V \tfrac{1}{2}\mu H^2 \, dV + \frac{d}{dt}\int_V \tfrac{1}{2}\epsilon E^2 \, dV \tag{15-2}$$

Let us now consider a series RLC circuit across a generator supplying a sinusoidal voltage v and current i. The circuit dimensions are, of course, assumed to be very small compared with the wavelength of the excitation. The power is

$$vi = i^2R + \frac{d}{dt}(\tfrac{1}{2}Li^2) + \frac{d}{dt}(\tfrac{1}{2}Cv_C{}^2) \tag{15-3}$$

The energy of the capacitor C is stored in the electric field between its plates. As the external electric field is negligible in comparison, it is evident that the energy $\frac{1}{2}Cv_C{}^2$ of the capacitor equals the total energy W_E stored in the electric field of the circuit. In terms of this energy the capacitance C is

$$C = \frac{2W_E}{v_C{}^2} = \frac{1}{v_C{}^2}\int_V \epsilon E^2 \, dV \tag{15-4}$$

The volume V is that between the plates, provided the energy stored in the electric field in other parts of the region around the circuit is negligible

We note that C is directly proportional to the permittivity of the dielectric, and it also depends on the dimensions of the capacitor. However, it is independent of time, because the field between the plates is obviously in time phase with the voltage drop. Equation (15-4) is frequently useful in finding C in terms of the dimensions and the dielectric constant of a capacitor.

It is now evident from comparison of Eqs. (15-2) and (15-3) that

$$i^2R + \frac{d}{dt}(\tfrac{1}{2}Li^2) = \int_V J^2/\sigma \, dV + \frac{d}{dt}\int_V \tfrac{1}{2}\mu H^2 \, dV \tag{15-5}$$

In general, the separate terms on the left side are not equal to the corresponding terms on the right side. However, they are equal if skin effect is negligible. For sufficiently low frequencies, the current density J is everywhere in time phase with the current i, and the volume integral of J^2/σ is proportional to i^2. The volume integral of $\frac{1}{2}\mu H^2$ is also proportional to i^2. This follows from the fact that H in the region outside the conducting material is proportional to i by the Biot-Savart law and H inside the conducting material is proportional to J by the Maxwell-Ampère curl equation. We conclude that i^2R in Eq. (15-5) equals the volume integral of J^2/σ, and $\frac{1}{2}Li^2$ equals the volume integral of $\frac{1}{2}\mu H^2$, provided skin effect is negligible. Consequently, at low frequencies the resistance and the inductance can be expressed as

$$R = p_d/i^2 = \frac{1}{i^2}\int_V J^2/\sigma \, dV \tag{15-6}$$

$$L = 2W_H/i^2 = \frac{1}{i^2}\int_V \mu H^2 \, dV \tag{15-7}$$

At sufficiently low frequencies the power i^2R to the resistance of the circuit denotes the instantaneous power dissipated, and the energy $\frac{1}{2}Li^2$ of the inductance denotes the instantaneous energy stored in the magnetic field of the circuit. At higher frequencies these relations are invalid because of skin effect. However, regardless of the frequency, the average power I^2R to the resistance equals the average power dissipated, and the average energy $\frac{1}{2}LI^2$ stored in the inductance equals the average energy stored in the magnetic field, with I denoting the rms current. Thus for a given current the resistance is a measure of the ability of the circuit to dissipate energy, and the inductance is a measure of the ability of the circuit to store energy in its magnetic field.

Substitution of i/S for J in Eq. (15-6) shows that the d-c resistance of a conductor of length l, constant cross-sectional area S, and constant conductivity σ is $l/(\sigma S)$. This same expression is often used to denote the a-c resistance with the understanding that S is the *effective* cross-sectional area. This effective area, which depends on the frequency, is always less than the actual area because of skin effect.

15-2. LOW-FREQUENCY INDUCTANCE

Often the inductance of a circuit does not differ appreciably from its d-c value. Such is the case when the energy stored in the magnetic field is not substantially influenced by the nonuniform current distribution

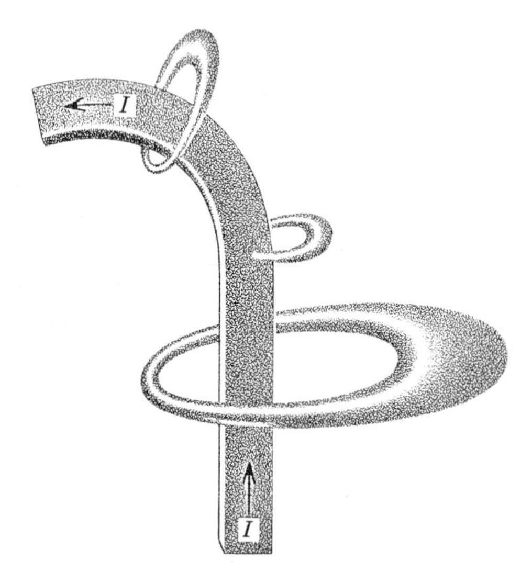

FIG. 15-1. A metallic strip with a steady current I and three associated flux tubes. Note that one tube links only a part of I.

resulting from skin effect. This condition is always met at very low frequencies, and it is, in fact, frequently satisfied at high frequencies. In this section we shall develop several very useful expressions for inductance, which are strictly applicable only for steady currents. However, we should keep in mind the fact that the a-c inductance is approximately equal to the d-c inductance, provided the magnetic energy is not appreciably affected by the phenomenon of skin effect.

Let us examine the energy stored in the magnetic field of a linear electric circuit carrying a steady current I. The magnetic field can be represented by means of field lines. Imagine such lines drawn through all points of a small surface located arbitrarily and oriented at right angles to the magnetic field. These lines form a *flux tube* which occupies a small volume of space. Shown in Fig. 15-1 is a conducting strip and three associated flux tubes.

All lines cutting a cross-sectional area of a tube are confined to the tube, for flux lines cannot cross one another. Let us consider a flux tube with a differential cross-sectional area dS. In a differential length of the tube the stored magnetic energy is $\frac{1}{2}\mu H^2 \, dS \, dl$, which can be expressed as $\frac{1}{2}(B \, dS) \times (H \, dl)$, or $\frac{1}{2} \, d\Phi(H \, dl)$. Integrating this around the closed path of the tube gives the differential energy dW_H. The flux $d\Phi$ is constant, and the integral of $H \, dl$ around the closed path is simply the electric current I' that is encircled by the flux tube. Therefore, $dW_H = \frac{1}{2}I' \, d\Phi$. All the flux tubes collectively occupy all of space, and the integral of dW_H over all flux tubes yields the total energy W_H stored in the magnetic field of the circuit. As $d\Phi = \mathbf{B} \cdot d\mathbf{S}$, this becomes

$$W_H = \frac{1}{2}\int_S I'\mathbf{B} \cdot d\mathbf{S} \tag{15-8}$$

with the surface S denoting any surface that cuts through each flux tube once and only once.

The current I' of Eq. (15-8) may be greater than, equal to, or less than the current I of the circuit. If the flux tube under consideration is outside the conducting material and links the circuit N times, then I' is the product NI. On the other hand, the flux tube may lie partly or wholly within the conducting material, and the current I' may be less than I. Of course, each flux tube must link at least a portion of the current I, for otherwise the Maxwell-Ampère law would be violated. It should be recalled that displacement currents, except those through capacitors, are considered negligible in circuit theory.

In terms of the steady current I, the low-frequency inductance L is $2W_H/I^2$. By means of Eq. (15-8) this can be expressed as

$$L = \left[\frac{1}{I}\int_S I'\mathbf{B} \cdot d\mathbf{S}\right]\left[\frac{1}{I}\right] \tag{15-9}$$

Suppose the circuit has a coil of N turns *with each flux tube linking all the turns of the coil.* Then $I' = NI$, and the first term in brackets represents the flux linkages $N\varphi$, with φ denoting the flux over the cross-sectional area of the coil. If the circuit consists of a single loop, N is unity, and the flux linkages equal the flux Φ over any surface S having the path of the circuit as its boundary. In general, however, there are *partial flux linkages* due to flux lines that link only a fraction of the N turns of a coil and also due to flux lines that lie within or pass through the metallic conductor. If we understand that Φ denotes the flux linkages of a circuit, including the partial flux linkages, then the inductance equals the flux linkages Φ per unit current. Mathematically

$$L = \Phi/I \tag{15-10}$$

with the flux linkages equal to

$$\Phi = \frac{1}{I}\int_S I'\mathbf{B} \cdot d\mathbf{S} \tag{15-11}$$

The surface S is any surface *that cuts through each flux tube once*, and the current I' is that current *encircled by a field line passing through the differential surface* $d\mathbf{S}$ *of* S. It should be noted that the energy stored in the magnetic field is

$$W_H = \tfrac{1}{2}LI^2 = \tfrac{1}{2}\Phi I \tag{15-12}$$

provided the permeability is independent of the current.

The flux linkages of a circuit, including the partial flux linkages, are defined by Eq. (15-11). The d-c inductance is the flux linkages per unit current. At higher frequencies, however, the flux linkages Φ and the instantaneous current i are not in time phase, because of skin effect, and inductance no longer equals the flux linkages per unit current. In fact, for alternating currents the ratio Φ/i is infinite at the instant of zero current, regardless of the frequency and the geometry of the circuit. Let us consider an example utilizing the concept of flux linkages.

EXAMPLE. By the flux-linkage method find the low-frequency internal inductance per unit length of a round wire of radius a and permeability μ. Assume circular flux lines, centered on the axis.

Solution. Inside the wire a flux tube through the differential rectangle of width dr in the radial direction and of unit length in the axial direction encircles the current I', which equals Ir^2/a^2, with I denoting the total current. The differential area of the rectangle is dr, and the magnetic flux density B is $\mu I'/(2\pi r)$, by the Maxwell-Ampère integral equation. Therefore, the magnetic flux $\mathbf{B} \cdot d\mathbf{S}$ over the surface of the rectangle is $\mu Ir/(2\pi a^2)\, dr$. Substituting into Eq. (15-11) and integrating with respect to r from zero to a gives the internal flux linkages Φ per unit length to be $\mu I/8\pi$ webers/m. It follows from Eq. (15-10) that the internal inductance per unit length is $\mu/8\pi$ henry/m. This same result was obtained in Sec. 14-9 by multiplying the energy stored in the magnetic field of a unit length of the wire by $2/I^2$.

In many cases some flux lines of a circuit will be partly in the dielectric and partly in the conducting material, and the flux linkages cannot be classified as internal and external. However, it may be that no lines cut through the surface of the conducting material. In this event some lines are entirely internal, linking only portions of the current, and the remainder of the lines are entirely external, linking all of the current one or more times; the internal and external inductances become the internal and external flux linkages per unit current, respectively.

Let us consider a circuit that has a geometry such that no flux lines cut through the surface of the conducting material. At any point on the surface the magnetic field is tangential. Let C denote a closed path around the circuit, with each point of C located somewhere on the surface of the conducting material so that no internal flux lines link the path; the flux linkages of C are entirely external. These external flux linkages are precisely equal to the magnetic flux Φ over any surface S having the path C as its contour. If the circuit has a coil of N turns, a flux line that links all N turns cuts the surface N times. This was discussed in Sec. 8-2. The magnetic flux Φ is the surface integral of the flux density $\mathbf{B}$. As $\mathbf{B} = \textbf{curl A}$, Φ is the surface integral of $\textbf{curl A}$, and by Stokes's theorem this equals the line integral of the vector potential $\mathbf{A}$ around the closed path C. Therefore, the external flux linkages are

$$\Phi = \int_S \mathbf{B} \cdot d\mathbf{S} = \oint_C \mathbf{A} \cdot d\mathbf{l}$$

In terms of the magnetic vector potential, the external inductance L_e is

$$L_e = \frac{1}{I} \oint_C \mathbf{A} \cdot d\mathbf{l} \tag{15-13}$$

The unretarded magnetic vector potential $\mathbf{A}$ of (15-13) is

$$\mathbf{A} = \frac{\mu}{4\pi} \int_V \frac{\mathbf{J}}{r}\, dV \tag{15-14}$$

Consequently, the external inductance expressed directly in terms of the current density $\mathbf{J}$ becomes

$$L_e = \frac{\mu}{4\pi I} \oint_C \left[\int_V \frac{\mathbf{J}}{r}\, dV \right] \cdot d\mathbf{l} \tag{15-15}$$

This result is sometimes used to calculate the low-frequency external inductance of a circuit. It applies only if the magnetic field is tangential to the metallic surface at every point. The path C is any path around the closed circuit, with each point of the path located on the surface of the conducting material.

If the wire of the circuit is filamentary, having a cross-sectional area that approaches zero, $\mathbf{J}\, dV$ in Eq. (15-15) can be replaced with $I\, d\mathbf{l}$, giving

$$L_e = \frac{\mu}{4\pi} \oint_C \left[\oint_C \frac{d\mathbf{l}}{r} \right] \cdot d\mathbf{l} \tag{15-16}$$

For the same $d\mathbf{l}$'s, r is zero, and L_e is infinite. Thus the inductance of a circuit approaches infinity as the cross-sectional area of the metallic conductor approaches zero. This is also evident from energy considerations. The magnetic field at the surface of a wire carrying a current I approaches infinity as the radius approaches zero. Consequently, the flux linkages and the energy stored in the external magnetic field approach infinity, and of course, the inductance does also. For circuits with wires of small cross-sectional areas the external inductance is usually much greater than the internal inductance, which is independent of the size of the wire.

We shall now develop an additional expression useful in calculating low-frequency inductance. As $\mu H^2 = \mathbf{B} \cdot \mathbf{H}$, Eq. (15-7) can be written

$$L = \frac{1}{I^2} \int_V \mathbf{B} \cdot \mathbf{H} \, dV \tag{15-17}$$

with I denoting the steady current. Substituting $\nabla \times \mathbf{A}$ for $\mathbf{B}$ and replacing $(\nabla \times \mathbf{A}) \cdot \mathbf{H}$ with $\nabla \cdot (\mathbf{A} \times \mathbf{H}) + \mathbf{A} \cdot (\nabla \times \mathbf{H})$, this being justified by the vector identity of Eq. (10-58), give

$$L = \frac{1}{I^2} \left[\int_V \nabla \cdot (\mathbf{A} \times \mathbf{H}) \, dV + \int_V \mathbf{A} \cdot (\nabla \times \mathbf{H}) \, dV \right]$$

By the divergence theorem the first integral can be replaced with the surface integral over the surface S that surrounds the volume V. As V denotes the volume of all space, the surface S is at infinity. At points on S both $\mathbf{A}$ and $\mathbf{H}$ are zero, and the surface integral is also zero. In the second integral we can replace $\nabla \times \mathbf{H}$ with the current density $\mathbf{J}$, because displacement currents in the dielectric around the circuit are negligible. We obtain

$$L = \frac{1}{I^2} \int_V \mathbf{A} \cdot \mathbf{J} \, dV \tag{15-18}$$

This is the low-frequency inductance, both internal and external. The volume V is that occupied by the conducting material, for $\mathbf{J}$ is zero outside this region. The unretarded magnetic vector potential $\mathbf{A}$ of Eq. (15-18) is given as Eq. (15-14).

Several illustrative examples involving the calculation of inductance are given in the following chapter on magnetostatics. Unfortunately, most practical problems utilizing the equations for low-frequency inductance are so complex, insofar as the geometry of the circuit is concerned, that advanced mathematics is required for evaluation of the integrals.

15-3. INCREMENTAL CIRCUIT PARAMETERS

Having defined the resistance, inductance, and capacitance of a circuit, we are now in an excellent position to consider the incremental circuit parameters so important in circuits with vacuum tubes, transistors, saturated iron-core inductors, or other nonlinear devices. The resistance R of a circuit is the ratio v_R/i, with v_R denoting the component of the sinusoidal applied voltage in time phase with the current. If R is independent of the current i, then v_R is directly proportional to i, and this relationship is often referred to as Ohm's law. R may be a function of temperature and other variables that directly affect the medium, but if Ohm's law applies, R must be independent of i. For media satisfying Ohm's law, a graphical plot of i versus v_R is a straight line passing through the origin. As this plot is linear, the resistance R is a *linear* resistance.

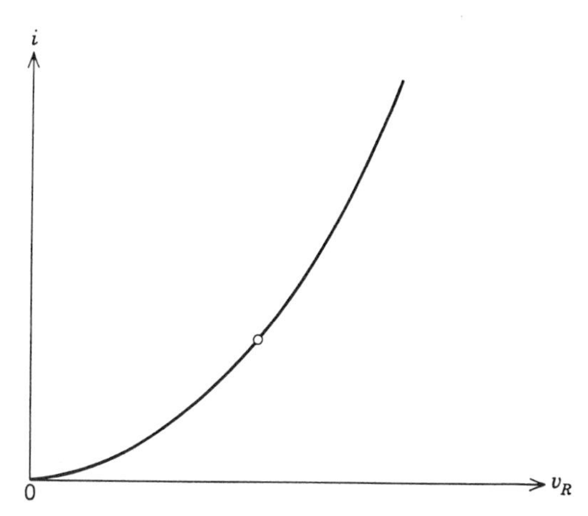

FIG. 15-2. Current-voltage plot of a nonlinear resistor R.

If R is a function of i, Ohm's law is not satisfied, the plot of i versus v_R is nonlinear, and R is a *nonlinear* resistance. Such resistors are of considerable importance in electrical engineering. For example, a thyrite lightning arrestor has a large resistance when v_R and i are small but has a small resistance when they are large. In a vacuum tube the plate current is not directly proportional to the applied plate voltage, and the average power dissipated is not proportional to the rms current squared. Thus the resistance is nonlinear. Shown in Fig. 15-2 is a current-voltage plot of a nonlinear resistor R, which is connected in series with the linear resistor R_1 of Fig. 15-3. By Kirchhoff's law

$$V = iR_1 + v_R \tag{15-19}$$

with V denoting the terminal voltage of the ideal battery.

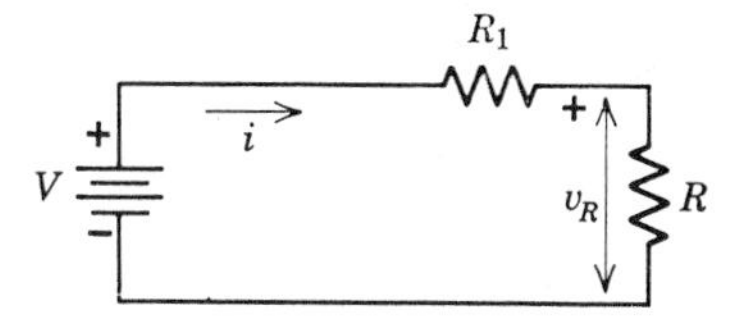

FIG. 15-3. A series circuit with a nonlinear resistor R.

A plot of Eq. (15-19), with i and v_R the variables, is a straight line, and this is shown in Fig. 15-4. The voltage v_R and the current i must satisfy the curves of both Fig. 15-2 and Fig. 15-4. Therefore, if we sketch these on the same set of axes, the intersection of the two curves determines the values of v_R and i. This graphical method is frequently utilized to solve a nonlinear circuit such as the one considered here.

Suppose a very small alternating voltage is applied to the circuit of Fig. 15-3, in addition to the d-c voltage of the battery. The d-c *operating*, or *quiescent*, point is indicated on the curve of Fig. 15-2 by the circle. The a-c voltage causes v_R and i to vary about their average values. Let these variations, which are functions of time, be denoted by Δv_R and Δi, which are referred to as the a-c components of the voltage and current.

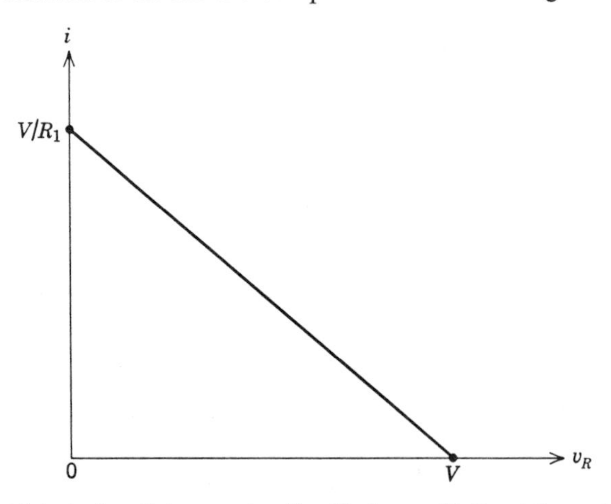

FIG. 15-4. A plot of the equation $V = iR_1 + v_R$, with V and R_1 constant.

Although the curve of Fig. 15-2 is nonlinear, it is essentially a straight line in the immediate vicinity of the operating point. In fact, a sufficiently small region of any smooth curve approximates a straight line. Consequently, the *incremental changes* Δv_R *and* Δi *are directly proportional to one another*, provided the changes are small enough so that the region of operation on the curve of Fig. 15-2 is reasonably linear. The limit of the ratio $\Delta v_R/\Delta i$, as Δi approaches zero, is the *incremental resistance* r, often referred to as the a-c, or dynamic, resistance. Thus

$$r = dv_R/di \tag{15-20}$$

For small signals it is evident that the a-c voltage Δv_R and current Δi are related by the equation $\Delta v_R = r\,\Delta i_R$. Even though the resistance R is nonlinear, the waveforms of the a-c voltage and current are identical, provided the signal is small, and the incremental resistance r is the constant of proportionality that relates these a-c quantities. It should be noted that r equals the reciprocal of the slope of the current-voltage characteristic curve, with a value that depends on the d-c operating point. The concept of incremental resistance is used extensively in the analysis of small-signal amplifier circuits that contain vacuum tubes or transistors. Let us consider an example utilizing this concept.

EXAMPLE 1. The current i of a certain PN junction diode is $0.03(e^{40v} - 1)$ milliamperes, with v denoting the applied voltage. If $v = 0.15 + 0.001 \sin \omega t$, find the resistance R, the incremental resistance r, and the a-c component of the diode current.

Solution. At the quiescent point $v = 0.15$, and the corresponding direct current is 12 ma. Consequently, the resistance R is 12.5 ohms. The incremental resistance is the reciprocal of di/dv at the operating point. As $di/dv = 1.2e^{40v} = 482$ millimhos at the operating point, r is 2.1 ohms. The alternating current is the a-c voltage divided by r, or $0.48 \sin \omega t$ milliampere. It is easily shown that the slope of the current-voltage curve does not change appreciably over the range of operation, and therefore, the use of the incremental resistance to determine the alternating current is justified.

An inductor frequently consists of a coil of wire mounted on a ferromagnetic core. This gives a large number of flux linkages for a given current. However, ferromagnetic materials are nonlinear, and the core flux is not directly proportional to the current i. Therefore, the inductance L is nonlinear, with L depending on the current i. If i is sinusoidal, L varies with time, and the inductive voltage drop is nonsinusoidal. Although the nonlinearity is frequently negligible, inductors with ferromagnetic cores are, in general, nonlinear.

Often a small alternating current is superimposed upon a large direct current in a ferromagnetic inductor. For such cases it is convenient to utilize the concept of *incremental inductance* L', defined at low frequencies by

$$L' = d\Phi/di \tag{15-21}$$

with $d\Phi$ denoting the differential change in the flux linkages corresponding to the differential change di in the current. The a-c inductive voltage drop in the direction of the positive current is, of course, equal to the product of the incremental inductance and the time rate of change of the alternating current. The incremental inductance is evaluated at the d-c operating point. It can be treated as a constant as long as the a-c quantities are small enough so that the slope of the curve of Φ versus i is essentially constant over the range of operation. Obviously, incremental inductance and inductance are equivalent if the medium is linear.

Occasionally the charges $+q$ and $-q$ stored in a capacitor are nonlinear functions of the applied voltage v_C. In such cases the capacitance C, which equals q/v_C, is a function of the voltage. Frequently, the engineer is primarily concerned with the capacitive effect on small alternating currents and voltages that are superimposed upon the quiescent d-c levels. Thus we define *incremental capacitance* C' as

$$C' = dq/dv_C \tag{15-22}$$

The differential charge dq is the increase in q resulting from the differential increase dv_C in the capacitive voltage. Although the capacitance C may be nonlinear, the incremental capacitance C' is a constant independent of the magnitude of the a-c voltage, provided the a-c variations about the quiescent level are very small. Let us consider an example.

EXAMPLE 2. Shown in Fig. 15-5 is a reverse-biased PN junction of a germanium crystal. In the immediate vicinity of the junction, charges of $+q$ and $-q$ are stored as illustrated. Suppose that $q = av^{1/2}$, with a denoting a constant dependent on the dimensions and properties of the crystal and with v denoting the sum of the d-c voltage V and the much smaller a-c voltage v_1. Find C, C', and the a-c charge q_1 of the capacitance.

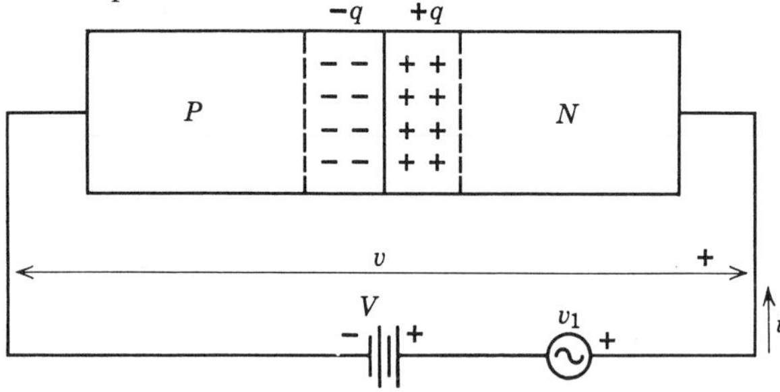

FIG. 15-5. A PN junction. In the vicinity of the junction between the P and the N regions there are net charges $\pm q$.

Solution. $C = q/v = av^{-1/2} = aV^{-1/2}$, for $v \approx V$. The incremental capacitance C', which equals dq/dv, is $\frac{1}{2}av^{-1/2}$, or $\frac{1}{2}aV^{-1/2}$. Thus the incremental capacitance is one-half the capacitance. The a-c charge q_1 equals the product of the incremental capacitance C' and the a-c voltage v_1, or $q_1 = (\frac{1}{2}aV^{-1/2})v_1$.

The analysis of a circuit involving transistors, vacuum tubes, or other nonlinear devices is usually rather difficult if the signals are large, because the response to a sinusoidal excitation is nonsinusoidal. For small-signal circuits, however, it is possible to employ an equivalent a-c circuit composed of linear parameters and internal linear generators, regardless of the d-c, or quiescent, level. Whenever nonlinear elements are present, the small-signal equivalent circuit utilizes the incremental parameters. This method accurately relates the alternating currents and voltages, provided the excursions about the d-c levels are sufficiently small to justify the use of the incremental parameters evaluated at the operating point. It should be noted that resistance and incremental resistance are equivalent for a linear element, and the same is true for both inductance and capacitance.

15-4. MUTUAL INDUCTANCE

We have learned that a linear circuit has an emf of self-induction equal to $L\,di/dt$ volts. This is the voltage drop in the direction of the positive current i and is induced in the circuit by the time-changing flux linkages produced by the changing current i. If a second linear circuit is present, as

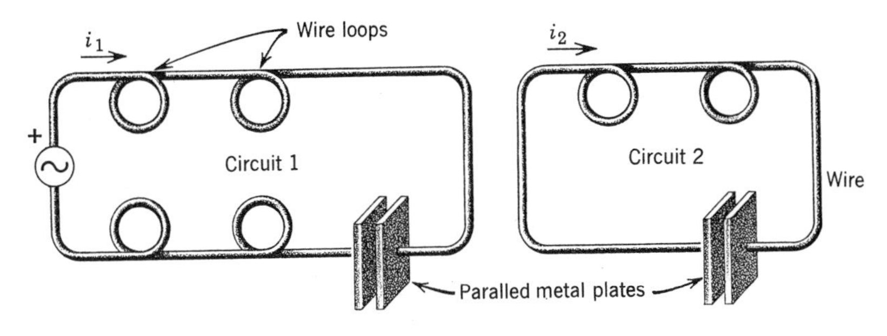

FIG. 15-6. Two nearby circuits.

shown in Fig. 15-6, the time-changing flux induces a voltage in this circuit also; the induced voltage is the emf of *mutual induction*. When both circuits are closed, the magnetic field in the region is the superposition of the fields produced by the individual currents. Each time-changing current has an associated changing magnetic field that induces a voltage in the other circuit as well as its own. The lines of magnetic flux that link both circuits constitute the *mutual flux*. Flux linking one but

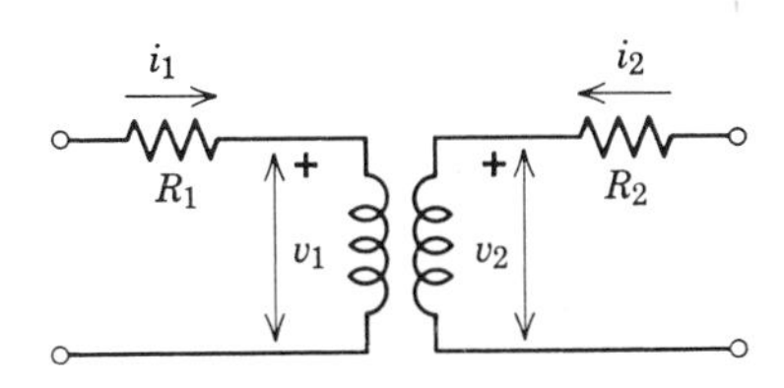

FIG. 15-7. Inductively coupled circuits with lumped resistances.

not the other is referred to as *leakage flux*. Obviously, the flux linkages of a circuit are the sum of the mutual and leakage flux linkages. The two circuits of Fig. 15-6 are said to be *inductively coupled*.

Two inductively coupled circuits, with their resistances regarded as lumped, are shown in Fig. 15-7. The reference directions of the voltages and currents are indicated, and their selection was arbitrary. As the voltages v_1 and v_2 are due to both self and mutual induction, each can be expressed as the sum of two components, one depending on the time rate of change of i_1 and the other depending on the time rate of change of i_2. Thus

$$v_1 = L_1 \frac{di_1}{dt} + M_{12} \frac{di_2}{dt} \tag{15-23}$$

$$v_2 = L_2 \frac{di_2}{dt} + M_{21} \frac{di_1}{dt} \tag{15-24}$$

with the constants M_{12} and M_{21} denoting the *mutual inductances* of their respective circuits. The mks unit of mutual inductance is the *henry*. Of course, L_1 and L_2 are the self-inductances of the circuits.

Suppose the *primary circuit* is open, so that i_1 is zero. It is then evident from Eq. (15-23) that

$$M_{12} = \frac{v_1}{di_2/dt} \tag{15-25}$$

On the other hand, if the *secondary circuit* is open so that i_2 is zero, we note from Eq. (15-24) that

$$M_{21} = \frac{v_2}{di_1/dt} \tag{15-26}$$

Equations (15-25) and (15-26) provide a method for measuring the mutual inductances.

Let us assume that the frequency is sufficiently low to justify our neglecting skin effect. With this assumption we can develop some very useful expressions for mutual inductance. If skin effect is negligible, the instantaneous power dissipated in the two circuits of Fig. 15-7 equals the instantaneous power supplied to the resistances R_1 and R_2; therefore, the sum of $v_1 i_1$ and $v_2 i_2$ must represent the instantaneous power supplied to the magnetic field.

For linear media the magnetic field $\mathbf{H}$ can be subdivided into two components $\mathbf{H}_1$ and $\mathbf{H}_2$, with $\mathbf{H}_1$ denoting the field due to i_1 and $\mathbf{H}_2$ the field due to i_2. As $H^2 = \mathbf{H} \cdot \mathbf{H}$ and as $\mathbf{H} = \mathbf{H}_1 + \mathbf{H}_2$, it is clear that

$$H^2 = H_1^2 + 2\mathbf{H}_1 \cdot \mathbf{H}_2 + H_2^2$$

Consequently, the instantaneous power supplied to the magnetic field is

$$v_1 i_1 + v_2 i_2 = \frac{d}{dt} \int_V \tfrac{1}{2}\mu(H_1^2 + 2\mathbf{H}_1 \cdot \mathbf{H}_2 + H_2^2)\, dV \tag{15-27}$$

By Eq. (15-7) the self-inductance L_1 is

$$L_1 = \frac{1}{i_1^2} \int_V \mu H_1^2\, dV \tag{15-28}$$

and the self-inductance L_2 is similarly defined. In terms of L_1 and L_2, Eq. (15-27) becomes

$$v_1 i_1 + v_2 i_2 = \frac{d}{dt}\left(\tfrac{1}{2}L_1 i_1^2 + M i_1 i_2 + \tfrac{1}{2}L_2 i_2^2\right) \qquad (15\text{-}29)$$

with M defined by

$$M = \frac{1}{i_1 i_2}\int_V \mu \mathbf{H}_1 \cdot \mathbf{H}_2 \, dV \qquad (15\text{-}30)$$

The constant M is independent of time, if skin effect is negligible, because $\mathbf{H}_1$ is everywhere in time phase with i_1 and $\mathbf{H}_2$ is everywhere in time phase with i_2. As the magnetic fields are proportional to their respective currents, M depends only on the geometry of the circuit and the permeability of the medium. In Eq. (15-29), L_1, L_2, and M are independent of time. Therefore, the instantaneous power p_H into the magnetic field can be expressed as

$$p_H = L_1 i_1 \frac{di_1}{dt} + M i_1 \frac{di_2}{dt} + M i_2 \frac{di_1}{dt} + L_2 i_2 \frac{di_2}{dt} \qquad (15\text{-}31)$$

Comparison of this with the sum of $v_1 i_1$ and $v_2 i_2$, with v_1 and v_2 as given in Eqs. (15-23) and (15-24), shows that

$$M_{12} = M_{21} = M \qquad (15\text{-}32)$$

Thus if skin effect is negligible, *the mutual inductances M_{12} and M_{21} of a linear system are both equal to M as defined by Eq. (15-30).*

Examination of Eq. (15-29) reveals that the energy stored in the magnetic field of the linear circuits is

$$W_H = \tfrac{1}{2}L_1 i_1^2 + M i_1 i_2 + \tfrac{1}{2}L_2 i_2^2 \qquad (15\text{-}33)$$

The energy terms involving the self-inductances L_1 and L_2 are the energies that would be stored if the circuits were isolated from one another. The term $M i_1 i_2$ represents the change in the stored energy due to the interaction of the magnetic fields of the circuits. It is sometimes referred to as a *mutual energy*. We note from Eq. (15-30) that M may be positive or negative, for the scalar product of $\mathbf{H}_1$ and $\mathbf{H}_2$ at a point may be positive or negative when both currents are positive. The mutual energy term may, of course, be positive or negative at a given instant, depending on the sign of M and also on the signs of i_1 and i_2 at the instant under consideration.

EXAMPLE. If $i_1 = 2 \sin \omega t$ and $i_2 = -1 \cos \omega t$ in the inductively coupled circuit of Fig. 15-7, with $\omega = 1000$, $L_1 = 2$ mh, $L_2 = 8$ mh, and $M = -3$ mh, find the voltages v_1 and v_2 and the energy W_H stored in the magnetic field. Calculate W_H for the instant at which $\omega t = -30°$.

Solution. In the primary circuit $L_1\, di_1/dt$ is $4 \cos \omega t$ and $M\, di_2/dt$ is $-3 \sin \omega t$. The sum of these is $5 \sin (\omega t + 126.9°)$ volts, and this is v_1. Note that the emfs of self and mutual induction are, in this special case, 90° out of time phase and, therefore, they alternately aid and oppose one another. Similarly, v_2 is found to be $10 \sin (\omega t - 36.9°)$.

The energy $\frac{1}{2}L_1 i_1^2 = 0.004 \sin^2 \omega t$, and $\frac{1}{2}L_2 i_2^2 = 0.004 \cos^2 \omega t$. The mutual energy $M i_1 i_2$ is $0.006 \sin \omega t \cos \omega t$. The sum of these gives W_H, which can be expressed as $0.004 + 0.003 \sin 2\omega t$. For $\omega t = -30°$, $\frac{1}{2}L_1 i_1^2$ is 0.001, $\frac{1}{2}L_2 i_2^2$ is 0.003, and the mutual energy is -0.0026. Thus W_H is 0.0014 joule at this instant.

15-5. INDUCTIVELY COUPLED CIRCUITS

We shall now examine the procedure for analyzing circuits with mutual inductance. Shown in Fig. 15-8 is an inductively coupled circuit in which the resistances and self-inductances are treated as lumped elements. The voltages v_1' and v_2' are due to mutual inductance, with $v_1' = M\, di_2/dt$ and $v_2' = M\, di_1/dt$. We can, if we wish, represent these voltages by means of

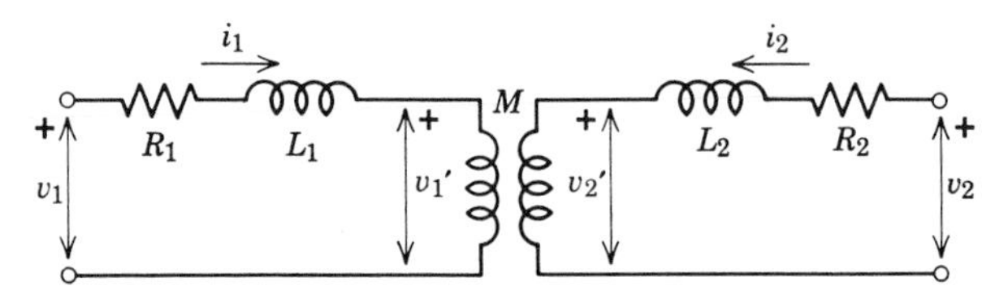

FIG. 15-8. Inductively coupled circuits.

ideal voltage generators, as shown in Fig. 15-9. This is an equivalent circuit that yields the proper relationships between the voltages and currents. The expressions $M\, di_2/dt$ and $M\, di_1/dt$ denote the terminal voltages of the two generators. By Kirchhoff's voltage law it is evident that

$$v_1 = i_1 R_1 + L_1 \frac{di_1}{dt} + M \frac{di_2}{dt} \tag{15-34}$$

$$v_2 = i_2 R_2 + L_2 \frac{di_2}{dt} + M \frac{di_1}{dt} \tag{15-35}$$

These are similar to Eqs. (15-23) and (15-24) except for the addition of the resistive terms.

The positive directions of the currents of Fig. 15-9 were selected arbitrarily. In the primary circuit the voltage drop in the direction of i_1, due to L_1, is $+L_1\, di_1/dt$. The voltage drop in the direction of i_1, due to M, is $+M\, di_2/dt$; this is in accordance with our definition of M. Therefore, regardless of the selection of the reference direction of i_1, the plus sign on the generator of voltage $M\, di_2/dt$ must be placed so that the positive current i_1 enters this terminal. The expression $M\, di_2/dt$ is understood, by definition, to represent the voltage drop in the positive direction of i_1. This voltage drop may be in phase with i_1, or it may lead or lag i_1, depending on the parameters of the circuit. In the secondary circuit the voltages $L_2\, di_2/dt$ and $M\, di_1/dt$ are voltage drops in the direction of the positive current i_2. Therefore, the same rule applies with regard to the reference direction of the emf of mutual induction. Thus for both primary and

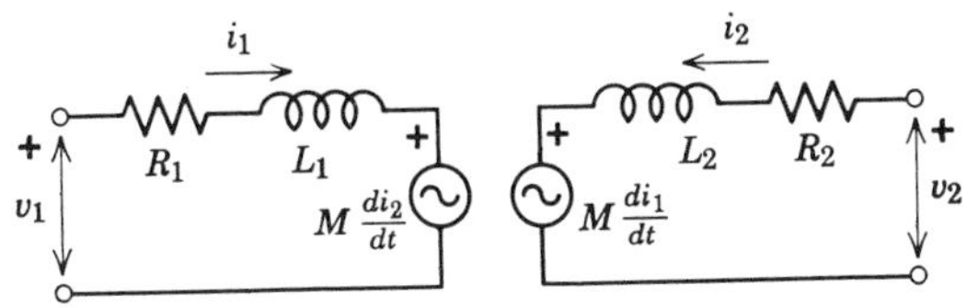

FIG. 15-9. A representation of the coupled circuits of Fig. 15-8.

secondary circuits, *the positive sign on the generator representing the induced voltage* $+M\, di/dt$ *should always be placed so that the positive current enters this terminal.* It is, of course, permissible to denote the induced voltage by $-M\, di/dt$ with the reference direction of the generator reversed, and this is often done. Clearly, the reference directions of the currents and other voltages are selected as desired.

For a given circuit the symbol M denotes a positive or negative number whose magnitude depends on the geometry of the circuit and the permeability of the medium and whose sign depends on both the geometry of the circuit and the reference currents. M is given by Eq. (15-30), provided skin effect is negligible. From this equation we note that, if positive currents i_1 and i_2 produce flux fields that have the same general direction in space, then M is positive. On the other hand, if the designated positive

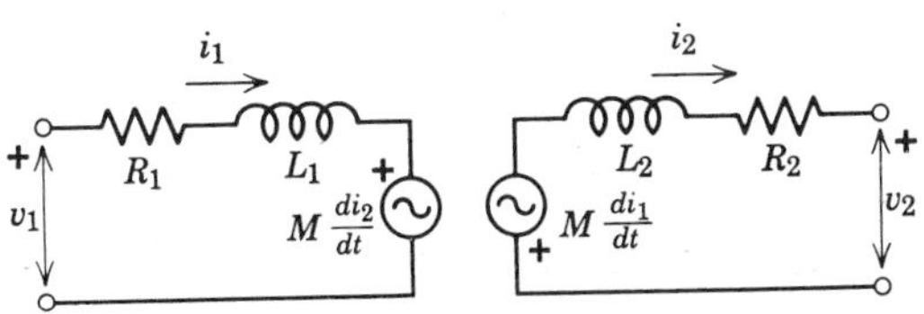

FIG. 15-10. The circuit of Fig. 15-9 with the positive direction of i_2 reversed. M in this illustration is the negative of the M in Fig. 15-9 because of the change in the positive direction of i_2.

currents produce component fields that are in opposition, M is negative. The sign of M is affected by the actual circuit orientations *and also by the reference directions selected for the currents.* Experimentally, the sign can be determined by driving the primary and the secondary with currents i_1 and i_2 that are *in time phase.* Then M is positive if the emf of mutual induction aids the emf of self-induction. Otherwise, M is negative.

The circuit of Fig. 15-9 is redrawn in Fig. 15-10 with the reference direction for i_2 reversed. This changes the sign of M and also the sign of di_2/dt, for the new current i_2 is the negative of that shown in Fig. 15-9. Consequently, the voltage $M\,di_2/dt$ induced in the primary is unchanged in sign, whereas the voltage $M\,di_1/dt$ induced in the secondary is changed.

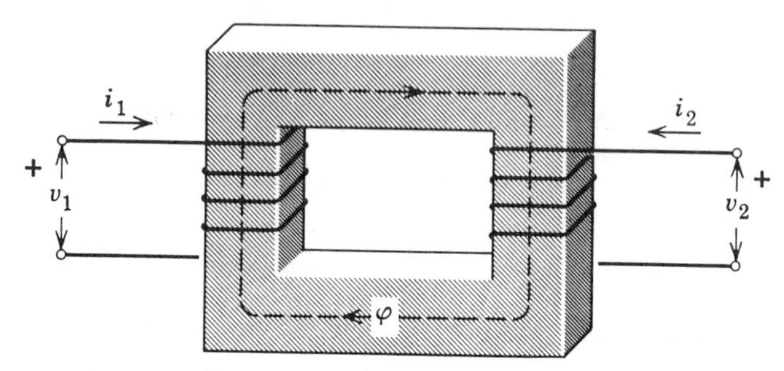

FIG. 15-11. Circuit with positive M.

For this reason the reference direction of this voltage is changed, with the plus sign placed on the bottom terminal of the generator, rather than on the top terminal as in Fig. 15-9. Note that the reference current enters the terminal marked with the plus sign.

Shown in Fig. 15-11 are two coils on an iron core. Most of the flux lines are confined to the iron core. We observe that the two reference currents produce magnetic fluxes directed similarly around the iron core. Consequently, M is positive.

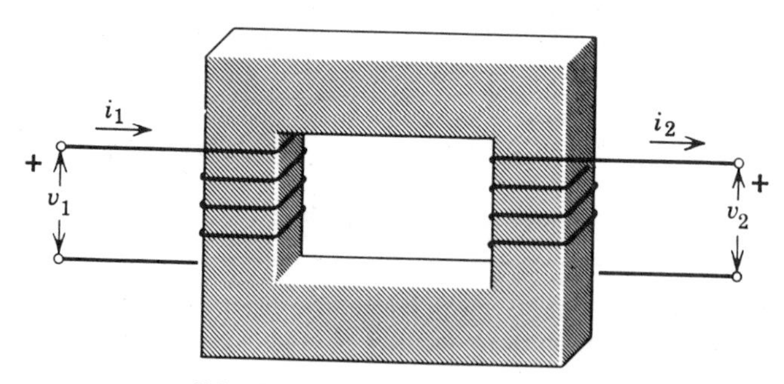

FIG. 15-12. Circuit with negative M.

The same circuit is shown in Fig. 15-12, but the specified positive direction of i_2 is changed. Positive currents now produce opposing fluxes in the iron core, and M is negative.

In Fig. 15-13 one coil winding is reversed. The reference currents produce fluxes in opposite directions, and M is negative.

It is not always possible to determine the way the coils are wound about a core by direct inspection. Therefore, coils are frequently marked in some manner to resolve this difficulty. One common method is the marking of

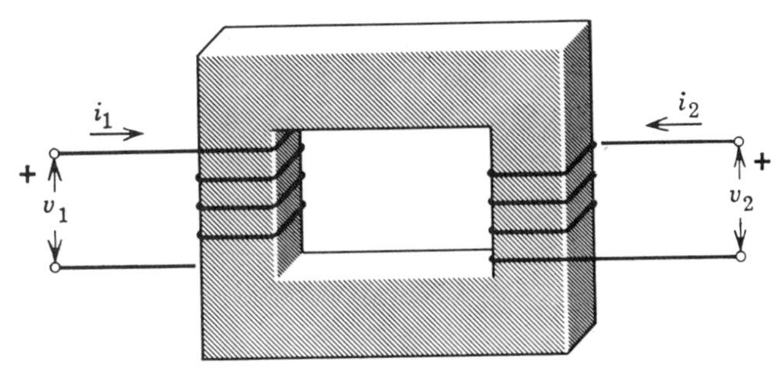

FIG. 15-13. Circuit with negative M.

one terminal of each coil with a heavy dot, placed so that M is positive if each reference current enters the dotted terminal of its coil. If the reference directions of both currents are reversed, so that the positive currents leave

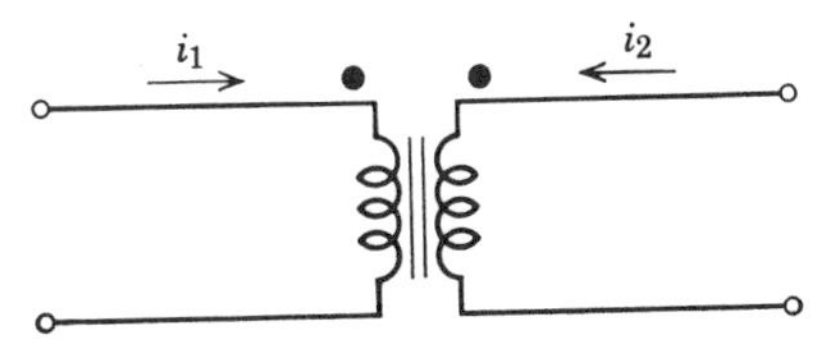

FIG. 15-14. Circuit of Fig. 15-11. M is positive.

the dotted terminals, M is, of course, also positive. However, if one positive current enters the marked terminal of its coil and the other leaves its dotted terminal, then M is negative.

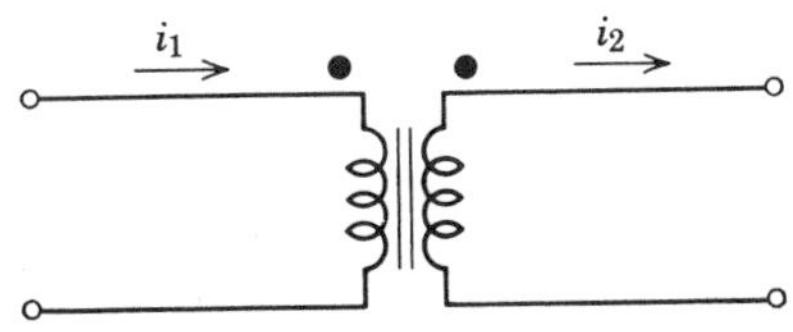

FIG. 15-15. Circuit of Fig. 15-12. M is negative.

Figure 15-14 corresponds to Fig. 15-11. As each positive current enters the marked terminal of its coil, M is positive. Figure 15-15 corresponds to Fig. 15-12 and M is negative. Figure 15-16 corresponds to Fig. 15-13, and M is again negative. In analyzing inductively coupled circuits considerable care must be exercised in determining the proper sign of M. It should be mentioned that some authors prefer to represent the emf of mutual induction as $\pm M\,di/dt$, *with M treated as a positive number*; if this is done, the rule which has been given for determining the sign of M is now employed to determine whether to use the positive or negative sign with the expression for the mutually induced voltage.

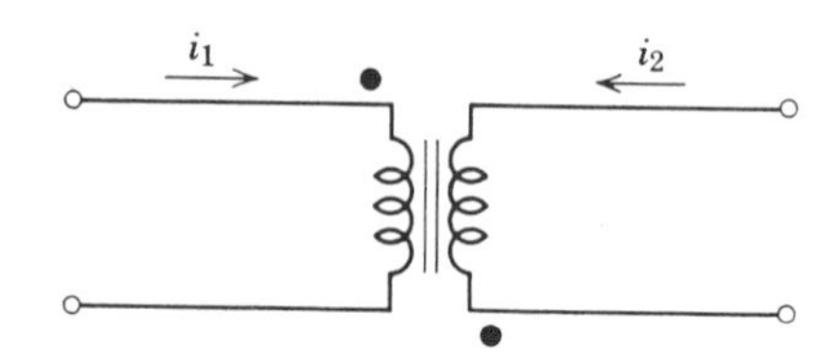

FIG. 15-16. Circuit of Fig. 15-13. M is negative.

EXAMPLE. The coupled circuit of Fig. 15-16 has a mutual inductance of magnitude 5 millihenrys and a secondary-winding resistance of 4 ohms. The primary is driven with a current $i_1 = 8 \sin 1000t$. If a capacitance C is placed across the terminals of the secondary, with C selected so that the sum of the drops due to C and the self-inductance L_2 of the secondary is zero at each instant, find i_2.

Solution. The equivalent circuit is that of Fig. 15-9 with C connected across the output. The sum of the voltage drops counterclockwise around the secondary circuit is $i_2R_2 + M\,di_1/dt$, and this sum is zero. Therefore, $i_2 = -(M/R_2)\,di_1/dt$. Substituting -0.005 for M, 4 for R_2, and the given current, we obtain $i_2 = 10 \cos 1000t$.

15-6. USEFUL EXPRESSIONS FOR MUTUAL INDUCTANCE

The mutual inductances M_{12} and M_{21} of a linear coupled circuit are defined by Eqs. (15-25) and (15-26) in terms of the currents and the emfs of mutual induction. It has been shown that these mutual inductances are both equal to M, defined by Eq. (15-30) with skin effect neglected. We shall now deduce several additional and important expressions for low-frequency mutual inductance. We shall not concern ourselves here with the sign of M, for we have already learned rules that serve this purpose quite well.

Shown in Fig. 15-17 are two coils of turns N_1 and N_2. Let the flux linkages of the coils be designated as follows:

$$\begin{aligned} N_1\varphi_{11} &= \text{flux linkages of coil 1 due to } i_1. \qquad (i_2 = 0) \\ N_1\varphi_{12} &= \text{flux linkages of coil 1 due to } i_2. \qquad (i_1 = 0) \\ N_2\varphi_{21} &= \text{flux linkages of coil 2 due to } i_1. \qquad (i_2 = 0) \\ N_2\varphi_{22} &= \text{flux linkages of coil 2 due to } i_2. \qquad (i_1 = 0) \end{aligned} \tag{15-36}$$

The reference direction of each flux is selected so that the flux linkages and the corresponding current are in time phase. It should be noted that the symbol φ does not represent flux linkages, but denotes flux linkages divided by N. If each flux line links all N turns, then φ is the core flux produced by its associated current.

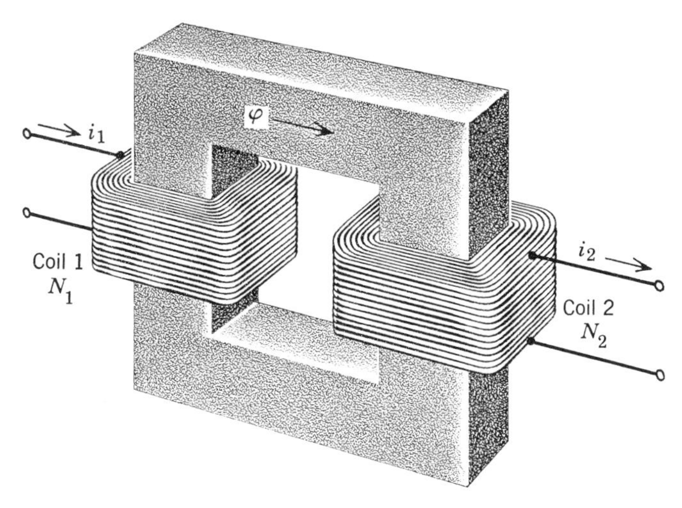

FIG. 15-17. Coupled circuits.

The self-inductance L_1 of the primary equals its flux linkages per unit current, with the secondary open, and the self-inductance L_2 of the secondary equals its flux linkages per unit current, with the primary open. Thus

$$L_1 = N_1\varphi_{11}/i_1 \qquad L_2 = N_2\varphi_{22}/i_2 \tag{15-37}$$

Suppose the primary is open and a current i_2 is driven in the secondary circuit. The voltage induced in the primary is $M_{12}\, di_2/dt$, and this equals the time rate of change of the flux linkages $N_1\varphi_{12}$ of the primary, according to the Maxwell-Faraday law. Therefore, $M_{12}i_2 = N_1\varphi_{12}$. A similar relation applies to the secondary circuit. Thus the mutual inductance M_{12} of the primary and the mutual inductance M_{21} of the secondary, in terms of flux linkages, are

$$M_{12} = N_1\varphi_{12}/i_2 \qquad M_{21} = N_2\varphi_{21}/i_1 \tag{15-38}$$

Of course, M_{12} and M_{21} are equal, and the sign of the mutual inductance may be positive or negative.

Assuming filamentary circuits, the flux linkages $N_1\varphi_{12}$ of coil 1 due to i_2, with $i_1 = 0$, is the surface integral of the magnetic flux density $\mathbf{B}$ over any surface having the path C_1 of the primary circuit as its boundary. As

$\mathbf{B} = \mathbf{curl}\,\mathbf{A}_2$, with $\mathbf{A}_2$ denoting the magnetic vector potential due to i_2, the application of Stokes's theorem to the surface integral gives

$$N_1\varphi_{12} = \oint_{C_1} \mathbf{A}_2 \cdot d\mathbf{l}_1 \tag{15-39}$$

Therefore,

$$M_{12} = \frac{1}{i_2}\oint_{C_1} \mathbf{A}_2 \cdot d\mathbf{l}_1 \tag{15-40}$$

This corresponds to Eq. (15-13) for self-inductance, and a similar expression applies to M_{21}. Substitution for $\mathbf{A}_2$ yields the *Neumann* expression for mutual inductance between filamentary circuits in a medium of constant permeability μ. The result is

$$M = \frac{\mu}{4\pi}\oint_{C_1}\oint_{C_2} \frac{d\mathbf{l}_1 \cdot d\mathbf{l}_2}{r} \tag{15-41}$$

with r denoting the distance between the elemental lengths $d\mathbf{l}_1$ and $d\mathbf{l}_2$. This equation is frequently utilized to calculate M. It clearly shows that the low-frequency mutual inductance between filamentary circuits depends only on the permeability of the medium and the geometry of the circuits. Problems 15-20 and 15-21 are interesting applications of Neumann's equation.

An expression for mutual inductance that corresponds to Eq. (15-18) for self-inductance is

$$M_{12} = \frac{1}{i_1 i_2}\int_V \mathbf{A}_2 \cdot \mathbf{J}_1\, dV \tag{15-42}$$

with $\mathbf{A}_2$ denoting the magnetic vector potential due to i_2 and with $\mathbf{J}_1$ denoting the current density in circuit 1. A similar relation applies to M_{21}. Equation (15-42) is easily deduced from (15-30) in the same manner that Eq. (15-18) was derived from (15-17). For filamentary circuits it is evident that Eq. (15-42) reduces to (15-40).

We note from Eqs. (15-37) and (15-38) that

$$\frac{M_{21}}{L_1} = \frac{N_2}{N_1}k_1 \qquad \frac{M_{12}}{L_2} = \frac{N_1}{N_2}k_2 \tag{15-43}$$

with the constants k_1 and k_2 defined by the relations

$$k_1 = \varphi_{21}/\varphi_{11} \qquad k_2 = \varphi_{12}/\varphi_{22} \tag{15-44}$$

The *primary coupling coefficient* k_1 is the fraction of the flux linking the N_1 turns of the primary that also links the N_2 turns of the secondary, with i_2 zero. The *secondary coupling coefficient* k_2 is similarly defined. Obviously,

k_1 and k_2 have values between zero and unity, but they are not necessarily equal. From Eq. (15-43) it is easily deduced that

$$M = k\sqrt{L_1 L_2} \tag{15-45}$$

with the *coefficient of coupling* k of the circuit defined as $(k_1 k_2)^{1/2}$. In terms of the coupling coefficients the ratio of the inductances is readily shown from (15-43) to be

$$\frac{L_1}{L_2} = \left(\frac{N_1}{N_2}\right)^2 \left(\frac{k_2}{k_1}\right) \tag{15-46}$$

If $k_1 = k_2$, the ratio of the inductances equals the turns ratio squared. This is usually the case. In the next section several of these relations are utilized in the investigation of circuits with unity coupling.

15-7. THE IDEAL TRANSFORMER

A transformer consists basically of two coils of many turns mounted on a common iron core. Most of the flux produced by the current of one coil links the other coil as well. That which does not is the leakage flux, and usually the leakage fluxes of the coils of an iron-core transformer are very small. Because of the high permeability of the iron and the many turns of wire, the self-inductances of the windings are normally so large that the voltages across circuit elements in series with them are negligible in comparison.

Linear transformer-coupled circuits can be analyzed by means of the equivalent circuit employing self and mutual inductances. However, the analysis is considerably simplified by idealizing the transformer in a manner that enables one to obtain with ease approximate relations between the currents and voltages. Accordingly, let us define an *ideal transformer* as a transformer that satisfies the following conditions:

1. The coefficient of coupling k is approximately unity. Specifically, the voltage induced in each coil by the leakage flux linkages of that coil is negligible in comparison with the terminal voltage. Many practical transformers have coefficients of coupling greater than 0.98.

2. The voltages across the self-inductances of the coils are very much greater than those across circuit elements in series with them. This implies that the inductive reactance ωL of each coil is considerably larger than the resistances and reactances of series-connected elements. Obviously, no transformer is ideal at very low frequencies.

3. The resistances of the windings are quite small in comparison with series-connected resistances. Thus we may neglect these winding resistances without appreciable error. The transformer losses are but a small fraction of the transmitted power.

Shown in Fig. 15-18 is a circuit with an iron-core transformer assumed to be ideal. The induced voltages v_1 and v_2 are

$$v_1 = L_1\, di_1/dt + M\, di_2/dt \tag{15-47}$$

$$v_2 = -L_2\, di_2/dt - M\, di_1/dt \tag{15-48}$$

The negative signs in Eq. (15-48) are a consequence of the reference direction selected for v_2, with v_2 denoting the induced voltage drop of the secondary coil in the direction opposite the positive current i_2 of the coil.

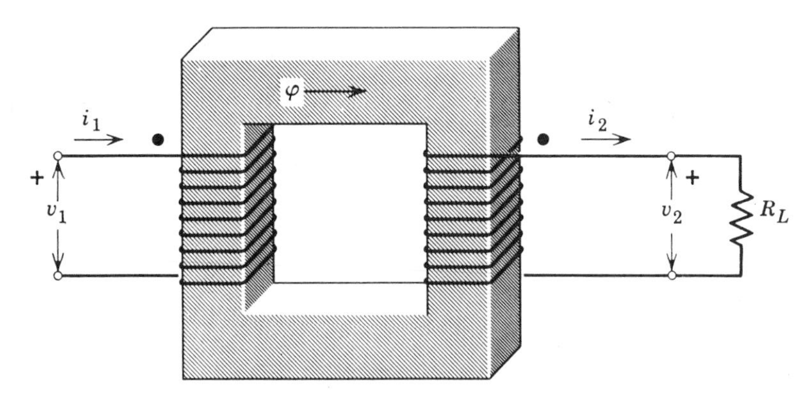

FIG. 15-18. Transformer.

If we replace M in Eq. (15-47) with $-L_2N_1/N_2$ and in Eq. (15-48) with $-L_1N_2/N_1$, these substitutions being justified by Eq. (15-43) and the knowledge that M is negative, comparison of the resulting expressions reveals that

$$\frac{v_1}{v_2} = \frac{N_1}{N_2} \tag{15-49}$$

The voltage ratio of a transformer with unity coupling equals the turns ratio. Furthermore, the voltages v_1 and v_2 are in time phase. In general, *the voltages of an ideal transformer are in time phase if the plus signs indicating the reference directions are both placed at the dotted terminals or if both are placed at the terminals not dotted.* However, if one plus sign is at a dotted terminal and the other is not, the voltages are 180° out of phase. No other phase relation is possible in an *ideal* transformer.

In order to determine the relation between the currents, we apply Kirchhoff's voltage law to the secondary circuit, obtaining

$$M\, di_1/dt + L_2\, di_2/dt + i_2R_L = 0$$

The i_2R_L term is negligible compared with the voltage across L_2 if the transformer is ideal. It follows that $M = -L_2i_2/i_1$. But M also equals $-L_2N_1/N_2$ from (15-43). Therefore

$$\frac{i_1}{i_2} = \frac{N_2}{N_1} \tag{15-50}$$

The current ratio of an ideal transformer equals the reciprocal of the turns ratio. The ampere-turns N_1i_1 of the primary equal the ampere-turns N_2i_2 of the secondary. Also, we note that i_1 and i_2 are in time phase. In general, *the currents of an ideal transformer are in time phase if the reference directions are selected so that one positive current enters the dotted terminal of its coil and the other positive current leaves the dotted terminal.* Otherwise, the currents are 180° out of time phase. No other phase relation is possible in an *ideal* transformer.

It is easily shown from Eqs. (15-49) and (15-50) that the ratio v_1/i_1 equals the product of v_2/i_2 and $(N_1/N_2)^2$. The ratio v_2/i_2 equals R_L, for a resistive load, and the input resistance R_i is

$$R_i = (N_1/N_2)^2R_L \tag{15-51}$$

All power supplied to this input resistance is delivered to R_L, for the ideal transformer is lossless. Ideal transformers are frequently used to match resistances in order to transfer maximum power from a source to a load.

The analysis of a circuit with ideal transformers is simplified by the use of Eqs. (15-49), (15-50), and (15-51). It is important to learn the proper phase relations. In Fig. 15-18 the voltages are in time phase, and so are the currents. If the secondary coil were dotted on the bottom terminal, then the voltages would be 180° out of phase, the currents would also be 180° out of phase, and Eqs. (15-49) and (15-50) should have negative signs inserted. These phase relations do not apply, of course, to transformers that are not ideal. In case the windings are shown but not dotted, it is suggested that they be marked before analyzing the circuit. To do this, determine the directions of the primary and secondary currents that produce core fluxes in the same direction, and then dot the terminals entered by the currents. After this is done, select the reference directions as desired. A transformer that is ideal except for appreciable resistances in its windings can be treated as ideal by regarding the resistances as lumped elements outside the windings. Also, if there are appreciable leakage fluxes, the theory applies provided lumped *leakage inductances*, due to the leakage flux linkages, are inserted in series with the windings. However, the inductive reactances of the coils must be large, as previously stated. Let us consider an example.

EXAMPLE. A certain generator can be represented by an ideal voltage source of $100\sqrt{2} \sin \omega t$ volts in series with a resistance of 1000 ohms. Find the average power supplied to a 1-ohm resistor across the terminals of this generator. Also, calculate this power if an ideal matching transformer is placed between the source and the load.

Solution. Without the transformer, the rms current I is 100/1001, or 0.1 ampere. The average power I^2R to the 1-ohm resistor is 0.01 watt.

With the transformer, the resistance looking into the primary is 1000 ohms, and the total resistance of the primary circuit is 2000 ohms. Therefore, the rms primary current I is 100/2000, or 0.05 ampere. The average power into the transformer is $(0.05)^2(1000)$, or 2.5 watts. This power, which is supplied to the load, is 250 times the power obtained without the transformer. The turns ratio N_1/N_2 equals the square root of the resistance ratio, by Eq. (15-51), and this is 31.6.

REFERENCES

Harnwell, G. P., *Principles of Electricity and Magnetism*, McGraw-Hill Book Co., New York, 2nd ed., 1949, Chap. 9.

PROBLEMS

Section 15-1

15-1. The current of a series RLC circuit, with $R = 10$ ohms, $L = 40$ mh, and $C = 100\ \mu$f, is $i = 5 \sin 377t$ amperes. Find as a function of time the power dissipated as heat, the power supplied to the magnetic field of the circuit, and the power supplied to the electric field of the circuit. Also, calculate the time-average power. Assume skin effect is negligible.

15-2. A wire of radius a and length l has a conductivity σ that varies with respect to the radial distance r from its axis. Using Eq. (15-6) with both i and J expressed in terms of the electric field E, show that the d-c resistance of the wire is $l\Big/\left(2\pi\int_0^a \sigma r\, dr\right)$. Deduce this same result from the ratio v_R/i. Evaluate R if $\sigma = ce^r$, with c a constant.

15-3. A power of $32 - 25 \cos (2\omega t + 30°)$ watts is dissipated in a series RL circuit whose current is $2 \sin \omega t$ amperes, with $\omega = 10^5$. If the inductance L is 10^{-4} henry, find the instantaneous energy stored in the magnetic field.

15-4. A power of $30 \sin (2000t - 60°)$ watts is supplied to the magnetic field of a series RL circuit whose current is $10 \sin 1000t$ amperes, and a power of $P + P_1 \sin (2000t + \theta)$ watts is dissipated as heat. If $R = 2$ ohms and $L = 1$ mh, find P, P_1, and θ.

Section 15-2

15-5. For the coaxial line of Prob. 14-31 assume equal-and-opposite direct currents and find the external inductance per unit length from the external flux linkages.

15-6. The expression for the low-frequency inductance of a coaxial line is given in Prob. 14-32. Deduce this expression by finding the internal and external flux linkages per unit current.

15-7. A wire of radius a and permeability μ, located in a dielectric of permeability μ_0, is formed into a large circular loop of radius b. If the wire carries a steady current I, the magnetic vector potential at points on the surface of the wire is directed along the wire with a magnitude of $(\mu_0 I/\pi)(-1 + \frac{1}{2} \ln 8b/a)$ weber/m. Show that the inductance of the loop is

$$L = \mu_0 b(-2 + \ln 8b/a) + \mu b/4$$

Calculate L for a nonferromagnetic wire of radius 0.1 cm with $b = 10$ cm.

15-8. The two conductors of a certain parallel-wire transmission line are nonferromagnetic, have equal radii a, are separated a distance D that is large compared with a, and carry equal and opposite steady currents I. The magnetic vector potential at points within either wire has the direction of the current density and a magnitude of $(\mu_0 I/4\pi)(1 - r^2/a^2 + 2 \ln D/a)$, with r denoting the distance from the axis. Show that the inductance L per unit length of the two-wire line is

$$L = (\mu_0/4\pi)(1 + 4 \ln D/a)$$

Section 15-3

15-9. The plate current i_b of a vacuum tube is $10^{-5}(e_b + 20e_c)^{1.5}$ ampere, with e_b and e_c denoting the voltage drops from the plate and grid, respectively, to the cathode. Calculate the resistance e_b/i_b of the tube at the operating point $e_b = 100$ and $e_c = -2$. At this same point also calculate the incremental plate resistance $\partial e_b/\partial i_b$, with e_c constant. If $e_b = 100 + 0.1 \sin \omega t$, with e_c fixed at -2 volts, find i_b.

15-10. The steady current I of a 1000-turn coil on a ferromagnetic core is one ampere. If the core flux φ is $10^{-4}I$ weber, determine the inductance and the incremental inductance. Repeat for a core flux of $10^{-4}\sqrt{I}$.

15-11. Suppose the charge q stored in the immediate vicinity of the PN junction of Fig. 15-5 is $10^{-9}v^{1/3}$ coulomb. If $v = 10 + 0.1 \sin 10^8 t$, find the alternating components of the charge q and the current i. The flow of charge through the junction is negligible.

Section 15-4

15-12. If $i_1 = 1 \sin 10^4 t$ and $i_2 = 2 \sin (10^4 t + 60°)$ in the coupled circuits of Fig. 15-7, with $L_1 = L_2 = 4$ mh and $M_{12} = M_{21} = -2$ mh, find the amplitudes and phase angles of the voltages v_1 and v_2.

15-13. Suppose a current $i_2 = 5 \sin 377t$ amperes is driven in the secondary circuit of Fig. 15-7, with the primary open. If the voltage v_1 induced in the primary is $-100 \cos 377t$, find M_{12}.

15-14. Suppose $L_1 = 4$ mh, $L_2 = 3$ mh, and $M = 2.5$ mh in the circuit of Fig. 15-7. Find the energy stored in the magnetic field if $i_1 = 3$ amperes with the secondary open. Repeat if $i_2 = -4$ amperes with the primary open. What is the stored energy if both currents are present?

Section 15-5

15-15. If $i_1 = 2 \sin 377t$ and $i_2 = 1 \cos 377t$ in the circuit of Fig. 15-11, with $R_1 = R_2 = 10$ and $L_1 = L_2 = M = 20$ mh, find the amplitudes and phase angles of the voltages v_1 and v_2.

15-16. The primary circuit of Fig. 15-12 is driven with a current $i_1 = 2 \sin 1000t$, and a resistance of 5 ohms is connected across the secondary. Find i_2, v_1, and v_2 if $L_1 = 10$ mh, $L_2 = 8$ mh, and M has a magnitude of 2 mh. The winding resistances are negligible.

15-17. Repeat Prob. 15-16 with a capacitor inserted in the secondary circuit, with the capacitance such that its voltage drop exactly cancels the secondary emf of self-inductance. The voltage v_2 includes that of the capacitor.

15-18. In Fig. 15-19 the squares and triangles have the same significance as the dots. Write the three volt-ampere equations, and determine the signs of the mutual inductances M_{12}, M_{13}, and M_{23}. If each has a magnitude of 1 mh, what is the open-circuit voltage v_3 for currents $i_1 = i_2 = 1 \sin 1000t$?

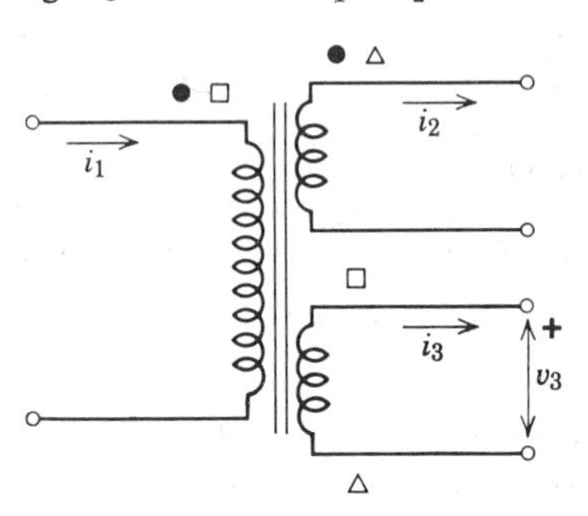

FIG. 15-19.

Section 15-6

15-19. Two coils of turns N_1 and N_2 are mounted on a common iron core. If a steady current I_1 in the coil of turns N_1 produces a core flux φ equal to $N_1 I_1/\mathscr{R}$, with $\mathscr{R}$ a constant that depends on the permeability and dimensions of the core, show that the mutual inductance is $N_1 N_2/\mathscr{R}$.

15-20. Using Eq. (15-41), show that the mutual inductance of the two parallel line segments of Fig. 15-20 is

$$M = \frac{\mu}{4\pi} \sum_{n=1}^{4} (-1)^n [c_n \ln (c_n + \sqrt{c_n^2 + d^2}) - \sqrt{c_n^2 + d^2}]$$

with $c_1 = a_3 - a_1$, $c_2 = a_2 - a_1$, $c_3 = a_2$, and $c_4 = a_3$.

The following integrals, with $z = \sqrt{(x - a)^2 + d^2}$, will be helpful:

$$\int 1/z \, dx = \ln (x - a + z)$$

$$\int \ln (a - x + z) \, dx = z - (a - x) \ln (a - x + z)$$

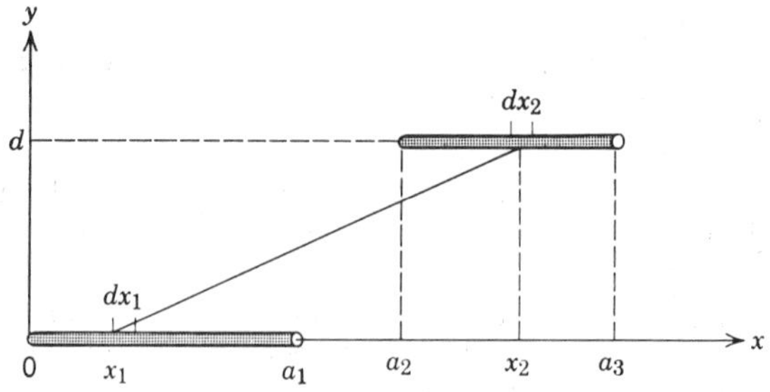

FIG. 15-20. Two parallel conductors.

15-21. Use the result of Prob. 15-20 to calculate the mutual inductance between the two square loops of Fig. 15-21. The medium is free space, the loops are 0.01 m apart, and the length of each side is 0.05 m. (*Ans.*: 0.00604 μh).

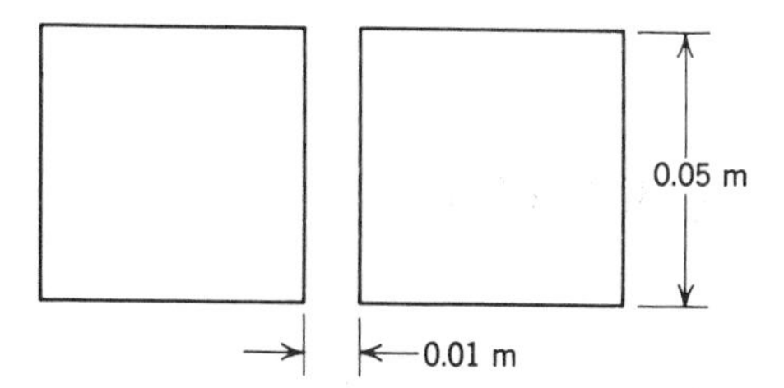

FIG. 15-21. Two square conducting loops.

15-22. A 15-turn coil with an inductance of 10 μh is inductively coupled to a 30-turn coil having an inductance of 50 μh. If the mutual inductance is 5 μh, calculate the coupling coefficients k_1, k_2, and k.

Section 15-7

15-23. The ideal transformer between the generator and the load of Fig. 15-22 has a turns ratio N_1/N_2 of 6.62. Calculate the input resistance, and for $v = 100 \sin \omega t$, find v_1 and i_1. Place dots on corresponding terminals, and determine v_2 and i_2. What is the average power to the load?

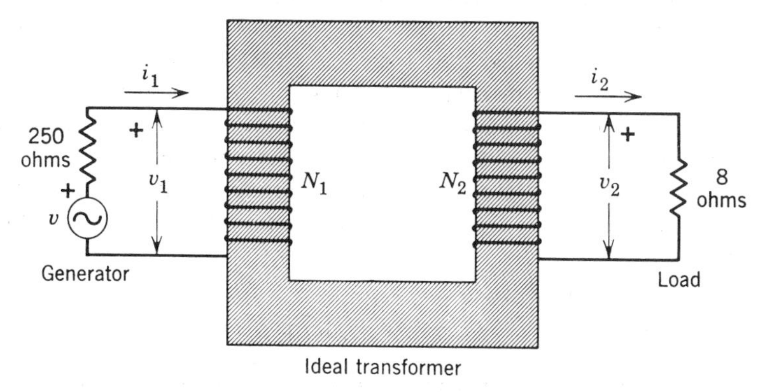

FIG. 15-22.

15-24. If the transformer of Fig. 15-22 is an ideal matching transformer, determine the turns ratio N_1/N_2. For $v = 100 \sin \omega t$, find v_1, v_2, i_1, and i_2. Also, calculate the average power supplied to the load.

15-25. Calculate the turns ratio of an iron-core transformer designed to match resistances of 5000 and 500 ohms. Explain why this transformer would be unsuitable for matching resistances of 500,000 and 50,000 ohms or resistances of 50 and 5 ohms.

Magnetostatics I

CHAPTER 16

Magnetostatics is that branch of electromagnetism that deals with electric currents that do not vary with time. The electric and magnetic fields are, of course, likewise steady with time. We shall discuss in this and the next chapter some of the basic concepts of the science of magnetostatics. The important equations are obtained from the general field equations by eliminating all terms with time derivatives. Thus we treat magnetostatics as a special case of electromagnetic field theory. Among the topics considered in this chapter are direct current and resistance, the static potential functions, the magnetic circuit, and calculation of inductance.

16-1. DIRECT CURRENT AND RESISTANCE

The expression for a sinusoidal current i is $I_m \sin(\omega t + \theta)$. If the angular frequency ω approaches the limit zero, the current i does not change appreciably in any finite time interval, and i becomes a direct current. The frequency is zero, and the wavelength is infinite. As direct current can be regarded as a limiting case of alternating current, it is evident that the magnetostatic equations can be applied to a-c problems at sufficiently low frequencies.

Shown in Fig. 16-1 is a linear d-c circuit with resistance and inductance. The resistive voltage drop is IR, and the inductive drop is zero because the current is steady. When the circuit is initially closed, the current must rise from zero to its d-c value. As long as the current changes with time, there is a voltage across the inductance L, but when the current becomes steady, this inductive voltage is zero. *A pure inductance has no effect on a steady current.* There is, however, energy stored in the magnetostatic field, and this energy equals $\frac{1}{2}LI^2$ and also the volume integral of $\frac{1}{2}\mu H^2$. Inductors are often used in electrical circuits to provide easy passage of direct currents while opposing alternating currents.

In Fig. 16-2 is shown a circuit with resistance and capacitance. When the circuit is initially closed, a transient current charges the capacitor as indicated, and the voltage drop across C is q/C. As the charge q increases, this voltage increases. When the capacitive voltage becomes equal to the battery voltage V, the drop across R is zero, and there is no current. The

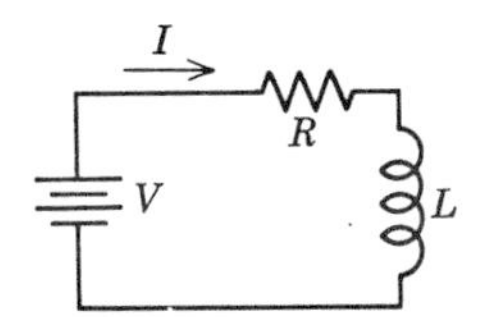

FIG. 16-1. An *RL* circuit.

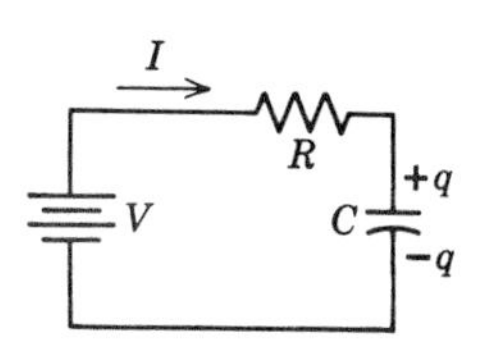

FIG. 16-2. An *RC* circuit.

electrostatic field of the capacitor has stored energy that is equal to $\frac{1}{2}CV^2$ and also to the volume integral of $\frac{1}{2}\epsilon E^2$. Capacitors are often used in electrical circuits to pass alternating currents while blocking direct currents.

As displacement currents in magnetostatic fields are nonexistent, each line of magnetic flux must link a convection current of moving charges. Clearly, the *convection* current over any closed surface is zero. The electric field is conservative, and the electric potential difference between two points equals the voltage along any path connecting the points. As the wavelength is infinite, there is neither skin effect nor radiation. Circuit theory becomes exact, of course, as the frequency approaches zero.

A wire of conductivity σ, length l, and cross-sectional area S has a d-c resistance R equal to $l/(\sigma S)$. In terms of the resistivity ρ in ohm-meters, $R = \rho l/S$. The power dissipated as heat by a steady current I is I^2R, and this is the instantaneous power and also the time-average power. Obviously, the rms value of a direct current I equals I. Frequently, the length l of a wire is expressed in feet, and the area S is given in *circular mils*, a circular mil being the area of a circle one mil, or 0.001 inch, in diameter. In this system the unit of resistivity ρ is the *ohm-circular-mil per foot*, sometimes referred to by the nondescriptive name *ohm per circular-mil-foot*. It is easily shown that the area of a wire in circular mils equals the square of its diameter in mils. Thus in the mil-foot system $R = \rho l/d^2$, with d denoting the diameter in mils.

Resistivity is a function of temperature. For metallic conductors it increases as the temperature rises, because the greater thermal vibrations of the atoms result in more frequent collisions between the free electrons and the positive ions. Over a considerable range of temperature the resistivity of metallic conductors is practically a linear function of temperature. Let ρ and ρ_0 represent the resistivities of a metal at T and T_0 degrees Centigrade, respectively. Then ρ is approximately

$$\rho = \rho_0[1 + \alpha_0(T - T_0)] \tag{16-1}$$

with α_0 denoting the *temperature coefficient of resistance*, in reciprocal degrees, at T_0. The equation is often written in terms of the resistances R and R_0, which replace ρ and ρ_0. Annealed copper has an α_0 of 0.00393 at 20°C. Thus the resistance of a copper conductor at 20°C changes 0.393% per degree change in temperature. A copper wire with a resistance of one ohm at 20°C has a resistance of approximately 1.039 ohms at 30°C. Semiconductors have resistivities that usually decrease as the temperature increases. This is, of course, the result of thermal generation of additional free electrons and holes at higher temperatures.

The reciprocal of resistance R is called the *conductance* G. Conductance has dimensions of reciprocal ohms, and its mks unit is the mho. In the direction of the voltage drop V across a resistor the current I is VG amperes.

Copper wire tables prepared by the National Bureau of Standards give at several temperatures the resistances per thousand feet of standard sizes of annealed copper wire. The wire sizes are designated by gauge numbers. The *Brown and Sharpe* (*B* & *S*) wire-gauge designation, often called the *American Wire Gauge* (*A.W.G.*), is in common use in the United States. Number 10 wire is approximately 0.1 inch (100 mils) in diameter, has an area of about 10,000 circular mils, and has a resistance of about one ohm per thousand feet. Larger gauge numbers are used for smaller wires, and smaller gauge numbers are used for larger wires. For every third larger gauge number the area is halved and the resistance is doubled. For example, No. 13 wire has an area of about 5000 circular mils and a resistance of two ohms per thousand feet. Number 12 and No. 14 wires are quite often used in low amperage circuits of residential wiring systems.

16-2. THE POTENTIAL FUNCTIONS

Currents and charges that do not vary with time give unretarded potential functions which are helpful in the analyses of important problems in magnetostatics. Although the static potentials have been utilized occasionally in earlier chapters, a review of the mathematical expressions should prove beneficial, for these are employed frequently in much of the work that follows.

For static fields in media that are linear, isotropic, and homogeneous, Maxwell's equations in terms of the magnetic vector potential **A** and the electric scalar potential ϕ are

$$\mathbf{B} = \nabla \times \mathbf{A} \tag{16-2}$$

$$\mathbf{E} = -\nabla\phi \tag{16-3}$$

$$\nabla \cdot \mathbf{A} = 0 \tag{16-4}$$

$$\nabla^2\phi = -\rho/\epsilon \tag{16-5}$$

$$\nabla^2\mathbf{A} = -\mu\mathbf{J} \tag{16-6}$$

These are Eqs. (13-67) through (13-71) with time derivatives set equal to zero. Equation (16-5) is Poisson's equation so important in electrostatics. The last equation (16-6), containing the vector Laplacian, represents three scalar equations. In rectangular coordinates each has the same form as Poisson's equation. The integral solutions of Eqs. (16-5) and (16-6) are

$$\phi = \frac{1}{4\pi\epsilon}\int_V \frac{\rho}{r}\,dV \tag{16-7}$$

$$\mathbf{A} = \frac{\mu}{4\pi}\int_V \frac{\mathbf{J}}{r}\,dV \tag{16-8}$$

These are Eqs. (13-72) and (13-73) without retardation.

In terms of the steady current I of a filamentary conductor, the vector potential becomes

$$\mathbf{A} = \frac{\mu}{4\pi}\int_C \frac{I}{r}\,d\mathbf{l} \tag{16-9}$$

For a single current element $I\,d\mathbf{l}$ the differential magnetic vector potential is

$$d\mathbf{A} = \frac{\mu I\,d\mathbf{l}}{4\pi r} \tag{16-10}$$

We note from Eq. (16-7) that the electric scalar potential of a single point charge q is

$$\phi = \frac{q}{4\pi\epsilon r} \tag{16-11}$$

The equations given in this section should be examined carefully. They are immensely important in static field theory, and they shall be used freely in this and the following two chapters, which present the science of magnetostatics and electrostatics. The next three sections are intended primarily to illustrate the utilization of the magnetostatic vector potential in the solution of physical problems. In addition, the results are of considerable practical value.

16-3. THE MAGNETIC VECTOR POTENTIAL AND FIELD OF A LONG STRAIGHT WIRE

As an example of how we can find the vector potential in a magnetostatic problem we shall obtain the potential of a long straight wire carrying a steady current I. The vector potential will be found at a point P located a distance r from the center of the wire of radius a. The result is utilized

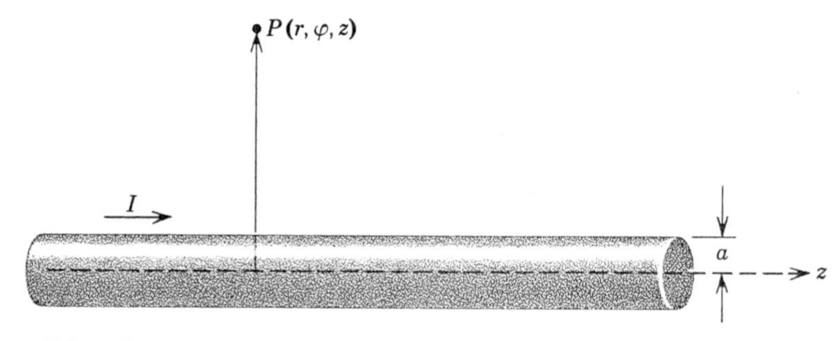

FIG. 16-3. Side view of section of a long straight wire with a steady current I.

in the next section in the determination of the magnetic field of a parallel-wire transmission line. Shown in Fig. 16-3 is the straight wire, with the z-axis oriented along the wire.

At P the magnetic potential is in the z-direction, because the current density $\mathbf{J}$ is directed along the z-axis. Therefore, the equation for $\mathbf{A}$ becomes $\nabla^2 A_z = -\mu J_z$, which can be written as

$$\boldsymbol{\nabla} \cdot (\boldsymbol{\nabla} A_z) = -\mu J_z \tag{16-12}$$

This equation has the same form as the differential form of Gauss's law ($\boldsymbol{\nabla} \cdot \mathbf{D} = \rho$). The integral form of Gauss's law equates the surface integral of $\mathbf{D}$ to the volume integral of ρ, with the surface S being that which encloses the volume V. By analogy, the integral form of Eq. (16-12) is

$$\oint_S (\boldsymbol{\nabla} A_z) \cdot d\mathbf{S} = -\int_V \mu J_z \, dV \tag{16-13}$$

This can be deduced directly from Eq. (16-12) by taking the volume integral of both sides and applying the divergence theorem. Let us apply the equation to a closed cylindrical surface of radius r and of unit length, the cylinder being concentric with the wire. The point P lies on the surface of this cylinder. In effect, the closed surface S is a Gaussian surface.

Inside the wire the current density J_z is everywhere constant, for there is no skin effect, and outside the wire J_z is zero. As the length of the cylinder is unity, the volume integral of μJ_z equals μI, provided $r > a$ as shown in Fig. 16-3. Equation (16-13) becomes

$$\oint_S (\nabla A_z) \cdot d\mathbf{S} = -\mu I \tag{16-14}$$

The cylindrical coordinates of the point P on the surface S are (r, φ, z), provided the origin of the coordinate system is located on the axis. As the wire is infinitely long, A_z does not vary with z. From symmetry, A_z does not vary with φ. Therefore, the gradient of A_z is $(\partial A_z/\partial r)\mathbf{a}_r$. The surface integral of ∇A_z over each end of the cylinder is zero, for the vector is directed radially outward. Over the curved surface, the integral of ∇A_z equals the product of $\partial A_z/\partial r$ and the area $2\pi r$ of this surface. This is a consequence of the fact that the gradient of A_z has magnitude independent of position on this curved surface, from symmetry considerations. Therefore, Eq. (16-14) becomes

$$\frac{\partial A_z}{\partial r} = -\frac{\mu I}{2\pi r} \tag{16-15}$$

Integration gives

$$A_z = -\frac{\mu I}{2\pi} \ln r + C_1 \qquad r > a \tag{16-16}$$

C_1 is a constant of integration, and its value depends on the zero reference selected for A_z. If A_z is to be zero at infinity, then C_1 is infinite. We are not really interested in this constant, because the magnetic field $\mathbf{B}$ is found from the curl of $\mathbf{A}$, and the constant C_1 has zero curl.

Next, suppose the point P is inside the wire. In this case r is less than the radius a. For $r < a$, the right side of Eq. (16-14) is $-\mu I r^2/a^2$, for only a portion of the current I is inside the cylinder. Following the same reasoning as before, we find that

$$A_z = -\frac{\mu I r^2}{4\pi a^2} + C_2 \qquad r < a \tag{16-17}$$

The magnetic field $\mathbf{B}$ is found by taking the curl of $\mathbf{A}$, and the resulting expressions are

$$\mathbf{B} = \frac{\mu I}{2\pi r}\mathbf{a}_\varphi \qquad r > a \tag{16-18}$$

$$\mathbf{B} = \frac{\mu I r}{2\pi a^2}\mathbf{a}_\varphi \qquad r < a \tag{16-19}$$

The external field of (16-18) was deduced in Sec. 8-5 directly from the Maxwell-Ampère law and again in the Example of Sec. 13-6 from the Biot-Savart law. The flux lines of **B** are circular about the wire.

16-4. THE VECTOR POTENTIAL AND FIELD OF TWO LONG PARALLEL WIRES

The problem of determining the magnetic vector potential of a parallel-wire transmission line carrying equal-and-opposite direct currents will now be considered. The result is used in Sec. 16-8 to find the low-frequency inductance per unit length. Shown in Fig. 16-4 is a cross-sectional

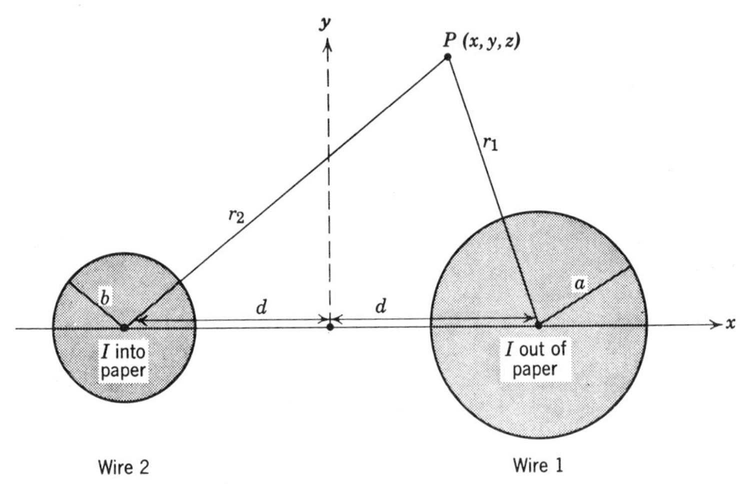

FIG. 16-4. Cross-sectional view of two long parallel wires with equal and opposite direct currents.

view of the wires, with the positive z-direction out of the paper. Wire 1 of radius a has a current I in the positive z-direction, and wire 2 of radius b has the current I in the negative z-direction. The point P is located at distances r_1 and r_2 from the centers of the wires 1 and 2, respectively. For the present we shall assume that P is outside the wires, as illustrated. The conductors are nonferromagnetic, and the permeability is everywhere equal to μ_0. Consequently, the presence of wire 2 does not affect the field due to the current of wire 1, and vice versa. Thus the results of the preceding section can be applied to the individual conductors.

At the point P the vector potential is the sum of those produced by each of the currents of the two wires. The component of A_z due to the current of wire 1 is given by Eq. (16-16) with $r = r_1$. The component due to the current of wire 2 is the negative of that given by Eq. (16-16) with $r = r_2$, for this current is in the negative z-direction. Therefore, the total vector potential is

$$A_z = -\frac{\mu_0 I}{2\pi}\ln r_1 + \frac{\mu_0 I}{2\pi}\ln r_2 + C \qquad (16\text{-}20)$$

The constant C depends on our selection of the zero reference. If we let A_z be zero at the origin of the coordinate system, the constant C is zero, and the equation becomes

$$A_z = \frac{\mu_0 I}{2\pi}\ln\frac{r_2}{r_1} \qquad (16\text{-}21)$$

For any point in the plane $x = 0$, r_1 and r_2 are equal, and A_z is zero. If r_2 is greater than r_1, A_z is positive, and if r_1 is greater than r_2, A_z is negative.

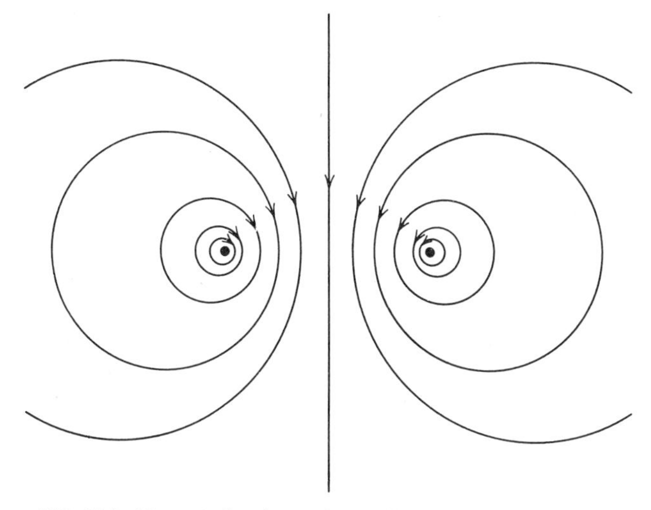

FIG. 16-5. Magnetic flux lines of a parallel-wire transmission line.

In terms of the rectangular coordinates (x, y, z) of the point P the distances r_1 and r_2 are $[(d - x)^2 + y^2]^{1/2}$ and $[(d + x)^2 + y^2]^{1/2}$, respectively. The magnetic flux density is obtained by substituting for r_1 and r_2 in Eq. (16-21) and evaluating the curl of **A**. The result is

$$\mathbf{B} = \frac{\mu_0 I}{2\pi}\left[y\left(\frac{1}{r_2^2} - \frac{1}{r_1^2}\right)\mathbf{i} - \left(\frac{d + x}{r_2^2} + \frac{d - x}{r_1^2}\right)\mathbf{j}\right] \qquad (16\text{-}22)$$

The magnetic flux lines in the xy-plane are shown in Fig. 16-5. Each line is a circle with its center on the x-axis at $x = (r_0^2 + d^2)^{1/2}$, with r_0 denoting the radius of the line (see Prob. 16-8).

Next, suppose the point P is located inside wire 1, making r_1 less than a. Utilizing Eq. (16-17) with $r = r_1$ and also Eq. (16-16) with $r = r_2$, we obtain

$$A_z = -\frac{\mu_0 I r_1^2}{4\pi a^2} + \frac{\mu_0 I}{2\pi}\ln r_2 + C \tag{16-23}$$

The constant C is evaluated by equating (16-23) and (16-21) at $r_1 = a$. The resulting expression for A_z becomes

$$A_z = \frac{\mu_0 I}{4\pi}\left(1 - \frac{r_1^2}{a^2} + \ln\frac{r_2^2}{a^2}\right) \qquad r_1 < a \tag{16-24}$$

The magnetic field **B** in rectangular form, obtained from the curl of **A**, is

$$\mathbf{B} = \frac{\mu_0 I}{2\pi}\left[y\left(\frac{1}{r_2^2} - \frac{1}{a^2}\right)\mathbf{i} - \left(\frac{d+x}{r_2^2} + \frac{d-x}{a^2}\right)\mathbf{j}\right] \tag{16-25}$$

It should be emphasized that the results are valid for steady currents and for alternating currents with frequencies so low that skin effect is negligible.

16-5. VECTOR POTENTIAL AND FIELD OF A SMALL CURRENT LOOP

An electron revolving in its orbit around the nucleus of an atom forms a tiny current loop, and so does an electron spinning about its axis. Both the orbital motion and the electron spin contribute to the magnetic properties of materials. Thus the magnetic field of a small current loop is of considerable importance.

Shown in Fig. 16-6 is a circular loop carrying a steady current I, with the z-axis of a rectangular coordinate system coinciding with the axis of the loop. The rectangular coordinates of the point P are (x, y, z) and the spherical coordinates are (r_0, θ, φ). From symmetry considerations it is evident that the magnitude of **A** is independent of φ. Therefore, no generality is lost by taking P at $\varphi = \frac{1}{2}\pi$. Let us consider two current elements *at equal distances* from P. The vector potential at P due to this pair of equidistant elements is normal to the yz-plane, because the y components of **A** at P cancel. All current elements can be grouped into equidistant pairs. It is evident that **A** has only the single spherical component $\mathbf{A}_\varphi$.

At the point P, $A_\varphi = -A_x$, and

$$A_x = \frac{\mu I}{4\pi}\oint_C \frac{dx}{r} \tag{16-26}$$

with C denoting the circular path of the current loop and with r denoting the distance from $d\mathbf{l}$ to P. Of course, dx is the x component of $d\mathbf{l}$, and dx equals $-(a\,d\varphi)(\sin\varphi)$. Clearly

$$A_\varphi = \frac{\mu I a}{4\pi}\int_0^{2\pi}\frac{\sin\varphi}{r}\,d\varphi \tag{16-27}$$

The distance r is a function of φ. If the rectangular coordinates of $d\mathbf{l}$ are $(x_1, y_1, 0)$, the distance r from $d\mathbf{l}$ to $P(0, y, z)$ is the square root of the

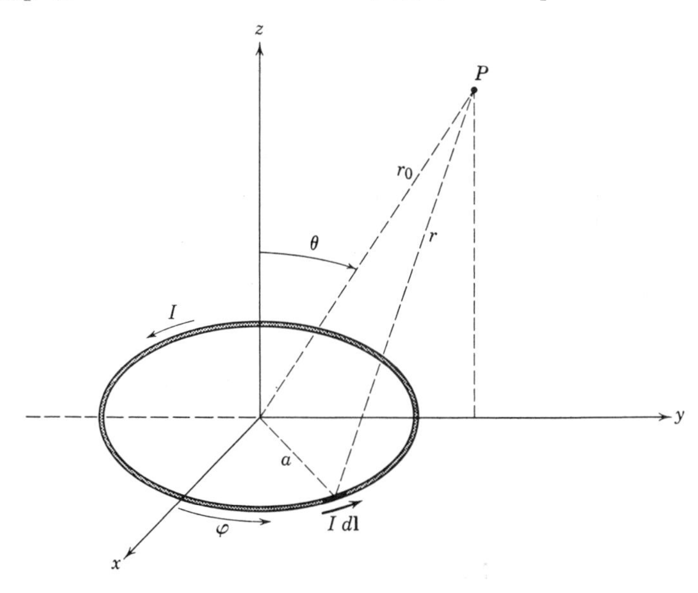

FIG. 16-6. A current loop in the *xy*-plane and a distant point *P* in the *yz*-plane.

sum of the squares of x_1, $y - y_1$, and z. As $x_1^2 + y_1^2 = a^2$, $y^2 + z^2 = r_0^2$, $y_1 = a\sin\varphi$, and $y = r_0\sin\theta$, it is easily shown that

$$A_\varphi = \frac{\mu I a}{4\pi}\int_0^{2\pi}\frac{\sin\varphi\,d\varphi}{\sqrt{a^2 + r_0^2 - 2ar_0\sin\theta\sin\varphi}} \tag{16-28}$$

This equation can be evaluated in terms of certain definite integrals known as *elliptic integrals*. However, we are interested here in a very small circular loop, and the integral is easily evaluated for a radius a that is small compared with r_0. If a^2 in the radical is neglected, Eq. (16-28) can be expressed in the form

$$A_\varphi = \frac{\mu I a}{4\pi r_0}\int_0^{2\pi}\frac{\sin\varphi\,d\varphi}{\sqrt{1 - (2a/r_0)\sin\theta\sin\varphi}} \tag{16-29}$$

The second term in the radical is very small compared with unity. Recall that $(1 - x)^{-1/2}$, with x considerably less than unity, is approximately equal to $1 + \frac{1}{2}x$. This is shown by application of the binomial expansion, neglecting all terms except the first two. It follows that Eq. (16-29) can be written

$$A_\varphi = \frac{\mu I a}{4\pi r_0} \int_0^{2\pi} (\sin \varphi)\left(1 + \frac{a}{r_0} \sin \theta \sin \varphi\right) d\varphi$$

Integration is now readily accomplished, and the result is

$$A_\varphi = \frac{\mu I S \sin \theta}{4\pi r^2} \tag{16-30}$$

with S denoting the area πa^2 of the loop and with the subscript on r_0 dropped. Thus r is the distance from the small loop at the origin to the point $P(r, \theta, \varphi)$.

The magnetic potential can be expressed in vector form. Let $\mathbf{n}$ denote a unit vector normal to the plane of the loop, directed out of the top side of the loop of Fig. 16-6. If the fingers of the right hand are curled around the loop in the direction of the positive current, the extended thumb gives the sense of $\mathbf{n}$. At P the vector potential $\mathbf{A}$ is normal to the plane of $\mathbf{n}$ and the unit radial vector $\mathbf{a}_r$. The cross product $\mathbf{n} \times \mathbf{a}_r$ has the direction of $\mathbf{A}$, with magnitude equal to $\sin \theta$. Therefore

$$\mathbf{A} = \frac{\mu I S \mathbf{n} \times \mathbf{a}_r}{4\pi r^2} \tag{16-31}$$

The distant magnetic field of a small current loop is found by taking the curl of $\mathbf{A}$. Equation (16-30) is convenient to use, and the result in spherical coordinates is

$$\mathbf{B} = \frac{\mu I S}{4\pi r^3}(2 \cos \theta \, \mathbf{a}_r + \sin \theta \, \mathbf{a}_\theta) \tag{16-32}$$

Although the loop considered is a circular loop, it can be shown that the result is valid for small loops of arbitrary shape. The magnetic field of a current loop is discussed further in the next section.

16-6. ELECTRIC AND MAGNETIC DIPOLES

Two point charges $+q$ and $-q$ separated a small distance l constitute an *electric dipole*. We shall determine, at distances large compared with l, the electrostatic field of the dipole shown in Fig. 16-7. Although this is properly a problem in electrostatics, it is desirable to treat this problem here before considering the magnetic dipole. The electric dipole is located at the origin of a spherical coordinate system, and the spherical coordinates of the distant point P are (r, θ, φ). The distances r_1 and r_2 are practically equal to r, because r is very large compared with l. At P the φ-direction is normal to the paper. From the symmetry of the problem the field is independent of the coordinate φ.

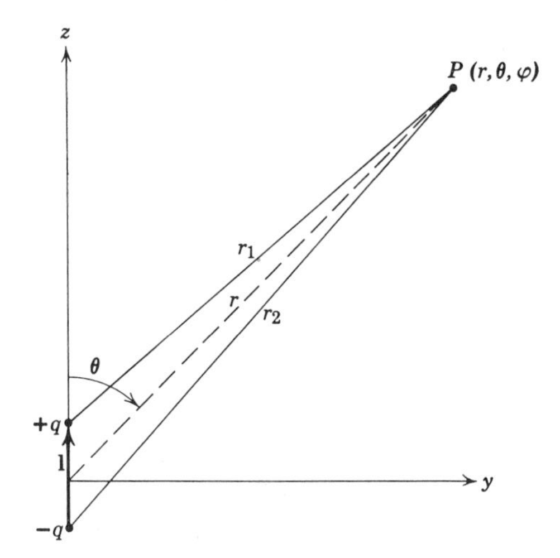

FIG. 16-7. An electric dipole and a distant point P.

The electric potential at P due to the two point charges is

$$\phi_P = \frac{q}{4\pi\epsilon r_1} - \frac{q}{4\pi\epsilon r_2} = \frac{q}{4\pi\epsilon}\left(\frac{r_2 - r_1}{r_1 r_2}\right) \tag{16-33}$$

Examination of Fig. 16-7 reveals that $r_2 - r_1$ is approximately equal to $l \cos \theta$, provided r is very much greater than l. Also, the product $r_1 r_2$ is practically r^2 for small l. Therefore, the electric scalar potential becomes

$$\phi_P = \frac{ql \cos \theta}{4\pi\epsilon r^2} = \frac{q\mathbf{l} \cdot \mathbf{a}_r}{4\pi\epsilon r^2} \tag{16-34}$$

with $\mathbf{l}$ denoting the vector length from $-q$ to $+q$ and with $\mathbf{a}_r$ denoting a unit vector at P directed radially outward. The vector $q\mathbf{l}$ is called the *electric dipole moment* $\boldsymbol{p}$. If $l \to 0$ and $q \to \infty$ such that ql remains finite, the dipole is a *point dipole.*

The electric field $\mathbf{E}$ is $-\nabla\phi$. In spherical coordinates this becomes

$$\mathbf{E} = \frac{ql}{4\pi\epsilon r^3}(2 \cos \theta\, \mathbf{a}_r + \sin \theta\, \mathbf{a}_\theta) \tag{16-35}$$

The field lines in a plane containing the point charges are illustrated in Fig. 16-8. For a constant θ the field varies inversely as the distance cubed.

Comparison of Eqs. (16-32) and (16-35) shows that the magnetic field of a small current loop has the same functional form as the electric field of an electric dipole. Because of this similarity, a small current loop is referred to as a *magnetic dipole*. The *magnetic dipole moment* **m** is defined as $I S \mathbf{n}$. Its magnitude is the product of the current and the area of the

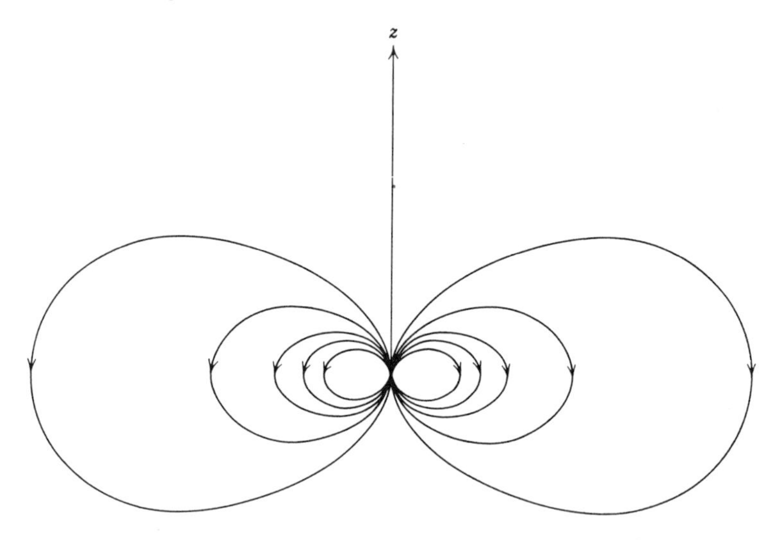

FIG. 16-8. Field lines of a point dipole with moment in the z-direction.

loop, and its direction is that of **n**, determined by the right-hand rule. The field of a magnetic dipole in a plane containing the vector **m** is shown in Fig. 16-8, which also illustrates the electric field of an electric dipole. In terms of the moment **m**, the vector potential of a magnetic dipole is obtained from Eq. (16-31), and the result is

$$\mathbf{A} = \frac{\mu \mathbf{m} \times \mathbf{a}_r}{4\pi r^2} \tag{16-36}$$

A large current loop, divided into many enlarged infinitesimal loops, is shown in Fig. 16-9. It should be noted that the net current of each internal path is zero. Consequently, the sum of the field components of all the differential current loops gives the field of the original loop. The field of each differential loop is given by Eq. (16-32), with S replaced with the differential area dS of the loop. Summing the fields of all infinitesimal loops by integrating Eq. (16-32) over the surface area of the large loop gives the magnetic field. Each differential loop is a magnetic dipole. Therefore, the field of a current loop *of arbitrary size and shape*, carrying a steady current I, is identical to the field of a surface distribution of magnetic dipoles, each of moment $I\,d\mathbf{S}$. The surface is *any* surface having the loop as its boundary. The use of a surface distribution of magnetic dipoles is sometimes a convenient way to find the magnetic field of a current loop.

In the next chapter we shall investigate briefly the magnetic theory of materials. We shall find that the concept of the magnetic dipole is used to

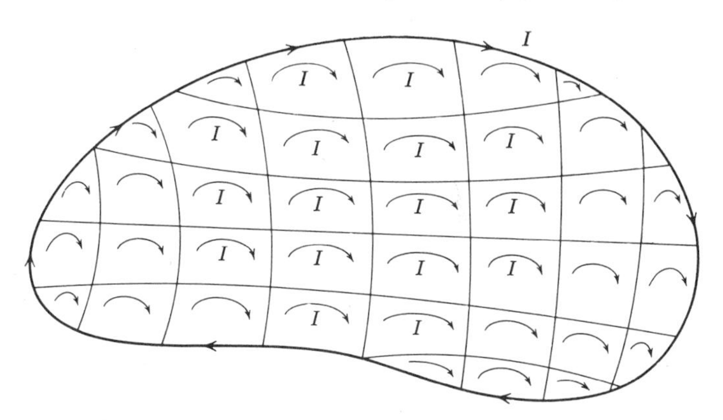

FIG. 16-9. A current loop subdivided into infinitesimal loops.

relate the observable magnetic behavior with the atomic behavior. The electric dipole is employed similarly in the study of the electric theory of materials in Chapter 18.

16-7. THE MAGNETIC CIRCUIT

An N-turn coil with a steady current I produces a magnetomotive force of NI amperes. This mmf acts along every closed path that links the coil and, consequently, magnetic flux lines extend throughout the region. However, if the coil is mounted on a ferromagnetic core of high relative permeability, the flux density in the core is very much greater than that in the surrounding air, and most of the flux lines are confined to the ferromagnetic material of the *magnetic circuit*. Such magnetic circuits are present in electric motors and generators, transformers, loudspeakers, telephone receivers, masers, magnetrons, nuclear accelerators, instruments, and innumerable other devices.

Although many magnetic circuits are entirely ferromagnetic, others contain one or more air gaps through which the magnetic flux must pass. Shown in Fig. 16-10 is an elementary magnetic circuit with an air gap. The magnetomotive force is NI amperes, and this mmf produces a core flux φ. We shall assume that the leakage flux, which is not confined to the magnetic circuit, is negligible. The ratio of the mmf to the core flux is called the *reluctance* $\mathscr{R}$ of the circuit, with $\mathscr{R}$ expressed in units of ampere-turns per weber. Thus

$$\text{mmf} = NI = \varphi\mathscr{R} \tag{16-37}$$

The illustrated path C of Fig. 16-10 represents a line of magnetic flux. Around this path the mmf is the circulation of **H**, or $\mathbf{B}/\mu$, and as **B** and $d\mathbf{l}$ have the same directions at points along C, the circulation becomes

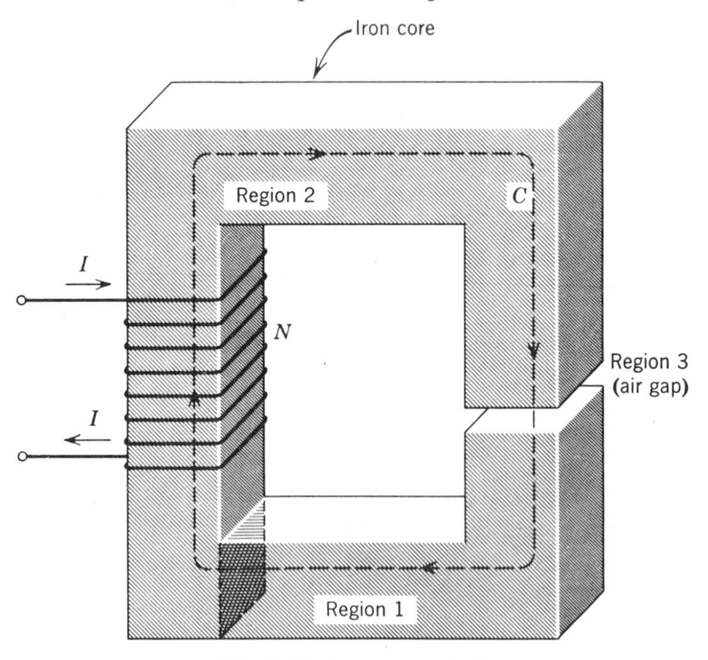

FIG. 16-10. A magnetic circuit.

$\oint(B/\mu)\,dl$. As a rough approximation, let us assume that the core flux is uniformly distributed over the cross-sectional area S of each portion of the path. Then $B = \varphi/S$ and the mmf is $\varphi \oint 1/(\mu S)\,dl$. Obviously the reluctance is

$$\mathscr{R} = \oint_C \frac{dl}{\mu S} = \frac{l_1}{\mu_1 S_1} + \frac{l_2}{\mu_2 S_2} + \frac{l_3}{\mu_3 S_3} \tag{16-38}$$

with the subscripts referring to the numbered regions of Fig. 16-10. The lengths l_1, l_2, and l_3 are the mean path lengths of the three regions. Although the equation is only approximate, it will yield a reasonable value for the reluctance, as defined in Eq. (16-37), provided the leakage flux is small, the flux density is nearly uniform over S, and the path C is carefully selected to correspond to a flux line of average length. In many magnetic circuits considerable judgment is required in the determination of the mean lengths of the various regions. The reciprocal of the reluctance $\mathscr{R}$ of a magnetic circuit is called the *permeance* $\mathscr{P}$, with $\mathscr{P}$ usually expressed in henrys.

In Fig. 16-10 the flux lines are directed clockwise. At the small air gap they leave region 2, pass across the gap, and enter region 1. The ferromagnetic region just above the gap is referred to as a *north*, or *positive, pole*. That region just below the gap is a *south*, or *negative, pole*. Flux lines in an air gap leave the north pole and enter the south pole. The magnetic poles of the earth are, of course, exceptions to the definitions. When a magnetic circuit contains an air gap, such as that of Fig. 16-10, it is usually referred to as an electromagnet. Let us now consider an example.

EXAMPLE 1. In the magnetic circuit of Fig. 16-10 the average path lengths l_1, l_2, and l_3 of the numbered regions are 10 cm, 20 cm, and 0.5 cm, respectively, and each cross-sectional area is 4 cm^2. The relative permeabilities of regions 1 and 2 are 1000 and 800, respectively. For 5000 ampere-turns determine the core flux φ and the mmf of each region. Also, find the energy stored in each region, assuming that the permeabilities are independent of the flux density.

Solution. The reluctance $l_1/(\mu_1 S_1)$ of region 1 is 199,000 ampere-turns per weber, and that of region 2 is 498,000. In the air gap the relative permeability is unity, and even though the path length of the gap is only $\frac{1}{2}$ cm, its reluctance is 9,950,000. Thus the total reluctance is 10,650,000. Dividing 5000 ampere-turns by this reluctance yields a core flux of 0.000469 weber, and the flux density is 1.17 weber/m^2.

The mmf of each region is determined from the product of the flux and the reluctance of the region. In region 1 the mmf is 93 amperes, and in region 2 it is 234 amperes. The remaining 4673 amperes of the applied mmf appear across the air gap. Note that most of the ampere-turns of the coil are accounted for by the air gap. In problems of this type a rough approximation of the magnetic flux density can be quickly determined by assuming that the mmf of the air gap equals the mmf of the coil.

The energy stored in each region is $(\frac{1}{2}BH)(lS)$, for $\frac{1}{2}BH$ is the energy density of a linear medium and the product lS is the volume. As $BS = \varphi$ and $Hl =$ mmf, it follows that the stored energy is $\frac{1}{2}\varphi$(mmf). The flux is 0.000469 and the mmf's of the regions are 93, 234, and 4673 amperes. Consequently, the stored energies are 0.022, 0.055, and 1.10 joules. Actually, iron is not a linear medium and, therefore, these calculated energies are only approximations. It is interesting to note that most of the energy is stored in the air gap.

The relationship between the magnetic flux density and the magnetic field intensity of a ferromagnetic material is nonlinear. This is discussed in the next chapter. In magnetic-circuit problems the permeability of a ferromagnetic material will normally not be known, for it depends on the flux density. Usually, the relationship between B and H is presented in the

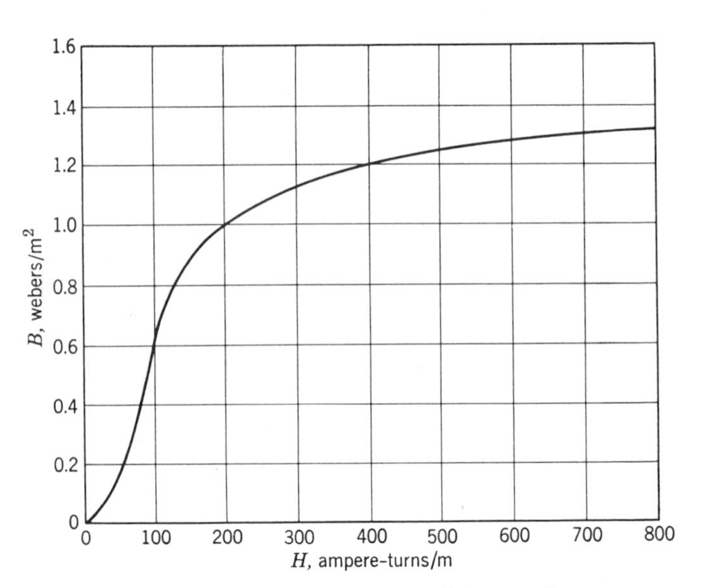

FIG. 16-11. Magnetization curve of sheet steel.

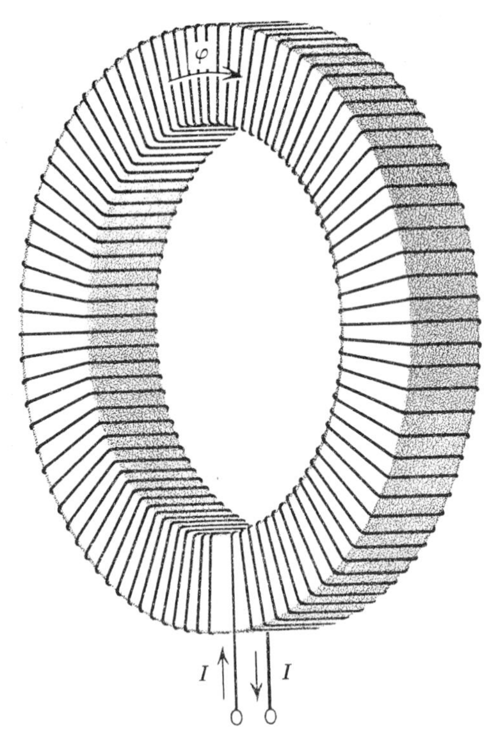

FIG. 16-12. Toroidal coil.

form of a curve known as a *magnetization*, or *B-H*, curve. A typical magnetization curve is shown in Fig. 16-11, and this curve is utilized in the next two examples.

EXAMPLE 2. Shown in Fig. 16-12 is a toroid of sheet steel, with an inner radius of 4 cm, an outer radius of 6 cm, and a depth of 2 cm. Uniformly wound about the core is a 200-turn copper coil carrying a steady current of one ampere. Find the flux.

Solution. The mmf of the toroid is 200 ampere-turns, and the flux lines are circular provided the uniform winding approximates a current sheet. As the mmf around the closed path of a flux line of radius r is $2\pi rH$, it follows that $H = 31.8/r$ amperes/m. Because the magnetic field intensity in the core varies with r, so does the magnetic flux density. Of course, the permeability also varies with r, for the magnetization curve is nonlinear.

An approximate solution is readily obtained by regarding the flux density at $r = 0.05$ m as the average flux density. At this radial distance, H is 636 ampere-turns/m. From the magnetization curve of Fig. 16-11 we find B to be 1.28 webers/m^2, and the flux φ is approximately BS, which is 0.000512 weber.

EXAMPLE 3. If the toroid of Example 2 has an air gap of length 0.2 cm introduced into the magnetic circuit, what current is required to give a core flux of 0.0004 weber?

Solution. The average flux density B is φ/S, or 1 weber/m^2. From the magnetization curve the field intensity in the iron is found to be 200 ampere-turns/m. As the average length of this ferromagnetic core is 0.314 m, the mmf of this portion of the magnetic circuit is 62.8 ampere-turns.

In the air gap the magnetic field intensity H is B/μ_0, or 796,000 ampere-turns/m, and the mmf Hl is 1592. Therefore, the total mmf of the magnetic circuit is about 1655 ampere-turns, and this requires a coil current of 8.28 amperes. Most of the applied magnetomotive force appears across the small air gap.

In the preceding example the air-gap flux was assumed to be known, and the required mmf was readily calculated. On the other hand, the problem of finding the flux *for a given mmf* is more involved. In this case the division of the applied ampere-turns between the air gap and the iron is unknown. The reluctance of the iron portion of the circuit depends on the permeability, which in turn depends on the unknown flux density. A problem such as this can be solved by assuming various flux densities and finding the corresponding ampere-turns as was done in Example 3, with the results used to plot a curve of the mmf versus the core flux. The curve can then be used to find the flux that corresponds to a given mmf. This procedure can be employed whenever the magnetic circuit has two or more regions with different permeabilities, with B and H of each ferromagnetic material related by a magnetization curve.

EXAMPLE 4. The electromagnet of Fig. 16-13 has two series-connected 1000-turn coils carrying a steady current I. The dimensions are indicated on the sketch, and the ferromagnetic material is cast iron, with B and H related by the expression

$$B = \frac{0.984H}{1457 + H} \tag{16-39}$$

Find the current I that produces an air-gap flux density of 0.5 weber/m^2.

Solution. In the air gap H is B/μ_0, or 398,000 amperes/m, and the mmf Hl of the gap is 1592 amperes. The air-gap reluctance is 796,000.

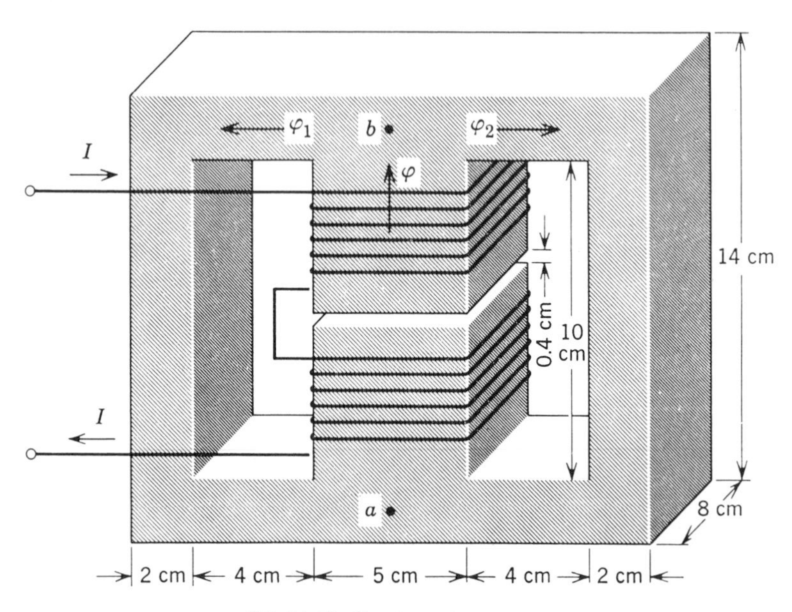

FIG. 16-13. Cast-iron electromagnet.

In the center leg from a to b the flux density B is 0.5, and H is found from Eq. (16-39) to be 1505 amp/m. As the path length from a to b, not including the air gap, is 11.6 cm, the mmf Hl is 175. Thus the total mmf of the center leg from a to b is 1592 + 175, or 1767 amperes. The permeability B/H of the iron of the center leg is 0.000332 henry/m, and the reluctance including that of the air gap is 883,000.

As the magnetic flux density is a solenoidal field, the flux $\varphi_1 + \varphi_2$ leaving the junction at b equals the flux φ that enters the junction. Thus the flux of each side leg is $\frac{1}{2}\varphi$, and $\varphi_1 = \varphi_2 = 0.001$ weber. The flux density is 0.625, and H is found from (16-39) to be 2537. As the path length is about 24 cm, the mmf from b to a along each side leg is 609 amperes. The permeability B/H is 0.000246, and the reluctance of each leg is 609,000.

Along the closed path of a flux line, the mmf is the sum of the 1767 ampere-turns of the center leg and the 609 ampere-turns of a side leg, or 2376 ampere-turns. This magnetomotive force is given by a current of 1.19 amperes in the 2000 turns of the two coils. Equation (16-39), which relates B and H, is a fair approximation of a limited range of the magnetization curve of cast iron.

16-8. CALCULATION OF INDUCTANCE

A fundamental problem of magnetostatics is the calculation of low-frequency inductance. In the preceding chapter we developed some equations useful in determining the self-inductance of a circuit and the mutual inductance of inductively coupled circuits. A few applications of these equations were encountered in the Problems of Chapter 15. Perhaps needless to say, the mathematics is often rather complex. In this section we shall consider several examples involving inductors of rather simple geometry.

Thus far we have considered the inductance only of linear circuits, with L defined as the ratio of the sinusoidal emf of self-induction to the time rate of change of the sinusoidal current. For circuits with negligible skin effect L equals the flux linkages per unit current. Inductors with iron cores are nonlinear and, therefore, a sinusoidal excitation produces a nonsinusoidal response. For such cases L is usually defined as the ratio Φ/i, with Φ denoting the flux linkages of the circuit. Mutual inductance M is similarly defined. The emf of self-induction $d\Phi/dt$ becomes $d(Li)/dt$, and inductance L varies with time if the current is alternating. The emf of mutual inductance in circuit 1 becomes $d(Mi_2)/dt$, with i_2 denoting the current of circuit 2. Frequently, the nonlinearity of iron-core inductors is small and can be ignored.

EXAMPLE 1. For the toroidal coil of Example 2 of the preceding section, find the inductance in terms of the inner radius r_1, the outer radius r_2, the depth D, the number N of turns, and the permeability μ of the iron. The coil is shown in Fig. 16-12 on p. 364.

Solution. In the iron the magnetic field intensity H is $NI/(2\pi r)$, and the flux density B is $\mu NI/(2\pi r)$. A differential area dS of a cross section is $D\,dr$. Evaluation of the surface integral of B over a cross section, with the limits of r being r_1 and r_2, gives the core flux φ. With the permeability treated as a constant independent of r, the resulting flux φ is $(\mu NID/2\pi)\ln r_2/r_1$. The inductance L is $N\varphi/I$, or $(\mu N^2D/2\pi)\ln r_2/r_1$, and μ is a function of the current.

An approximate value of L is readily found by assuming that the flux density B at an average radius r is approximately the average flux density. The core flux φ becomes $\mu NIS/(2\pi r)$, with S denoting the area of a cross section, and the flux linkages per unit current are $\mu N^2S/(2\pi r)$. This is the approximate inductance, regardless of the shape of the cross section.

In Example 2 of Sec. 16-7 the core flux was found to be 0.000512 weber for a current of one ampere in the 200-turn coil. Therefore, the inductance is (200)(0.000512), or 102 millihenrys. The internal inductance is negligible. As each turn has a length of about 0.08 m, the wire is about 16 m long. Neglecting proximity effect, this gives an internal inductance of $(\mu_0/8\pi)(16)$, or 0.8 microhenry.

It should be noted that the inductance of the toroidal coil is proportional to the product of the permeability and the square of the number of turns.

EXAMPLE 2. Shown in Fig. 16-14 is a section of a solenoidal coil of infinite length, with N_1 turns per meter. The cross-sectional area of the core is S, and its permeability is μ. Assuming that the coil approximates a uniform current sheet, find the inductance per unit length.

Solution. A steady current I produces a magnetic field in the core, and this field is directed along the length of the core. The mmf around the closed path $abcd$ of Fig. 16-14 is simply equal to H, for the path length bc is unity. As the enclosed current is N_1I, the magnetic field intensity in the core is N_1I. The flux density is μN_1I, and the core flux φ is μN_1IS. Multiplying this by N_1 gives the flux linkages

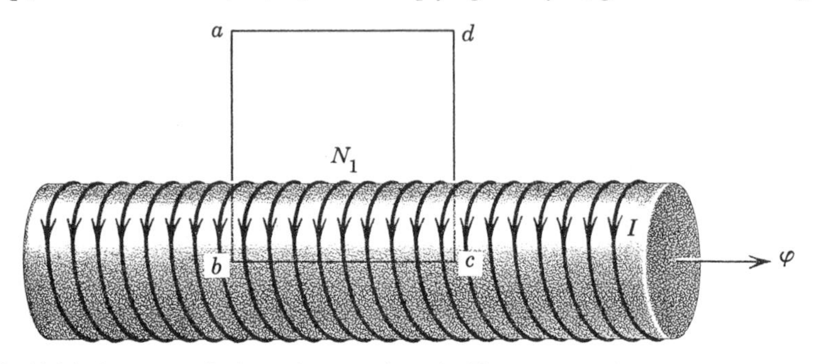

FIG. 16-14. A section of a long electric solenoid. The square path $abcd$ has unit length and links N_1 turns of the coil.

per unit length, and dividing the result by I gives the inductance L per unit length, which is $L = \mu N_1{}^2S$ henrys/m. The internal inductance is negligible in comparison, assuming the core is ferromagnetic.

For a solenoid of finite length l, the magnetic field in the core is not substantially different provided the length l is large compared with the transverse dimensions. As $N_1 = N/l$, with N denoting the total number of turns of the solenoid, the inductance L becomes approximately

$$L = \mu N^2S/l \text{ henrys} \tag{16-40}$$

It should be noted that the inductance is proportional to the product μN^2. Large inductances are obtained from solenoids with many turns of wire around ferromagnetic cores.

A toroidal coil, such as that of Example 1, can be viewed as a solenoid bent into a circle, closing on itself. Equation (16-40), with l denoting the mean path length of the toroid, gives the approximate inductance.

EXAMPLE 3. Calculate the mutual inductance of the coils of Fig. 16-15, assuming a ferromagnetic core with a relative permeability of 5000. The flux φ_1 of the left leg from a to b has a mean path length of one meter, and so does the flux φ_3 of the right leg. The length of the center leg from a to b is 0.4 m. Each path has a cross-sectional area of 0.01 m^2, and leakage flux is negligible.

Solution. Assume a current I_1 of coil 1 equal to one ampere, with coil 2 open. The flux linkages $N_2\varphi_2$ of coil 2 are, therefore, equal to the mutual inductance M. Thus we must determine the flux φ_2.

The reluctances $\mathscr{R}_1$, $\mathscr{R}_2$, and $\mathscr{R}_3$ of the three paths are easily calculated from the relation $l/(\mu S)$. $\mathscr{R}_1$ and $\mathscr{R}_3$ are 15,900, and $\mathscr{R}_2$ is 6,360. Around the closed magnetic circuit consisting of the left and center legs the mmf N_1I_1 equals $\varphi_1\mathscr{R}_1 + \varphi_2\mathscr{R}_2$. Therefore, $200 = 15{,}900\varphi_1 + 6{,}360\varphi_2$. Around the closed magnetic circuit consisting of the center and right legs the mmf is zero. Consequently, $\varphi_2\mathscr{R}_2 = \varphi_3\mathscr{R}_3$, or $6{,}360\varphi_2 = 15{,}900\varphi_3$. These two equations in terms of the three fluxes, with the

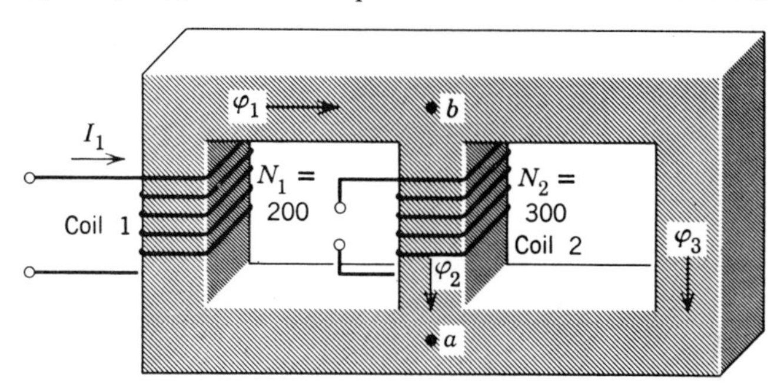

FIG. 16-15. Two coils and a ferromagnetic circuit.

aid of the relation $\varphi_1 = \varphi_2 + \varphi_3$, can be solved for φ_2, giving $\varphi_2 = 0.00699$ weber. $N_2\varphi_2$ is 2.1, and the mutual inductance M is 2.1 henrys. The sign of M depends on the positive directions selected for the coil currents.

Fig. 16-16 is a circuit representation of this magnetic-circuit problem, with the reluctances shown as lumped elements.

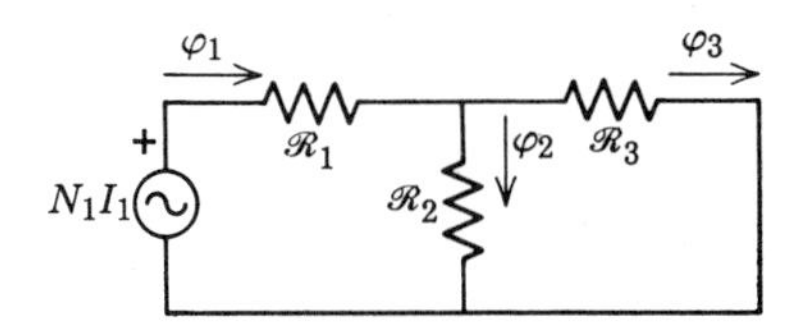

FIG. 16-16. Circuit representation of magnetic-circuit problem, with I_2 of coil 2 equal to zero.

EXAMPLE 4. Find the external inductance per unit length of a coaxial transmission line. The radius of the inner conductor is a, the inner radius of the outer conductor is b, and the permeability of the dielectric is μ.

Solution. Assume a current I in the inner conductor. The current of the outer conductor is also I, but in the opposite direction. From symmetry it is evident that the magnetic flux lines in the dielectric are circular. Consequently, $H = I/(2\pi r)$, with r denoting the distance from the axis of the inner conductor to a point in the dielectric. The flux density B is $\mu I/(2\pi r)$, and the flux *per unit length* that links the current I of the inner conductor is the integral of B with respect to r from a to b, or $(\mu I/2\pi)\ln b/a$. Dividing by the current I gives an external inductance of $(\mu/2\pi)\ln b/a$ henrys/meter, and this result is valid regardless of the frequency.

The internal inductance per unit length is a function of the frequency. At low frequencies the expression for the total inductance is given in Prob. 14-32. At very high frequencies the internal inductance can be found from the principles of Sec. 14-9 (see Prob. 14-31). As the internal inductance of a coaxial line is often quite appreciable, the total inductance per unit length varies with frequency.

EXAMPLE 5. Determine the d-c inductance per unit length of the parallel-wire transmission line shown in Fig. 16-17. Assume nonferromagnetic conductors.

Solution. Figure 16-17 is similar to Fig. 16-4, except for the point P being located inside wire 1. The inductance will be found by evaluating the volume integral of $\mathbf{A} \cdot \mathbf{J}$ and multiplying the result by $1/I^2$. This is Eq. (15-18). Only the volume of the conductors need be considered, for the current density $\mathbf{J}$ is zero in the dielectric. Both $\mathbf{A}$ and $\mathbf{J}$ are independent of the axial coordinate z. Therefore,

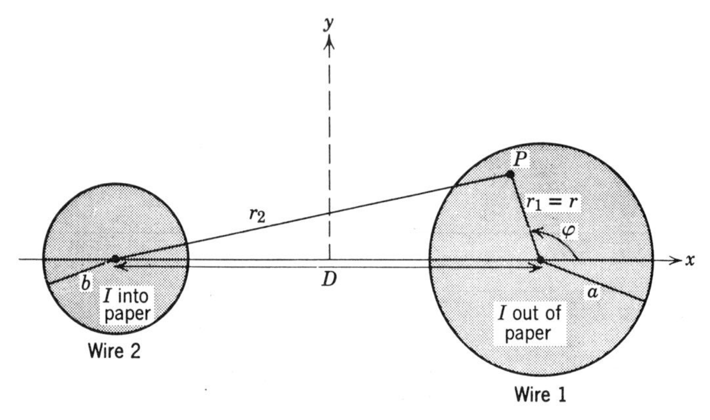

FIG. 16-17. Cross-sectional view of two long parallel wires with equal and opposite direct currents.

the volume integral in one meter of length equals the surface integral of $\mathbf{A} \cdot \mathbf{J}$ over the cross sections of the wires. Let L_1 and L_2 denote the respective contributions of wires 1 and 2 to the inductance per unit length. As $\mathbf{A}$ and $\mathbf{J}$ have only z components, it follows that

$$L_1 = \frac{1}{I^2} \int_{S_1} A_z J_z \, dS \tag{16-41}$$

with S_1 denoting the cross-sectional area of wire 1. A similar expression applies to L_2.

The current density J_z in wire 1 is the constant $I/(\pi a^2)$. The magnetic vector potential A_z, for $r_1 < a$, is given by Eq. (16-24). Let us locate the origin of a cylindrical coordinate system at a point on the axis of wire 1. The cylindrical coordinate φ is indicated on the illustration, and r_1 becomes equal to the cylindrical coordinate r. A differential surface area dS is $r\,dr\,d\varphi$. The limits for r are 0 and a, and we may choose 0 and π as the limits for φ provided we multiply the integral by 2. Substituting for A_z, J_z, and dS in Eq. (16-41), we obtain

$$L_1 = \frac{\mu_0}{2\pi^2 a^2} \int_0^{\pi} \int_0^{a} \left(1 - \frac{r^2}{a^2} + \ln \frac{r_2^{\,2}}{a^2}\right) r \, dr \, d\varphi$$

Before the integration can be performed, r_2 must be expressed in terms of the cylindrical coordinates. Noting that $-\cos(\pi - \varphi) = \cos\varphi$, it is easily deduced from the law of cosines that

$$r_2^{\,2} = D^2\left(1 + \frac{r^2}{D^2} + \frac{2r}{D}\cos\varphi\right)$$

with D denoting the distance between the centers of the wires. The expression for L_1 becomes

$$L_1 = \frac{\mu_0}{2\pi^2 a^2}\int_0^{\pi}\int_0^{a}\left[1 - \frac{r^2}{a^2} + \ln\frac{D^2}{a^2} + \ln\left(1 + \frac{r^2}{D^2} + \frac{2r}{D}\cos\varphi\right)\right] r\,dr\,d\varphi$$

First, we shall integrate with respect to φ. From a table of definite integrals (Pierce 523), it is found that the integral of the last logarithmic function with respect to φ, from 0 to π, is zero. Thus this term can be dropped from the integral expression for L_1. As the remaining terms of the integrand are independent of φ, the φ integration yields the multiplier π, giving

$$L_1 = \frac{\mu_0}{2\pi a^2}\int_0^{a}\left(1 - \frac{r^2}{a^2} + \ln\frac{D^2}{a^2}\right) r\,dr$$

This is easily evaluated. The result is

$$L_1 = \frac{\mu_0}{8\pi} + \frac{\mu_0}{2\pi}\ln\frac{D}{a}$$

The expression for L_2 is the same except that b replaces a. The sum of L_1 and L_2 gives the inductance L per unit length, and the result is

$$L = \frac{\mu_0}{4\pi} + \frac{\mu_0}{\pi}\ln\frac{D}{\sqrt{ab}} \tag{16-42}$$

REFERENCES

See Bibliography.

PROBLEMS

Section 16-1

16-1. The resistivity of aluminum at 20°C is 2.645 microhm-cm. Find the resistivity in ohm-circular-mils per foot, and also determine the conductivity in mks units.

16-2. A pair of annealed copper wires is to supply a steady current of 40 amperes at 220 volts to a load 1200 feet from a substation. If the voltage at the substation is 230 volts, what must be the diameter of the wire? The resistivity is 10.4 ohms per circular-mil-foot.

16-3. Let R_1 and R_2 denote the resistances of a conductor at temperatures T_1 and T_2 degrees Centigrade, respectively. Show that $R_2/R_1 = (C + T_2)/(C + T_1)$, with the constant $C = 1/\alpha_0 - T_0$. Verify that C is 234.5 for annealed copper. What is the resistance of a copper wire at 35°C if its resistance is 1 ohm at 10°C?

16-4. Show that the temperature coefficient of resistance α_1 at temperature T_1 is $1/(T_1 + C)$, with C denoting the constant defined in Prob. 16-3. Find the temperature coefficient of resistance of copper at $-20°C$.

16-5. Determine the approximate diameter in inches, the area in circular mils, and the resistance per 1000 feet of No. 1 annealed copper wire. Repeat for No. 18 wire.

Section 16-3

16-6. Write Eq. (16-12) in cylindrical coordinates. Noting that $J_z = 0$ at points outside the wire, find Eq. (16-16) by direct integration of (16-12) with respect to r. Evaluate one of the constants of integration by using the known magnetic field and the relation $\mathbf{B} = \nabla \times \mathbf{A}$. Similarly, derive Eq. (16-17).

Section 16-4

16-7. Derive Eq. (16-22) from (16-21).

16-8. Show that the equation of the family of flux lines described by Eq. (16-22) and sketched in Fig. 16-5 is

$$(x \pm \sqrt{r_0^2 + d^2})^2 + y^2 = r_0^2$$

with r_0 a constant. First show by the methods of Sec. 4-1 that the differential equation is $(d^2 - x^2 + y^2)\,dx = 2xy\,dy$. Multiplication by $1/x^2$ makes this an exact equation.

16-9. Derive Eq. (16-25) from Eqs. (16-16) and (16-17), clearly showing the details of each mathematical operation.

Section 16-6

16-10. A differential vector length of a field line described by Eq. (16-35) and shown in Fig. 16-8 is $d\mathbf{l} = dr\,\mathbf{a}_r + r\,d\theta\,\mathbf{a}_\theta$. Using this and Eq. (16-35), deduce that the family of field lines is represented by the equation $r = C \sin^2 \theta$, with C a constant. Plot carefully the flux line in the yz-plane for $C = 1$.

Section 16-7

16-11. In Example 1 of Sec. 16-7, find the core flux if the ferromagnetic material of both regions 1 and 2 is cast iron with B and H related by Eq. (16-39).

16-12. In Example 2 of Sec. 16-7, find the current required to produce a core flux of 0.00044 weber.

16-13. In Example 3 of Sec. 16-7, find the current required to produce an average air-gap flux density of 1.25 webers/m^2.

16-14. In Example 4 of Sec. 16-7, find the current I that produces an air-gap flux density of 0.6 weber/m^2.

16-15. In Example 4 of Sec. 16-7, find the air-gap flux density for a current of 1 ampere.

Section 16-8

16-16. If the coil of Example 1 of Sec. 16-7 has 1000 turns, calculate its inductance corresponding to the given mmf. Also, find the internal inductance.

16-17. Find the inductance of the winding of the electromagnet of Example 4 of Sec. 16-7 corresponding to the current of 1.23 amperes.

16-18. A superpowerful electromagnet consists of a solenoid 10 cm long with 20,000 turns of wire made of a compound of niobium and tin that is superconductive at temperatures below 18°K. If the diameter of the solenoid is small compared with the length, calculate the approximate magnetic flux density in the nonferromagnetic core for a current of 25 amperes.

16-19. Calculate both the internal and external inductances of the toroidal coil of Example 2 of Sec. 16-7 if the ferromagnetic core is replaced with a nonferromagnetic core. Neglect leakage flux.

16-20. Sketch Fig. 16-15 with a third coil of 400 turns placed on the third leg, with its winding similar to that of coils 1 and 2. Using dots, triangles, and squares, mark the corresponding terminals of each pair of coils. Select reference directions for the coil currents I_1, I_2, and I_3, and determine the mutual inductances, including their signs, for each pair of coils. Use the data of Example 3 of Sec. 16-8.

16-21. If No. 10 annealed copper wire is used to construct a parallel-wire transmission line, what spacing is required to give a d-c inductance of 3.67 mh/mile? If the same wire is used as the inner conductor of a coaxial cable, what must be the inner radius of the outer conductor to give an inductance of 0.425 mh/mile at a frequency so high that internal inductance is negligible?

Magnetostatics II

CHAPTER 17

We have learned that electric currents in nearby conductors exert magnetic forces on one another. In fact, as Ampère showed us in 1820, each current element produces a magnetic field that acts on every other current element in the region. If two or more closed circuits are present, there are, in general, magnetic forces and torques exerted on each. The operation of most electromechanical-energy-conversion devices depends on these forces and torques. In the first part of this chapter we shall develop a basic theory for determining the forces and torques produced by magnetic fields. The remainder of the chapter is devoted to a study of the magnetic theory of materials, with special emphasis on ferromagnetism. Hysteresis and eddy currents are discussed, and the important concept of *magnetization* is introduced in order to link the macroscopic, or observable, viewpoint with the microscopic, or atomic, viewpoint. Let us begin our investigation of magnetic force with a review of the important Biot-Savart law, from which the mechanical forces between individual current elements and also between closed electric circuits can be formulated.

17-1. THE BIOT-SAVART LAW

From the general expressions for the fields of a current element, derived in Chapter 13, the near magnetic field at a point P was found to be

$$d\mathbf{H} = \frac{i\, d\mathbf{l} \times \mathbf{a}_r}{4\pi r^2} \tag{17-1}$$

This mathematical statement of the Biot-Savart law was given in Chapter 13 as Eq. (13-63). The unit vector $\mathbf{a}_r$ at P is, of course, directed radially outward from the current element, and the distance r from the current element to the point P is understood to be very small compared with the wavelength. Otherwise, Eq. (17-1) is not a reasonable approximation of the magnetic field. For a steady current I the wavelength is infinite, and the Biot-Savart law is exact.

The Biot-Savart law can be deduced directly from Maxwell's equations without utilizing the results of the current-element problem of Chapter 13. Let us consider an isolated current element $I\,d\mathbf{l}$ in a single infinite dielectric. The steady current I produces charges $+q$ and $-q$ at the ends of the differential length, and q increases linearly with time with $\dot{q}$ equal to I. The time-changing point charges produce an electric field that increases linearly with time. However, the magnetic field is steady because the current is steady. This is a very special case of a time-changing electric field *not* accompanied by a time-changing magnetic field.

The charges $+q$ and $-q$, separated a distance $d\mathbf{l}$, constitute an electric dipole. If the dipole is located at the origin of a coordinate system with the dipole moment in the positive z-direction, the electric field $\mathbf{E}$ is given in spherical coordinates by Eq. (16-35). Multiplication by the permittivity ϵ gives the electric flux density $\mathbf{D}$, and the time derivative of $\mathbf{D}$ is the displacement current density. As $\dot{q}$ equals I, it follows from Eq. (16-35) that the displacement current density at the point $P(r, \theta, \varphi)$ is

$$\dot{\mathbf{D}} = \frac{I\,dl}{4\pi r^3}(2\cos\theta\,\mathbf{a}_r + \sin\theta\,\mathbf{a}_\theta) \tag{17-2}$$

Consider the spherical cap shown in Fig. 17-1. The mmf around the contour C of the spherical cap equals the displacement current I_d over the surface S of the cap. This displacement current is the surface integral of $\dot{\mathbf{D}}$. Noting that each vector differential surface area is $r^2 \sin\theta\, d\theta\, d\varphi\, \mathbf{a}_r$, with the limits of θ being 0 and θ_1 and the limits of φ being 0 and 2π, evaluation of the surface integral is easily accomplished, giving

$$I_d = \frac{I\,dl \sin^2\theta_1}{2r} \tag{17-3}$$

This equals the mmf around the path C, and the mmf is the product of the differential magnetic field dH_φ of the current element and the path length $2\pi r \sin\theta_1$. Clearly

$$dH_\varphi = \frac{I\,dl\sin\theta}{4\pi r^2} \tag{17-4}$$

with the subscript 1 on θ dropped. This is the Biot-Savart law of Eq. (17-1).

The Biot-Savart law can also be deduced from the magnetic vector potential of a steady current element. This is suggested as an exercise (see Prob. 17-1).

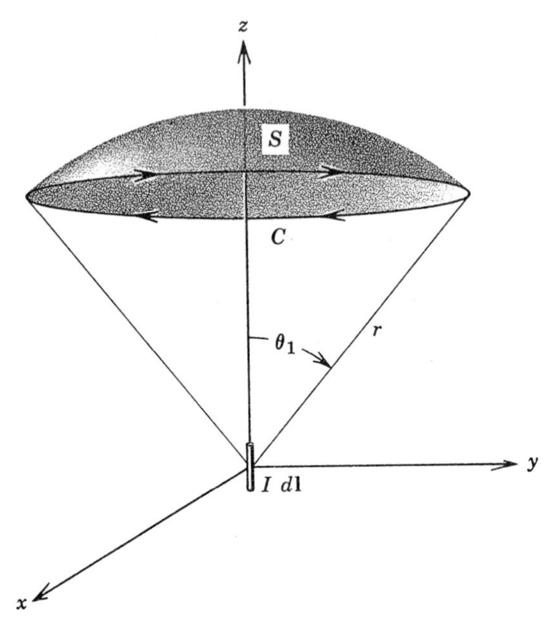

FIG. 17-1. A spherical cap of area S centered on the axis of a current element $I\,d\mathbf{l}$.

EXAMPLE 1. Find the magnetic field at the center of a circular loop with current I and radius a.

Solution. Consider the current element $I\,d\mathbf{l}$ shown on the loop of Fig. 17-2. The unit vector $\mathbf{a}_r$ at the center of the loop is drawn away from the current element. As the vectors $\mathbf{a}_r$ and $d\mathbf{l}$ are normal, the cross product $d\mathbf{l} \times \mathbf{a}_r$ equals $dl\,\mathbf{n}$, with $\mathbf{n}$ denoting a unit vector normal to the loop out of the paper. By the Biot-Savart law the differential field of this current element is $I\,dl\,\mathbf{n}/(4\pi a^2)$. Therefore, the total field at the center of the loop is

$$\mathbf{H} = \frac{I\mathbf{n}}{4\pi a^2}\oint dl = \frac{I}{2a}\mathbf{n}$$

The Biot-Savart law can be used to obtain an expression for the force between two current elements. The magnetic flux density $d\mathbf{B}_1$ produced by a current element $I_1\,d\mathbf{l}_1$ is $\mu I_1\,d\mathbf{l}_1 \times \mathbf{a}_r/(4\pi r^2)$. If a second current element $I_2\,d\mathbf{l}_2$ is located in this magnetic field, the magnetic force $d\mathbf{F}_2$ on it is $I_2\,d\mathbf{l}_2 \times d\mathbf{B}_1$. It follows that the differential force on $I_2\,d\mathbf{l}_2$ is

$$d\mathbf{F}_2 = \frac{\mu I_1 I_2\,d\mathbf{l}_2 \times (d\mathbf{l}_1 \times \mathbf{a}_r)}{4\pi r^2} \tag{17-5}$$

with $\mathbf{a}_r$ denoting a unit vector directed from $d\mathbf{l}_1$ to $d\mathbf{l}_2$. This equation is often referred to as *Ampère's law of force between current elements.*

In order to find the force on a closed circuit 2 due to the current of a closed circuit 1, we must integrate Eq. (17-5) around the closed paths of both circuits. The integral around the path of circuit 1 gives the force on a single current element of circuit 2. The total force is then obtained by integrating around the path of circuit 2. Although Eq. (17-5) gives the force between current elements in a direct manner, without resort to the concept of a magnetic field, it is usually rather difficult to apply directly.

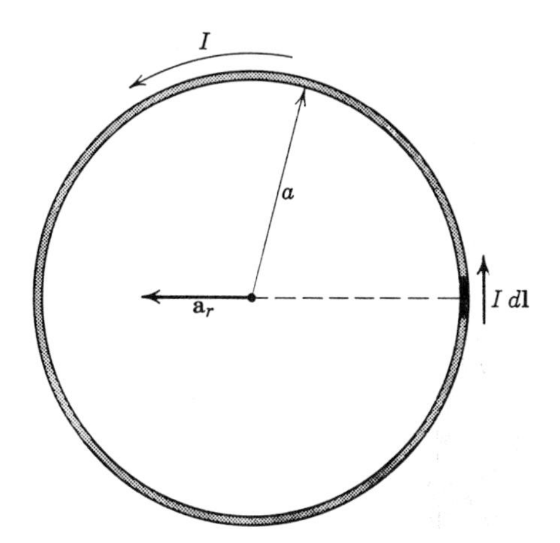

FIG. 17-2. A current loop.

EXAMPLE 2. Determine the force acting on each current element of Fig. 17-3 due to the other element.

Solution. First, we shall utilize Eq. (17-5) to find the force on $I_2\,d\mathbf{l}_2$. As $d\mathbf{l}_2 = dl_2\,\mathbf{k}$ and $d\mathbf{l}_1 = dl_1\,\mathbf{j}$, the equation becomes

$$d\mathbf{F}_2 = \frac{\mu I_1 I_2\,dl_1\,dl_2}{4\pi r^2}\,\mathbf{k} \times (\mathbf{j} \times \mathbf{a}_r)$$

The unit vector $\mathbf{a}_r$ at $d\mathbf{l}_2$ is directed away from $d\mathbf{l}_1$. In rectangular form $\mathbf{a}_r = -\sin\theta\,\mathbf{j} + \cos\theta\,\mathbf{k}$. Therefore, $\mathbf{j} \times \mathbf{a}_r = \cos\theta\,\mathbf{i}$. As $\cos\theta$ equals b/r and as $\mathbf{k} \times \mathbf{i}$ equals $\mathbf{j}$, the differential force becomes

$$d\mathbf{F}_2 = \frac{\mu I_1 I_2\,dl_1\,dl_2\,b}{4\pi r^3}\,\mathbf{j}$$

The force $d\mathbf{F}_1$ that acts on $I_1\,d\mathbf{l}_1$ is determined in a similar manner. The subscripts 1 and 2 of Eq. (17-5) are interchanged, and the unit vector $\mathbf{a}_r$ at $d\mathbf{l}_1$ is directed away from $d\mathbf{l}_2$. The resulting force is

$$d\mathbf{F}_1 = \frac{\mu I_1 I_2\,dl_1\,dl_2\,a}{4\pi r^3}\,\mathbf{k}$$

It is interesting to note that the forces $d\mathbf{F}_1$ and $d\mathbf{F}_2$ are not equal and opposite as one might expect. However, isolated current elements do not exist physically. When Ampère's force law is applied to closed circuits, Newton's law of action and reaction is obeyed.

The Biot-Savart law applies to alternating current elements if the distances involved are very small compared with the wavelength. With the

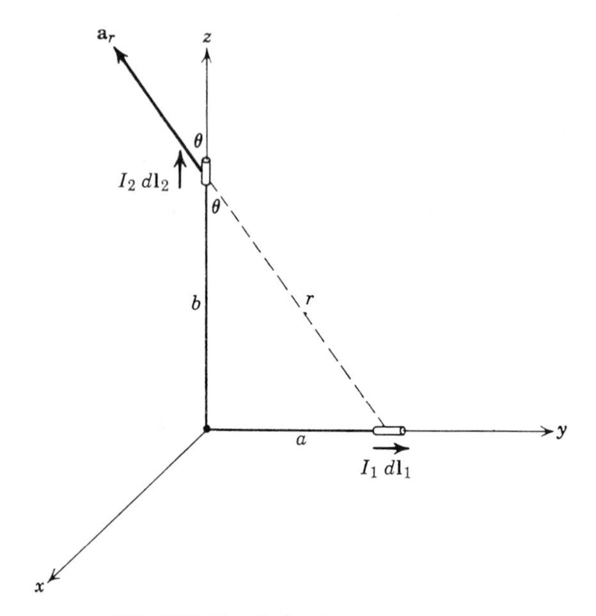

FIG. 17-3. Two isolated current elements.

same restriction Ampère's law of force between current elements also applies to alternating currents. In the next two sections we shall examine a very useful method of calculating magnetic forces from changes in magnetic energy.

17-2 FORCE AND MAGNETIC ENERGY

A force F_x of magnetic origin can be expressed in terms of the change dW that occurs in the magnetic field energy if the force acts through a differential distance dx. Let us investigate this *method of virtual work* by first considering a single electric circuit with a current i and flux linkages Φ. In the differential time dt suppose the current and the flux linkages increase by di and $d\Phi$, respectively. The changes may be due to the motion of an armature in the magnetic circuit, causing the reluctance to vary, or they may result from a variation in the applied voltage, or they may be due to other effects. In any event di and $d\Phi$ are the increases that occur in the time dt. During this differential time the voltage induced in the circuit by the changing flux is $d\Phi/dt$, according to the Maxwell-Faraday law, and the product $i\,d\Phi/dt$ is the power supplied to the magnetic field by the electric circuit. Therefore, the differential energy dW_{elec} supplied to the magnetic field by the electric circuit in the time dt is

$$dW_{\text{elec}} = i\,d\Phi \tag{17-6}$$

It should be noted that the differential change in i is not involved, for $(i + di)d\Phi \approx \mathrm{i}\,d\Phi$.

We shall now consider the possible disposition of the electrical energy supplied to the magnetic field. Some of the energy may be stored in the field. There may be iron losses that convert part of the energy into heat. This is discussed in Secs. 17-6 and 17-7. In addition, there may be mechanical work done by the magnetic field. These energies require closer examination.

By Eq. (15-12), the energy W stored in the magnetic field of the circuit is $\frac{1}{2}\Phi i$, assuming a linear relationship between the flux linkages and the current. The assumption of linearity certainly restricts the analysis, for if iron is present, the nonlinearity may be appreciable. However, many ferromagnetic circuits contain air gaps; the relationship between Φ and i in such circuits is nearly linear, because most of the magnetic energy is stored in the air gaps. This is true, for example, in the magnetic circuits of most electric motors and generators even though a considerable amount of iron is usually present. In the time dt the increase dW in the field energy, due to the changes di and $d\Phi$, is

$$dW = \tfrac{1}{2}\Phi\,di + \tfrac{1}{2}i\,d\Phi \tag{17-7}$$

We shall assume that iron losses, if any, are negligible. The effect of these losses on the result is usually not very great and, in fact, magnetic circuits that are truly linear, as assumed, are lossless. If there is no mechanical work done, the electrical energy supplied in the time dt equals dW.

The magnetic field of the circuit exerts a force on any current in this field and also on the moving charges and magnetic dipole moments associated with the atoms of physical media that are present. In order to determine the force acting on any part of the electric or magnetic circuit, we can imagine that the part is allowed to move through the distance dx in the time dt due to the magnetic force F_x. Then the mechanical work $F_x\,dx$ done in the time dt must equal the electrical energy supplied to the field less the increase in the field energy; that is,

$$F_x\,dx = i\,d\Phi - dW \tag{17-8}$$

By utilizing Eq. (17-7), we can put this in the form

$$F_x\,dx = dW - \Phi\,di \tag{17-9}$$

Suppose that the flux linkages Φ are maintained constant as the part moves through the distance dx. Then $d\Phi$ of (17-8) is zero, and it is evident that

$$F_x = -\left.\frac{\partial W}{\partial x}\right|_{\Phi\ \text{constant}} \tag{17-10}$$

On the other hand, if the current i is held constant, it is evident from (17-9) that

$$F_x = +\left.\frac{\partial W}{\partial x}\right|_{i\ \text{constant}} \tag{17-11}$$

From Eq. (17-10) we see that the force tending to increase a coordinate of a system equals the space rate of *decrease*, as the selected coordinate is increased, of the magnetic energy of the system, provided the magnetic flux linkages are kept constant. For constant Φ there is no electrical energy supplied, and the mechanical work $F_x\,dx$ equals the decrease $-dW$ in the stored magnetic energy. On the other hand, from Eq. (17-11) we see that the force tending to increase a coordinate of a system equals the space rate of *increase* of the magnetic energy of the system provided the current is kept constant. In this case it is evident that electrical energy is supplied, with half of the energy used to increase the stored magnetic energy and the other half converted into mechanical work.

Another useful form of the force equation is obtained by substituting the expression for dW in Eq. (17-7) into Eq. (17-8), giving

$$F_x = \tfrac{1}{2} i \frac{d\Phi}{dx} - \tfrac{1}{2}\Phi \frac{di}{dx} \tag{17-12}$$

If the current i is maintained constant, the force acts on each part of the electric and magnetic circuits in a direction that tends to increase the flux linkages. On the other hand, if the flux linkages are maintained constant, action of the force requires a decrease in the current. As inductance $L = \Phi/i$, Eq. (17-12) can be written

$$F_x = \tfrac{1}{2} i^2 \frac{dL}{dx} \tag{17-13}$$

Thus *the force tends to increase the inductance L*. Equation (17-12) can also be written in terms of the reluctance $\mathscr{R}$ of the magnetic circuit. As $\mathscr{R} = Ni/\varphi$, with the flux $\varphi = \Phi/N$, it is evident that

$$F_x = -\tfrac{1}{2}\varphi^2 \frac{d\mathscr{R}}{dx} \tag{17-14}$$

The force tends to decrease the reluctance of the magnetic circuit.

Let us now consider several examples illustrating the use of the force equations.

EXAMPLE 1. Shown in Fig. 17-4 is a section of a thin cylindrical conducting shell of radius a and infinite length in a dielectric of permeability μ. If the shell carries a steady current I, determine the magnetic force per unit area that acts on the shell.

Solution. Suppose the *inward* radial force F per unit surface area compresses the shell so as to *decrease* its radius by a differential amount dR, with I maintained constant. By Eq. (17-11), $F = dW/dR$, with dW denoting the differential increase in the magnetic-field energy due to the displacement of a unit area of the surface. Thus $dW = \frac{1}{2}\mu H^2\, dR$ joule/m², with $H = I/(2\pi a)$, and consequently, $F = \frac{1}{2}\mu H^2$ newtons/m², or $\mu I^2/(8\pi^2 a^2)$. This is the inward force per unit area acting on each differential surface area. According to Eqs. (17-11) and (17-12), the force tends to increase the magnetic-field energy and the flux linkages, provided the current is regarded as constant. By Eqs. (17-13) and (17-14) the force tends to increase the

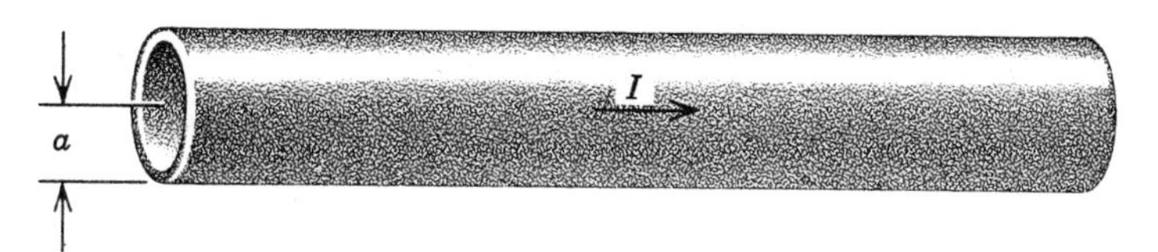

FIG. 17-4. Cylindrical conducting shell.

inductance of the electric circuit and to decrease the reluctance of the magnetic circuit. It is evident that the inward force on the cylindrical shell satisfies these requirements.

The force can also be determined from the differential force on a current element $\mathbf{J}_s\, dS$, with $\mathbf{J}_s$ denoting the surface current density of magnitude $I/(2\pi a)$. In accordance with the principles of Sec. 7-6, the magnetic force per unit area is $\mathbf{J}_s \times \mathbf{B}'$, and the magnitude F of this inward force is $\mu J_s H'$, with the primes used to indicate that the fields are evaluated *precisely at* $r = a$. Inside the shell $H = 0$. At a point P outside the shell barely off the surface of the current element, $H = J_s$. The point P is assumed to be so close to the differential surface dS that *the surface current element appears from P to be an infinite current sheet* whose magnetic field intensity is, by the Maxwell-Ampère law, equal to $\frac{1}{2}J_s$. Therefore, the field at P due to all current elements *except the one located at P* is $\frac{1}{2}J_s$ amperes/m, and this is H'. Thus the inward force $\mu J_s H'$ per unit area becomes $\frac{1}{2}\mu J_s^2$, or $\frac{1}{2}\mu H^2$, with $H = I/(2\pi a)$.

A round wire can be regarded as made up of a number of cylindrical shells of differential thickness. If the wire carries a steady current, each of these differential shells is acted upon by an inward magnetic force per unit area. For intense currents, such as those sometimes encountered in lightning strokes, these magnetic forces may crush the wire. This phenomenon is known as the *pinch effect*. It is oftentimes convenient to regard the lines of magnetic flux as stretched elastic bands. The circular lines around the wire tend to compress the wire. An alternative viewpoint is that of Ampère's law of force between current elements, which states that each element exerts a force on every other current element. In spite of these forces the direct-current distribution in a conductor with constant conductivity is uniform, because any appreciable change in this distribution would be strongly opposed by the resulting charge separation. Thus magnetic forces are transmitted to the medium by means of the electric current.

EXAMPLE 2. Find the magnetic force of attraction on the armature of the electromagnet of Fig. 17-5, in terms of the magnetic field in the air gaps and the

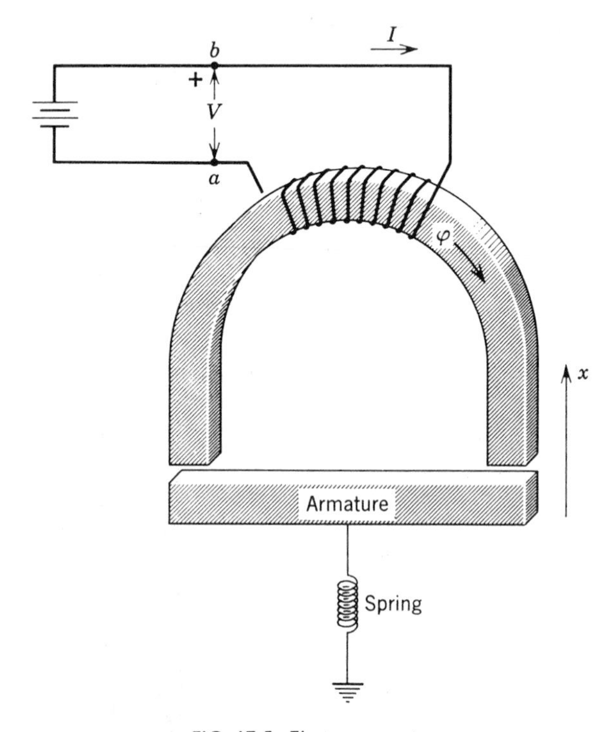

FIG. 17-5. Electromagnet.

cross-sectional area S of each gap. The ferromagnetic material has high permeability and fringing is negligible.

Solution. Suppose the armature moves through a differential distance dx. The reluctance of each gap decreases by $dx/(\mu_0 S)$, and $-d\mathcal{R}/dx$, with $\mathcal{R}$ denoting the total reluctance of the magnetic circuit, is $2/(\mu_0 S)$. Therefore, by Eq. (17-14) the force F_x of attraction is $\varphi^2/(\mu_0 S)$, or $B^2 S/\mu_0$, or BHS, with B and H denoting the air-gap fields. The force of attraction at each air gap is $\frac{1}{2}BHS$, and the force per unit area is $\frac{1}{2}BH$, or $\frac{1}{2}\mu_0 H^2$, or $\frac{1}{2}B^2/\mu_0$. This result applies when magnetic flux lines cross a small air gap separating parallel ferromagnetic surfaces.

EXAMPLE 3. A d-c voltage V is applied to the electromagnet of Fig. 17-5, and each of the N turns of the coil has a resistance r. The length of each air gap is a, and the area of each pole face is S. If the reluctance of the ferromagnetic material is negligible, find the force of attraction between the magnet and the armature, and determine the power dissipated in the winding. Calculate these quantities for $N = 2000$, $r = 0.04$, $a = 0.001$, $S = 0.0001$, and $V = 10$.

Solution. The magnetic flux $\varphi = NI/\mathscr{R}$. As the reluctance of the two air gaps is $2a/(\mu_0 S)$, the flux φ is $\frac{1}{2}\mu_0 NIS/a$. In the preceding example the force F of attraction was found to be $\varphi^2/(\mu_0 S)$. Therefore, $F = \frac{1}{4}\mu_0 N^2 I^2 S/a^2$. As the current I is $V/(Nr)$, the force becomes

$$F = \frac{\mu_0 S V^2}{4a^2 r^2}$$

This force is proportional to the voltage squared and is independent of the number of turns. The power P dissipated in the coil is $V^2/(Nr)$. For the data given, $F = 1.96$ newtons and $P = 1.25$ watts.

The electromagnet of Fig. 17-5 is an example of an electromagnetic device consisting of an exciting coil wound on a magnetic circuit, part of which is movable. A wide variety of such moving-iron devices are utilized in electro-mechanical energy conversion. The magnetic forces always tend to move rigid bodies into positions of minimum reluctance. The force relations of this and the next section apply to permanent magnets as well as to electromagnets.

17-3. TORQUE AND MAGNETIC ENERGY

If a torque T in newton-meters rotates a rigid body through a differential angle $d\theta$, the mechanical work done is $T\,d\theta$ joule. The expressions of the preceding section, with $F_x\,dx$ replaced with $T\,d\theta$, can be used to find the magnetic torque that tends to rotate a body through the angle $d\theta$. In particular, Eq. (17-14) becomes

$$T = -\tfrac{1}{2}\varphi^2 \frac{d\mathscr{R}}{d\theta} \qquad (17\text{-}15)$$

The magnetic torque on a body tends to decrease the reluctance of the magnetic circuit.

Shown in Fig. 17-6 is a simple reluctance motor. The angle θ is measured counterclockwise from the vertical to the dashed line along the shaft of the rotor, as indicted. In Fig. 17-6*a* an increase $d\theta$ in the angular position of the rotor results in a decrease in the reluctance of the magnetic circuit. Therefore, $d\mathscr{R}/d\theta$ is negative, and the torque T of Eq. (17-15) is positive. Thus the torque on the rotor of Fig. 17-6*a* tends to pull it counterclockwise. On the other hand, the torque on the rotor of Fig. 17-6*b* is clockwise, because an increase $d\theta$ in θ results in an increase in the reluctance of the magnetic circuit, and the torque T of Eq. (17-15) is negative.

Suppose the rotor rotates with angular velocity ω. If the flux φ were maintained steady, the torque on the rotor would be alternately positive and negative, and the average torque would be zero. However, an average torque is developed if the flux φ is made to vary sinusoidally with time with angular frequency ω, provided the flux is a maximum at the instant when the rotor is approximately as shown in Fig. 17-6*a*. At this instant a strong positive torque acts on the rotor. When the rotor has moved

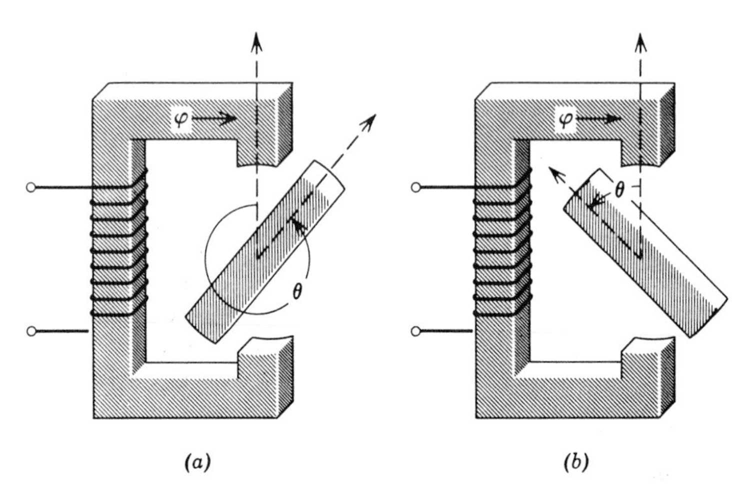

FIG. 17-6. Simple reluctance motor.

to the position shown in Fig. 17-6*b*, the flux has become very weak, and the negative torque is weak. Thus a net average torque is obtained, and the motor is able to convert electrical energy into mechanical energy. As the motor is not self-starting, it must be brought to the proper speed by auxiliary means. The rotor makes one revolution for each cycle of the applied voltage that produces the alternating flux. Therefore, the speed in revolutions per second equals the frequency, and this speed is called the *synchronous speed*. The most common application of reluctance motors is in driving electric clocks.

EXAMPLE 1. Suppose the reluctance of the magnetic circuit of Fig. 17-6 is

$$\mathscr{R} = C_1 - C_2 \cos 2\theta$$

with C_1 and C_2 denoting constants. When $\theta = 0$, the reluctance is $C_1 - C_2$, the minimum value of $\mathscr{R}$. When $\theta = 90°$, the reluctance is $C_1 + C_2$, the maximum value of $\mathscr{R}$. If $\theta = \omega t - \delta$ and if the flux φ is $\varphi_m \cos \omega t$, find the time-average counterclockwise torque.

Solution. When $\omega t = 0$, the flux φ is a maximum, and the angular position of the rotor is as shown in Fig. 17-6*a*, with δ being the angle between the two dashed arrows. This angle is called the *torque angle*. The instantaneous torque T is found by substituting the expressions for φ and $\mathscr{R}$ into Eq. (17-15) and replacing θ with $\omega t - \delta$. The result is

$$T = -C_2\varphi_m{}^2 \cos^2 \omega t \sin (2\omega t - 2\delta)$$

The time-average torque is easily found by substituting $\frac{1}{2}(1 + \cos 2\omega t)$ for $\cos^2 \omega t$ and by applying another identity to the product of the sine and cosine functions. The resulting time-average torque is $\frac{1}{4}C_2\varphi_m{}^2 \sin 2\delta$. It should be noted that this is a maximum when δ is 45°. If there is no load on the motor, the torque angle is practically zero. At maximum load, δ is 45°.

Thus far we have considered the magnetic forces and torques associated with a single electric circuit. Let us now investigate these quantities when there are two electric circuits involved, and we shall assume that the currents i_1 and i_2 are maintained constant. The differential energy supplied to the magnetic field by the two electric circuits in the differential time dt is

$$dW_{\text{elec}} = i_1\, d\Phi_1 + i_2\, d\Phi_2 \tag{17-16}$$

with Φ_1 and Φ_2 denoting the respective flux linkages of the circuits. This equation corresponds to Eq. (17-6). As Φ_1 is the sum of $L_1 i_1$ and Mi_2 and as Φ_2 can be expressed similarly, Eq. (17-16) can be written

$$dW_{\text{elec}} = i_1^2\, dL_1 + i_2^2\, dL_2 + 2i_1 i_2\, dM \tag{17-17}$$

The field energy W is $\frac{1}{2}L_1 i_1^2 + \frac{1}{2}L_2 i_2^2 + Mi_1 i_2$. Therefore, the differential increase dW in this energy in the time dt is

$$dW = \tfrac{1}{2}i_1^2\, dL_1 + \tfrac{1}{2}i_2^2\, dL_2 + i_1 i_2\, dM \tag{17-18}$$

Comparison of Eqs. (17-17) and (17-18) shows that

$$dW_{\text{elec}} = 2\, dW \tag{17-19}$$

Thus for constant currents the electrical energy supplied to the magnetic field in the differential time dt is twice the increase in the stored energy. Half of the electrical energy supplied does mechanical work, and this mechanical work in the time dt equals the increase dW in the energy stored in the magnetic field. If the force on a body is desired, we equate $F_x\, dx$ and dW. To determine the torque, we equate $T\, d\theta$ and dW. The expression for the torque is

$$T = \frac{\partial W}{\partial \theta} = \tfrac{1}{2}i_1{}^2 \frac{\partial L_1}{\partial \theta} + \tfrac{1}{2}i_2{}^2 \frac{\partial L_2}{\partial \theta} + i_1 i_2 \frac{\partial M}{\partial \theta} \tag{17-20}$$

with partial derivatives used to signify that the currents are regarded as constants. T is the torque that tends to increase the angle θ of the body. If θ in Eq. (17-20) is replaced with x, the expression gives the force on the body that tends to increase the coordinate x.

In many cases the motion of the body does not change the self-inductances of the circuits. If L_1 and L_2 are constant, Eq. (17-20) becomes

$$T = i_1 i_2 \frac{\partial M}{\partial \theta} \tag{17-21}$$

The mutual inductance M is positive or negative, depending on the orientation of the circuits and the reference directions selected for the currents. The magnitude of M equals Φ_{12}/i_2 and also Φ_{21}/i_1, with Φ_{12} denoting the flux linkages of circuit 1 due to i_2 and with Φ_{21} similarly defined. Note that the torque tends to increase the mutual inductance of the circuits. Let us now consider a very important example illustrating the use of Eq. (17-21).

EXAMPLE 2. Shown in Fig. 17-7 is a loop of wire enclosing a planar area S and located in a uniform magnetic field **B** produced by a current of a distant

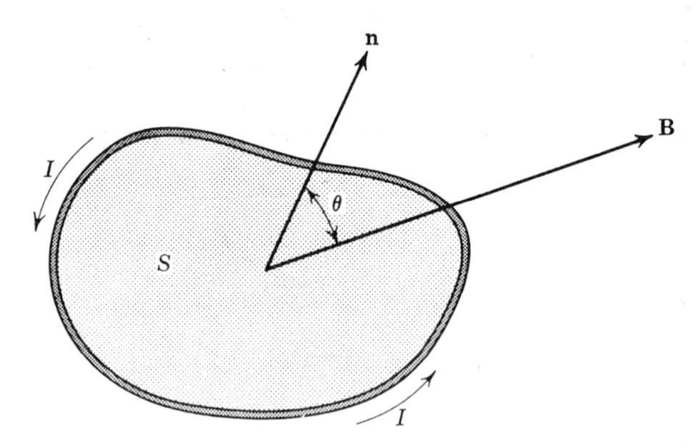

FIG. 17-7. A current loop in a uniform field **B**. The unit vector **n** is normal to the plane of the loop.

circuit. The size and shape of the loop is arbitrary, and the unit vector **n** out of the positive side of the surface S makes the angle θ with the field **B**. If the wire carries a steady current I, determine the torque on the loop.

Solution. From Eq. (17-21) it follows that the torque acts so as to decrease the angle θ between **n** and **B**, for the mutual inductance between the loop and the distant circuit that produces the field **B** is a maximum when the vectors **n** and **B** are aligned. As $I_2 M = \Phi_{12}$, it is evident from Eq. (17-21) that the torque that tends to *decrease* the angle θ is $-I\,\partial\Phi_{12}/\partial\theta$, with Φ_{12} denoting the flux over S due to the uniform field **B**. Obviously, $\Phi_{12} = BS\cos\theta$, and the torque that tends to decrease θ becomes $ISB\sin\theta$. This can be written as the magnitude of $\mathbf{m} \times \mathbf{B}$ with the magnetic moment $\mathbf{m} = IS\mathbf{n}$.

Torque is often treated as a vector. Shown in Fig. 17-8 is a force **F** acting at a point P located a vector distance **r** from the origin 0. The vector torque **T** about the origin has a magnitude of $Fr \sin \theta$, and its direction is out of the paper normal to the vectors **r** and **F**. In vector notation torque **T** is defined as $\mathbf{r} \times \mathbf{F}$.

In the preceding example we found that the torque on the current loop tends to decrease the angle θ, with the magnitude of the torque equal to the magnitude of $\mathbf{m} \times \mathbf{B}$. It is evident that the direction of the vector torque **T** is the direction of the vector $\mathbf{m} \times \mathbf{B}$. Therefore

$$\mathbf{T} = \mathbf{m} \times \mathbf{B} \tag{17-22}$$

This is the vector torque on a planar current loop of arbitrary size and shape, located in a uniform magnetic field **B**. A magnetic force acts on

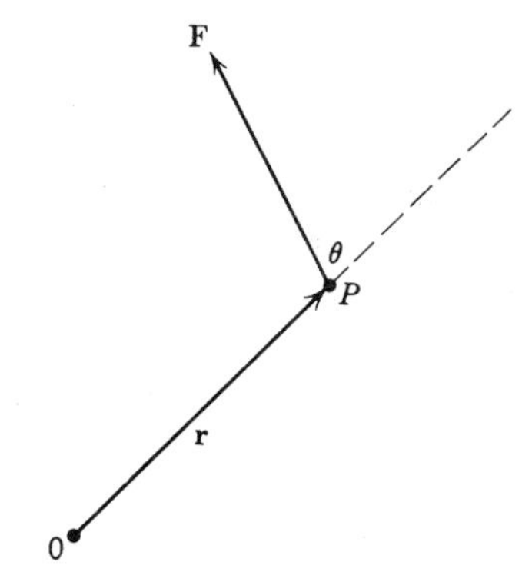

FIG. 17-8. A force **F** acting at *P* located a vector distance **r** from the origin 0.

each current element of the loop, and the resulting torque tends to rotate the loop so as to align its magnetic field with the applied field **B**. If the loop were perfectly free to rotate, it would orient its plane normal to the applied field **B**, and the magnetic field of the loop would reinforce the field **B**. Equation (17-22) applies to all current loops of differential dimensions, because the magnetic field in a very small region is always approximately uniform.

17-4. MAGNETIC THEORY OF MATERIALS

Both the orbital and spin motions of the electrons of atoms have magnetic effects somewhat similar to small current loops. Although neither the current nor the area can be accurately defined for either type of motion, each electron has an *orbital magnetic moment* and a *spin magnetic moment*. An atom may have a number of electrons occupying principal energy levels, or shells, which have certain allowed quantum states. A shell is said to be closed if all of its quantum states are filled with electrons.

Atoms with only closed shells do not have permanent magnetic moments, because there are just as many spin moments and orbital moments in one direction as in the opposite direction. In incomplete shells, however, electrons may or may not produce a net moment, depending on the quantum states that are occupied. The individual atoms of many elements have no magnetic moments, and such materials are said to be *diamagnetic*. On the other hand, materials with atoms having permanent magnetic moments are classified as *paramagnetic*, *ferromagnetic*, *antiferromagnetic*, or *ferrimagnetic*, based upon the alignment of the atomic dipoles. The relative permeabilities depend on the behavior of the electronic magnetic moments. Nuclear spin may also have an effect, though this is usually negligible.

Diamagnetic materials have relative permeabilities slightly less than unity. When a magnetic field is applied, the magnetic force on the moving charges of the atoms causes a slight modification of the quantum states of all the electrons. The modified motion of each electron produces a magnetic moment that opposes the applied field, and the magnetic flux density is, therefore, less than it would be in free space. Actually, all materials exhibit diamagnetism. However, if the atoms have permanent magnetic moments, the diamagnetic effects are usually overshadowed. Most common insulators and many of the common metals are diamagnetic. It is evident from Eq. (17-11) that a diamagnetic material in a nonuniform field experiences a force toward the weaker parts of the field.

In a paramagnetic material the permanent magnetic moments of the atoms, due to both the spins and orbital motions of the electrons, are oriented so as to give zero net magnetization. In an applied field, however, there is a partial alignment of the atoms, resulting in a small magnetic field that adds positively to the applied field. Many insulators and metals are paramagnetic, with relative permeabilities slightly greater than unity. It is evident from Eq. (17-11) that a paramagnetic material in a nonuniform field experiences a force toward the stronger parts of the field. For engineering purposes the relative permeabilities of both diamagnetic and paramagnetic materials can usually be taken as unity with negligible error.

The most important magnetic materials are the ferromagnetic solids. In diamagnetic and paramagnetic materials the electrons in incomplete shells of atoms usually pair off with opposite spin moments. However, in the ferromagnetic elements there are as many as five extra electrons, in the incomplete third shell, that have *aligned spin magnetic moments*. The explanation relies on quantum-mechanical theory, which shows that this arrangement gives the lowest net energy for these materials. In the solid the atomic dipoles interact with one another, and *the resulting alignment yields a net magnetization*. This interaction is not, as one might expect, due to the magnetic moments, because the magnetic forces are far too weak. Much stronger quantum-mechanical "exchange forces" are involved. The energy of the electrons of a ferromagnetic specimen in the magnetized state is a minimum. However, if the solid were in an unmagnetized state, the energy would be but slightly greater; furthermore, the difference in these energies decreases as the temperature rises. At the *Curie temperature* the spontaneous magnetization disappears, and the specimen becomes paramagnetic. The Curie temperatures of iron, cobalt, and nickel are 1043°K, 1388°K, and 631°K, respectively. The spontaneous magnetization of ferromagnetic materials is confined to very small regions, or *domains*, which are normally oriented in a random manner.

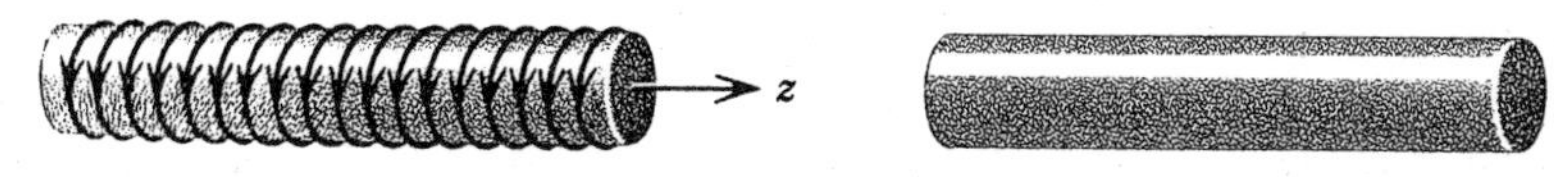

FIG. 17-9*a*. Solenoid. FIG. 17-9*b*. Core of solenoid.

Consequently, a virgin sample of iron does not usually exhibit an appreciable magnetization. This is discussed further in the next section.

In some materials a quantum-mechanical exchange force produces an antiparallel alignment of the electron spins of neighboring atoms. This is a spontaneous effect, independent of an applied field. If the neighboring dipoles having opposite directions are approximately equal in magnitude, the material is antiferromagnetic, and the relative permeability is nearly unity. On the other hand, if the neighboring dipoles with opposite directions are of unequal magnitudes, the material has a pronounced magnetic effect and a large relative permeability. Such materials are ferrimagnetic. A special group are the *ferrites*, which have large resistivities as well as large relative permeabilities. Because of their large resistivities, currents are not readily induced in ferrite cores by time-changing magnetic fields, and the eddy-current loss, discussed in Sec. 17-7, is minimized. Ferrites are used in transformer cores at frequencies up to the microwave region.

We shall now develop a relation between the *microscopic* magnetic moments of the atoms and the *macroscopic*, or observable, magnetic quantities. In Fig. 17-9*a* is shown a material surrounded by a long solenoid parallel with the z-axis and carrying a steady current. The axial field **H** within this approximate current sheet has a magnitude equal to the current per unit length. This was discussed in Example 2 of Sec. 16-8. There is partial alignment of the magnetic moments of the atoms. From the microscopic viewpoint we regard the medium as consisting of point magnetic dipoles *in free space*. With this understanding it is clear that the flux density **B** is the sum of the flux density $\mu_0\mathbf{H}$, which is produced directly by the applied field **H**, and the induced flux density $\mathbf{B}_i$, which is produced by the point dipoles. On the other hand, we know that the flux density is $\mu_0\mu_r\mathbf{H}$, this being the macroscopic viewpoint. Equating the relations gives

$$\mathbf{B} = \mu_0\mu_r\mathbf{H} = \mu_0\mathbf{H} + \mathbf{B}_i \tag{17-23}$$

The flux density induced by the magnetic dipoles becomes

$$\mathbf{B}_i = \mu_0(\mu_r - 1)\mathbf{H} \tag{17-24}$$

In Fig. 17-9*b* the winding of the solenoid is eliminated, but the magnetic dipoles of the atoms are assumed to be precisely the same as in Fig. 17-9*a*. We shall now determine the induced flux density $\mathbf{B}_i$ in terms of the magnetic moment per unit volume, or *magnetization* $\mathbf{M}$, of the medium. For a differential volume of cross section dS and length dz, the magnetic moment is $\mathbf{M}\,dS\,dz$. In Sec 16-6 a magnetic dipole was defined as the product of the current and the area of a current loop. Accordingly, let the differential dipole $dI\,dS\,\mathbf{k}$ be equivalent to the magnetic moment $\mathbf{M}\,dS\,dz$, with $\mathbf{k}$ denoting a unit vector normal to the area dS. From this equivalence we deduce that the magnetization $\mathbf{M}$ is

$$\mathbf{M} = dI/dz\,\mathbf{k} \tag{17-25}$$

Now consider a long axial section of the material, with the differential cross section dS. If each length dz is regarded as having a circulating current dI, then the magnetization equals the current dI/dz per unit length by Eq. (17-25). The flux density that would be produced by this imaginary current sheet is $\mu_0\,dI/dz\,\mathbf{k}$, which must equal the induced flux density $\mathbf{B}_i$. From this and Eq. (17-25) we obtain

$$\mathbf{B}_i = \mu_0\mathbf{M} \tag{17-26}$$

Clearly, $\mu_0\mathbf{M}$ is the magnetic field induced by a uniform distribution of magnetic dipoles in free space, with the magnetization $\mathbf{M}$ denoting the magnetic moment per unit volume.

From Eqs. (17-24) and (17-26) it is evident that

$$\mathbf{M} = (\mu_r - 1)\mathbf{H} \tag{17-27}$$

The induced flux density $\mathbf{B}_i = \mu_0\mathbf{M}$, and the total flux density is

$$\mathbf{B} = \mu_0(\mathbf{H} + \mathbf{M}) \tag{17-28}$$

The expression $\mu_r - 1$ in (17-27) is called the *magnetic susceptibility* χ_m of the material. From (17-27) we obtain

$$\mu_r = 1 + M/H = 1 + \chi_m \tag{17-29}$$

For free space the magnetization is zero, and μ_r is unity. Equation (17-29) relates the magnetization and the relative permeability. The microscopic viewpoint treats a magnetic material as consisting of innumerable differential dipoles uniformly distributed in free space; the macroscopic viewpoint ignores the individual dipoles but considers their effect on the magnetic flux density by means of the concept of relative permeability.

17-5. FERROMAGNETISM

Common ferromagnetic materials are iron, cobalt, nickel, and many alloys containing one or more of these metals. There are two additional ferromagnetic elements, gadolinium and dysprosium, but their Curie temperatures are 289°K and 105°K, respectively; hence they are of little practical interest. A virgin specimen of iron is known to be composed of many small regions, or domains, each magnetized to saturation in some direction and having dimensions of approximately 10^{-5} meter. The flux density of a domain is large, being of the order of 2 webers/m^2. Normally the domains are oriented so that the external magnetic field is zero, for this condition gives the minimum stored energy. Of course, there is energy stored in the internal field, and there is also energy associated with the domain walls and with the direction of magnetization relative to the crystal axes. The actual configuration of the domains is the one of minimum energy.

Domain walls and their behavior as a specimen is magnetized can be observed under the microscope by placing a drop of a colloidal suspension of ferromagnetic particles on a prepared surface. The particles congregate near the domain boundaries due to the strong local magnetic fields. When a magnetizing force **H** is applied, the walls move, and this motion is found to be irregular because of the tendency of the walls to cling to impurities, strains, and other imperfections present. Consequently, the magnetization increases irregularly. This is known as the *Barkhausen effect*, which can be detected by wrapping a sample being magnetized with a coil of wire connected through an amplifier to a loudspeaker. A series of audible clicks can be heard, resulting from the small abrupt changes in the flux density that produce voltage pulses in the coil. The boundaries move so that those domains that are spontaneously magnetized in the approximate direction of the applied field grow at the expense of others. As the applied field is increased, the process continues until *saturation* is reached, with the sample essentially one large domain. However, there is also some domain rotation at the higher field strengths. Both the movement of the boundaries and the rotation of the domains contribute to the net magnetization. Impurities have considerable effect, and these can be partially controlled in the production of ferromagnetic materials.

Magnetization of a ferromagnetic specimen is accompanied by a small change in its length. This effect, which is also exhibited by the ferrites, is known as *magnetostriction*. If a current is driven through a coil about a ferromagnetic rod, the rod expands and contracts as the current changes. Such a magnetostrictive transducer is often used to convert electrical signals into mechanical vibrations.

The net magnetization of a ferromagnetic specimen is a nonlinear function of the applied field **H**. The nonlinear nature is shown in the typical magnetization curve of Fig. 17-10, with the origin representing the virgin state. When the magnetizing force is gradually increased from zero by a small amount, the domain walls move, producing a net flux density. The walls that respond initially are mainly those not held by imperfections,

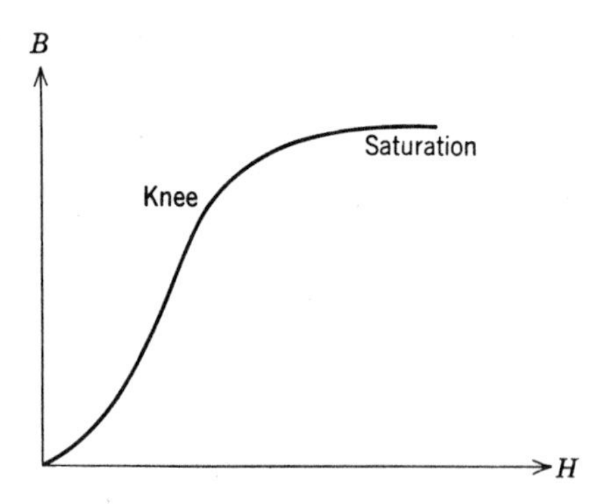

FIG. 17-10. Typical magnetization curve.

and this movement is *reversible*. There is also some reversible domain rotation. If the applied field is reduced to zero, the return path follows approximately the same magnetization curve, and there is but little energy loss. The slope of the magnetization curve at the origin is called the *initial permeability*. Transformers used to transmit small radio signals are usually made of materials with high initial permeability, such as permalloy and supermalloy. Supermalloy has an initial relative permeability of about 100,000. Obviously the magnetic nonlinearity is negligible for small radio signals.

As the magnetizing force is further increased, the flux density rises more rapidly, and the slope of the magnetization curve between the origin and the *knee* is relatively steep. In this region of *easy* magnetization, the wall movement is largely *irreversible*. The stronger applied field enables the walls to move through imperfections with irregular motion and an expenditure of energy. If the magnetizing force is reduced, the return path does not follow the same magnetization curve. Near the knee of the curve the maximum value of the ratio B/H is obtained. This is clearly equal to the slope of the straight line extending from the origin and drawn tangent to the B–H curve in the vicinity of the knee. The maximum value is, of course, the *maximum permeability*. Power transformers are usually constructed of magnetic materials with maximum relative permeabilities ranging from 5,000 to 50,000. In the region above the knee of the magnetization curve the increase in the magnetization is due mostly to domain rotation. When saturation is reached, all the atomic dipoles are aligned with $\mathbf{H}$,

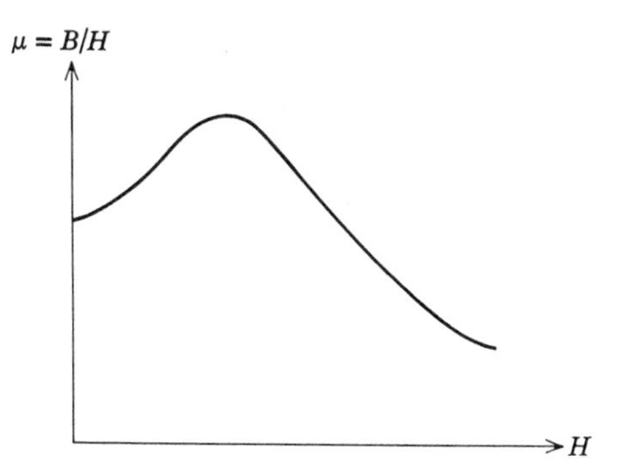

FIG. 17-11. Permeability versus magnetic field intensity for magnetization curve of Fig. 17-10.

and no further increase in the magnetization $\mathbf{M}$ is possible. Additional flux density, given by the term $\mu_0\mathbf{H}$ in Eq. (17-28), is usually negligible.

Shown in Fig. 17-11 is a typical curve of the permeability B/H versus H. Note the initial and maximum permeabilities and the declining permeability as H is increased in the saturation region.

17-6. HYSTERESIS

If the magnetic field intensity applied to a ferromagnetic specimen is increased to saturation and is then decreased, the return curve does not retrace the initial curve but lies above it as shown in Fig. 17-12. This lag in the demagnetization is a consequence of inclusions that impede the motion of domain walls, earlier referred to as irreversible boundary displacement. When the field intensity is reduced to zero, the flux density still has a positive value, called the *residual flux density*, or *remanence*, B_r. In order to bring the flux density back to zero, the magnetizing force must be reversed and given a magnitude H_c known as the *coercive force*. A sufficiently negative magnetizing force gives saturation in the opposite direction. If the field intensity is now brought to zero, a residual flux density $-B_r$ exists, and a positive coercive force H_c must be applied to reduce the flux density to zero. A further increase in the magnetizing force is required to saturate once again the material and to close the loop of Fig. 17-12. The phenomenon which has been described is known as *hysteresis*, and the closed magnetization curve of Fig. 17-12 is the *hysteresis loop*.

The loop of Fig. 17-12 is the *saturation*, or *major*, hysteresis loop; the magnetizing force carries the specimen into saturation at both ends. Smaller loops are obtained for magnetizing forces that do not saturate

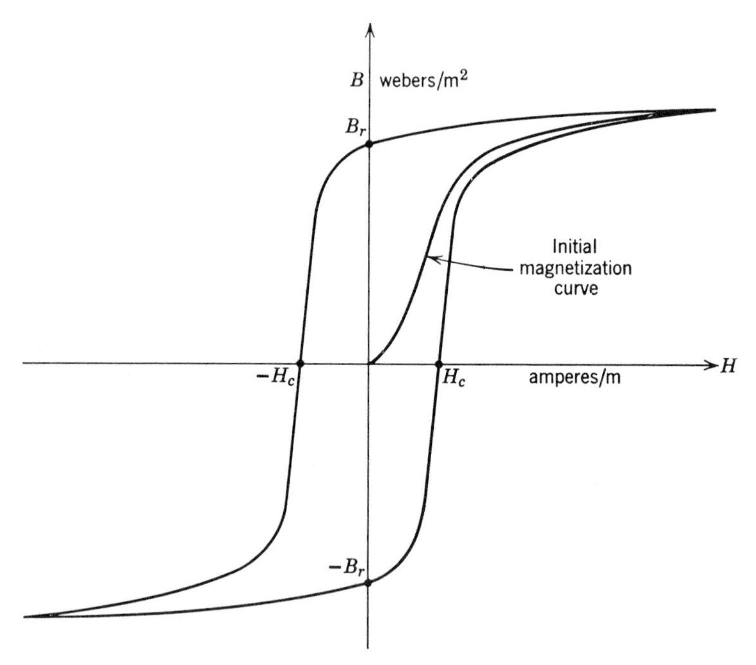

FIG. 17-12. Typical hysteresis loop.

the iron, and each of these is completely within the major loop. It is not possible to reach a point outside the saturation loop, but any point inside can be reached by means of a smaller loop. Occasionally it is necessary to demagnetize an object, such as a watch that has been brought too close to a magnet. A method of accomplishing this is to place the object inside a coil carrying an alternating current of sufficient magnitude to give the saturation loop; by gradually decreasing the amplitude of the current, the size of the loop is reduced to zero.

The permeability of a ferromagnetic specimen that has an alternating magnetizing force is rather meaningless. In the second and fourth quadrants the permeability is negative, with **B** and **H** oppositely directed.

When the field intensity is zero, the permeability is infinite, but it is zero for a flux density of zero.

The section of the saturation loop in the second quadrant is known as the *demagnetization curve*. This is of special interest with regard to permanent magnets. The magnetic circuit of a permanent magnet consists of magnetized iron and an air gap, and the flux lines around this circuit form closed loops. The line integral of **H** around the path of one of these lines is zero, for no electric current is encircled. In the air gap **H** and **B** certainly have the same direction. It follows that they are oppositely directed in the iron, and the operating point lies in the second quadrant where **H** and **B** have unlike signs. To obtain appreciable magnetization the remanence B_r should be large. Also, the coercive force should be large in order that the magnet will not easily be demagnetized. These requirements are best met by materials with hysteresis loops that enclose large areas. The maximum value of the product BH along the demagnetization curve is often used as a criterion for judging the quality of materials for permanent magnets. An excellent permanent-magnet material is *Alnico* 5, an alloy containing iron, cobalt, nickel, aluminum, and copper. It has a $BH_{\max}$ value of 36,000 joules/m³.

Energy is expended when a ferromagnetic specimen is carried through its hysteresis loop. This is caused by the irreversible domain-wall movement, with heat generated as the walls move past strains and imperfections. We shall now investigate this *hysteresis loss*. Let us recall that the energy per unit volume supplied to the magnetic field of a region is the integral of $H\,dB$. If the hysteresis loop is traversed once, the net energy supplied to a unit volume is

$$W = \oint H\,dB \text{ joules/m}^3 \tag{17-30}$$

with the circle on the integral sign signifying that the integration is over a complete loop. This is Eq. (11-12) applied to this special case, and clearly W denotes the hysteresis loss.

Shown in Fig. 17-13 is that portion of a hysteresis loop in the first quadrant. The integral of Eq. (17-30), when applied to the path from a to b, yields a positive value equal to the area enclosed by the path *abdoa*. Application to the path *bc* of the loop yields a negative value, for dB is negative for a decreasing flux density; the magnitude of this integral is the area *bdcb*. We deduce that the integral from a to b to c gives a positive value equal to the area of that part of the loop in the first quadrant. Similar results are obtained in the other quadrants and, therefore, the integral of Eq. (17-30) is the area of the loop. When an a-c magnetizing force is applied, the loop is traversed once per cycle. Consequently, *for a unit volume the hysteresis loss per cycle equals the area of the hysteresis loop.*

The energy loss per second is the product of the area of the loop and the frequency. Clearly *the hysteresis power loss is directly proportional to the frequency.* If a wire that is coiled around an iron core has an alternating current, the average power supplied to the coil and its magnetic circuit includes this loss, and the effective resistance of the coil may be much

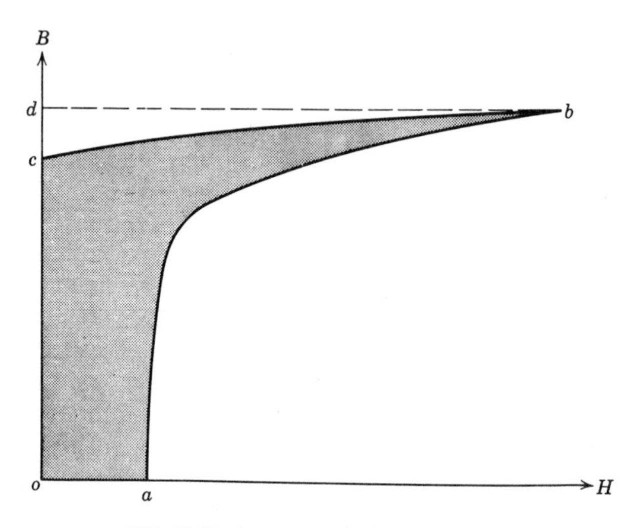

FIG. 17-13. A portion of a hysteresis loop.

greater than the resistance of the metallic wire. The core loss also includes that due to eddy currents; this is discussed in the next section. To minimize hysteresis loss, materials with loops of small area should be utilized, and such materials are used in power transformers, rotating electric machinery, and many other electromagnetic devices. These low-loss materials are relatively pure metals composed of large crystals with a minimum of impurities.

An ideal hysteresis loop is shown in Fig. 17-14. As the enclosed area is zero, there is no loss. Regardless of the magnitude of the applied magnetizing force, all the atomic dipoles are aligned, and the magnetization $\mathbf{M}$ has its saturation value. Such an ideal curve would be obtained from a single crystal of ferromagnetic material that is completely devoid of impurities. The movement of the domain walls would be perfectly free from restraint. Many practical materials have loops that are very thin and nearly rectangular, thus approaching the curve of Fig. 17-14; as these materials are easily magnetized, they are said to be *magnetically soft.*

Materials with loops of large area, such as those used in permanent magnets, are *magnetically hard*. In the next section we shall consider another phenomenon that contributes to the core loss of magnetic materials.

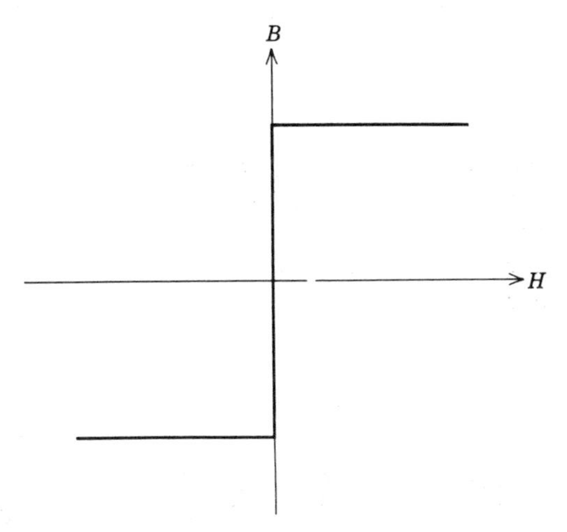

FIG. 17-14. Ideal B-H curve.

17-7. EDDY CURRENTS

A time-changing magnetic field in a conducting solid, either ferromagnetic or nonferromagnetic, produces a transformer emf around each closed path that encircles lines of magnetic flux. The motion of the specimen in a magnetic field yields a motional emf. Circulating currents induced in the conductor by these voltages are known as *eddy currents*, and the resulting heat losses, as a rule, are undesirable. Special efforts must be made to minimize the eddy-current losses of magnetic devices with transformer or motional emfs induced in ferromagnetic material. Usually the magnetic material is made of thin sheets, or *laminations*, that are placed parallel to the flux and insulated from one another. These insulated sheets break up the paths of the eddy currents, thereby reducing the currents and their associated heat losses.

Shown in Fig. 17-15 is an iron lamination having a magnetic flux density $B\mathbf{k}$, with B approximately equal to $B_m \sin \omega t$. The time-changing magnetic field induces an electric field E, and the E lines in the iron are similar to the closed loops shown on the face of the sheet. The current density and the electric field are, of course, related by the point form of Ohm's law. Consider a closed E-line whose parallel sides are each a distance y from the xz-plane. In terms of the total length l of this closed line, the enclosed area is approximately $(\frac{1}{2}l)(2y)$, or ly, and consequently the emf El equals $\dot{B}ly$. As the current density J equals σE, it follows that J equals $\sigma y \omega B_m \cos \omega t$. At any point the dissipated power per unit volume is J^2/σ, which has the time-average value $\frac{1}{2}\sigma y^2 \omega^2 B_m{}^2$. If this is integrated over the volume of the lamination, with the result divided by the volume hab, the dissipated power P per unit volume is found to be

$$P = (\sigma/6)(\pi f B_m h)^2 \text{ watts/m}^3 \tag{17-31}$$

Because of imperfect insulation between the individual laminations, the nonuniformity of the flux density, and other factors, the expression is somewhat in error.

It should be noted that the eddy-current loss is proportional to the square of the thickness h of the laminations. If the ferromagnetic material

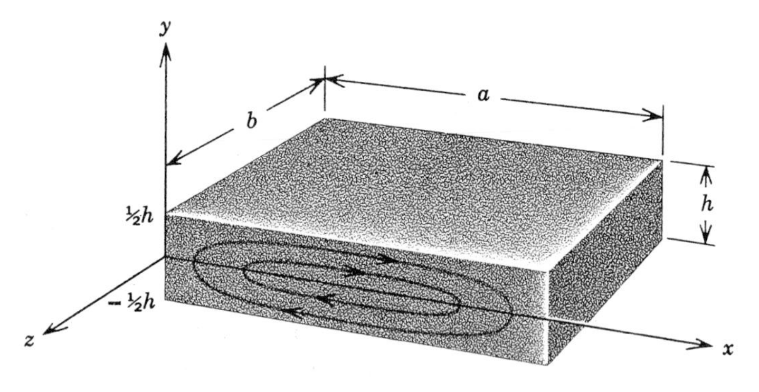

FIG. 17-15. An iron lamination.

of d-c generators, transformers, and other similar devices were not made of thin laminations, the loss would be intolerable. In addition to the use of laminated material, eddy-current loss can be reduced by employing high-resistivity materials. Good silicon steel has a resistivity several times greater than ordinary sheet steel, and this accounts for the widespread use of silicon steel in machines and transformers. As eddy-current loss in laminated iron is proportional to the square of the frequency, it is particularly objectional at high frequencies. Radio-frequency transformers often have ferromagnetic cores made of powdered iron with the minute ferromagnetic particles electrically insulated from one another. However, the magnetic ferrites are more suitable for magnetic cores at high frequencies. The ferrites have resistivities of the order of magnitude of semiconductors, and the eddy currents of ferrites are usually small.

If the closed B–H curve of a laminated ferromagnetic material is obtained with an alternating magnetizing force, the area of the loop equals the total core loss per unit volume per cycle. This core loss is, of course, the sum of the hysteresis and eddy-current losses. The hysteresis loss is proportional to the frequency, and the eddy-current loss varies as the square of the frequency. Thus the area enclosed by the B–H loop increases as the frequency is increased. If the amplitude of the flux density is maintained constant as the frequency is varied, the power dissipated in the ferromagnetic core is $C_1 f + C_2 f^2$, with these terms denoting the respective power losses due to hysteresis and eddy currents. The constants C_1 and C_2 can be determined by measurement of the power supplied to the iron at two different frequencies (see Prob. 17-32).

REFERENCES

See Bibliography.

PROBLEMS

Section 17-1

17-1. Derive the Biot-Savart law by taking the curl of the differential magnetic vector potential of a direct current element. The vector identity of Eq. (10-56) will be helpful. Note that the curl of the vector $d\mathbf{l}$ at an arbitrary point in the medium is zero, for $d\mathbf{l}$ is not a function of the space coordinates.

17-2. Shown in Fig. 17-16 is a straight section of a filamentary conductor with a steady current I. Deduce that the magnetic field H at the point P is $I(\cos\theta_1 + \cos\theta_2)/(4\pi a)$, with the field at P directed out of the paper. Use this result to find the magnetic field intensity at the center of a square conducting loop of side length 10 cm and carrying a 5-ampere current.

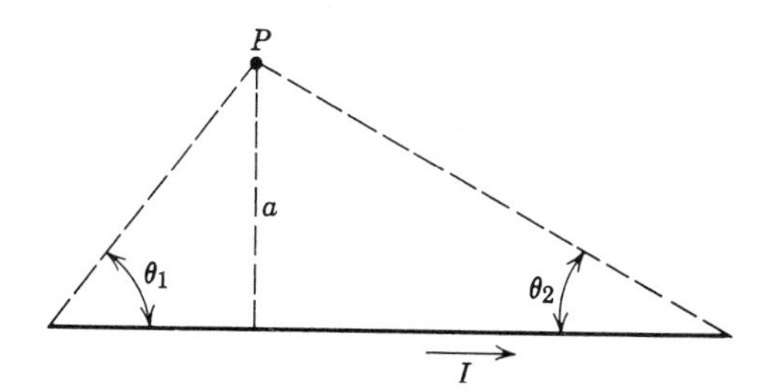

FIG. 17-16. Straight conductor with current I.

17-3. Using the result of Prob. 17-2 show that the magnetic flux density at the point P of the rectangular current loop of Fig. 17-17 is directed out of the paper with magnitude

$$B = \frac{\mu I}{4\pi}\left(\sqrt{\frac{1}{a^2}+\frac{1}{c^2}} + \sqrt{\frac{1}{b^2}+\frac{1}{c^2}} + \sqrt{\frac{1}{a^2}+\frac{1}{d^2}} + \sqrt{\frac{1}{b^2}+\frac{1}{d^2}}\right)$$

17-4. Find the magnetic flux density of the square loop of Prob. 17-2 at a point on the axis of the square 5 cm from its center. The dielectric is free space. (*Ans.:* 23.1 microwebers/m^2).

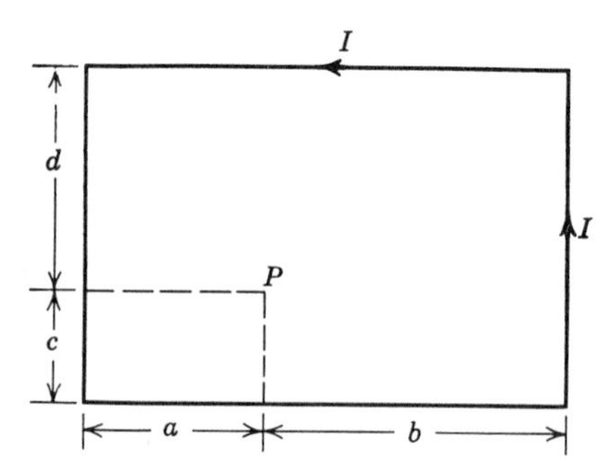

FIG. 17-17. Rectangular current loop.

17-5. A circuit has the form of a regular polygon of n sides inscribed in a circle of radius a. Show that the magnetic flux density at the center of the circle is

$$B = \frac{\mu n I}{2\pi a} \tan(\pi/n)$$

Also show that, as n is indefinitely increased, this approaches the value of B at the center of a circular current.

17-6. A circular current loop of radius a carries a steady current I. A point P is located on the axis of the loop a distance d from its center. Show that the magnetic flux density at P is directed along the axis with a magnitude of $\frac{1}{2}\mu I a^2(a^2 + d^2)^{-3/2}$.

17-7. If the point P of Fig. 17-17 is located on the bottom side of the rectangular current loop, with $c = 0$, show that the magnetic force per unit length acting on a current element at P is

$$\frac{dF}{dl} = \frac{\mu I^2}{4\pi}\left(\sqrt{\frac{1}{a^2} + \frac{1}{d^2}} + \sqrt{\frac{1}{b^2} + \frac{1}{d^2}}\right)$$

To do this, first find at the point P on the bottom side the magnetic field due to the other three sides. Refer to Prob. 17-2.

17-8. A certain 60-cycle transmission line consists of three long wires a, b, and c parallel to the z-axis of a rectangular coordinate system. The respective (x, y) coordinates of the wires are $(0, 0)$, $(0, 1)$, and $(\frac{1}{2}, \frac{1}{2}\sqrt{3})$, and their respective currents in the positive z-direction are, at a certain instant, 100, 125, and -225 amperes. At this instant find the force per unit length on conductor c, expressed in terms of the unit vectors **i**, **j**, and **k**.

Section 17-2

17-9. The magnetic circuit of the electromagnet of Fig. 17-5, including the armature, has an average length of 30 cm and a cross-sectional area of 6 cm^2. Find the magnetic flux density required to develop a pull of 100 newtons on the armature. If the relative permeability of the iron at this flux density is 3000 and if each air gap has a length of 0.1 cm, calculate the required ampere-turns of the coil. Neglect fringing.

17-10. The magnetic circuit of the electromagnet of Fig. 17-5, including the armature, has an average length of 30 cm and a cross-sectional area of 6 cm^2.

Each air gap has a length of 0.1 cm with negligible fringing. The relative permeability of the iron is 3000, and the mmf of the coil is 500 ampere-turns. Calculate the pull on the armature.

17-11. If the armature of the electromagnet of Prob. 17-10 moves upward a distance of 0.0001 cm, with the ampere-turns maintained constant, calculate (*a*) the work done on the armature by the magnetic force, (*b*) the increase in the energy stored in the magnetic field, and (*c*) the energy supplied by the electric circuit.

17-12. If the armature of the electromagnet of Prob. 17-10 moves upward a distance of 0.0001 cm, with the flux maintained constant by changing the current, calculate (*a*) the work done on the armature by the magnetic force, (*b*) the increase in the energy stored in the magnetic field, and (*c*) the energy supplied by the electric circuit.

17-13. A long cylindrical solenoid in a region of free space has a steady current I and N_1 turns per unit length. The turns are so closely spaced that the coil approximates a current sheet. From Eq. (17-11), (17-13), or (17-14), deduce that the force per unit area that tends to increase the radius of the coil is $\frac{1}{2}\mu_0 N_1^2 I^2$, provided end effects are negligible.

17-14. A long solenoid carrying a steady current I has a square cross section of side length l and N_1 turns per unit length in free space. The turns are so closely spaced that the coil approximates a current sheet. Using Eq. (17-11), (17-13), or (17-14), deduce that the outward force on one side of one turn is $\frac{1}{2}\mu_0 N_1 I^2 l$, provided end effects are negligible.

17-15. The nonferromagnetic conductors of a certain parallel-wire transmission line carry equal and opposite direct currents. The round wires have radii a and b, and the separation between their centers is D. Using Eq. (17-13), show that the repulsion force per unit length is $2 \times 10^{-7}(I^2/D)$. Note that this force is independent of the radii.

Section 17-3

17-16. The axis of a coil that is located off the end of a permanent bar magnet is aligned with the axis of the magnet. If the current of the coil produces a flux that generally reinforces the field of the magnet, deduce from Eq. (17-11) the direction of the force on the coil. What is the direction of this force if the current produces a flux that opposes the field of the magnet? Also, prove that unlike magnetic poles attract one another, whereas like poles repel.

17-17. Two series-connected coils with a current $10 \sin \omega t$ have self- and mutual inductances of $L_1 = 0.02$, $L_2 = 0.01$, and $M = 0.004 \cos \theta$, with θ denoting the angle between the axes of the coils. Find the time-average torque that tends to increase θ, as a function of θ.

17-18. Two coaxial circular coils, each of radius a, are separated a distance d that is large compared with a. For loop currents I_1 and I_2 the mutual inductance M is $-\frac{1}{2}\pi\mu a^4/(a^2 + d^2)^{3/2}$. Find the force exerted on each coil by the other.

17-19. If the inductance of a certain solenoid is given by Eq. (16-40), determine the force that tends to decrease the length l of the solenoid. The current is i.

17-20. Suppose the variable-reluctance motor of Example 1 of Sec. 17-3 has maximum and minimum reluctances, as the armature rotates, of 10^7 and 10^6. If a sinusoidal voltage impressed on the coil produces a flux φ of $0.0004 \cos 377t$, calculate the synchronous speed in revolutions per minute (rpm) and find the maximum time-average torque that can be developed. Also, determine the torque angle for a torque equal to one-half this maximum.

17-21. The *electrodynamometer*-type instrument of Fig. 17-18 has two fixed coils and a movable coil with a pointer. (*a*) If the mutual inductance between the movable coil and the fixed coils is $-C_1 \cos \theta$, show that the torque that tends to increase the angle θ of the movable coil is $C_1 I^2 \sin \theta$. Note that this torque does not depend upon the direction of the current. (*b*) If the opposing torque due to a spring is $C_1(\theta - \pi/4)$, find the current I for deflections of 45°, 60°, 90°, and 135°.

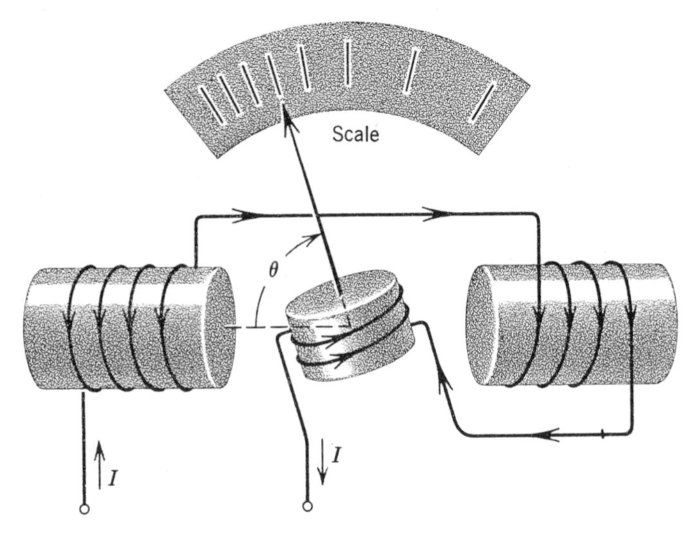

FIG. 17-18. Electrodynamometer.

17-22. In the magnetic circuit of Fig. 17-19 the reluctances of the ferromagnetic regions are negligible compared with those of the air gaps, and fringing is negligible. Using Eq. (17-20) with force and distance replacing torque and angle, show that the force of attraction between the ferromagnetic regions is

$$F = \frac{\mu_0 S}{4l^2}(I_1 N_1 + I_2 N_2)^2$$

with S denoting the cross-sectional area of the magnetic circuit and l denoting the length of each air gap. Note that the coefficient of coupling is unity and $L = N^2/\mathscr{R}$.

17-23. Calculate the force of Prob. 17-22 for $S = 25\text{ cm}^2$, $l = 0.4$ cm, $N_1 = 500$, $N_2 = 100$, $I_1 = 2$, and $I_2 = 4$. Repeat for $I_1 = -2$ with the other quantities unchanged.

17-24. In a region of free space a small current loop of magnetic moment 2**k** is located at the origin of a rectangular coordinate system, and a second small current loop of magnetic moment 1.5**j** is located at the point (0, 1, 1). Using Eqs. (16-32) and (17-22), calculate the vector torque, in rectangular form, on the second loop.

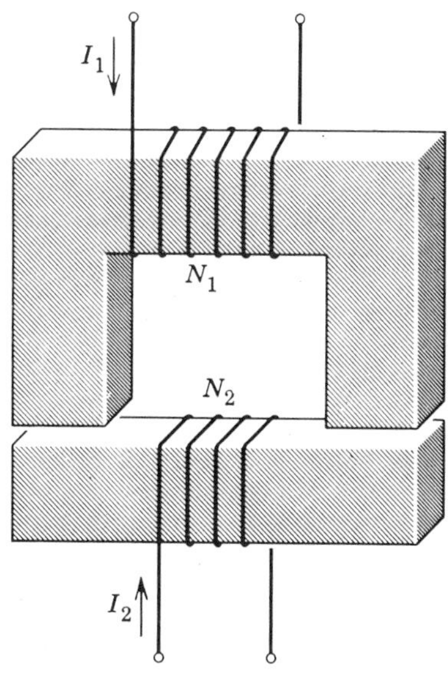

FIG. 17-19.

Section 17-4

17-25. The current I in a coil about a ferromagnetic core produces a magnetic field intensity of 400 amperes/m at a point P in the core. If the magnetic flux density at P is 0.1 weber/m^2, calculate the magnetization, the magnetic susceptibility, and the relative permeability. What is the flux density at P produced *directly* by the coil current I, and what is the flux density produced by the atomic magnetic moments?

17-26. At room temperature the magnetic susceptibility of copper is approximately -0.9×10^{-5}. For an applied magnetizing force of 10,000**i** amperes/m, find the flux density **B**, the magnetization **M**, and the relative permeability.

Sections 17-5, 17-6, and 17-7

17-27. From the magnetization curve of Fig. 16-11 (p. 364) determine the initial permeability, the maximum permeability, and the permeability when the field intensity is 800 amperes/m. Also, calculate the corresponding relative permeabilities.

17-28. A certain permanent magnet has the shape of a ring with a small air gap. The closed magnetic circuit is 30 cm long, and the length of the air gap is 1 cm. If the magnetic flux density is 1 weber/m^2, determine the field intensity in the air gap, the field intensity in the iron, and the negative relative permeability of the iron. Note that the mmf around the closed magnetic circuit is zero.

17-29. Using the law of refraction of the magnetic field, given in Prob. 9-23, deduce that practically every line of magnetic flux in air enters or leaves a high-permeability ferromagnetic material with an angle α, between the surface and the line, that nearly equals 90°. Show that $\tan \alpha = \mu_r \tan \alpha_i$, with α_i denoting the angle between the surface and the line in the iron. For $\mu_r = 7000$, calculate α for angles α_i of 30°, 2°, 0.1°.

17-30. If the expression $B = 0.9H/(1500 + H)$ describes the approximate magnetization curve of a piece of iron, find the energy per unit volume supplied to the magnetic field when the field intensity is increased from zero to 1500 amperes/m.

17-31. The hysteresis loop of a ferromagnetic sample, plotted with an abscissa of 1 inch equal to 100 amperes/m and an ordinate of 1 inch equal to 0.2 weber/m^2, has an area of 5.6 square inches. Find the power loss due to hysteresis at a frequency of 60 cps in a volume of 0.001 m^3.

17-32. The power supplied to a laminated iron-core reactor is measured at both 40 and 60 cycles with the same maximum flux density. If the power is 100 watts at 40 cycles and 162 watts at 60 cycles, determine the hysteresis loss and the eddy-current loss at 60 cycles. The copper loss is negligible.

Electrostatics

CHAPTER 18

Electrostatics is that branch of electromagnetism that deals with static electric fields, such fields being produced by stationary charges. In a region containing charged conductors it is often desirable to find the potentials of the conductors, the distribution of the electric charges of the conductors, and the field distribution in the dielectric. These results can be used to determine the difference of potential between any two points, the capacitance between any two conductors, the maximum voltage gradient in the dielectric, the force on an electron in the region, or some other quantity that may be of interest.

The main purpose of this chapter is to familiarize the student with the equations of electrostatics and their applications to some problems of considerable practical importance. For example, the potential distributions in a vacuum diode and a PN junction are determined. Certainly, one of the fundamental problems of electrostatics is the calculation of capacitance, and this is done for various systems of conductors. Also included is a discussion of the electric theory of materials, intended to prepare the student for a study of the microscopic behavior of dielectrics.

The preceding chapters have emphasized either time-changing electromagnetism or magnetostatics. However, it was occasionally quite desirable to include electrostatics in the discussion. For example, several problems involving static electric fields were presented in Sec. 9-4 to illustrate the laws of Coulomb and Gauss. The application of the electric scalar potential to static fields has been briefly considered, and the concept of capacitance has been introduced. The field of an electric dipole was determined in Sec. 16-6, along with the field of a magnetic dipole. Thus the subject of electrostatics is not new to us. In fact, the electrostatic field equations have already been given individually in various sections of the preceding chapters, in each case deduced from a general field equation by elimination of terms containing time derivatives. Let us now summarize and review these equations.

18-1. THE ELECTROSTATIC FIELD EQUATIONS

By the Maxwell-Faraday law the electrostatic field has zero curl and, therefore, the voltage drop along a fixed path C depends only on the end points of the path. As the time derivative of the magnetic vector potential is zero, the electrostatic field is the negative of the gradient of the electric scalar potential; that is,

$$\mathbf{E} = -\nabla\phi \tag{18-1}$$

Clearly, the voltage drop v from point 1 to point 2 along with any path C is

$$v = \int_C \mathbf{E} \cdot d\mathbf{l} = \phi_1 - \phi_2 \tag{18-2}$$

with ϕ_1 and ϕ_2 denoting the potentials of points 1 and 2, respectively. In statics, voltage and potential difference are exactly equivalent.

We have learned that electric fields are produced by electric charges and time-varying magnetic fields. It is evident that the electrostatic field is produced only by electric charges, with each flux line beginning on a positive charge and ending on a negative charge. Gauss's law relates the flux density $\mathbf{D}$ and the charge density ρ, and the point and integral forms are

$$\nabla \cdot \mathbf{D} = \rho \tag{18-3}$$

$$\oint_S \mathbf{D} \cdot d\mathbf{S} = \int_V \rho\, dV \tag{18-4}$$

This law is a basic equation of electrostatics.

For constant permittivity ϵ, Gauss's law can be written $\nabla \cdot \mathbf{E} = \rho/\epsilon$. As $\mathbf{E} = -\nabla\phi$, it follows that

$$\nabla^2\phi = -\rho/\epsilon \tag{18-5}$$

This is Poisson's equation, which we have encountered before. It is a special case of the wave equation for ϕ, given as Eq. (13-12), with the term $\partial^2\phi/\partial t^2$ eliminated. The integral solution of Poisson's equation is Eq. (13-35), which is

$$\phi = \frac{1}{4\pi\epsilon}\int_V \frac{\rho}{r}\, dV \tag{18-6}$$

This gives the electric scalar potential in an infinite dielectric of constant permittivity ϵ, in terms of the charge distribution. There is, of course, no retardation in statics. For a single point charge q the potential at a point P a distance r from q is

$$\phi = \frac{q}{4\pi\epsilon r} \tag{18-7}$$

The electric field $\mathbf{E}$ of a point charge q is the negative of the gradient of the potential of Eq. (18-7). Using spherical coordinates, we obtain

$$\mathbf{E} = \frac{q}{4\pi\epsilon r^2}\,\mathbf{a}_r \tag{18-8}$$

This is, of course, Coulomb's law.

When Poisson's equation is applied to a region in which the net electric charge density is everywhere zero, the equation becomes

$$\nabla^2\phi = 0 \tag{18-9}$$

This is Laplace's equation. If the potential ϕ varies with respect to one space coordinate only, the equation is an ordinary differential equation. On the other hand, if ϕ varies with respect to two or three space coordinates, a partial differential equation results, and the separation-of-variables method is frequently employed. By this method the Laplace equation can often be converted into several ordinary differential equations, one for each space coordinate. The solutions of these equations contain arbitrary constants that must be evaluated so as to satisfy the boundary conditions. Ordinarily, this is very difficult to do unless the boundaries of the problem coincide with coordinate surfaces.

In any region with static fields the electric potential function must satisfy Poisson's equation or, in the absence of charge, Laplace's equation. In addition, the function must satisfy the boundary conditions. The boundary conditions of Sec. 9-5 apply to static fields as well as to time-varying fields. Thus the tangential component of the electric field intensity is continuous across the boundary of two different physical media, and the normal component of the electric flux density is discontinuous by an amount equal to the surface charge density ρ_s coulombs/m^2. Let us consider the important case of a conducting body containing a net static charge. In Sec. 7-3 it was shown that the drift current density $\sigma\mathbf{E}$ at each point of such a conductor is essentially zero. Therefore, within the conductor the electric field is zero and, by Gauss's law, so is the electric charge density. The net charge, of course, resides on the surface. As $\mathbf{E}$ is zero within the conductor, the tangential component of the field at a point P barely outside the conductor is zero, and the normal flux density equals the surface charge density ρ_s. In terms of the unit vector **n** at P normal to the surface and directed outward, the flux density is

$$\mathbf{D} = \rho_s \mathbf{n} \tag{18-10}$$

This is the electrostatic boundary condition at the surface of a conductor.

There is always one, and only one, potential function that satisfies Poisson's equation and the boundary conditions of a problem. This is known as the *uniqueness theorem*. In a physical problem, if a potential function can be found that satisfies Poisson's equation and also the boundary conditions, we know from the uniqueness theorem that this function is the correct solution.

It should be kept in mind that the equations of this section, except for Gauss's law, are restricted to fields that are invariant with respect to time.

18-2. FIELD LINES AND EQUIPOTENTIAL SURFACES

In many electrostatic problems it is desirable to plot the field and potential distributions. Such plots not only serve as aids for visualizing the fields, but they also are tools useful in obtaining approximate solutions to problems in which mathematical solutions are impractical. Although such problems are not considered in this text, we shall examine some of the properties of the field lines and equipotential surfaces.

One of the simplest field distributions is that of a point charge q in an infinite medium of permittivity ϵ. With the origin of a spherical coordinate system located at the charge q, the electric potential ϕ at a point P is $q/(4\pi\epsilon r)$, and the electric field intensity $\mathbf{E}$ is $q/(4\pi\epsilon r^2)\, \mathbf{a}_r$. Obviously, a spherical surface of radius r is an equipotential surface. Also, the field lines of $\mathbf{E}$ are directed radially outward from q, provided q is positive. As indicated in Fig. 18-1, the field lines are normal to the equipotential surfaces. It should be noted that the equipotential lines are plotted for equal increments of potential and, therefore, the spacing between the lines increases with distance. Also, the spacing between the field lines is a measure of the field strength.

It is easily shown that the field lines are normal to the equipotential surfaces for any system of charges. The voltage drop along a differential vector path length is $\mathbf{E} \cdot d\mathbf{l}$, and this is zero if all points of the differential length lie on an equipotential surface. It follows that the electric field at a point is normal to any differential path located in the equipotential surface that passes through the point. Thus *the field lines of a static electric field are everywhere normal to the equipotential surfaces.* An exception to this might occur at a point at which the field is zero.

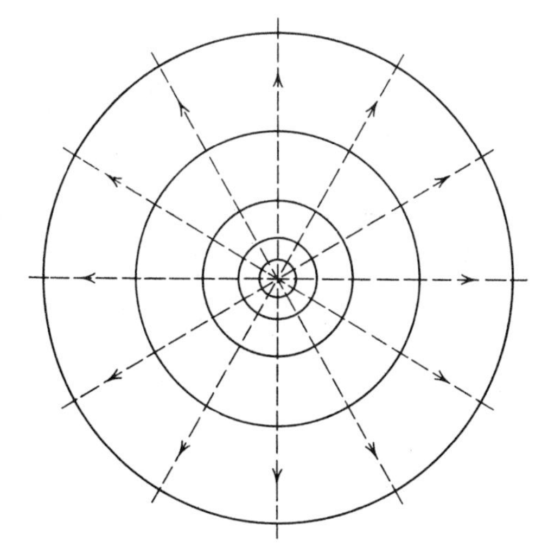

FIG. 18-1. Field and equipotential lines of a point charge, in a plane containing the charge.

Shown in Fig. 18-2 is a point P $(x, y, 0)$ at distances r_1 and r_2 from two equal point charges of magnitude q, located on the x-axis at $+d$ and $-d$. The electric potential ϕ at P is $(q/4\pi\epsilon)(1/r_1 + 1/r_2)$, with $r_1 = \sqrt{(x-d)^2 + y^2}$ and $r_2 = \sqrt{(x+d)^2 + y^2}$. The equations of the equipotential curves in the xy-plane are

$$1/r_1 + 1/r_2 = \text{constant}$$

A number of these curves are shown in Fig. 18-3 as solid lines. The electric field lines can be plotted by constructing them carefully so as to intersect the equipotential lines at right angles. Each field line begins at

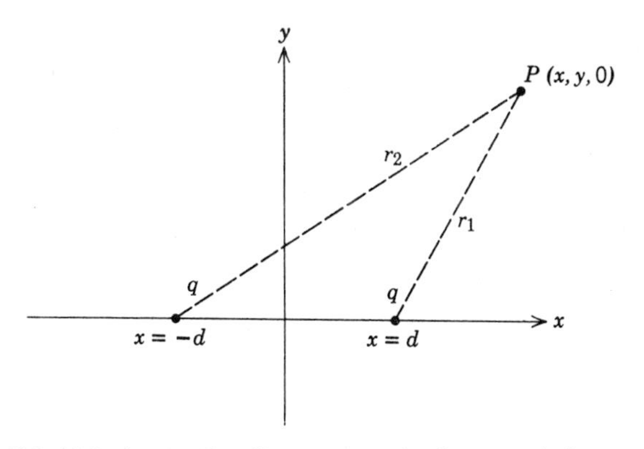

FIG. 18-2. A point P at distances r_1 and r_2 from equal charges.

one of the point charges and continues to infinity, except for the lines through the midpoint.

The mathematical expression for **E** is readily obtained from the electric scalar potential ϕ, and the resulting expression for the field in the xy-plane is

$$\mathbf{E} = \frac{q}{4\pi\epsilon}\left[\left(\frac{x-d}{r_1^{\,3}} + \frac{x+d}{r_2^{\,3}}\right)\mathbf{i} + \left(\frac{y}{r_1^{\,3}} + \frac{y}{r_2^{\,3}}\right)\mathbf{j}\right]$$

The slope dy/dx of the field lines is E_y/E_x. At $y = 0$ the slope is zero, and the x-axis is a field line. At $x = 0$ the slope is infinite, and the y-axis is

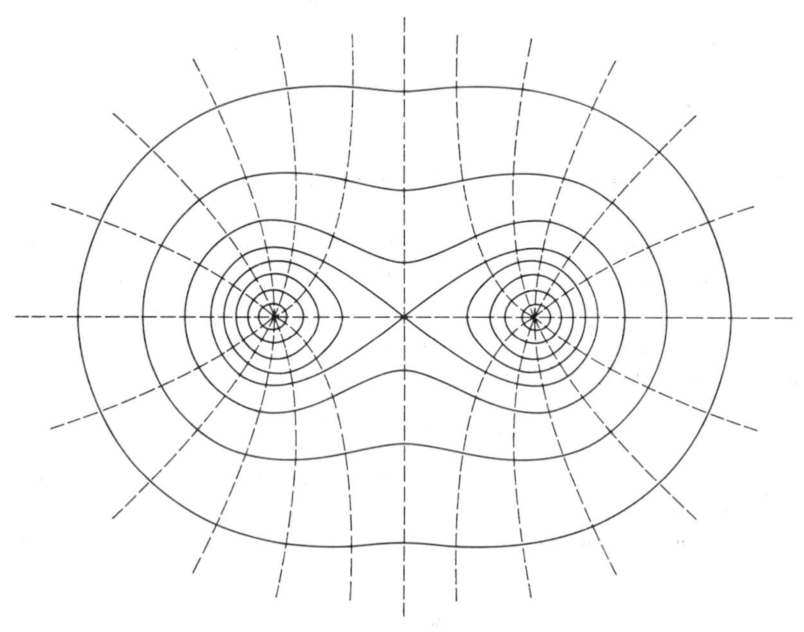

FIG. 18-3. Field and equipotential lines in a plane with two equal point charges.

also a field line. At the origin the electric field is zero. At this point an equipotential line intersects itself. If the field were not zero at the origin, the field and equipotential lines at this point would meet at right angles, and the equipotential line could not possibly cross itself.

In electrostatics, field lines meet the surface of a conductor at right angles in accordance with Eq. (18-10), and the surface of a conductor is an equipotential surface. In fact, the conductor is an equipotential body, with all points at the same potential, for the electric field is zero within the conductor. If any closed surface has all of its points within a conductor, it is clear from Gauss's law that the net charge within the volume enclosed by the surface is zero. For example, if a hollow spherical conducting shell has a charge q at a point in the dielectric inside the shell there must be an induced charge equal to $-q$ on the inner surface of the conductor. Field lines leaving the charge q terminate on the inner surface of the conductor, and these lines are, of course, normal to the surface. If the conductor is electrically neutral, a charge q is uniformly distributed over its outer surface.

It is important to keep in mind that we are considering static electric fields. When the fields vary with time, the electric field lines are not, in general, normal to the equipotential surfaces. Furthermore, the lines need not begin and end on charges, but may form closed loops.

18-3. FIELD AND POTENTIAL OF A VACUUM DIODE

A problem of considerable importance in electronics is the determination of the field and potential in the region between the plates of a vacuum tube. In this section we shall investigate the conditions inside a parallel-plate diode.

Electrons in a conductor have high thermal velocities. When an electron moves through the surface of a conductor, the surface region is left with a net positive charge, because a negative electron has left a region that was electrically neutral. Normally, the Coulomb force pulls the electron back into the conductor. If the conductor is heated to a very high temperature, some thermal energy is imparted to the free electrons, increasing their kinetic energies. Many electrons that pass through the surface may now have sufficient kinetic energy to overcome the Coulomb force and leave the conductor. Such emission of electrons is referred to as *thermionic emission*.

A parallel-plate diode consists basically of two parallel conducting plates enclosed in a near vacuum. One plate, designated the *cathode*, is heated to a high temperature which produces a copious emission of electrons from the surface. The other is called the *anode*, or *plate*, and normally is maintained at a higher potential than that of the cathode. The electrons emitted by the cathode are collected by the plate. Shown in Fig. 18-4 is a side view of the diode, with the cathode located at $x = 0$ and the plate at $x = d$.

Electrons emitted by the cathode are attracted to the positively charged plate. The charge density ρ is negative, and the convection current density $\mathbf{J}$, which equals $\rho\mathbf{v}$, is in the negative x-direction. As the electric current over each cross-sectional area is the same, $\mathbf{J}$ is independent of the space coordinates for a separation d that is considerably smaller than the transverse dimensions of the plates. The charge density ρ and the drift velocity $\mathbf{v}$ are both functions of x, but the product $\rho\mathbf{v}$ is assumed to be constant in the region between the plates.

The zero, or reference, potential can be selected as desired, because only potential difference is of interest. In this problem it is convenient to select the cathode as the reference. Thus the cathode potential is zero, and the plate potential relative to the cathode is ϕ_P. If there were no space charge in the region between the plates, the electric field would be a uniform

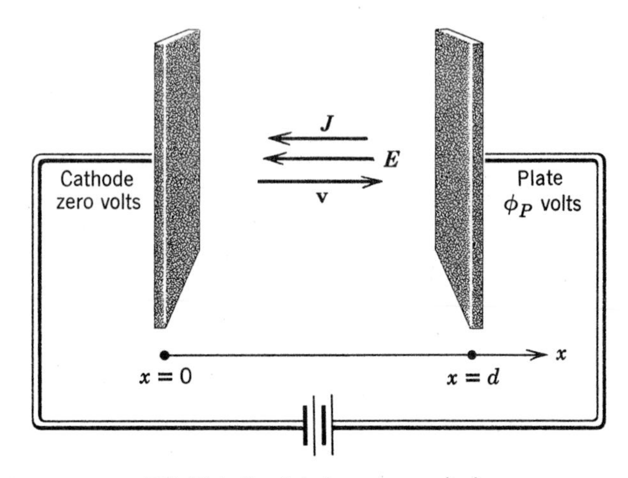

FIG. 18-4. Parallel-plate vacuum diode.

field directed from the plate to the cathode. However, the presence of the space charge of electrons affects the field considerably. Electrons "boil off" the cathode at a very rapid rate, and a dense space charge forms just off the surface, provided the plate voltage is not too large. As electrons leave this space charge and move toward the plate, additional electrons are supplied by the cathode. The negative space charge exerts a small repelling force on electrons leaving the cathode. Consequently, the field just off the cathode is very small and is in the positive x-direction. Electrons with sufficient kinetic energy can overcome this repelling force, and under equilibrium conditions the flow of electrons from the cathode to the dense space charge is exactly equal to the flow from the dense space charge to the plate.

At some point P just off the cathode the electric field goes to zero, with the direction of the field reversed beyond this point. The potential at P is a minimum, with a negative value of a small fraction of a volt, and the potential gradient is zero. As an approximation we shall assume that the potential minimum occurs *at the cathode surface*. This is equivalent to assuming that the field is zero at the surface of the cathode. Actually the electric field at this surface is very small, though not zero, and our assumption is only a fair engineering approximation.

In order to find the field and potential we shall utilize Poisson's equation. The one-dimensional form applicable to our problem is

$$d^2\phi/dx^2 = -\rho/\epsilon_0$$

Both ϕ and ρ are functions of x, and consequently, we must find some relation between them before solving Poisson's equation.

An electron moving through a potential rise ϕ acquires $e\phi$ joules of energy, with e denoting the magnitude of the electronic charge. Assuming the initial velocity of the emitted electron is negligible, we can equate $e\phi$ and the kinetic energy $\frac{1}{2}mv^2$. Therefore, in terms of ϕ the velocity v is $(2e\phi/m)^{1/2}$. The charge density ρ is $-J/v$, with J denoting the magnitude of the current density. It follows that $\rho = -J(2e\phi/m)^{-1/2}$, and the Poisson equation becomes

$$\frac{d^2\phi}{dx^2} = k\phi^{-1/2}$$

with $k = (J/\epsilon_0)\sqrt{m/2e}$.

Let us multiply both sides of the equation by $d\phi/dx$, giving

$$\frac{d\phi}{dx}\frac{d}{dx}\left(\frac{d\phi}{dx}\right) = k\phi^{-1/2}\frac{d\phi}{dx}$$

This can be expressed as

$$\frac{1}{2}\frac{d}{dx}\left(\frac{d\phi}{dx}\right)^2 = 2k\frac{d}{dx}(\phi^{1/2})$$

Integration yields

$$\frac{1}{2}\left(\frac{d\phi}{dx}\right)^2 = 2k\phi^{1/2} + C_1$$

At the cathode surface the potential and the field are zero. Therefore, both the potential ϕ and the potential gradient $d\phi/dx$ are zero at the cathode and, consequently, the constant C_1 is zero. Taking the square root of both sides of the equation and separating the variables, we find that

$$\phi^{-1/4}\,d\phi = 2k^{1/2}\,dx$$

Integrating and solving for ϕ, we obtain

$$\phi = \left(\frac{3}{2}\right)^{4/3} k^{2/3} x^{4/3}$$

The constant of integration was dropped, because ϕ is zero at $x = 0$.

We note that the potential ϕ varies as the four-thirds power of x. Differentiation of the potential shows that the field intensity varies as the cube root of x. The velocity v and the charge density ρ have been expressed in terms of the potential and can, therefore, be expressed in terms of dis-

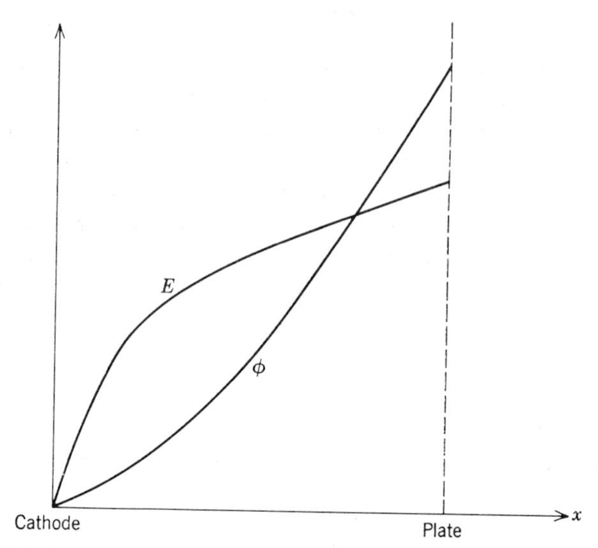

FIG. 18-5. The potential ϕ and the field E between the cathode and the plate.

tance x if this information is desired. Let us now substitute for k and solve for the current density J. The result is

$$J = \frac{4}{9}\epsilon_0(2e/m)^{1/2}\phi^{3/2}/x^2$$

At $x = d$, $\phi = \phi_P$. Making these substitutions and evaluating the constant term give

$$J = 2.34 \times 10^{-6}\, \phi_P^{3/2}/d^2 \tag{18-11}$$

This is the *space-charge equation* for a parallel-plate diode. It is often referred to as the *three-halves power law*, or the *Langmuir-Child law*.

As several simplifying approximations were employed in its development, the space-charge equation is not exact. In actual diodes the exponent of ϕ_P is usually between 1.4 and 1.6. The plate current of a diode whose plates are concentric cylinders also varies approximately as the three-halves power of the plate voltage. Clearly the diode is a nonlinear device, because its current is not proportional to its voltage.

Shown in Fig. 18-5 is the variation of potential ϕ and field intensity E with respect to distance x from the cathode. As a consequence of our approximations, the field is zero and the potential is a minimum at the cathode surface. In an actual diode the potential is very slightly negative at a point just off the cathode. Figure 18-6 shows the variation of charge density ρ and velocity v with respect to x. The product ρv is, of course, independent of x. At the cathode the charge density is infinite, this absurdity due to our assumption of zero emission velocities.

The analysis of this section is inapplicable if the plate voltage is so large that the emitted electrons are drawn away from the cathode as fast as the

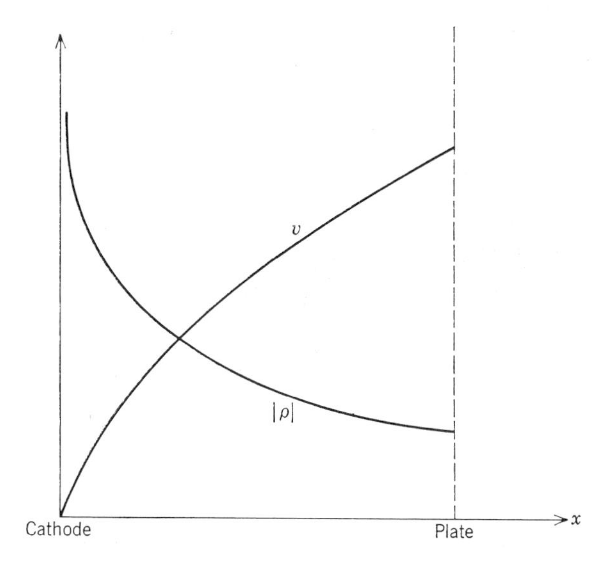

FIG. 18-6. The charge density ρ and the velocity v of the electrons between the cathode and plate.

cathode is able to emit electrons. Such large plate voltages, normally avoided, prevent the formation of the dense space charge.

18-4. FIELD AND POTENTIAL OF A PN JUNCTION

A semiconductor diode consists of a single crystal of semiconducting material, such as germanium or silicon, with impurities added to make one portion of the crystal P-type and the remaining portion N-type. The impurities of the P region are acceptor atoms, and each can readily accept one electron into the orderly crystal structure. The N region is doped with donor atoms, each of which gives up an electron that becomes a free charge carrier. The process of conduction in the P and N regions was discussed briefly in Chapters 6 and 7.

Let us consider a PN junction with the ideal geometry of Fig. 18-7. The simple geometry is chosen to make our analysis one-dimensional. We shall assume that the acceptor and donor atoms are uniformly distributed throughout the P and N regions, respectively. When the crystal is formed, some of the electrons in the N region diffuse through the junction into the P region. As a consequence, the P region has a net negative charge, and the N region is left with a net positive charge. The acceptor atoms in the P region near the junction acquire electrons and become unneutralized negative ions. The donor ions in the N region are positive ions, and those very near the junction are unneutralized because of the migration of electrons from the N to the P region. The positive and negative ions in the

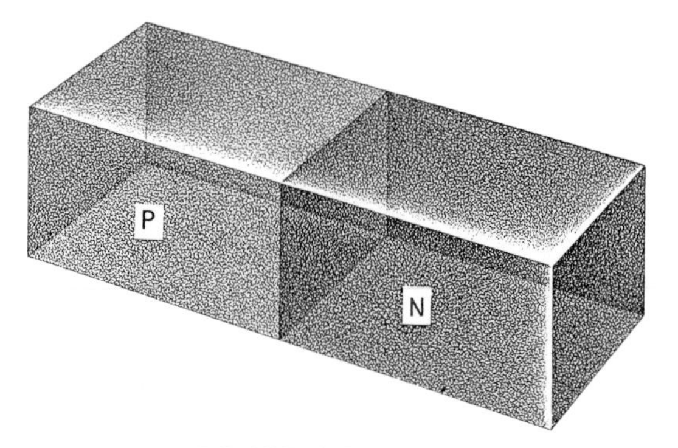

FIG. 18-7. A PN junction.

vicinity of the junction produce an electric field that opposes the movement of electrons from the N to the P region. Under equilibrium conditions there is no net flow of charge carriers across the junction.

The space occupied by the unneutralized ions near the junction is called the *depletion region*. The electric field here is fairly intense, and the region is nearly depleted of free charge carriers. The positive and negative ions are not free charge carriers, for they are bound in the crystal structure.

Let W_1 denote the width of that part of the depletion region in the P-type material, and let W_2 denote the corresponding width in the N-type material. The density of the acceptor atoms in the P region is N_a per cubic meter, and the density of the donor atoms in the N region is N_d. Each ion has one electronic charge of magnitude e. Therefore, the charge density in depletion region 1 of width W_1 is $-eN_a$, and that in depletion region 2 of width W_2 is eN_d. Outside the depletion region there is electrical neutrality. Shown in Fig. 18-8 is this charge distribution, with the junction located at $x = 0$. Because N_a is greater than N_d, clearly the P region is more heavily doped than the N region.

The field and potential distributions can be determined readily by applying Poisson's equation. As the potential ϕ varies with respect to x only, the Laplacian of ϕ is $d^2\phi/dx^2$. In region 1 of width W_1 the charge density is $-eN_a$. Therefore

$$d^2\phi_1/dx^2 = eN_a/\epsilon$$

with ϕ_1 denoting the potential in this region. Integration gives

$$d\phi_1/dx = (eN_a/\epsilon)x + C_1$$

To evaluate C_1 we note that there is no electric field outside the depletion

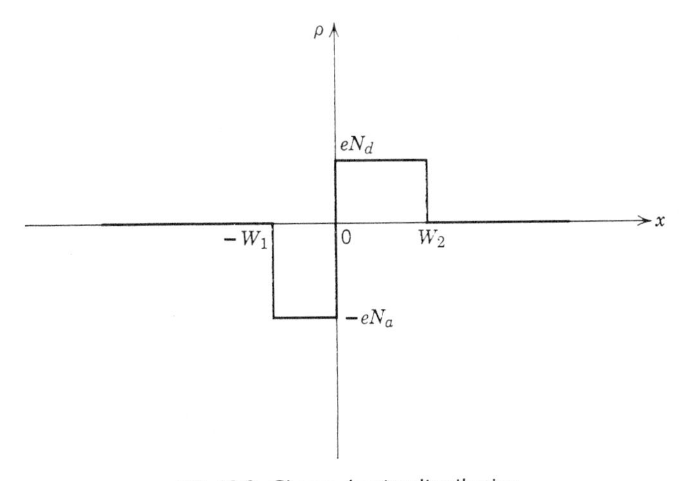

FIG. 18-8. Charge-density distribution.

region, for the current is zero. Consequently, $d\phi_1/dx$ is zero at $x = -W_1$. From this boundary condition we find C_1 to be eN_aW_1/ϵ, and

$$d\phi_1/dx = (eN_a/\epsilon)(x + W_1)$$

Integrating again gives

$$\phi_1 = (eN_a/\epsilon)(\tfrac{1}{2}x^2 + W_1x) + C_2$$

We can select the reference potential arbitrarily. Let the potential be zero at $x = -W_1$. Then C_2 can be evaluated, yielding

$$\phi_1 = (eN_a/\epsilon)(\tfrac{1}{2}x^2 + W_1x + \tfrac{1}{2}W_1^2) \qquad (18\text{-}12)$$

To find the potential ϕ_2 in region 2 we follow the same procedure. The integration constants are evaluated by utilizing the boundary conditions $E = 0$ at $x = W_2$ and $\phi_2 = \phi_1$ at $x = 0$. The result is

$$\phi_2 = (eN_d/\epsilon)(-\tfrac{1}{2}x^2 + W_2x + \tfrac{1}{2}W_1^2\,N_a/N_d) \qquad (18\text{-}13)$$

The potential rise across the depletion region is ϕ_2 evaluated at $x = W_2$, because ϕ is zero at $x = -W_1$. Therefore, the junction voltage v is

$$v = (\tfrac{1}{2}e/\epsilon)(N_a W_1^2 + N_d W_2^2) \tag{18-14}$$

The potential and field distributions are shown in Fig. 18-9. The electric field intensity in each region is easily found from the potential function.

The charges in regions 1 and 2 are $-eN_a W_1 S$ and $eN_d W_2 S$, respectively, with S representing the cross-sectional area. As charge is conserved, these

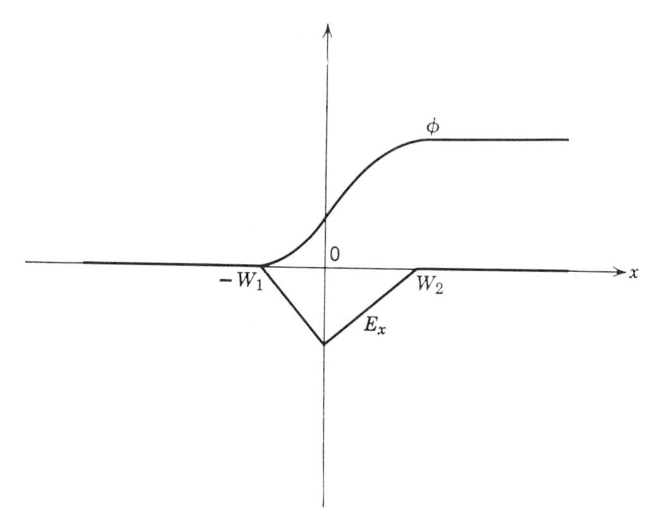

FIG. 18-9. Potential and field distributions of an abrupt PN junction.

charges have equal magnitudes, and $N_a W_1 = N_d W_2$. From this and Eq. (18-14), we find W_1 to be

$$W_1 = \left[\frac{2\epsilon v}{eN_a(1 + N_a/N_d)}\right]^{1/2} \tag{18-15}$$

Of course, $W_2 = (N_a/N_d)W_1$, and the total width W of the depletion region is the sum of W_1 and W_2.

The voltage v of the preceding equations is the *built-in* junction voltage. This voltage creates a barrier that opposes the flow of the majority charge carriers across the junction. If an external voltage is applied to the PN junction with a polarity such that the junction voltage is increased in magnitude, the barrier that opposes the flow of the majority charge carriers is increased, and the electric current is negligible. On the other hand, if the external voltage has a polarity that decreases the magnitude of the junction voltage, the barrier is decreased, and the charge carriers readily diffuse across the junction, producing an appreciable electric current. The field in the region of the diode outside the depletion zone is no longer zero. However, this field is very small, and the boundary conditions employed in evaluation of the integration constants are not substantially changed. Consequently, the preceding equations apply, provided the voltage v is understood to represent the total junction voltage which equals the sum of the built-in and applied voltages. The built-in voltage of a PN junction is normally several tenths of a volt.

Examination of the expressions for W_1 and W_2 shows that the width of the depletion region is proportional to the square root of the junction voltage. Also, if the P region is doped with an impurity concentration that is much greater than the impurity concentration of the N region, so that $N_a \gg N_d$, then the depletion zone is almost completely confined to the N region. The width in the region of lower impurity concentration is greater than that in the other region.

When an external voltage is applied, the charges stored at the junction change. If the applied voltage has a polarity that increases the total junction voltage, the stored charge is increased. The increased charges are supplied by the source, and the junction has the effect of a nonlinear capacitor. Of particular interest is the incremental capacitance dq/dv, with dq representing the differential increase in the charge due to the increase dv in the voltage. Clearly, $dq = eN_aS\,dW_1$. The differential increase in W_1 due to dv is found from Eq. (18-15) to be

$$dW_1 = \left[\frac{\epsilon}{2eN_a(1 + N_a/N_d)}\right]^{1/2} v^{-1/2}\,dv$$

It follows that the incremental junction capacitance dq/dv is

$$C = \left[\frac{\frac{1}{2}\epsilon e N_a N_d}{N_a + N_d}\right]^{1/2} v^{-1/2} S \tag{18-16}$$

The incremental junction capacitance is proportional to the cross-sectional area of the junction and inversely proportional to the square root of the voltage v. If the applied voltage opposes the flow of majority charge carriers and if this voltage is at least several volts, the built-in voltage can be neglected.

In actual PN diodes the idealized geometry which we assumed is never achieved, and consequently, the equations which we have developed are only approximations. In some types of PN junctions the impurity density through the depletion region is graded so that the ion charge density varies linearly with distance from the junction. The analysis of such a graded junction is performed in a similar manner (see Prob. 18-17).

18-5. CAPACITANCE

The calculation of capacitance is certainly one of the major problems of electrostatics. We shall consider in this section a few capacitors of simple geometry, primarily for the purpose of illustrating some useful methods for determining capacitance. In the next section several capacitors of more complicated geometry are treated, using an altogether different procedure. Let us begin with the parallel-plate capacitor.

Shown in Fig. 18-10 is a parallel-plate capacitor charged with equal and opposite charges by means of an impressed d-c voltage V. The

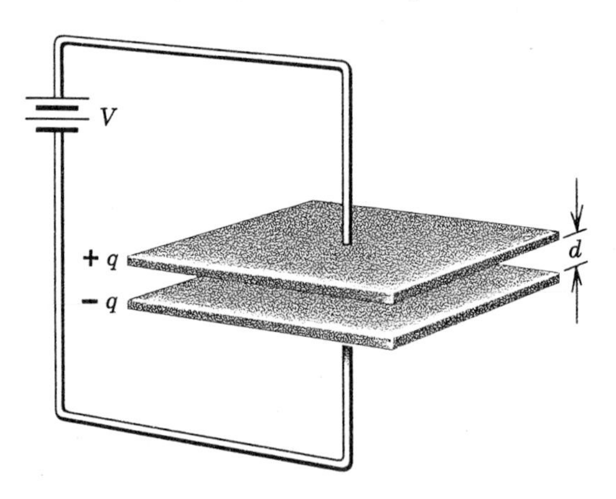

FIG. 18-10. Parallel-plate capacitor.

charge-voltage ratio q/V is the capacitance C. Assuming the plates are very closely spaced, the field lines in the dielectric between them are straight lines, and fringing at the edges is negligible. It is obvious that the electric field intensity E between the plates equals V/d, with d denoting the separation. Therefore, the electric flux density $D = \epsilon V/d$, and this is a constant independent of the space coordinates. As the magnitude of the surface charge density of each plate equals D, it is evident that the charges on the surfaces facing one another are uniformly distributed over the area S, provided fringing is negligible. Thus $q = \rho_s S = \epsilon VS/d$, and the ratio q/V is $\epsilon S/d$. This is the capacitance in farads of two parallel plates spaced a distance that is very small compared with the dimensions of the plates. Clearly, this can be written

$$C = 8.854\epsilon_r S/d \quad \mu\mu\text{f} \tag{18-17}$$

To obtain a large capacitance the dielectric constant and the area of the plates should be large, and the spacing d should be very small.

With reference to Fig. 18-10, suppose the top half of the space between the plates has a dielectric of permittivity ϵ_1 and the bottom half has a dielectric of permittivity ϵ_2. The flux density $D = q/S$, and the field intensities in the two regions are $q/(\epsilon_1 S)$ and $q/(\epsilon_2 S)$. The voltage V between the plates is found by multiplying each of these fields by $\frac{1}{2}d$ and adding the results. The charge-voltage ratio, or capacitance, is found to be

$$C = \frac{2\epsilon_1\epsilon_2 S}{(\epsilon_1 + \epsilon_2)\, d} \tag{18-18}$$

Next, let us consider a capacitor consisting of two concentric spherical conducting shells separated by a dielectric of permittivity ϵ. The outer

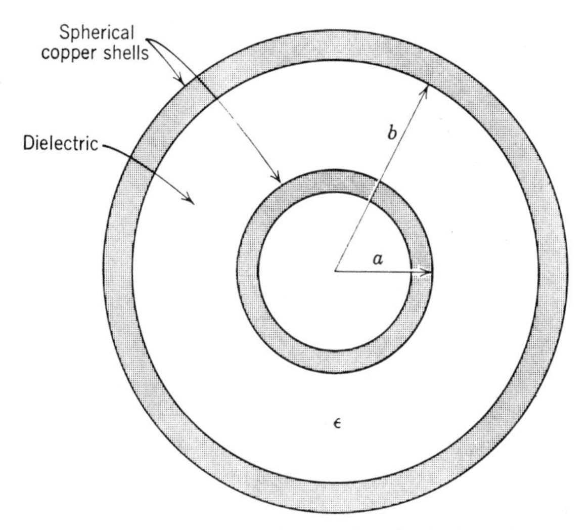

FIG. 18-11. Cross-sectional view of a spherical capacitor.

radius of the inner conductor is a and the inner radius of the outer conductor is b, as shown in Fig. 18-11.

Imagine a charge q on the outer conductor and a charge $-q$ on the inner conductor. As the unlike charges attract one another, they reside on the surfaces of the conductors adjacent to the dielectric shell. From symmetry we know that each charge is uniformly distributed over its respective surface, and the field lines in the dielectric shell are radially inward. Let us apply Gauss's law to a closed spherical surface between the two conductors and concentric with them. With r denoting the radius of this Gaussian surface, the net outward flux is $4\pi r^2 D_r$ coulombs, and this equals the total charge $-q$ enclosed. Therefore, $D_r = -q/(4\pi r^2)$, and $E_r = -q/(4\pi\epsilon r^2)$. The voltage rise V from the inner conductor to the outer conductor is the negative of the line integral of **E** from $r = a$ to $r = b$. From the resulting voltage the charge-voltage ratio, or capacitance, is found to be

$$C = 4\pi\epsilon ab/(b - a) \tag{18-19}$$

This same result can be found by solving Laplace's equation. As the potential ϕ in the dielectric shell is a function of r only, the Laplace equation becomes

$$\frac{d}{dr}\left(r^2 \frac{d\phi}{dr}\right) = 0$$

Two integrations yield $\phi = C_1/r + C_2$. If the inner conductor is taken as the reference potential, then $\phi = 0$ at $r = a$, and $\phi = V$ at $r = b$. These conditions enable us to evaluate the constants, and we obtain

$$\phi = \frac{Vb}{b - a}\left(1 - \frac{a}{r}\right)$$

As $\mathbf{E} = -\nabla\phi$, the electric field intensity is

$$\mathbf{E} = \frac{Vab}{(b - a)r^2}\,\mathbf{a}_r$$

The electric flux density $\mathbf{D} = \epsilon\mathbf{E}$. At the surface of the outer conductor the magnitude of **D** is $\epsilon Va/(b^2 - ab)$, and this equals the surface charge density $q/(4\pi b^2)$. Equation (18-19) follows.

Suppose the radius b of the outer conductor of the spherical conductor is infinite. For a dielectric of free space the capacitance becomes

$$C = 4\pi\epsilon_0 a \tag{18-20}$$

This is the capacitance of a spherical conductor of radius a. The capacitance of a single conductor, such as this ball, is simply the ratio of its charge to its absolute potential.

Finally, let us determine from Laplace's equation the capacitance per unit length of a coaxial transmission line. Shown in Fig. 18-12 is a section of the line. Let the inner conductor of radius a have a charge $-q$ per unit length, and let the outer conductor of inner radius b have a charge q per unit length. The electric scalar potential ϕ in the dielectric is a function only of the cylindrical coordinate r and, therefore, the Laplace equation becomes

$$\frac{d}{dr}\left(r \frac{d\phi}{dr}\right) = 0$$

It is clear that $r\,d\phi/dr = C_1$, or $d\phi/dr = C_1/r$. Integrating gives $\phi = C_1 \ln r + C_2$. At $r = a$, the potential $\phi = 0$, and at $r = b$, $\phi = V$. Evaluation of the constants gives

$$\phi = V \frac{\ln r/a}{\ln b/a}$$

The electric field $\mathbf{E} = -\nabla\phi$, and $\mathbf{D} = \epsilon\mathbf{E}$. The magnitude of the flux density is found to be $\epsilon V/(r \ln b/a)$. As this must equal the surface

FIG. 18-12. Section of a coaxial transmission line.

charge density $q/(2\pi b)$ at $r = b$, we deduce that the ratio of the charge q per unit length to the voltage V is

$$C = 2\pi\epsilon/\ln(b/a) \quad \text{farad/m} \tag{18-21}$$

This result can also be obtained rather easily from the integral form of Gauss's law (see Prob. 9-13). The capacitance per unit length of a parallel-wire transmission line is investigated in the following section.

18-6. CAPACITANCE BETWEEN TWO PARALLEL CYLINDERS

We shall now find the capacitance of two infinite cylinders of radii a and b, whose centers are separated a distance D. The cylinders may be external to each other as shown in Fig. 18-13a, or one may be inside the other as shown in Fig. 18-13*b*. First, we must find the potential distribution in the region around two infinite lines having equal and opposite charges per unit length. The geometry of the problem is illustrated in Fig. 18-14. The lines are normal to the paper, separated a distance $2d$, and their per-unit-length charges are $+q$ and $-q$ coulombs per meter. The point P is located a distance r_1 from line 1 and a distance r_2 from line 2.

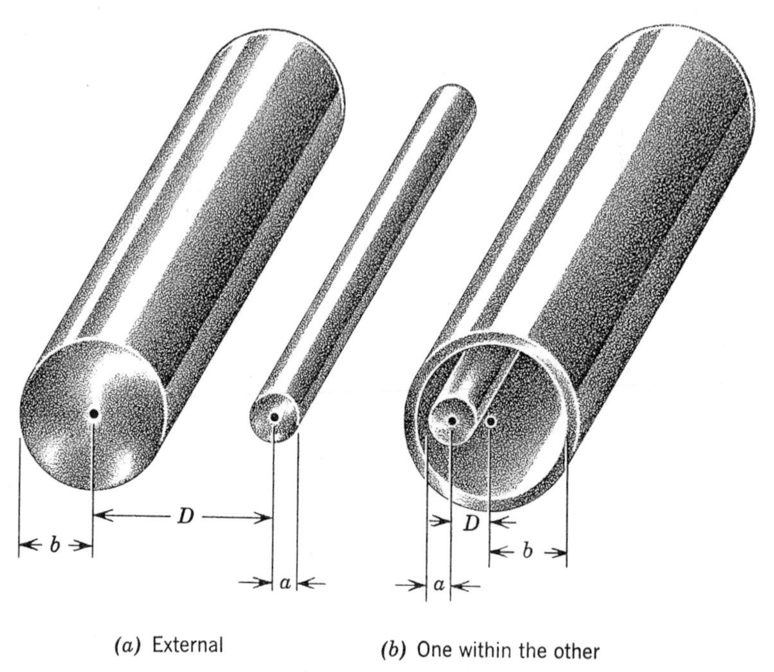

(*a*) External (*b*) One within the other

FIG. 18-13. Parallel infinite cylinders.

Let us imagine a cylindrical Gaussian surface concentric with line 1, having radius r and unit length. Neglecting line 2 for the present, we note that the flux lines from line 1 are radially outward. The flux out of the Gaussian cylinder of unit length is $2\pi r D_r$, and this equals the enclosed charge q. It follows that the electric field E_r is $q/(2\pi\epsilon r)$. This field equals $-d\phi'/dr$, with ϕ' denoting the potential due to the charges of line 1. By integration we find the potential ϕ' at P to be $(q/2\pi\epsilon) \ln d/r_1$, with the zero reference potential selected as the point midway between the lines. Similarly, the potential ϕ'' at P, due to line 2, is found to be $(q/2\pi\epsilon) \ln r_2/d$, and the total potential ϕ at P is the sum of ϕ' and ϕ'', or

$$\phi = \frac{q}{2\pi\epsilon} \ln \frac{r_2}{r_1} \tag{18-22}$$

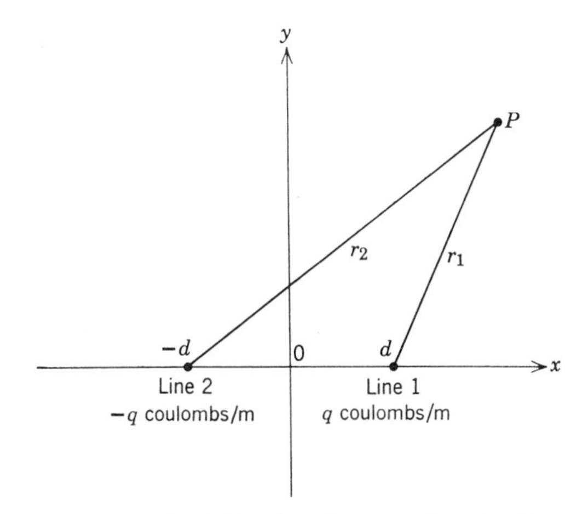

FIG. 18-14. Two line charges and a point P.

The equipotential and field lines in a plane normal to the line charges are circular as shown in Fig. 18-15. To verify that the equipotential lines are circular, we note from Eq. (18-22) that ϕ is constant if r_2/r_1 is constant.

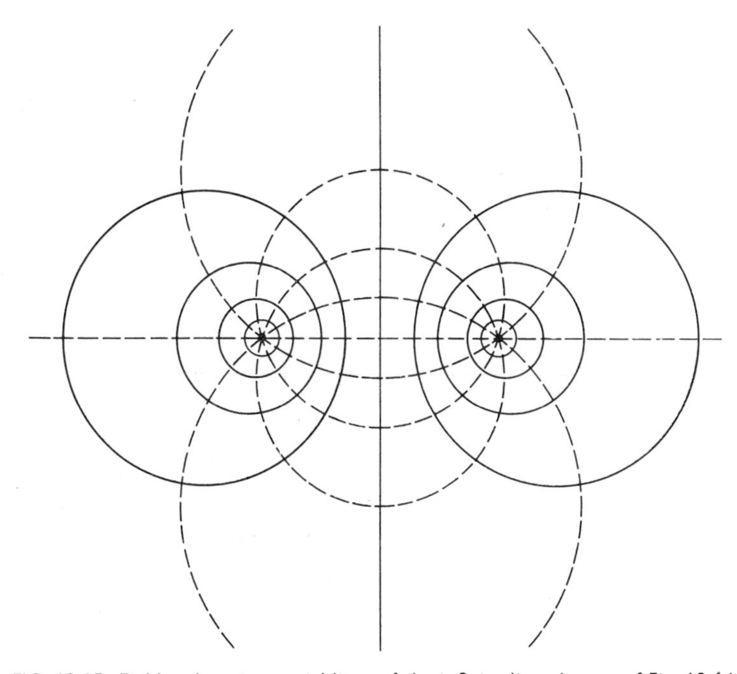

FIG. 18-15. Field and equipotential lines of the infinite line charges of Fig. 18-14.

Thus the equation of the family of equipotential lines is

$$k = \frac{r_2}{r_1} = \left[\frac{(x + d)^2 + y^2}{(x - d)^2 + y^2}\right]^{1/2} \tag{18-23}$$

with k constant. By squaring and separating terms we obtain

$$x^2 - 2d\left(\frac{k^2 + 1}{k^2 - 1}\right) x + y^2 = -d^2$$

Completing the square in x by adding $d^2(k^2 + 1)^2/(k^2 - 1)^2$ to both sides gives

$$\left[x - \left(\frac{k^2 + 1}{k^2 - 1}\right) d\right]^2 + y^2 = \left(\frac{2dk}{k^2 - 1}\right)^2 \tag{18-24}$$

For constant k this is the equation of a circle whose center is on the x-axis at

$$x = \frac{k^2 + 1}{k^2 - 1}\, d \tag{18-25}$$

and with radius r equal to

$$r = \pm\, \frac{2dk}{k^2 - 1} \tag{18-26}$$

Each equipotential line has a corresponding k. If r_2 is greater than r_1, k is greater than unity, the center of the circle is on the positive x-axis, and the positive sign in Eq. (18-26) applies. On the other hand, if r_2 is less than r_1, k is less than unity, the center of the circle is on the negative x-axis, and the negative sign in Eq. (18-26) applies. Proof that the field lines are also circular is suggested as an exercise; this can be done by expressing the circular field lines of Fig. 18-15 in mathematical form in terms of two arbitrary constants, and then verifying that the expression can be made to satisfy the result of Prob. 18-25.

The results can be utilized to obtain the capacitance per unit length of two circular cylinders of infinite length. The cylinders have charges q and $-q$ coulombs per meter, and are located so that *their charged surfaces coincide with two equipotential surfaces of the line charges.* The field and potential distributions *in the dielectric between the conductors* are the same as those of the line charges. The boundary conditions at the surfaces of the cylinders are, of course, satisfied, and the potential satisfies Laplace's equation. The capacitance per unit length is the ratio of the charge q per unit length to the potential difference.

Let the cylinder of radius a, with charge q coulombs per meter and potential ϕ_1 corresponding to k_1, be centered at x_1 on the positive x-axis. As k is the constant ratio r_2/r_1 for all points on an equipotential line, it follows from Eq. (18-22) that $k_1 = \exp(2\pi\epsilon\phi_1/q)$. Also, $x_1 = d(k_1^2 + 1)/(k_1^2 - 1)$, and $a = 2dk_1/(k_1^2 - 1)$, from Eqs. (18-25) and (18-26). The cylinder of radius b, with charge $-q$ coulombs per meter and potential ϕ_2 corresponding to k_2, is centered at x_2 on the x-axis. If the cylinders are external as shown in Fig. 18-13*a*, x_2 is negative, but if one cylinder is inside the other as shown in Fig. 18-13*b*, x_2 is positive. Clearly, $k_2 = \exp(2\pi\epsilon\phi_2/q)$, $x_2 = d(k_2^2 + 1)/(k_2^2 - 1)$, and $b = \pm 2dk_2/(k_2^2 - 1)$, with the *negative* sign taken for external cylinders. The distance D between the centers of the cylinders is the difference between x_1 and x_2. Using the preceding relations it is easily shown by direct substitution that

$$\frac{k_1}{k_2} + \frac{k_2}{k_1} = \pm \frac{D^2 - a^2 - b^2}{ab} \tag{18-27}$$

with the *positive* sign taken for cylinders that are external to one another.

Substitution of the exponential expressions for k_1 and k_2 into (18-27) reveals that the left side of the equation is twice the hyperbolic cosine of $2\pi\epsilon(\phi_1 - \phi_2)/q$. As the capacitance C per unit length is $q/(\phi_1 - \phi_2)$, we obtain

$$C = \frac{2\pi\epsilon}{\cosh^{-1}\left[\pm \dfrac{D^2 - a^2 - b^2}{2ab}\right]} \tag{18-28}$$

The positive sign is taken for cylinders external to each other, and the negative sign is taken when one cylinder is inside the other. Hyperbolic functions are discussed in Secs. 19-6 and 19-7.

An important special case is the parallel-wire transmission line whose conductors have equal radii a. For $b = a$ it can be shown (Prob. 18-27) that the denominator of Eq. (18-28) equals twice the inverse hyperbolic cosine of $\frac{1}{2}D/a$. Therefore, the capacitance per unit length of a parallel-wire transmission line is

$$C = \frac{\pi\epsilon}{\cosh^{-1}(\frac{1}{2}D/a)} \tag{18-29}$$

Another important special case is that of a wire parallel to an infinite conducting plane. The infinite plane can be regarded as a cylinder whose radius approaches infinity. Shown in Fig. 18-16 is a cylinder of radius a inside the much larger cylinder of radius b. The distance D between their centers is $b - h$, with h denoting the minimum distance from the center of the smaller cylinder to the surface of the larger cylinder. Substituting $b - h$ for D in Eq. (18-28) and then letting b approach infinity, we obtain

$$C = \frac{2\pi\epsilon}{\cosh^{-1}(h/a)} \tag{18-30}$$

with h denoting the distance from the center of the wire to the conducting plane. This can be used to calculate the capacitance per unit length between a horizontal wire and earth.

The capacitance per unit length of a coaxial cable has already been found by other methods. However, the expression for this capacitance

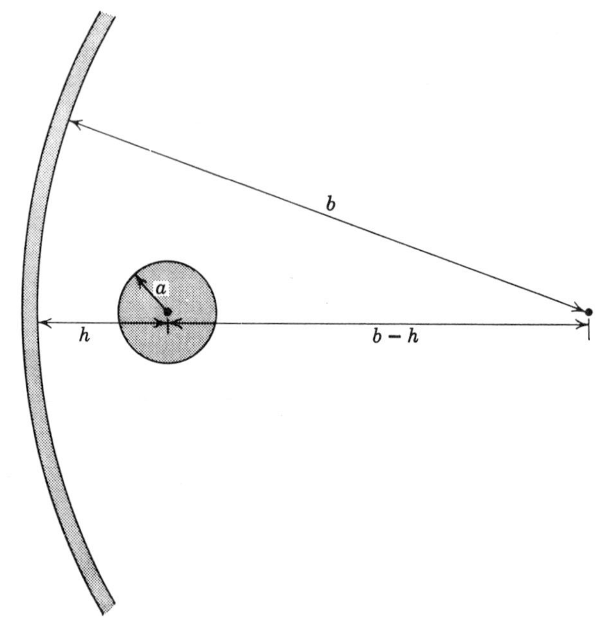

FIG. 18-16. Cross-sectional view of small cylinder within a much larger one.

can be determined from Eq. (18-28) by letting D equal zero (see Prob. 18-28).

18-7. METHOD OF IMAGES

We have learned how to use the potential function of oppositely charged parallel lines to determine the capacitance of long parallel cylinders. Let us now consider the inverse problem of finding the potential function in the dielectric between two cylinders. To do this we must deduce the proper location of the imaginary line charges with respect to the given cylinders. These charges, which give the same field in the dielectric between the cylinders as that produced by the actual charges of the cylinders, are referred to as *image charges*.

The cylinders and their image charges are shown in Fig. 18-17. The cylinder of radius a, with a positive charge q coulombs per meter, has its center at $x = x_1$, and the cylinder of radius b, with charge $-q$ coulombs/m, has its center at $x = x_2$. The image charges are located at $x = d$ and $x = -d$. We must determine d in terms of the radii a and b and the spacing D between the centers of the cylinders.

From Eq. (18-25), with x_1 substituted for x, and Eq. (18-26), with a substituted for r, it is easily shown that $x_1 = \pm(a^2 + d^2)^{1/2}$. Similarly,

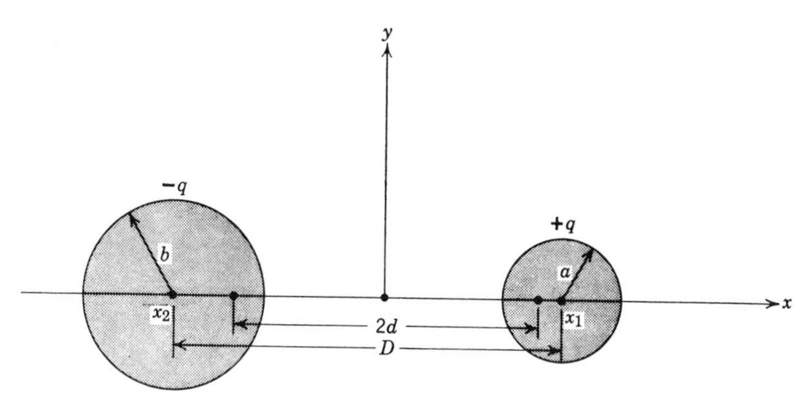

FIG. 18-17. Cross-sectional view of infinite cylinders and their image line charges.

$x_2 = \pm(b^2 + d^2)^{1/2}$. The distance D between the centers of the cylinders is the magnitude of $x_1 - x_2$. From these relations it is not difficult to show that

$$d = \frac{1}{2D}[(D^2 - a^2 - b^2)^2 - 4a^2b^2]^{1/2} \tag{18-31}$$

This equation enables us to determine, from the geometry of the cylinders, the location of the image charges. Also, of course, the coordinates x_1 and x_2 of the centers of the cylinders can be found from d and the radii. These coordinates have opposite signs for cylinders that are external to each other, as shown in Fig. 18-17, but their signs are alike if one cylinder is within the other.

The potential ϕ in the dielectric between the cylinders is given as a function of the space coordinates by Eqs. (18-22) and (18-23). From this potential function the electric field is readily found (see Prob. 18-25). The charge distribution can also be determined, for the surface charge density at a point on the surface of a cylinder equals the electric flux density at that point. Thus we are able to find the potential, field, and charge distributions by utilizing image charges that do not, of course, actually exist. It should be noted that the method can also be applied to a line charge and a parallel conducting cylinder, having equal and opposite charges per unit length, by treating the line charge as a cylinder whose radius is zero.

Next, let us consider the problem of determining the force on a point charge q located between two infinite planar conductors meeting at an angle of 90°. The charge and the conductors are shown in Fig. 18-18*a*. The net charge induced on the surfaces of the conductors in the vicinity of the corner is $-q$. Field lines leaving the point charge q terminate on the surface charges. Shown in Fig. 18-18*b* are the image charges, placed so that every point of the conducting surface is a point of zero potential. Each such point is equidistant from the charges of each of two pairs of equal-and-opposite point charges. Clearly, the charge q and the three image charges produce a field in the dielectric region of the corner that is

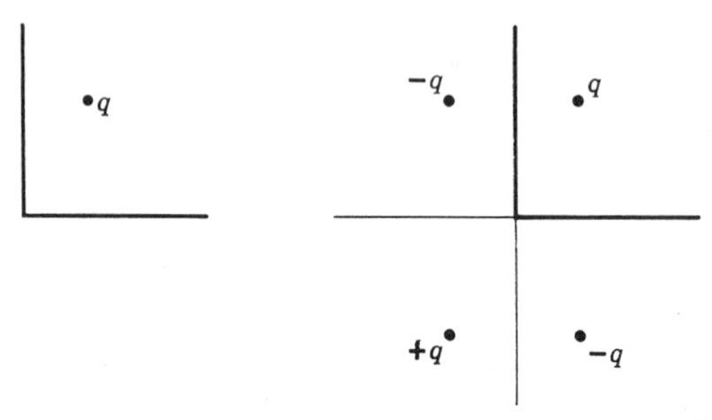

FIG. 18-18*a*. Corner and charge. FIG. 18-18*b*. The charge and its images.

identical with that produced by the point charge q and the induced surface charges. For either case, both Laplace's equation and the boundary conditions are satisfied. The force on the charge q can be readily found from Coulomb's law and the superposition principle. Also, the potential, field, and surface-charge distributions can be determined from the four point charges. This method can be applied for angles other than 90°, but the number of image charges depend on the angle. For example, a point charge in a 60° corner has five image charges. The number of image charges is finite only when the angle is a submultiple of 360°. Of special importance is the case of a point charge near a large conducting plane, which can be regarded as a 180° corner. In this case there is only a single image charge.

EXAMPLE. A charge q is located a small distance d off the surface of a large planar conductor. Find the force exerted on the charge by the induced surface charges.

Solution. The effect of the induced surface charges is identical with that of the imaginary image charge $-q$ a distance d inside the conductor. Therefore, the force pulling the charge q toward the surface is $q^2/(16\pi\epsilon d^2)$ by Coulomb's law, for the distance between the charge and its image is $2d$. This force is often referred to as an image force. It is this image force that prevents the free electrons of a conductor from escaping from the surface under ordinary conditions.

We have found that the method of images sometimes enables us to reduce a field problem to one that has been previously solved. We applied the method to parallel cylinders and to a point charge near a conducting corner. A line charge near a conducting corner can be treated just as we did the point charge, using image line charges, of course. There are many other field problems involving planes, cylinders, and spheres that can be simplified by utilizing image charges. However, we shall now proceed to a study of the method of virtual work as applied to charged conductors.

18-8. ELECTRIC FORCES ON CONDUCTORS

The static charges of conductors, residing on the surfaces of the conductors, exert forces on one another. The force on each charge is normal to the surface and directed outward because otherwise the charge would move. *Assuming linear dielectrics*, we shall now determine several useful expressions for the force per unit area.

Let us consider a differential surface area of the surface S of a conductor in a region containing an electric field $\mathbf{E}$. The charge on dS is $\rho_s\, dS$, and $\mathbf{E}$ is normal to dS with a magnitude equal to ρ_s/ϵ. Not all of this field acts on the charge, for part of the field is produced by the charge on dS and part is produced by other charges. Only those charges not on dS exert a force on the differential area.

The differential surface is, of course, a plane area, and the outward electric flux equals $\rho_s\, dS$. The flux *due only to the charge on dS* leaves both sides of this plane surface, with half the flux leaving one side and half the other. Clearly, the electric field intensity at the surface of dS, due only to the charge on dS, is $\frac{1}{2}\rho_s/\epsilon$. As the total electric field just off the surface is ρ_s/ϵ, it follows that one-half the field is produced by the charge on dS and the other half is produced by other charges. Therefore, the field that acts on the charge is $\frac{1}{2}\rho_s/\epsilon$, and the force on dS is $(\frac{1}{2}\rho_s/\epsilon)(\rho_s\, dS)$ newton. Thus the outward force per unit area is

$$\tfrac{1}{2}\rho_s^2/\epsilon = \tfrac{1}{2}D^2/\epsilon = \tfrac{1}{2}\epsilon E^2 \text{ newtons/m}^2 \tag{18-32}$$

This force is directed outward regardless of the sign of the surface charge density.

The same result can be obtained from the method of virtual work. Shown in Fig. 18-19 are two parallel conducting plates charged with equal-and-opposite charges. These unlike charges attract each other, and the plates tend to pull together. Suppose one plate is moved through the differential distance dx in the time dt. During this time interval the electrical energy supplied to the field by the source is

$$dW_{\text{elec}} = v\, dq \tag{18-33}$$

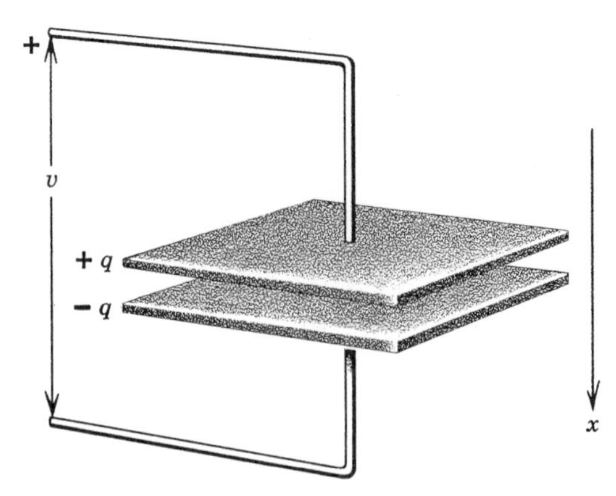

FIG. 18-19. Charged conducting plates.

with v and q denoting the voltage and charge of the capacitor. By Eq. (14-24) the energy W stored in the electric field of the capacitor is $\frac{1}{2}qv$, and the differential increase in W in the time dt is

$$dW = \tfrac{1}{2}q\,dv + \tfrac{1}{2}v\,dq \tag{18-34}$$

The mechanical work $F_x\,dx = dW_{\text{elec}} - dW$. Substitution gives

$$F_x\,dx = \tfrac{1}{2}v\,dq - \tfrac{1}{2}q\,dv \tag{18-35}$$

If the charge q is maintained constant during the motion of the plate, it is evident from Eqs. (18-34) and (18-35) that

$$F_x = -\left.\frac{\partial W}{\partial x}\right|_{q\text{ constant}} \tag{18-36}$$

On the other hand, if the voltage v is maintained constant, the force becomes

$$F_x = +\left.\frac{\partial W}{\partial x}\right|_{v\text{ constant}} \tag{18-37}$$

From Eq. (18-36) we note that the force tending to increase a coordinate of a conductor equals the space rate of decrease of the electric energy stored in the field, provided the charge q of the conductor is maintained constant. For constant charge there is no electrical energy supplied, and the mechanical work $F_x\,dx$ equals the decrease $-dW$ in the stored electric energy. On the other hand, we note from Eq. (18-37) that the force tending to increase a coordinate of the conductor equals the space rate of increase of the stored electric energy provided the voltage is kept constant. In this case there is electrical energy supplied, with half of the energy used to increase the stored energy and the other half converted into mechanical work.

Another useful form of the force equation, easily deduced from Eq. (18-35) and the relation $C = q/v$, is

$$F_x = \tfrac{1}{2}v^2 \frac{dC}{dx} \qquad (18\text{-}38)$$

Clearly, the electric force on a charged body tends to increase the capacitance, or charge-voltage ratio, of the body.

Let us now apply the method of virtual work to the capacitor of Fig. 18-19. The dimensions of the plates are very large compared with the spacing between the plates and, consequently, edge effects are negligible. Accordingly, the charge of each plate is uniformly distributed over the surface facing the other plate, and the resulting electric field between the conductors is uniform. The stored energy equals the energy density $\frac{1}{2}\epsilon E^2$ multiplied by the volume between the plates. Suppose the positive conductor is moved through a differential distance dx, decreasing the spacing by this amount. If the charge q is maintained constant, the electric field in the dielectric is also constant, for the flux density equals the surface charge density. The stored energy decreases by $(\frac{1}{2}\epsilon E^2)(S\,dx)$, with S denoting the area of a plate, and the force on the conductor is $\frac{1}{2}\epsilon E^2 S$ by Eq. (18-36). Obviously, the force per unit area is $\frac{1}{2}\epsilon E^2$ newtons/m^2, a result in agreement with Eq. (18-32).

EXAMPLE 1. A copper ball with a radius of 0.1 m is charged to a potential of 1000 volts. The dielectric is free space. Find the force that tends to expand the ball.

Solution. From symmetry the charge q of the ball is uniformly distributed over the surface, and the flux lines are radially outward. Therefore, the electric field outside the ball is the same as though the charge were located at the center. Clearly, the potential ϕ at the surface is $q/(4\pi\epsilon a)$, with a denoting the radius, and the charge $q = 4\pi\epsilon a\phi$. The surface charge density is $q/(4\pi a^2)$, or $\epsilon\phi/a$. Thus $D = \epsilon\phi/a$, and $E = \phi/a$ at the surface.

The force per unit area is $\frac{1}{2}\epsilon E^2$, or $\frac{1}{2}\epsilon\phi^2/a^2$. As $\epsilon = \epsilon_0$, $\phi = 1000$, and $a = 0.1$, the force per unit area is 0.000443, and the total force is 0.0000556 newton.

EXAMPLE 2. Two conducting balls, each of radius a, are separated a distance r that is very much greater than a. If the charge of each ball is q, employ the method of virtual work to find the force of repulsion.

Solution. As $r \gg a$, the charges are uniformly distributed over the surfaces. The field and potential at a point in the dielectric are the same that would be produced by the charges concentrated at the centers of the balls. Therefore, the potential ϕ at a point on the surface of either ball is $(q/4\pi\epsilon)(1/a + 1/r)$. The potential energy of each ball, with the potential energy at infinity taken as zero, is $\frac{1}{2}\phi q$. The total energy W is ϕq, or $(q^2/4\pi\epsilon)(1/a + 1/r)$, and $-\partial W/\partial r$ is $q^2/(4\pi\epsilon r^2)$, with q regarded as constant. As this force tends to increase the distance r, it is a force of repulsion. Of course, the result is simply Coulomb's law.

EXAMPLE 3. A parallel-plate capacitor has square plates of edge a separated a distance d that is very small compared with a. The region between the plates is initially filled with a solid dielectric slab of relative permittivity ϵ_r, but then this dielectric is withdrawn parallel to an edge through a distance x less than a. If the voltage between the plates is v, find the force on the dielectric slab. Neglect fringing.

Solution. As fringing is negligible, the field lines are straight lines normal to the plates, and the field intensity at each point of the region between the plates is v/d. Therefore, the energy density is $\frac{1}{2}\epsilon v^2/d^2$. The free-space volume between the plates is xad, and the energy of this region is $(\frac{1}{2}\epsilon_0 v^2/d^2)(xad)$. The volume between the plates filled with the dielectric slab is $ad(a - x)$, and the energy stored in this region is $(\frac{1}{2}\epsilon_r\epsilon_0 v^2/d^2)(ad)(a - x)$. Consequently, the total energy stored in the electric field is

$$W = \tfrac{1}{2}\epsilon_0 v^2(a/d)[x + \epsilon_r(a - x)]$$

By Eq. (18-37) the force that tends to increase x is $+\partial W/\partial x$, with v constant. Therefore, the force that tends to decrease x is $-\partial W/\partial x$, with v constant. Evaluation gives a force of $\frac{1}{2}\epsilon_0 v^2(a/d)(\epsilon_r - 1)$ newtons. If the dielectric were free to move, it would be pulled back into the entire volume between the plates. The force on the dielectric is the result of the electric forces on the atomic electric dipoles. It should be noted that the method of virtual work applies to dielectrics as well as to conductors.

EXAMPLE 4. Two long parallel wires, each of radius a, are charged with equal and opposite charges. In terms of the radius a, the permittivity ϵ, the distance D between the axes, and the charge q per unit length, find the force of attraction per unit length.

Solution. The force that tends to *decrease* the distance D between the axes of the cylinders is $-\frac{1}{2}v^2\, dC/dD$, by (18-38). The capacitance C per unit length is $\pi\epsilon/\cosh^{-1}(\frac{1}{2}D/a)$, by (18-29). It is easily shown that

$$\frac{dC}{dD} = -\frac{C^2}{\pi\epsilon}(D^2 - 4a^2)^{-1/2}$$

Noting that $vC = q$, the force of attraction on each conductor becomes

$$F = \frac{q^2}{2\pi\epsilon}(D^2 - 4a^2)^{-1/2} \text{ newtons/m}$$

This result can also be obtained from the method of images.

18-9. ELECTRIC THEORY OF MATERIALS

From the microscopic viewpoint a dielectric material consists of many atoms held closely together in free space. Each atom has a positive nucleus surrounded by a cloud of negative electrons, and normally the atom is electrically neutral. When an electric field is applied, a force is exerted on the charged particles of each atom. This causes the electron cloud to be slightly displaced relative to the nucleus, for the force on the negative electrons and the force on the positive nucleus are opposite.

Consequently, each atom becomes a small electric dipole, as indicated in Fig. 18-20. Recalling that the dipole moment **p** is directed along the axis of the charges from the negative to the positive charge, with magnitude equal to the product of charge and distance, we note that the dipole moment has the same direction as the applied field. In the presence of an electric field the atomic dipole moments are aligned with the applied field, and the dielectric is said to be *polarized*.

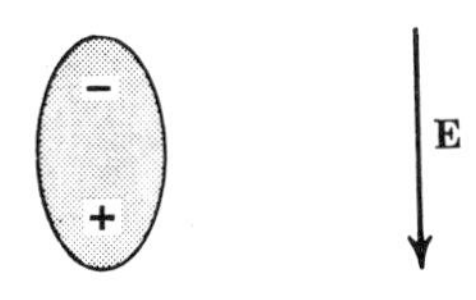

FIG. 18-20. Polarized atom.

Let us consider two parallel conducting plates located in free space and charged with equal and opposite charges. A side view of the plates is shown in Fig. 18-21. Let d represent the distance between the plates and S represent the cross-sectional area. We shall assume that the plate dimensions are large compared with the spacing d so that edge effects are negligible. If the charge on the top plate is q, the surface charge density is q/S, and the electric flux density

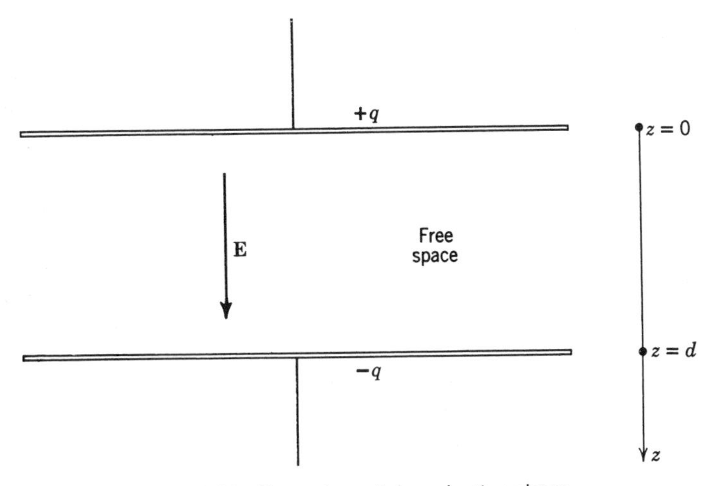

FIG. 18-21. Charged parallel conducting plates.

D is $q\mathbf{k}/S$, with **k** denoting a unit vector directed from the top to the bottom plate. The field intensity is

$$\mathbf{E} = \frac{\mathbf{D}}{\epsilon_0} = \frac{q}{\epsilon_0 S}\mathbf{k} \tag{18-39}$$

Now suppose the region between the plates is filled with a dielectric. The applied field polarizes the dielectric somewhat as shown in Fig. 18-22. Observe that the atomic charges at points inside the dielectric tend to cancel. There are, however, induced charges on the dielectric surfaces at the plates. These induced charges are bound to the atoms of the dielectric and should not be confused with the charges on the conducting plates. The induced charge at the top plate is negative, and the induced charge at the bottom plate is positive. These induced charges produce an induced field $\mathbf{E}_i$ directed opposite to the applied field. Thus the effect of the electric dipoles of the dielectric is to *reduce* the electric field.

Consider a *very small* elemental volume ΔV of length Δz and cross-sectional area ΔS. Each such volume of the dielectric is a small electric dipole. If the elemental charges of the dipole are Δq and $-\Delta q$, the dipole

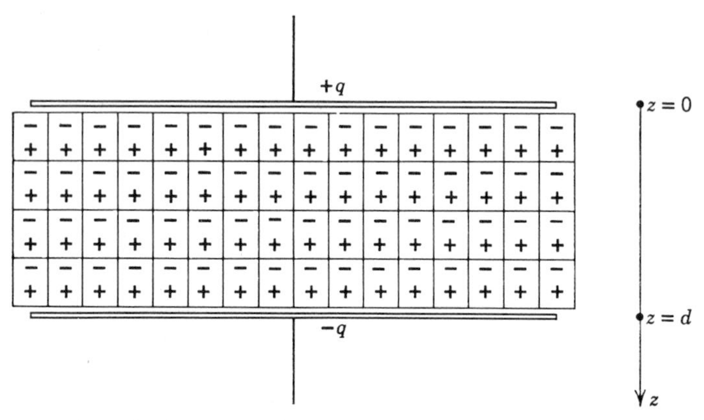

FIG. 18-22. Polarized dielectric between plates of Fig. 18-21.

moment $\Delta\mathbf{p}$ is $\Delta q\ \Delta z\ \mathbf{k}$. The dipole moment per unit volume is called the *polarization* $\mathbf{P}$. Dividing the dipole moment by the volume $\Delta S\ \Delta z$ gives $\mathbf{P} = (\Delta q/\Delta S)\mathbf{k}$. Clearly $\Delta q/\Delta S$ is the magnitude of the surface charge density of the top and bottom surfaces of the dielectric. The induced field $\mathbf{E}_i$ due to these dielectric charges is directed from the positive surface charge to the negative surface charge, this being in the direction $-\mathbf{k}$; the magnitude of $\mathbf{E}_i$ equals the surface charge density divided by ϵ_0. It is evident that $\mathbf{E}_i = -\mathbf{P}/\epsilon_0$, with the induced field and the polarization having opposite directions. The permittivity of free space is used here, for we are examining the electric behavior from the microscopic viewpoint.

The polarization $\mathbf{P}$ is the electric dipole moment per unit volume. In studying magnetic theory we learned that the magnetization $\mathbf{M}$ is the magnetic dipole moment per unit volume. For comparison, these definitions in mathematical form are

$$\mathbf{P} = \lim_{\Delta V \to 0} \frac{\Delta\mathbf{p}}{\Delta V} \qquad \mathbf{M} = \lim_{\Delta V \to 0} \frac{\Delta\mathbf{m}}{\Delta V} \tag{18-40}$$

with $\Delta\mathbf{p}$ and $\Delta\mathbf{m}$ denoting the electric and magnetic dipole moments of the volume ΔV. When an electric field is applied to a dielectric, there is an induced field due to the polarization of the material. Similarly, when a magnetic field is applied to a magnetic material, there is an induced magnetic field due to the magnetization of the medium. These induced fields have been determined to be

$$\mathbf{E}_i = -\mathbf{P}/\epsilon_0 \quad \mathbf{B}_i = \mu_0\mathbf{M} \tag{18-41}$$

The induced electric field is directed opposite to the polarization, whereas the induced magnetic field has the same direction as the magnetization, by Eq. (17-26).

The total electric field $\mathbf{E}$ in the dielectric is the vector sum of the applied field, which is produced by the charges on the conducting plates, and the field produced by the polarization. The applied field is given by Eq. (18-39), and the induced field is given by Eq. (18-41). Thus the total field $\mathbf{E}$ is

$$\mathbf{E} = \frac{1}{\epsilon_0}(\mathbf{D} - \mathbf{P}) \tag{18-42}$$

with $\mathbf{D}$ representing the electric flux density resulting from the charges on the conducting plates. In studying magnetic theory we found that the magnetic field $\mathbf{B}$ is the sum of the applied flux density $\mu_0\mathbf{H}$ and the induced flux density $\mu_0\mathbf{M}$, or

$$\mathbf{B} = \mu_0(\mathbf{H} + \mathbf{M}) \tag{18-43}$$

In Eqs. (18-42) and (18-43) the quantities $\mathbf{D}$ and $\mathbf{H}$ are due to the charges and currents, respectively, *not including those of the atoms.* The quantities $\mathbf{E}$ and $\mathbf{B}$ are the total electric and magnetic quantities, including the atomic effects.

Now let us return to the macroscopic, or observable, viewpoint. From this viewpoint we utilize the concept of relative permittivity to describe the dielectric property of a medium, and the electric field $\mathbf{E}$ is expressed by

$$\mathbf{E} = \mathbf{D}/(\epsilon_r\epsilon_0) \tag{18-44}$$

The flux density $\mathbf{D}$ is that produced by electric charges *excluding those of the atomic dipoles*, and the field $\mathbf{E}$ is the total electric field, including the induced field. This should be clearly understood.

The macroscopic quantity ϵ_r and the microscopic quantity $\mathbf{P}$ are related. Comparison of Eqs. (18-42) and (18-44) reveals that $\mathbf{D} - \mathbf{P}$ equals $\mathbf{D}/\epsilon_r$, or

$$\mathbf{P} = \frac{\epsilon_r - 1}{\epsilon_r}\mathbf{D} \tag{18-45}$$

As $\mathbf{D} = \epsilon_r\epsilon_0\mathbf{E}$, the polarization $\mathbf{P}$ in terms of $\mathbf{E}$ is

$$\mathbf{P} = \epsilon_0(\epsilon_r - 1)\mathbf{E} \tag{18-46}$$

The polarization is expressed in coulombs per square meter. The quantity $\epsilon_r - 1$ is called the *electric susceptibility* of the material. For most dielectrics ϵ_r is constant, except for very strong fields, and the polarization is directly proportional to the total field **E**. For comparison we recall that the magnetization **M** is $(\mu_r - 1)\mathbf{H}$, with $\mu_r - 1$ being the magnetic susceptibility.

In order to measure the relative permittivity, or dielectric constant, of a dielectric, we can utilize a parallel-plate capacitor having a capacitance of $\epsilon S/d$, with ϵ denoting the permittivity of the dielectric. It is evident that $\epsilon_r = C/C_0$, with C_0 denoting the capacitance with the dielectric replaced with free space or air. Thus by measuring the capacitance both with and without the dielectric, we can determine the relative permittivity.

In *isotropic* dielectrics the polarization **P** and the electric field **E** have the same orientation, and the electric flux density **D** is

$$\mathbf{D} = \epsilon_0\mathbf{E} + \mathbf{P} = \epsilon\mathbf{E} \tag{18-47}$$

However, in *anisotropic* materials the orientations of **P** and **E** do not usually coincide. For example, in single crystals the dielectric constant generally depends on the direction in which it is measured relative to the crystal axes. For such cases each rectangular component of **D** depends on the three components of **E**, and the dielectric constant becomes a "nine-component tensor". The expression $\mathbf{D} = \epsilon\mathbf{E}$ is applicable only to isotropic media, whereas the relation $\mathbf{D} = \epsilon_0\mathbf{E} + \mathbf{P}$ always applies.

Many solids have molecules with permanent electric dipole moments. Such molecules are called *polar molecules*. Normally these dipole moments are fixed in position in the solid and cannot be aligned by an applied field. In the liquid state, however, the polar molecules are free to align with the applied field, and this alignment will increase the polarization. Suppose a liquid with permanent electric dipoles is subjected to an electric field, which causes the dipole moments to align with the field, and then is frozen into a solid. The polarization becomes fixed, remaining when the applied field is reduced to zero. Such a polarized solid is called an *electret*. When suspended like a compass needle, an electret aligns itself with an electric field just as a suspended permanent magnet aligns itself with a magnetic field. Electrets can be used as substitutes for batteries in certain applications requiring a voltage but no current.

In some dielectric materials the atoms interact with one another in a manner that induces electric dipoles in the atoms. Such materials, called *ferroelectric materials*, exhibit spontaneous polarization just as ferromagnetic materials exhibit spontaneous magnetization. A specimen of a ferroelectric material consists of a number of small domains, each of which is spontaneously polarized. The direction of polarization varies from one domain to another. If an electric field is applied, the domains polarized in the direction of the field grow larger at the expense of other domains. This process is somewhat similar to that encountered in our study of ferromagnetism. The relative permittivity of ferroelectric materials is a function of the electric field, and thus ferroelectric materials are nonlinear. In addition, these materials exhibit *hysteresis* effects. Shown in Fig. 18-23 is a typical hysteresis loop of a ferroelectric specimen. The *remanent flux density* D_r and the *coercive field* E_c are indicated on the illustration.

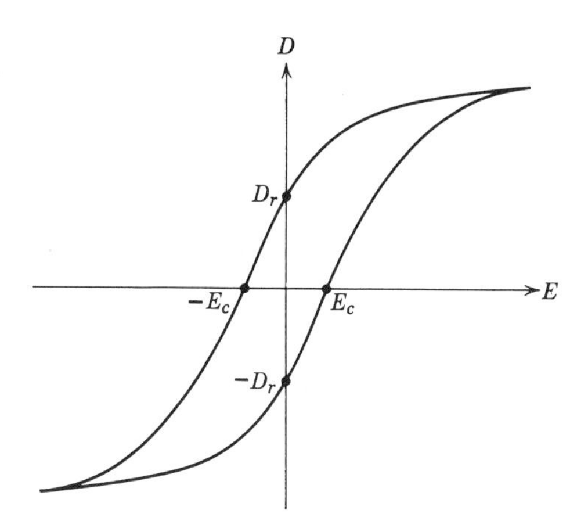

FIG. 18-23. Hysteresis loop of ferroelectric specimen.

When an electric field is applied to a solid, the separation of the atomic charges, producing atomic dipoles, causes a slight change in the physical dimensions of the solid. This electromechanical effect is known as *electrostriction* and is present to some degree in all materials. In addition, some solids become polarized when subjected to mechanical forces. Such materials are said to be *piezoelectric*. Piezoelectric solids are used to convert mechanical energy into electrical energy and also to convert electrical energy into mechanical energy.

Every dielectric has a maximum electric field that can be tolerated. If the field exceeds this maximum value, the electrons are pulled from the atoms, and a temporary discharge occurs. This maximum electric field is known as the *dielectric strength* of the material. The dielectric strength of air at normal temperature and pressure is about 30,000 volts per cm, and for mica it is about 1.5 million volts per cm. Electric fields are intense in the vicinity of sharp points of charged conductors. Therefore, in order to minimize the danger of dielectric breakdown, sharp points should be avoided in the design of electric equipment.

When an alternating field is applied to a dielectric, the polarization alternates. The electronic charges of each atom shift their position relative to the nucleus when the field reverses direction, and there is a slight motion of the bound charges. The displacement current in a dielectric material is greater than the displacement current in free space, for the same electric field intensity, because of this slight motion of the atomic charges. From Eq. (18-47) we note that the displacement current density $\dot{\mathbf{D}}$ at a point in a medium is the sum of $\epsilon_0\dot{\mathbf{E}}$ and $\dot{\mathbf{P}}$. The term $\dot{\mathbf{P}}$, which is the rate of change of the polarization, is associated with the actual motion of the bound charges of the dielectric. Thus a part of the displacement current in a dielectric consists of moving electric charges. For example, if the dielectric between the plates of a capacitor has a relative permittivity of 10, then 90% of the displacement current is a current of moving charges, with the motion of each charge carrier restricted to the vicinity of its associated atom. These bound charge carriers do not, of course, contribute to the conductivity.

REFERENCES

See Bibliography.

PROBLEMS

Section 18-1

18-1. Deduce directly from Eq. (18-1) that the electrostatic field is conservative. Also, show that the expression $y\mathbf{i} - x\mathbf{j}$ cannot possibly represent a static electric field.

18-2. From Gauss's law and the equation of continuity deduce that the net charge density at each point within a conductor carrying a *steady drift current* is zero.

18-3. A charge q is located at the point (x_1, y_1, z_1) in an infinite medium of permittivity ϵ. Find the electric scalar potential as a function of the rectangular coordinates, and from this potential function determine the electric field intensity in rectangular form.

18-4. In rectangular coordinates a charge of 5 μc is located in free space at the point (1, 1, 1), and a second charge of 10 μc is located at (1, 2, 3). Find the electric potential as a function of the space coordinates, and determine from Eq. (18-1) the field intensity at (2, 2, -1).

18-5. If a charge q is uniformly distributed throughout a spherical volume of radius a in a region of permittivity ϵ, find the electric potential and the field intensity as functions of the distance r from the center of the sphere.

Section 18-2

18-6. If the point P of Fig. 18-2 is located at (x, y, z), determine the potential at P, and use this result to derive the expression for the electric field intensity at P. Calculate ϕ and $\mathbf{E}$ at the point (3, 2, 1) for $q = 0.2$ μc and $d = 1$ m. The dielectric is free space.

18-7. If a copper ball with a charge q is placed in the dielectric within an uncharged hollow copper box, what is the net charge on the inner surface of the box? What is the charge on the outer surface of the box? What are these charges if the ball is placed in contact with the inner surface?

18-8. A small copper ball with a charge q is placed in the dielectric within an uncharged hollow copper box. The box is then momentarily connected to earth, after which the ball is withdrawn from the box through a small opening. What is the net charge of the box?

18-9. In the free space in the vicinity of the 90° conducting corner shown in Fig. 18-24, the potential ϕ is $100xy$ volts. Plot the equipotential curves in the xy-plane for potentials of 0, 25, 50, 75, and 100 volts for values of x and y between 0 and 2. Also, deduce that the family of field lines is described by the equation $x^2 - y^2 = C$, and plot the field lines in the xy-plane for $C = 0, \pm 0.5, \pm 1.0$, and ± 1.5.

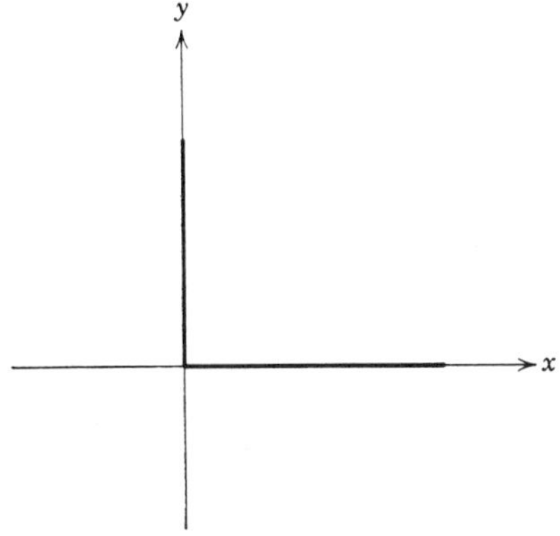

FIG. 18-24. 90° conducting corner.

18-10. For the conducting corner of Prob. 18-9 determine the surface charge density in the xz-plane as a function of x. What is this charge density at the corner?

18-11. In the vicinity of the 270° conducting corner of Fig. 18-25 the potential

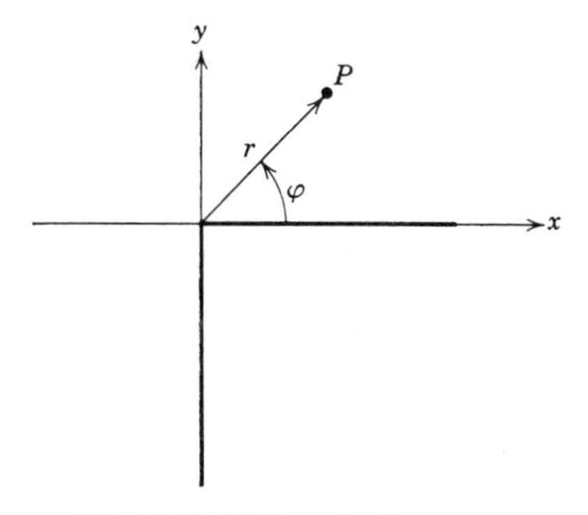

FIG. 18-25. 270° conducting corner.

ϕ in cylindrical coordinates is $100r^{2/3} \sin 2\varphi/3$ volts. Find the electric field intensity in terms of the cylindrical coordinates, and from this field deduce that the family of field lines is described by the equation $r^{2/3} \cos 2\varphi/3 = C$. Make a rough sketch of the approximate equipotential and field lines.

Section 18-3

18-12. If 300 volts are applied to a vacuum diode whose parallel plates are 0.5 cm apart, with the anode positive, find as functions of distance x from the cathode the following: the current density J, the electric scalar potential ϕ, the field intensity E, the velocity v of the electrons, and the charge density ρ. The emission velocities of the electrons are negligible, and space-charge conditions apply.

18-13. With reference to the preceding problem, calculate J, ϕ, E, v, and ρ for values of x from 0 to 0.5 cm in 0.1 cm increments. Carefully plot the results.

18-14. The space-charge equation (18-11) also applies to a cylindrical diode whose cathode is a straight filamentary wire and whose anode is a concentric cylinder of radius d, provided end effects are negligible. Noting that the current density is a function of the radial distance r, deduce from Eq. (18-11) the relationship between ϕ and r, and show that the result satisfies Poisson's equation in cylindrical coordinates.

Section 18-4

18-15. Derive Eq. (18-13), which gives the potential function within that part of the depletion region to the right of the PN junction of Fig. 18-7. The charge distribution is shown in Fig. 18-8.

18-16. A PN junction diode, made of germanium having a dielectric constant of 16, has a charge distribution as shown in Fig. 18-8. The diode is 2 mm long, with a rectangular cross section of 0.5 mm by 1 mm, and there are 10^{23} acceptor atoms/m^3 in the P region and 10^{22} donor atoms/m^3 in the N region. If the applied junction voltage v is $4 + 0.1 \sin 10^7 t$, determine the displacement current through the junction.

18-17. The charge density in the depletion region of a *graded* PN junction is $\rho = ax$ from $x = -W$ to $x = +W$. The total width of the depletion region is $2W$. Find the potential ϕ as a function of x, in terms of a, W, and ϵ, with zero potential at $x = -W$.

18-18. In terms of a, ϵ, and the junction voltage v, determine the incremental capacitance per unit area for the graded PN junction of Prob. 18-17.

Section 18-5

18-19. Use Laplace's equation to find the capacitance of a parallel-plate capacitor. Neglect fringing.

18-20. The space between the plates of a parallel-plate capacitor is filled with three thin dielectric slabs of permittivities ϵ_1, ϵ_2, and ϵ_3 and of thicknesses $d/4$, $d/4$, and $\frac{1}{2}d$, respectively, with d denoting the distance between the plates. The plate area is S. Find the capacitance, assuming negligible fringing.

18-21. The inner conductor of a spherical capacitor has a radius of 0.2 m and is surrounded, in order, with spherical dielectric shells of relative permittivities 1, 2, and 3 with thicknesses 0.01, 0.01, and 0.02 m, respectively. The inner radius of the outer conductor is 0.24. Find the capacitance.

18-22. A charged copper ball in free space has a radius of 9 cm and a potential of 100,000 volts. Calculate the capacitance of the ball, its charge, and the maximum voltage gradient.

18-23. A coaxial transmission line has two dielectrics of permittivities ϵ_1 and ϵ_2, each of which fills the space between the conductors throughout an angle of π radians. The radius of the inner conductor is a, and the inner radius of the outer conductor is b. Find the capacitance per unit length.

18-24. A diode vacuum tube consists of two concentric metallic cylinders 3 cm long, having radii 0.3 cm and 0.6 cm. If the voltage drop from plate to cathode is $10 + 0.5 \sin 10^9 t$, find the charge q on the plate and the displacement current from plate to cathode. Neglect end effects.

Section 18-6

18-25. For the oppositely charged infinite lines of Fig. 18-14 find the electric field intensity at $P(x, y)$, and deduce that the slope of the field line at P is $2xy/(x^2 - y^2 - d^2)$, with d denoting one-half the distance between the lines. Calculate $\mathbf{E}$ at $P(5, 4)$, for $q = 1\ \mu\text{c/m}$, $d = 3$ m, and $\epsilon_r = 1$.

18-26. Verify Eqs. (18-27) and (18-28).

18-27. Employ the relation $\cosh^{-1} x = \ln (x \pm \sqrt{x^2 - 1})$ to show that the inverse hyperbolic cosine of $(\frac{1}{2}D^2/a^2 - 1)$ equals twice the inverse hyperbolic cosine of $\frac{1}{2}D/a$, a relation utilized in the derivation of Eq. (18-29).

18-28. Deduce Eq. (18-21), which gives the capacitance of a coaxial cable, from Eq. (18-28), which gives the capacitance between two cylinders whose centers are a distance D apart.

18-29. Two parallel cylinders, each of radius a, are charged with equal and opposite charges per unit length. The distance between the centers of the conductors is D. Show that the field distribution outside the conductors is identical with that of two similarly charged lines spaced a distance $2d$ apart, provided $d^2 = (\frac{1}{2}D)^2 - a^2$. To do this, first deduce that $k_1 = 1/k_2$, and then find D and a in terms of d and k_1.

18-30. The potential of a point charge q is $q/(4\pi\epsilon r)$, and the equipotential surfaces are concentric spheres. Using this information and the method of Sec. 18-6, find the capacitance between two conducting spheres of radii a and b.

18-31. For a dielectric of free space calculate the capacitance per unit length between (*a*) two long cylinders, each of radius 0.4 cm, whose axes are 20 cm apart; (*b*) two long cylinders of radii 1 cm and 5 cm, whose centers are 2 cm apart; (*c*) a horizontal wire and earth, if the wire has a radius of 0.2 cm and a height of 5 meters.

Section 18-7

18-32. A line charge is located a distance D from the axis of a long parallel cylinder of radius a. The line and the cylinder have equal and opposite charges per unit length. Show that the distance between the center of the cylinder and its image line charge is a^2/D.

18-33. Determine the force per unit length that acts on the line charge of Prob. 18-32 if the charge per unit length is q and the dielectric is free space.

18-34. Two parallel cylinders of infinite length, each of radius a, have equal and opposite charges per unit length. The distance between the axes is D. Find the distance between the center of a cylinder and its image line charge, and calculate this distance for $a = 1$ cm and $D = 4$ cm.

18-35. If the voltage between the cylinders of the preceding problem is 100 volts, find the maximum and minimum values of the surface charge density of a cylinder. The dielectric is free space.

18-36. Two long parallel cylinders of radii 2 cm and 1 cm have charges of $+q$ and $-q$ coulombs/m, respectively. The axes of the cylinders are 5 cm apart, and the dielectric is free space. If the voltage between the cylinders is 100 volts, find the charge density on the larger cylinder at a point that is 4 cm from the center of the smaller cylinder. (*Ans.*: 0.0252 μc/m^2).

18-37. A grounded hollow cylinder of infinite length has an inner radius of 3 cm. A parallel cylinder with a radius of 1 cm is inside the larger one, with the axes 1.5 cm apart. The relative permittivity of the dielectric is 4. If the smaller cylinder is charged to a potential of 100 volts, calculate the maximum and minimum surface charge densities of each cylinder.

18-38. From Eq. (18-29), which gives the capacitance per unit length of a parallel-wire transmission line, derive Eq. (18-30), which gives the capacitance per unit length between a cylinder and a ground plane. Use the method of images.

18-39. A point charge of 5 μc is located in the free-space dielectric between two grounded planar conductors that meet at an angle of 90°. If the charge is 1 cm away from each conductor, calculate the force on the charge.

18-40. Repeat Prob. 18-39 for an angle of 120° instead of 90°.

18-41. An infinite line with a charge of 5 μc/m is located in the free-space dielectric between two grounded planar conductors that meet at an angle of 90°. If the line is 1 cm away from each conductor, calculate the force per unit length on the line.

Section 18-8

18-42. The axis of a long horizontal wire of radius a is at a height h above earth. The charge on the wire is q coulombs/m, and the surface of the earth is approximately planar. Using Eq. (18-38), deduce that the downward electric force on the wire is $(q^2/4\pi\epsilon_0)(h^2 - a^2)^{-1/2}$ newtons/m.

18-43. Using Eq. (18-38), calculate the force per unit length acting on each of the cylinders of Prob. 18-36.

18-44. Using Eq. (18-38), calculate the force per unit length acting on each of the cylinders of Prob. 18-37.

18-45. Show that the force that tends to increase the radius a of the inner conductor of a spherical capacitor is $q^2/(8\pi\epsilon a^2)$. Also, find the work done by this force if the inner sphere expands from radius a to radius a_1, with the stored charge q constant.

18-46. With the aid of Eq. (18-38), show that the capacitance of a spherical capacitor is increased if the inner sphere is moved out of position.

Section 18-9

18-47. Prove that the torque **T** on a point dipole of moment **p** in an electric field **E** is **p** × **E**. Compare with Eq. (17-22).

18-48. A dipole of moment **p** is perpendicular to a uniform electric field **E**. If the dipole is now rotated, show that its potential energy is increased by $-\mathbf{E}\cdot\mathbf{p}$ joule. Use the result of Prob. 18-47, recalling that the work done by the torque T acting through $d\theta$ is $T\,d\theta$.

18-49. A certain parallel-plate capacitor has a surface charge density of 10 $\mu c/m^2$ and a dielectric constant of 8. Find that part of the electric field intensity produced directly by the charges on the conducting plates and that part produced directly by the electric dipoles. Neglect fringing.

18-50. A series electric circuit with a current of $0.001 \sin 10^6 t$ ampere contains a parallel-plate capacitor with a cross-sectional area of 0.01 m^2 and a dielectric constant of 4. Assuming negligible fringing, find **D**, **E**, and **P** in the dielectric, and calculate the electric susceptibility. Also, determine the percentage of the displacement current that actually consists of moving charges.

Complex Exponentials

CHAPTER 19

Field and circuit problems are commonly analyzed for assumed sinusoidal time variations. The results can be applied to nonsinusoidal waveforms by utilizing the concepts of the Fourier series and integral and employing the principle of superposition. For sinusoidal time variations the mathematics of complex numbers and complex exponentials can be used to eliminate the time variable from the field and circuit equations. This greatly simplifies analysis.

In the first part of this chapter the mathematics of complex numbers is discussed. For students who have previously encountered complex numbers, the discussion may prove to be a worthwhile review. In the latter portion of the chapter, applications to electric circuits are considered, and the electromagnetic field equations are presented in complex-exponential form.

19-1. COMPLEX NUMBERS

The square root of a negative number is called an *imaginary number*. Let us denote the imaginary number $\sqrt{-1}$ by the symbol j. Then

$$j = \sqrt{-1} \tag{19-1}$$

Frequently, the symbol i is used in place of j, especially by mathematicians and physicists. If j is multiplied by a real number y, the product jy equals $\sqrt{-y^2}$, and jy is an imaginary number. By definition a *complex number* z is

$$z = x + jy \tag{19-2}$$

with x and y denoting real numbers. The number x is called the *real part of* z, often designated as Re z; the number y is called the *imaginary part of* z, often designated as Im z. Thus

$$x = \text{Re } z \qquad y = \text{Im } z \tag{19-3}$$

As j represents $\sqrt{-1}$, we note that $j^2 = -1$ and $1/j = -j$. Addition, subtraction, multiplication, and division of complex numbers are defined so that the fundamental rules of algebra apply. Accordingly,

$$z_1 + z_2 = (x_1 + x_2) + j(y_1 + y_2)$$

$$z_1 z_2 = (x_1 + jy_1)(x_2 + jy_2) = (x_1x_2 - y_1y_2) + j(x_1y_2 + x_2y_1)$$

$$\frac{z_1}{z_2} = \frac{x_1 + jy_1}{x_2 + jy_2} = \frac{(x_1 + jy_1)(x_2 - jy_2)}{(x_2 + jy_2)(x_2 - jy_2)} = \frac{x_1x_2 + y_1y_2}{x_2^2 + y_2^2} + j\frac{x_2y_1 - x_1y_2}{x_2^2 + y_2^2}$$

Two complex numbers z_1 and z_2 are equal if, and only if, $x_1 = x_2$ and $y_1 = y_2$. If $z = 0$, it follows that $x = y = 0$.

19-2. THE EXPONENTIAL FUNCTION

The exponential function of a complex number z, often expressed as exp z, can be defined by the infinite series

$$\exp z = 1 + z + \frac{z^2}{2!} + \frac{z^3}{3!} + \frac{z^4}{4!} + \cdots \tag{19-4}$$

with $z = x + jy$. Letting $x = 1$ and $y = 0$, we obtain

$$\exp 1 = 1 + 1 + \frac{1}{2!} + \frac{1}{3!} + \frac{1}{4!} + \cdots = 2.718 \cdots$$

The exponential of unity is designated by the symbol e. Thus

$$e = \exp 1 = 2.718 \cdots \tag{19-5}$$

The product (exp z_1)(exp z_2) is the product of two infinite series. Multiplication of the two series term by term* reveals that

$$(\exp z_1)(\exp z_2) = 1 + (z_1 + z_2) + \frac{(z_1 + z_2)^2}{2!} + \frac{(z_1 + z_2)^3}{3!} + \cdots$$

From this result we deduce that

$$(\exp z_1)(\exp z_2) = \exp (z_1 + z_2) \tag{19-6}$$

* The infinite series presented in this chapter are uniformly convergent for all values of the complex variable z. Such series can, term by term, be added, subtracted, multiplied, differentiated, and integrated. See, for example, Bronwell, A., *Advanced Mathematics in Physics and Engineering*, McGraw-Hill Book Co., New York, 1953, Chap. 1.

If $z_1 = z_2 = 1 + j0$, Eq. (19-6) becomes $(\exp 1)^2 = \exp 2$. It is evident that exp 1 raised to the power x equals $\exp x$, or

$$(\exp 1)^x = e^x = \exp x \tag{19-7}$$

Replacing x with the imaginary number jy gives

$$e^{jy} = \exp jy \tag{19-8}$$

Thus *the symbol* e^{jy} *is understood to represent* $\exp jy$.

Multiplication of Eqs. (19-7) and (19-8) gives $e^x e^{jy} = (\exp x)(\exp jy)$. The product $e^x e^{jy}$ equals e^z, and the product $(\exp x)(\exp jy)$ equals $\exp z$ by Eq. (19-6). Therefore

$$e^z = \exp z \tag{19-9}$$

If x and y are variables, the derivative of $\exp z$ with respect to z is defined by

$$\frac{d}{dz}(\exp z) = \lim_{\Delta x, \Delta y \to 0} \frac{\exp[(x + \Delta x) + j(y + \Delta y)] - \exp(x + jy)}{\Delta x + j\,\Delta y}$$

The power series of Eq. (19-4), when differentiated term by term, yields a series that is identical to the original series. Hence,

$$\frac{d}{dz}(e^z) = e^z \tag{19-10}$$

By differentiating the power series for $\exp az$ term by term we obtain

$$\frac{d}{dz}(e^{az}) = ae^{az} \tag{19-11}$$

The constant a in Eq. (19-11) may be real or complex.

From Eq. (19-10) it follows that the integral of $\exp z$ with respect to z equals $\exp z$. That is,

$$\int e^z\,dz = e^z \tag{19-12}$$

Also, it is evident from Eq. (19-11) that

$$\int e^{az}\,dz = \frac{1}{a}e^{az} \tag{19-13}$$

and the constant a may be complex. Equations (19-12) and (19-13) can be obtained directly from the power series of Eq. (19-4) by integrating the series term by term.

The expression e^z is referred to as a *complex exponential.* In general, mathematical operations involving complex exponentials follow the ordinary rules of algebra.

19-3. TRIGONOMETRIC FUNCTIONS

The sine and cosine functions of a complex number z can be defined in terms of infinite series as follows.

$$\sin z = z - \frac{z^3}{3!} + \frac{z^5}{5!} - \frac{z^7}{7!} + \cdots \tag{19-14}$$

$$\cos z = 1 - \frac{z^2}{2!} + \frac{z^4}{4!} - \frac{z^6}{6!} + \cdots \tag{19-15}$$

The tangent, cotangent, secant, and cosecant of z are defined in terms of the sine and cosine functions in the same manner as for real numbers. Accordingly,

$$\tan z = \frac{\sin z}{\cos z} \qquad \sec z = \frac{1}{\cos z}$$

$$\cot z = \frac{\cos z}{\sin z} \qquad \csc z = \frac{1}{\sin z}$$

If the infinite series of Eqs. (19-14) and (19-15) are each squared and then added together, all the terms containing z cancel. The result is

$$\sin^2 z + \cos^2 z = 1 \tag{19-16}$$

Differentiation of the series of Eq. (19-14) term by term yields the cosine series. Therefore,

$$\frac{d}{dz}(\sin z) = \cos z \tag{19-17}$$

In a similar manner we find that

$$\frac{d}{dz}(\cos z) = -\sin z \tag{19-18}$$

In general, the trigonometric functions of complex numbers are treated in the same manner as the trigonometric functions of real numbers, with j representing the imaginary number $\sqrt{-1}$ and obeying the usual algebraic laws. The same identities apply, and the rules of integration and differentiation are the same. The series of Eqs. (19-14) and (19-15) can be used to verify the common trigonometric identities.

If z in Eqs. (19-14) and (19-15) is a real number, the definitions for the sine and cosine functions are equivalent to those given in elementary texts on trigonometry. To show this, let us consider the equations

$$x = r\cos\theta \qquad y = r\sin\theta \tag{19-19}$$

with r and θ denoting real numbers. Utilizing the identity of Eq. (19-16), we obtain

$$x^2 + y^2 = r^2 \cos^2 \theta + r^2 \sin^2 \theta = r^2$$

For all values of θ the sum of x^2 and y^2 is r^2, and for constant r the equation is that of a circle. Thus the equations of (19-19) are the parametric equations of a circle. Figure 19-1 illustrates a circle of radius r. The point $P(x_1, y_1)$ on the circle is the point determined from equations (19-19)

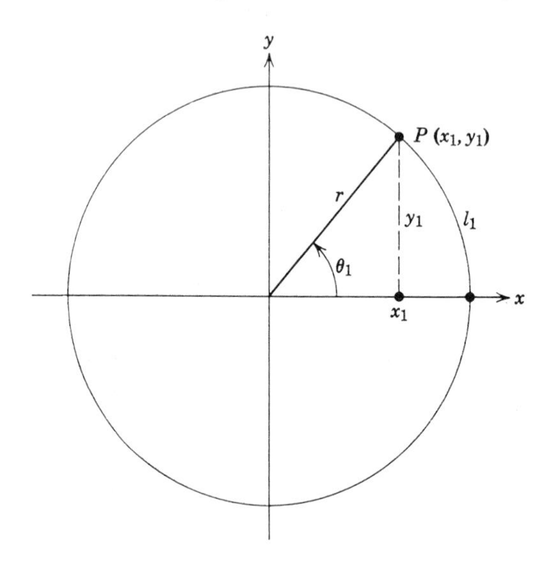

FIG. 19-1. A point $P(x_1, y_1)$ on a circle of radius r.

with $\theta = \theta_1$. The angle θ_1 is indicated on the illustration. From (19-19) we note that $\cos \theta_1 = x_1/r$ and $\sin \theta_1 = y_1/r$. From Fig. 19-1 we observe that x_1, y_1, and r form a right triangle. It is now necessary to show that the angle θ_1 equals the arc length l_1 divided by the radius r.

Let dl represent a differential length of the circular path. In terms of dx and dy the length dl is $\sqrt{(dx)^2 + (dy)^2}$. In terms of a differential change $d\theta$ in θ, the length dl is

$$dl = \sqrt{(dx/d\theta)^2 + (dy/d\theta)^2}\, d\theta$$

From equations (19-19) we note that $dx/d\theta = -r \sin \theta$ and $dy/d\theta = r \cos \theta$. Therefore,

$$dl = \sqrt{r^2 \sin^2 \theta + r^2 \cos^2 \theta}\, d\theta = r\, d\theta$$

As $dl = r\, d\theta$, with r constant, it is evident that $l_1 = r\theta_1$, or

$$\theta_1 = l_1/r \tag{19-20}$$

The angle θ_1 of Fig. 19-1 is the ratio of the arc length to the radius. The angle is dimensionless, and its dimensionless unit is the *radian*.

The angle subtended by the entire circumference of the circle is $2\pi r/r$, or 2π radians. It is evident that the sine and cosine functions are periodic in the interval 2π radians. Angles are frequently expressed in degrees, with 360° corresponding to 2π radians, or 1° corresponding to $\pi/180$ radian. The expression $\sin \theta°$ is understood to represent $\sin (\theta° \times \pi/180)$. For example, $\sin 45° = \sin \pi/4$. In order to evaluate the sine and cosine functions the infinite series can be utilized. By way of illustration,

$$\sin 1 = 1 - 1/3! + 1/5! - 1/7! + \cdots \approx 0.841$$

One radian is approximately 57.3°.

We know that the sine and cosine functions of real angles have values between +1 and −1. However, the sine and cosine functions of complex numbers are not so restricted. For example, for $z = 1 + j1$ the sine of z is $1.30 + j0.635$. This is readily verified by substituting $1 + j1$ for z in the series of Eq. (19-14), noting that only the first four terms of the power series are of appreciable consequence for this particular value of z. If $z = j1$, $\cos z = 1.543$, obtained by considering the first few terms of the cosine series.

The sine and cosine functions can be expressed in terms of the exponential function. The infinite series defining the exponential function is given as Eq. (19-4). If z in the series is replaced with the imaginary number $j\theta$, the even powers of z become real numbers and the odd powers of z become imaginary numbers. Arranging the real numbers together and the imaginary numbers together gives

$$\begin{aligned} e^{j\theta} &= (1 - \theta^2/2! + \theta^4/4! - \theta^6/6! + \cdots) \\ &\quad + j(\theta - \theta^3/3! + \theta^5/5! - \theta^7/7! + \cdots) \end{aligned}$$

These are the cosine and sine series. Therefore,

$$e^{j\theta} = \cos \theta + j \sin \theta \tag{19-21}$$

This important relation is known as *Euler's identity*. The imaginary part of $\exp j\theta$ is $\sin \theta$, and the real part is $\cos \theta$. Thus,

$$\sin \theta = \text{Im } e^{j\theta} \tag{19-22}$$

$$\cos \theta = \text{Re } e^{j\theta} \tag{19-23}$$

These provide a way of expressing the sine and cosine functions of real angles in terms of complex exponentials.

Euler's identity is obviously valid if θ is complex. Therefore,

$$e^{jz} = \cos z + j \sin z$$

As $\cos(-z) = \cos z$ and $\sin(-z) = -\sin z$, it is evident that

$$e^{-jz} = \cos z - j \sin z$$

If these two equations are added together, we obtain the cosine function in terms of the exponential functions. By subtracting one equation from the other we obtain the sine function in terms of the exponentials. The results are

$$\sin z = \frac{1}{2j}(e^{jz} - e^{-jz}) \qquad (19\text{-}24)$$

$$\cos z = \frac{1}{2}(e^{jz} + e^{-jz}) \qquad (19\text{-}25)$$

These could have been selected as the defining equations for the sine and cosine functions.

19-4. POLAR AND EXPONENTIAL REPRESENTATIONS OF COMPLEX NUMBERS

A complex number, $z = x + jy$, can be plotted as a point in the xy-plane as shown in Fig. 19-2. This plane is referred to as the *complex plane*, with the x-axis called the *real axis* and the y-axis called the *imaginary axis*. The value of z at the point $P(x, y)$ is $x + jy$. The variables x and y are not to be regarded as space variables. The directed segment r of the illustration is not a space vector.

From Fig. 19-2 we note that $x = r \cos \theta$ and $y = r \sin \theta$, with (r, θ) denoting the polar coordinates of the point P. Therefore, in *polar form*

$$z = r(\cos \theta + j \sin \theta) \qquad (19\text{-}26)$$

Clearly,

$$r = \sqrt{x^2 + y^2} \qquad (19\text{-}27)$$

$$\theta = \tan^{-1} y/x \qquad (19\text{-}28)$$

The positive number r is called the *amplitude*, or *absolute value*, of z; θ is the *angle*, or *phase*, of z. The angle θ is multivalued, for if the angle is increased or decreased by 2π radians, the arctangent of θ is unchanged. The value of θ between 0 and 2π radians is the *principal value*. Positive angles are measured counterclockwise from the x-axis, and negative angles are measured clockwise.

By employing Euler's identity we can express Eq. (19-26) in the *exponential form*

$$z = re^{j\theta} \qquad (19\text{-}29)$$

This form is very useful in performing certain mathematical operations. For example,

$$z_1 z_2 = (r_1 e^{j\theta_1})(r_2 e^{j\theta_2}) = r_1 r_2 e^{j(\theta_1+\theta_2)} \tag{19-30}$$

$$z_1/z_2 = (r_1/r_2)e^{j(\theta_1-\theta_2)} \tag{19-31}$$

Thus two complex numbers can be multiplied by multiplying their amplitudes and adding their angles. They can be divided by dividing their amplitudes and subtracting their angles according to Eq. (19-31).

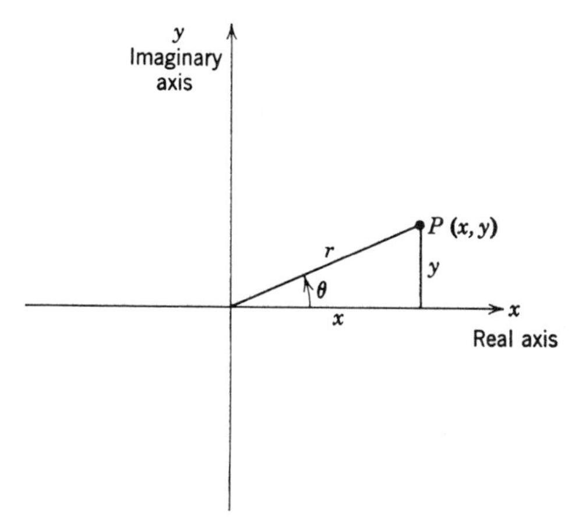

FIG. 19-2. A complex number $z = x + jy$, plotted as a point in the complex plane.

The exponential form is useful in raising a complex number z to a power n. We have

$$z^n = r^n e^{jn\theta} = r^n(\cos n\theta + j \sin n\theta)$$

The nth root of z is

$$z^{1/n} = r^{1/n} e^{j(1/n)(\theta \pm 2\pi k)} \qquad k = 0, 1, 2, \text{etc.}$$

The more general form of the multivalued angle is used, for there are n principal angles, with values less than 2π. For example, the square roots of $9e^{j\pi/2}$ are $3e^{j\pi/4}$ and $3e^{j5\pi/4}$. The cube roots of unity are $e^{j2\pi k/3}$, with principal values obtained by setting k equal to 0, 1, and 2. In rectangular form these roots are 1 and $-\frac{1}{2}(1 \pm j\sqrt{3})$.

The exponential and polar forms of complex numbers are often written in the form $r \underline{/\theta}$. Equivalent expressions are

$$re^{j\theta} = r(\cos \theta + j \sin \theta) = r \underline{/\theta}$$

The form $r \underline{/\theta}$ should be regarded as shorthand notation. It is evident that

$$(r_1 \underline{/\theta_1})(r_2 \underline{/\theta_2}) = r_1 r_2 \underline{/\theta_1 + \theta_2}$$

$$(r_1 \underline{/\theta_1})/(r_2 \underline{/\theta_2}) = (r_1/r_2) \underline{/\theta_1 - \theta_2}$$

$$1/(r \underline{/\theta}) = (1/r) \underline{/-\theta}$$

$$(r \underline{/\theta})^n = r^n \underline{/n\theta}$$

$$(r \underline{/\theta})^{1/n} = r^{1/n} \underline{/\theta/n \pm 2\pi k/n}$$

In exponential form j is $e^{j\frac{1}{2}\pi}$, or $1 \underline{/\frac{1}{2}\pi}$. Also, $-j$ is $1 \underline{/-\frac{1}{2}\pi}$. If $z = r \underline{/\theta}$, then $jz = r \underline{/\theta + \frac{1}{2}\pi}$ and $-jz = r \underline{/\theta - \frac{1}{2}\pi}$. Thus *multiplying a complex number by* $\pm j$ *changes its angle by* $\pm\frac{1}{2}\pi$. The number -1 in exponential form is $e^{\pm j\pi}$. Therefore, $-1 = 1 \underline{/\pm\pi}$. It follows that *multiplication of a complex number by* -1 *changes the angle of the complex number by* $\pm\pi$ *radians.* When the shorthand notation is used, angles are frequently expressed in degrees.

EXAMPLE. Evaluate $\sqrt{jz_1z_2/z_3}$, if $z_1 = 1 + j1$, $z_2 = 3e^{j\pi/3}$, and $z_3 = 4 - j3$.

Solution. $j = 1 \underline{/90°}$, $z_1 = \sqrt{2} \underline{/45°}$, $z_2 = 3 \underline{/60°}$, and $z_3 = 5 \underline{/-36.9°}$. Therefore

$$\frac{jz_1z_2}{z_3} = \frac{(1 \underline{/90°})(\sqrt{2} \underline{/45°})(3 \underline{/60°})}{5 \underline{/-36.9°}} = 0.6\sqrt{2} \underline{/231.9°}$$

This result can be expressed as $0.849 \underline{/-128.1°}$. The principal square roots are $\pm 0.921 \underline{/-64°}$, which can be expressed as $0.921 \underline{/-64°}$ and $0.921 \underline{/116°}$. In rectangular form they are $\pm(0.403 - j0.827)$.

Let z be represented by

$$z = x + jy = re^{j\theta} = r \cos\theta + jr \sin\theta$$

Then the *complex conjugate* z^* of z is

$$z^* = x - jy = re^{-j\theta} = r \cos\theta - jr \sin\theta$$

We note that the magnitude $|z|$ of z is $\sqrt{zz^*}$.

19-5. THE LOGARITHM

If $z_2 = e^{z_1}$, then the complex number z_1 is said to be the *logarithm* of z_2, or

$$z_1 = \ln z_2$$

Substitution of e^{z_1} for z_2 gives $z_1 = \ln e^{z_1}$. Clearly, *the logarithm of* e^{z_1} *equals* z_1.

In order to express the logarithm of a complex number in rectangular form, the number should first be expressed in exponential form. The logarithm becomes

$$\ln (re^{j\theta}) = \ln r + \ln e^{j\theta} = \ln r + j\theta$$

As θ is multivalued, this can be expressed as

$$\ln z = \ln r + j(\theta_1 \pm 2\pi k) \qquad (19\text{-}32)$$

with θ_1 representing the principal angle. It follows that a complex number has an infinite number of logarithms.

EXAMPLE. Find the ln of $1 - j1$.

Solution. $1 - j1 = \sqrt{2}\underline{/-45^\circ}$. Therefore,

$$\ln (1 - j1) = \ln \sqrt{2} - j(\pi/4 \pm 2\pi k) = 0.346 - j(0.785 \pm 6.283k)$$

with $k = 0, 1, 2$, etc.

19-6. HYPERBOLIC FUNCTIONS

The hyperbolic sine of z and the hyperbolic cosine of z are defined by

$$\sinh z = \tfrac{1}{2}(e^z - e^{-z}) \qquad (19\text{-}33)$$

$$\cosh z = \tfrac{1}{2}(e^z + e^{-z}) \qquad (19\text{-}34)$$

Replacing the exponential functions with their infinite series gives

$$\sinh z = z + \frac{z^3}{3!} + \frac{z^5}{5!} + \frac{z^7}{7!} + \cdots \qquad (19\text{-}35)$$

$$\cosh z = 1 + \frac{z^2}{2!} + \frac{z^4}{4!} + \frac{z^6}{6!} + \cdots \qquad (19\text{-}36)$$

From the infinite series for $\sin z$, $\cos z$, $\sinh z$, and $\cosh z$ it is easily shown that

$$\sin jz = j \sinh z \qquad \cos jz = \cosh z$$

$$\sinh (z_1 + z_2) = \sinh z_1 \cosh z_2 + \cosh z_1 \sinh z_2$$

$$\cosh (z_1 + z_2) = \cosh z_1 \cosh z_2 + \sinh z_1 \sinh z_2$$

$$\cosh^2 z - \sinh^2 z = 1$$

$$\frac{d}{dz}(\sinh z) = \cosh z \qquad \frac{d}{dz}(\cosh z) = \sinh z$$

It is evident from the above that

$$\sinh (x + jy) = \sinh x \cos y + j \cosh x \sin y$$

$$\cosh (x + jy) = \cosh x \cos y + j \sinh x \sin y$$

These relations enable us to express the hyperbolic functions as complex numbers. Also, it is easily shown that

$$\sin(x + jy) = \sin x \cosh y + j \cos x \sinh y$$

$$\cos(x + jy) = \cos x \cosh y - j \sin x \sinh y$$

The hyperbolic tangent, cotangent, secant, and cosecant are defined in terms of the hyperbolic sine and cosine functions. These definitions are similar to those of the corresponding trigonometric functions.

19-7. INVERSE TRIGONOMETRIC AND HYPERBOLIC FUNCTIONS

If $\sin z_1 = z$, then z_1 is the function whose sine equals z. The function z_1 is referred to as the arcsine of z, usually expressed by

$$z_1 = \sin^{-1} z$$

We note that $\sin(\sin^{-1} z) = z$. The sine and the arcsine functions are inverse functions.

The arcsine of z can be expressed as a logarithmic function of z. We note that

$$z = \sin z_1 = \frac{1}{2j}(e^{jz_1} - e^{-jz_1})$$

Therefore,

$$e^{jz_1} - e^{-jz_1} = 2jz$$

By multiplication by $\exp jz_1$ and rearrangement of terms, we obtain

$$(e^{jz_1})^2 - 2jz(e^{jz_1}) - 1 = 0$$

This is a quadratic equation in e^{jz_1}, whose solution is

$$e^{jz_1} = jz \pm \sqrt{1 - z^2}$$

Therefore,

$$z_1 = \sin^{-1} z = -j \ln(jz \pm \sqrt{1 - z^2})$$

In a similar manner it can be shown that

$$\cos^{-1} z = \pm j \ln(z + \sqrt{z^2 - 1})$$

$$\tan^{-1} z = \tfrac{1}{2} j \ln \frac{1 - jz}{1 + jz}$$

$$\sinh^{-1} z = \ln(z + \sqrt{z^2 + 1})$$

$$\cosh^{-1} z = \pm \ln(z + \sqrt{z^2 - 1})$$

$$\tanh^{-1} z = \tfrac{1}{2} \ln \frac{1 + z}{1 - z}$$

19-8. COMPLEX EXPONENTIALS AND SINUSOIDS

Time-varying quantities in field and circuit problems are often approximately sinusoidal. Even if this is not the case, it is usually advantageous to analyze a problem on the basis of a sinusoidal waveform; other time-functions can be regarded as consisting of the superposition of a number of sinusoidal waveforms of different frequencies and phases. The reason for selecting the sinusoid as our basic waveform for analysis is that its shape is unchanged when integrated or differentiated or when two sine functions of the same frequency are added or subtracted. Usually, sinusoidally time-varying quantities are expressed in terms of complex exponentials, the use of which enables us *to eliminate the time variable from our field and circuit equations.*

The general expression for a sinusoidally time-varying quantity i is $I_m \sin(\omega t + \theta)$. The angle θ may be a function of variables other than time. For example, θ may be a function of the space coordinates. It may be constant, depending on the particular situation. In any event, we shall regard it as independent of the variable time. A cosine function has the same waveform as the sine function, and thus the quantity i could be represented as $I_m \cos(\omega t + \phi)$. Both the sine and the cosine functions are classified as sinusoidal functions.

Let us consider a problem with all time variables represented by sine functions with angular frequency ω. For example, suppose the voltage v and the current i in a series circuit are designated $V_m \sin \omega t$ and $I_m \sin(\omega t + \theta)$, respectively. At time zero the voltage is zero, and the current is $I_m \sin \theta$. However, these values at some particular instant are of no consequence, for the selection of zero time is an arbitrary selection. The significant quantities are the amplitudes V_m and I_m and the phase angle θ. If we wished, we could change our selection of zero time so that the voltage and current are $V_m \cos \omega t$ and $I_m \cos(\omega t + \theta)$, respectively. We are at liberty to express all sinusoidal quantities as sine functions or all quantities as cosine functions. Suppose the sine function is selected. Then changing all sines to cosines, without changing the phase angles, is equivalent simply to shifting the zero time reference.

By Euler's identity

$$e^{j(\omega t+\theta)} = \cos(\omega t + \theta) + j \sin(\omega t + \theta)$$

The real and imaginary parts of $\exp j(\omega t + \theta)$ are

$$\text{Re}\, e^{j(\omega t+\theta)} = \cos(\omega t + \theta) \qquad \text{Im}\, e^{j(\omega t+\theta)} = \sin(\omega t + \theta)$$

The voltage v and the current i of the series circuit can be expressed as

$$v = V_m e^{j\omega t}$$

$$i = I_m e^{j(\omega t + \theta)} = I_m e^{j\theta} e^{j\omega t}$$

provided we understand that the voltage and current are represented by the real parts of the expressions, or the imaginary parts. However, we must be consistent; we cannot choose the real part for v and the imaginary part for i.

When using complex exponentials to represent sinusoids, we must take care to perform only those mathematical operations that keep the real and imaginary parts properly separated. First, let us consider the addition of the currents i_1 and i_2 with

$$i_1 = I_{m1} e^{j(\omega t + \theta_1)} = I_{m1} \cos(\omega t + \theta_1) + jI_{m1} \sin(\omega t + \theta_1)$$

$$i_2 = I_{m2} e^{j(\omega t + \theta_2)} = I_{m2} \cos(\omega t + \theta_2) + jI_{m2} \sin(\omega t + \theta_2)$$

The currents i_1 and i_2 are understood to be the real parts of the expressions, or the imaginary parts. In adding complex numbers we add the reals together, and we add the imaginaries together. Consequently, the cosine and sine functions are kept separated, and addition of sinusoids in complex-exponential form is justified. It follows that

$$i_1 + i_2 = (I_{m1} e^{j\theta_1} + I_{m2} e^{j\theta_2}) e^{j\omega t}$$

Of course both i_1 and i_2 must have the same angular frequency ω. As subtraction is a special case of addition, subtraction of sinusoids in complex exponential form is also permissible.

EXAMPLE 1. Express $5 \sin(\omega t + 90°) + 10 \sin(\omega t + 30°)$ as a single sine function.

Solution. With the imaginary part understood, the complex-exponential representation of the addition is

$$(5e^{j\pi/2} + 10e^{j\pi/6}) e^{j\omega t} = (j5 + 8.66 + j5) e^{j\omega t}$$

The exponential form of $8.66 + j10$, with the angle expressed in degrees, is $13.2e^{j49.1°}$. Multiplying this by $e^{j\omega t}$ and taking the imaginary part yields the expression $13.2 \sin(\omega t + 49.1°)$.

The above result can be obtained more directly by omitting the expression $e^{j\omega t}$. The amplitude and angle of the addition are found from

$$5\underline{/90°} + 10\underline{/30°} = 8.66 + j10 = 13.2\underline{/49.1°}$$

Therefore, the result is $13.2 \sin(\omega t + 49.1°)$.

EXAMPLE 2. Express $A \sin \omega t + B \cos \omega t$ as a single sine function.

Solution. As $\cos \omega t = \sin(\omega t + 90°)$, the magnitude and angle of the result is found by adding $A\underline{/0°}$ and $B\underline{/90°}$. This gives $A + jB$. The polar form in shorthand notation is $\sqrt{A^2 + B^2}\underline{/\tan^{-1}(B/A)}$. Therefore,

$$A \sin \omega t + B \cos \omega t = \sqrt{A^2 + B^2} \sin(\omega t + \tan^{-1} B/A)$$

We utilized this identity in some of the earlier chapters.

Next, let us consider time differentiation and time integration of the sinusoid i which equals the real or imaginary part of

$$i = I_m e^{j\theta} e^{j\omega t} = I_m \cos(\omega t + \theta) + jI_m \sin(\omega t + \theta)$$

It is evident that differentiation or integration, with respect to time, will keep the real and imaginary parts properly separated. Using the exponential form, we obtain

$$\frac{di}{dt} = j\omega(I_m e^{j\theta} e^{j\omega t})$$

$$\int i\, dt = \frac{1}{j\omega}(I_m e^{j\theta} e^{j\omega t})$$

Thus *the time derivative introduces $j\omega$ as a multiplying factor, and the time integral introduces $1/(j\omega)$, or $-j/\omega$, as a multiplying factor.*

EXAMPLE 3. If $i = 10 \cos(400t - 45°)$, find di/dt and $\int i\, dt$, using complex exponentials.

Solution. With the real part understood, the current i is $10e^{-j45°}e^{j400t}$, and di/dt is $(j400)(10e^{-j45°}e^{j400t})$. As $j = e^{j90°}$, this becomes $4000e^{j45°}e^{j400t}$. The real part is $4000 \cos(400t + 45°)$.

This result could be determined with less work by noting that the current is $10\underline{/-45°}$ with $e^{j\omega t}$ understood. The time derivative of the current is $(j400)(10\underline{/-45°})$, or $4000\underline{/45°}$. Therefore, $di/dt = 4000 \cos(400t + 45°)$.

The time integral is $(10\underline{/-45°})/(j400)$, with $e^{j\omega t}$ understood. As $1/j$ equals $1\underline{/-90°}$, this becomes $0.025\underline{/-135°}$, and $\int i\, dt$ is $0.025 \cos(400t - 135°)$.

It has been shown that sinusoids represented by complex exponentials can be added, subtracted, differentiated, or integrated in complex-exponential form. A time derivative introduces the multiplying factor $j\omega$, and a time integral introduces the factor $1/(j\omega)$. Other mathematical operations must be performed with care. For example, instantaneous power p equals vi. If v and i are in complex exponential form, the product of the complex exponential forms does *not* give the power p. This is due to the fact that the real and imaginary parts of the exponentials are not kept properly separated in the multiplication process.

A sinusoidal current $I_m \sin(\omega t + \theta)$ equals the imaginary part of $I_m e^{j\theta} e^{j\omega t}$. The expression $I_m e^{j\theta}$ is called the *phasor current*, which will be designated $\bar{I}$. Accordingly, the current i is the imaginary part of $\bar{I}e^{j\omega t}$, with the phasor current $\bar{I}$ equal to

$$\bar{I} = I_m e^{j\theta} = I_m \underline{/\theta} \tag{19-37}$$

In this book a bar over a quantity is employed to indicate the product of the maximum value and the exponential of $j\theta$, with θ representing the phase angle of a sinusoid. Phasor quantities are frequently expressed in terms of rms values rather than maximum values.

19-9. CIRCUIT EQUATIONS AND SINUSOIDS

As an application of the use of complex exponentials in a linear equation with a time derivative and a time integral, let us consider the integro-differential equation of a series RLC circuit. Letting v and i represent the voltage and current respectively, we have

$$v = iR + L\frac{di}{dt} + \frac{1}{C}\int i\,dt$$

Assuming sinusoidal time variations, we can replace v and i with $\bar{V}e^{j\omega t}$ and $\bar{I}e^{j\omega t}$, respectively. The circuit equation becomes

$$\bar{V}e^{j\omega t} = R\bar{I}e^{j\omega t} + j\omega L\bar{I}e^{j\omega t} + \frac{1}{j\omega C}\bar{I}e^{j\omega t}$$

The exponential of $j\omega t$ is common to all terms and can, therefore, be canceled. The equation becomes

$$\bar{V} = \bar{I}\left(R + j\omega L + \frac{1}{j\omega C}\right)$$

The resulting circuit equation does not contain the variable time. The use of complex exponentials to represent sinusoids has enabled us *to reduce the integro-differential equation to an algebraic equation that does not involve time.* The ratio of the phasor voltage $\bar{V}$ to the phasor current $\bar{I}$ is the *complex impedance* Z of the circuit; that is,

$$Z = \frac{\bar{V}}{\bar{I}} = \frac{V_m e^{j\theta}}{I_m e^{j\alpha}}$$

For the series RLC circuit the complex impedance Z is $R + j(\omega L - 1/\omega C)$.

Suppose $R = 3$, $\omega L = 4$, $1/(\omega C) = 8$. Then the impedance Z is $3 - j4$, or $5\underline{/-53.1^\circ}$. If the phasor voltage $\bar{V}$ is $10\underline{/0^\circ}$, the phasor current $\bar{I}$ is

$$\bar{I} = \frac{\bar{V}}{Z} = \frac{10\underline{/0^\circ}}{5\underline{/-53.1^\circ}} = 2\underline{/53.1^\circ}$$

In order to express the voltage and current as instantaneous functions of time we must multiply the phasors by $e^{j\omega t}$ and take either the real or imaginary parts of the results. However, we know the magnitudes and phase angles and, consequently, we can write the expressions for v and i directly. Using sine functions, we obtain

$$v = 10 \sin \omega t \qquad i = 2 \sin (\omega t + 53.1°)$$

The current i is said to *lead* the voltage v by 53.1°, because the phase angle of i is 53.1° greater than the phase angle of v.

The phasors $\bar{V}$ and $\bar{I}$ of the preceding example are shown in Fig. 19-3 plotted in the complex plane. If we imagine that they rotate counterclockwise with angular velocity ω radians/sec, then their projections on the

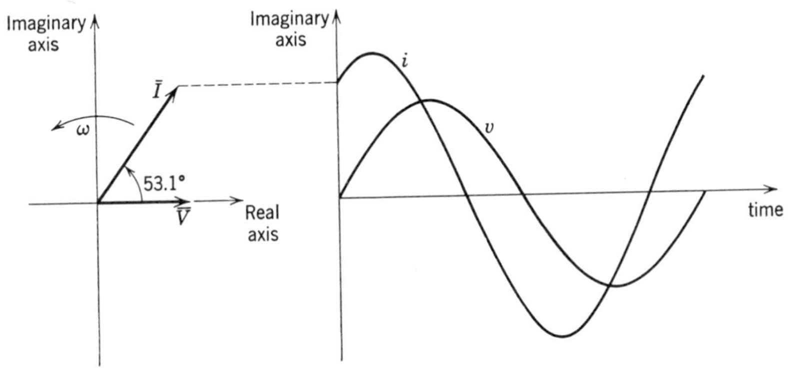

FIG. 19-3. Rotating phasors and their sinusoidal projections on the imaginary axis.

imaginary axis are the instantaneous voltage and current. These sine functions are sketched to the right as functions of time t. As the amplitudes and phase angles may depend on the frequency, but are independent of time, the phasors are said to be in the *frequency domain*. An observer in this domain would revolve with the phasors, with angular velocity ω; such an observer would see stationary phasors. In the frequency domain a phasor can be operated upon by some function of frequency to give some desired result. For example, in the problem that we have been discussing, the phasor voltage was divided by the complex impedance, a function of frequency, to obtain the current. Transformation back to the *time domain* is accomplished by considering the projections of the rotating phasors onto the imaginary axis, or the real axis; this is mathematically equivalent to multiplication by $\exp j\omega t$.

When writing circuit equations for sinusoidally time-varying quantities, it is customary to omit the factor $e^{j\omega t}$. This factor may be tacitly understood to be present, or it may be considered as canceled. *The equations* *with $e^{j\omega t}$ omitted give the proper relations between the magnitudes and phase angles of the sinusoids involved.*

If a voltage is impressed across a pure resistance R, the voltage drop v_R in the direction of the positive current i is iR. In complex-exponential form this voltage drop is $\bar{I}R$ with $e^{j\omega t}$ understood. The phasor voltage drop $\bar{V}_R$ equals $\bar{I}R$ and, obviously, the voltage and the current are in time phase. The voltage drop in the direction opposite to the positive current is $-iR$, and the corresponding phasor voltage drop is $-\bar{I}R$. In this case the voltage and the current are 180° out of time phase.

Across a pure inductance L, the voltage drop v_L in the direction of the positive current i is $L\,di/dt$. The corresponding phasor voltage drop $\bar{V}_L$

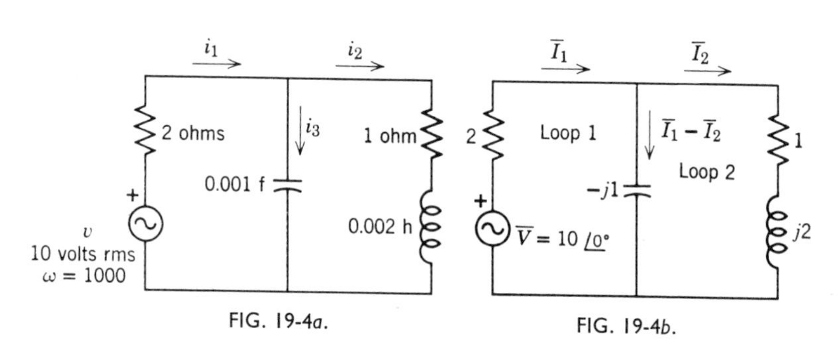

FIG. 19-4*a*. FIG. 19-4*b*.

is $j\omega L\bar{I}$. As $j = 1\underline{/90^\circ}$, this can be expressed as $\omega LI_m\underline{/\theta + 90^\circ}$, with θ denoting the phase angle of the phasor current. Thus the voltage leads the current by 90°. The phasor voltage drop across L in the direction opposite to the positive current is $-j\omega L\bar{I}$, and this voltage lags the current by 90°.

Across a pure capacitance C the voltage drop v_C in the direction of the positive current is $(1/C)\int i\,dt$. The corresponding phasor voltage drop is $\bar{I}/(j\omega C)$, or $-j\bar{I}/(\omega C)$. It is evident that this voltage drop lags the current by 90°. In the direction opposite to the positive current the phasor voltage drop is $-\bar{I}/(j\omega C)$, or $j\bar{I}/(\omega C)$, and this drop leads the current by 90°.

The rules discussed for pure resistances, inductances, and capacitances are very useful in analyzing circuit problems. Kirchhoff's laws apply to phasor voltages and currents as well as to instantaneous voltages and currents. An example will now be considered.

EXAMPLE. Find the currents in each branch of the circuit illustrated in Fig 19-4*a*, if the generator supplies 10 volts rms at an angular frequency ω of 1000.

Solution. As time variations are sinusoidal, Kirchhoff's laws can be expressed in terms of phasor voltages and currents. We shall express the phasors in terms of rms values. Selecting the voltage of the generator as our phase reference, we let its angle be zero; therefore, its rms phasor voltage $\bar{V}$ is $10\underline{/0^\circ}$, or $10 + j0$.

The positive directions of the currents were selected arbitrarily. Application of Kirchhoff's junction rule to one of the junctions reveals that $i_3 = i_1 - i_2$.

In Fig. 19-4*b* the circuit is shown with phasor quantities and complex impedances indicated. The phasor current $\bar{I}_3$ is replaced with $\bar{I}_1 - \bar{I}_2$. The impedances of the capacitance and the inductance were obtained from $-j/(\omega C)$ and $j\omega L$, respectively.

The sum of the phasor voltage drops around each of the closed loops 1 and 2 must equal zero. Adding the drops around loop 1 in a clockwise direction gives

$$-10 + 2\bar{I}_1 + (-j1)(\bar{I}_1 - \bar{I}_2) = 0$$

Adding the drops around loop 2 in a clockwise direction gives

$$-(-j1)(\bar{I}_1 - \bar{I}_2) + \bar{I}_2 + j2\bar{I}_2 = 0$$

The negative sign on the left side is the result of our taking the voltage drop across the capacitor in a direction opposite to the current arrow. The preceding equations can be written in the form

$$10 = (2 - j1)\bar{I}_1 + j\bar{I}_2$$

$$0 = j\bar{I}_1 + (1 + j1)\bar{I}_2$$

These are algebraic equations with two unknown phasor currents. They are readily solved by utilizing determinants. The resulting phasor currents are $\bar{I}_1 = 3.43 \,\underline{/\,31.0^\circ}$ and $\bar{I}_2 = 2.42 \,\underline{/\,-104.0^\circ}$. The phasor current $\bar{I}_3$, which equals $\bar{I}_1 - \bar{I}_2$, is $5.42 \,\underline{/\,49.4^\circ}$.

The instantaneous voltage v and the instantaneous currents, expressed in terms of sine functions, are

$$v = 10\sqrt{2} \sin 1000t$$

$$i_1 = 3.43\sqrt{2} \sin (1000t + 31^\circ)$$

$$i_2 = 2.42\sqrt{2} \sin (1000t - 104^\circ)$$

$$i_3 = 5.42\sqrt{2} \sin (1000t + 49.4^\circ)$$

The current i_1 leads the voltage v by 31°, the current i_2 lags v by 104°, and i_3 leads v by 49.4°. Cosine functions could have been used in place of sine functions.

19-10. MAXWELL'S EQUATIONS IN COMPLEX-EXPONENTIAL FORM

Maxwell's equations are frequently applied to problems in which the time variations are sinusoidal at angular frequency ω. Suppose each rectangular component of the electric field intensity **E** varies sinusoidally with time. Then

$$\mathbf{E} = E_1 \sin (\omega t + \theta_1)\,\mathbf{i} + E_2 \sin (\omega t + \theta_2)\,\mathbf{j} + E_3 \sin (\omega t + \theta_3)\,\mathbf{k}$$

The amplitudes E_1, E_2, and E_3 and the angles θ_1, θ_2, and θ_3 may be functions of the space coordinates. In complex-exponential form

$$\mathbf{E} = (E_1 e^{j\theta_1}\,\mathbf{i} + E_2 e^{j\theta_2}\,\mathbf{j} + E_3 e^{j\theta_3}\,\mathbf{k})e^{j\omega t}$$

If we let

$$\bar{\mathbf{E}} = E_1 e^{j\theta_1}\mathbf{i} + E_2 e^{j\theta_2}\mathbf{j} + E_3 e^{j\theta_3}\mathbf{k} \tag{19-38}$$

then $\mathbf{E} = \bar{\mathbf{E}}e^{j\omega t}$. This is the complex-exponential form of a vector whose components vary sinusoidally with time. *The vector* $\bar{\mathbf{E}}$ *is independent of time, and its components are complex numbers.* As each of these complex numbers represents the amplitude and phase angle of a sinusoid, the components of $\bar{\mathbf{E}}$ are *phasors*, and $\bar{\mathbf{E}}$ is often referred to as a *phasor-vector.*

When Maxwell's equations are written in complex-exponential form, the factor $e^{j\omega t}$ cancels, leaving time-independent equations. In differential form these are

$$\textbf{curl}\ \bar{\mathbf{E}} = -j\omega\bar{\mathbf{B}} \tag{19-39}$$

$$\textbf{curl}\ \bar{\mathbf{H}} = \bar{\mathbf{J}} + j\omega\bar{\mathbf{D}} \tag{19-40}$$

$$\text{div}\ \bar{\mathbf{B}} = 0 \tag{19-41}$$

$$\text{div}\ \bar{\mathbf{D}} = \bar{\rho} \tag{19-42}$$

$$\text{div}\ \bar{\mathbf{J}} = -j\omega\bar{\rho} \tag{19-43}$$

The last one is, of course, the equation of continuity. These should be compared with Eqs. (11-1), (11-2), (11-3), (11-4), and (11-6). Note that a partial time derivative introduces the factor $j\omega$. The quantities $\bar{\mathbf{E}}$, $\bar{\mathbf{D}}$, $\bar{\mathbf{H}}$, $\bar{\mathbf{B}}$, and $\bar{\mathbf{J}}$ are phasor-vectors, and the scalar $\bar{\rho}$ is simply a phasor. The integral equations can be expressed in terms of complex exponentials in a similar manner. Recalling that the divergence of the curl of any vector is zero, it follows from Eq. (19-39) that div $(-j\omega\bar{\mathbf{B}}) = 0$, or div $\bar{\mathbf{B}} = 0$. This is Eq. (19-41). Similarly, Eq. (19-42) can be derived from (19-40), utilizing the equation of continuity.

Let us apply Maxwell's equations to the usual case of an uncharged medium with $\mathbf{J} = \sigma\mathbf{E}$. For sinusoidal time variations the two curl equations, in terms of $\bar{\mathbf{E}}$ and $\bar{\mathbf{H}}$, become

$$\textbf{curl}\ \bar{\mathbf{E}} = -j\omega\mu\bar{\mathbf{H}} \tag{19-44}$$

$$\textbf{curl}\ \bar{\mathbf{H}} = (\sigma + j\omega\epsilon)\bar{\mathbf{E}} \tag{19-45}$$

and both $\bar{\mathbf{E}}$ and $\bar{\mathbf{H}}$ have zero divergence. Taking the curl of both sides of

Eq. (19-44), using Eq. (19-45) to eliminate **curl** $\bar{\mathbf{H}}$, and employing the vector identity of Eq. (10-57), we obtain

$$\nabla^2\bar{\mathbf{E}} = j\omega\mu(\sigma + j\omega\epsilon)\bar{\mathbf{E}} \tag{19-46}$$

This is Eq. (11-22) in complex-exponential form. It is easily deduced directly from (11-22), noting that two partial time derivatives introduce the factor $j\omega$ twice. The wave equation for $\bar{\mathbf{H}}$ can be developed similarly.

The time-dependent wave equation for the electric field is often written as

$$\nabla^2\bar{\mathbf{E}} + k^2\bar{\mathbf{E}} = 0 \tag{19-47}$$

with the complex constant k equal to

$$k = \sqrt{\omega^2\mu\epsilon - j\omega\mu\sigma} \tag{19-48}$$

Equation (19-47) is referred to as the *vector Helmholtz equation*. The magnetic field $\bar{\mathbf{H}}$ in an uncharged medium with drift current densities also satisfies the vector Helmholz equation.

19-11. THE POTENTIAL FUNCTIONS

In Sec. 13-8 Maxwell's equations are given in terms of the potential functions $\mathbf{A}$ and ϕ. In complex-exponential form these become

$$\bar{\mathbf{B}} = \nabla \times \bar{\mathbf{A}} \tag{19-49}$$

$$\bar{\mathbf{E}} = -\nabla\bar{\phi} - j\omega\bar{\mathbf{A}} \tag{19-50}$$

$$\nabla \cdot \bar{\mathbf{A}} = -j\omega\mu\epsilon\bar{\phi} \tag{19-51}$$

$$\nabla^2\bar{\phi} = -\omega^2\mu\epsilon\bar{\phi} - \bar{\rho}/\epsilon \tag{19-52}$$

$$\nabla^2\bar{\mathbf{A}} = -\omega^2\mu\epsilon\bar{\mathbf{A}} - \mu\bar{\mathbf{J}} \tag{19-53}$$

Suppose the electric charge density in a region varies sinusoidally with time with angular frequency ω. Then $\rho = \rho_m \sin(\omega t + \Theta)$, with the amplitude ρ_m and the angle Θ being functions of the space coordinates. In terms of complex exponentials $\rho = \bar{\rho}e^{j\omega t}$, with the phasor $\bar{\rho}$ denoting the complex number $\rho_m e^{j\Theta}$. The *retarded* charge density $[\rho]$, used to determine the retarded electric scalar potential at a distant point P, is $\rho_m \sin(\omega t - \beta r + \Theta)$ by Eq. (13-33). The phase constant β is ω/v, with v denoting the velocity of propagation of the wave, and the term βr is the product of ω and the time r/v of propagation. As the wave velocity in the unbounded dielectric is $(\mu\epsilon)^{-1/2}$, $\beta = \omega(\mu\epsilon)^{1/2}$. In complex-exponential form the retarded charge density is $\bar{\rho}e^{-j\beta r}e^{j\omega t}$. Consequently, the phasor electric potential is

$$\bar{\phi} = \frac{1}{4\pi\epsilon}\int_V \frac{\bar{\rho}e^{-j\beta r}}{r}\,dV \tag{19-54}$$

This is equivalent to Eq. (13-31). The angle βr is the phase retardation due to the finite time of propagation through the distance r.

Similarly, we reason that the current density [**J**] in the integral expression for the magnetic vector potential is $\bar{\mathbf{J}}e^{-j\beta r}e^{j\omega t}$, with $\bar{\mathbf{J}}$ denoting the phasor-vector current density. The magnetic vector potential becomes

$$\bar{\mathbf{A}} = \frac{\mu}{4\pi}\int_V \frac{\bar{\mathbf{J}}e^{-j\beta r}}{r}\,dV \tag{19-55}$$

This is the complex-exponential form of Eq. (13-43). It is, of course, independent of time, because the exponential of $j\omega t$ has been canceled. If the currents are confined to filamentary paths, the vector potential becomes

$$\bar{\mathbf{A}} = \frac{\mu}{4\pi}\int_C \frac{\bar{I}e^{-j\beta r}}{r}\,d\mathbf{l} \tag{19-56}$$

The phasor current $\bar{I}$ is $I_m\underline{/\Theta}$, and both the amplitude I_m and the phase angle Θ are, in general, functions of the space coordinates.

In order to illustrate the use of the potential functions in complex-exponential form, let us once again consider the important problem of determining the fields of an alternating current element. Let the current element be $i\,dz\,\mathbf{k}$, with the current i equal to the imaginary part of $\bar{I}e^{j\omega t}$. The vector potential has only a z component, and the phasor $\bar{A}_z$ is $\mu\bar{I}\,dz\,e^{-j\beta r}/(4\pi r)$, by Eq. (19-56). Utilizing Eq. (13-49), we find the phasor-vector $\bar{\mathbf{A}}$ in spherical coordinates to be

$$\bar{\mathbf{A}} = \frac{\mu\bar{I}\,dz}{4\pi r}e^{-j\beta r}(\cos\theta\,\mathbf{a}_r - \sin\theta\,\mathbf{a}_\theta) \tag{19-57}$$

The magnetic field $\bar{\mathbf{H}}$ can be found from the phasor-vector $\bar{\mathbf{A}}$ and Eq. (19-49). The result is

$$\bar{H}_\varphi = \frac{\bar{I}\,dz}{4\pi}\left(j\frac{\beta}{r} + \frac{1}{r^2}\right)e^{-j\beta r}\sin\theta \tag{19-58}$$

The components $\bar{H}_r$ and $\bar{H}_\theta$ are zero. The instantaneous field H_φ is, of course, the imaginary part of $\bar{H}_\varphi e^{j\omega t}$, and this is given as Eq. (13-52). It is suggested that the student deduce Eq. (19-58) directly from Eq. (13-52) (see Prob. 19-36). The electric field $\bar{\mathbf{E}}$ can be found from the magnetic field $\bar{\mathbf{H}}$, using Eq. (19-40) with $\bar{\mathbf{J}} = 0$, or the electric scalar potential $\bar{\phi}$ can be determined from Eq. (19-51), with the result employed in Eq. (19-50) to determine $\bar{\mathbf{E}}$. The phasor potential $\bar{\phi}$ and the phasor components of $\bar{\mathbf{E}}$

are

$$\bar{\phi} = \frac{\bar{I}\,dz}{4\pi\omega\epsilon}\left(\frac{\beta}{r} - j\frac{1}{r^2}\right)e^{-j\beta r}\cos\theta \tag{19-59}$$

$$\bar{E}_r = \frac{\bar{I}\,dz}{2\pi\omega\epsilon}\left(\frac{\beta}{r^2} - j\frac{1}{r^3}\right)e^{-j\beta r}\cos\theta \tag{19-60}$$

$$\bar{E}_\theta = \frac{\bar{I}\,dz}{4\pi\omega\epsilon}\left(j\frac{\beta^2}{r} + \frac{\beta}{r^2} - j\frac{1}{r^3}\right)e^{-j\beta r}\sin\theta \tag{19-61}$$

Equations (19-60) and (19-61) correspond to Eqs. (13-53) and (13-54), respectively. The phase constant $\beta = \omega(\mu\epsilon)^{1/2}$.

The use of phasors to represent sinusoids is conventional in both field and circuit theory. The differential equations are simplified by the elimination of the variable time. In our study of waveguides we shall employ complex exponentials to eliminate not only the time variable but also one of the space variables. A thorough understanding of the mathematics of this chapter is essential to the study of wave propagation in the chapters that follow.

REFERENCES

Bronwell, A., *Advanced Mathematics in Physics and Engineering*, McGraw-Hill Book Co., New York, 1953, Chaps. 1, 2.

Moon, P., and D. E. Spencer, *Foundations of Electrodynamics*, D. Van Nostrand Co., Princeton, N. J., 1960, Chap. 6.

Plonsey, R., and R. E. Collin, *Principles and Applications of Electromagnetic Fields*, McGraw-Hill Book Co., New York, 1961, Chap. 9.

PROBLEMS

Sections 19-1 and 19-2

19-1. If $z_1 = 5 + j2$ and $z_2 = 3 - j7$, find the real and imaginary parts of $z_1 + z_2$, $z_1 - z_2$, z_1z_2, and z_1/z_2.

19-2. Evaluate the exponential of 0.5, accurate to *five* significant figures.

19-3. Using the infinite series, evaluate exp $(1 + j1)$.

Section 19-3

19-4. Find the sine and cosine of $1 - j1$.

19-5. Evaluate the derivative with respect to x of the function $\sin (x - 45°)^2$ at $x = 1$. Note that the angle is squared, not the function.

19-6. Evaluate sin 0.02°, accurate to *five* significant figures.

19-7. Using Eqs. (19-24) and (19-25), verify the trigonometric identity of Eq. (19-16).

19-8. Evaluate exp $(j0.5)$ from the infinite series that defines the exponential function, and also from Euler's identity.

Sections 19-4 and 19-5

19-9. Find the three principal cube roots of -1. Also, evaluate j^j.

19-10. Find the amplitude and angle of $(3\underline{/30^\circ})(8e^{-j50^\circ})(5 - j6)/(2 + j15)$.

19-11. Determine the real and imaginary parts of $(860 + j5)/(215 - j1)$.

19-12. Find all possible logarithms of $-3 - j4$.

19-13. If $\ln z = -2 + j10$, determine the real and imaginary parts of z.

Sections 19-6 and 19-7

19-14. Evaluate $\tanh (2 - j1)$ and $\coth (1\underline{/30^\circ})$.

19-15. Verify that $\cosh^{-1} z = \pm \ln (z + \sqrt{z^2 - 1}) = \ln (z \pm \sqrt{z^2 - 1})$.

19-16. If $\sinh z = j2$, find all possible values of z.

19-17. If $\cosh z = j2$, find all possible values of z.

19-18. If $\sin z = 2$, find all possible values of z.

Sections 19-8 and 19-9

19-19. Express $2 \sin (\omega t + 60^\circ) - 5 \sin (\omega t - 20^\circ)$ as a single sine function.

19-20. $A \sin (x + \theta) = 3 \sin (x - 80^\circ) + 6 \sin (x - 20^\circ)$. Find A and θ.

19-21. Find the currents i_1, i_2, and i_3 of the electric circuit of Fig. 19-4*a*, if the angular frequency ω is 500.

19-22. Find the phasor currents $\bar{I}_1$ and $\bar{I}_2$ of the electric circuit of Fig. 19-4*b*, if the 2-ohm and 1-ohm resistances are doubled in value.

Section 19-10

19-23. If the x, y, and z components of the phasor-vector $\bar{\mathbf{E}}$ of Eq. (19-38) are $50 + j20$, $100 - j35$, and $75\underline{/20^\circ}$, express the vector $\mathbf{E}$ in terms of sinusoidal time functions.

19-24. Write Maxwell's equations in integral form using complex exponentials. Include the equation of continuity.

19-25. Derive Eq. (19-42) from Eqs. (19-40) and (19-43).

19-26. Equation (19-46) is the wave equation for the electric field intensity in complex-exponential form. Deduce this equation directly from Eq. (11-22).

19-27. For an uncharged medium with $\mathbf{J} = \sigma \mathbf{E}$, derive the vector Helmholtz equation for the magnetic field intensity from Maxwell's equations in complex-exponential form and also from Eq. (11-24).

19-28. If μ and ϵ are constant, deduce that the general propagation equations for the electric and magnetic fields are

$$\nabla^2 \bar{\mathbf{E}} = -\omega^2 \mu \epsilon \bar{\mathbf{E}} + j\omega\mu \bar{\mathbf{J}} + \nabla(\bar{\rho}/\epsilon)$$

$$\nabla^2 \bar{\mathbf{H}} = -\omega^2 \mu \epsilon \bar{\mathbf{H}} - \nabla \times \bar{\mathbf{J}}$$

19-29. The voltage along a transmission line is the sum of the incident voltage wave v_1 and the reflected voltage wave v_2, with

$$v_1 = 50e^{-0.05z} \cos (\omega t - 0.1z + 35^\circ)$$

$$v_2 = 6e^{0.05z} \cos (\omega t + 0.1z - 40^\circ)$$

What does an rms voltmeter read at $z = 20$?

19-30. Deduce that the phasor $e^{-\gamma z}$, with $\gamma = \alpha + j\beta$, represents a wave traveling in the positive z-direction, whereas the phasor $e^{\gamma z}$ denotes a wave traveling the negative z-direction. Also, show that the amplitudes of these waves decrease exponentially with distance and that the wave velocities are equal to ω/β.

19-31. If the phasor-vector $\bar{\mathbf{H}} = \cos \beta z\, \mathbf{i}$ in a region of free space, with $\omega = 10^6$, find (*a*) β, (*b*) $\bar{\mathbf{E}}$, (*c*) the Poynting vector **S**, and (*d*) the time-average Poynting vector.

19-32. The electric field E_x of a uniform plane wave traveling in the z-direction in a lossless dielectric is governed by Eq. (11-30). Assuming sinusoidal time variations, use complex exponentials to eliminate the time variable, thus reducing the equation to an ordinary differential equation. Show that $e^{-\gamma z}$ and $e^{\gamma z}$, with $\gamma = j\omega(\mu\epsilon)^{1/2}$, are solutions, and deduce Eq. (11-32), which gives E_x.

19-33. The current density J_z of the semi-infinite planar conductor of Sec. 14-1 is governed by Eq. (14-2). Using complex exponentials, reduce this equation to an ordinary differential equation, and show that $e^{-\gamma x}$ and $e^{\gamma x}$ are solutions, with $\gamma = (j\omega\mu\sigma)^{1/2}$. Deduce Eq. (14-3), which gives J_z.

19-34. Suppose $\mathbf{E} = \text{Re}\, \bar{\mathbf{E}} e^{j\omega t}$, with the phasor-vector $\bar{\mathbf{E}}$ equal to

$$\bar{\mathbf{E}} = (3 - j4)\mathbf{i} - 6e^{j20^\circ}\mathbf{j} + 4\underline{/-30^\circ}\,\mathbf{k}$$

Express the vector **E** in terms of cosinusoidal time functions.

19-35. The approximate current density J_z in a brass rod with a circular cross section of radius 2.1 cm is

$$J_z = 0.001e^{\pi r} \sin(\omega t + \pi r) \text{ amperes/cm}^2$$

with $\omega = 10^4$ and with the distance r from the axis measured in centimeters. Express J_z in complex-exponential form, and integrate the phasor $\bar{J}_z$ over a cross-sectional area to obtain the phasor current $\bar{I}$. Compare with the answer to Example 1 of Sec. 7-5.

Section 19-11

19-36. The phasor $\bar{H}_\varphi$ of a current element is given in Eq. (19-58). Deduce this directly from Eq. (13-52). First, change the cosinusoidal time function to a sine function by adding 90° to the angle, and recall that $\exp(j90^\circ) = j$. Also, deduce $\bar{H}_\varphi$ from the vector potential of Eq. (19-57).

19-37. Derive Eq. (19-59), which gives the electric potential $\bar{\Phi}$ of a current element, from the phasor-vector $\bar{\mathbf{A}}$ of a current element.

19-38. Derive Eq. (19-60), which gives the phasor $\bar{E}_r$ of a current element, from the magnetic field $\bar{H}_\varphi$ of Eq. (19-58).

19-39. Derive Eq. (19-61), which gives the phasor $\bar{E}_\theta$ of a current element, from Eq. (13-54).

19-40. The Maxwell-Ampère curl equation (19-45) can be written $\textbf{curl}\,\bar{\mathbf{H}} = j\omega\epsilon'\bar{\mathbf{E}}$, with $\epsilon' = \epsilon - j\sigma/\omega$; for a lossless medium it becomes $\textbf{curl}\,\bar{\mathbf{H}} = j\omega\epsilon\bar{\mathbf{E}}$. The equations are identical except for the constants ϵ' and ϵ. Consequently, mathematical relations determined for a lossless medium can be extended to a dissipative medium by replacing ϵ with $\epsilon - j\sigma/\omega$. From this, deduce that the vector potential $\bar{\mathbf{A}}$ of Eq. (19-56), for a medium with conductivity σ, becomes

$$\bar{\mathbf{A}} = (\mu/4\pi) \int_C (\bar{I}/r)e^{-\gamma r}\, d\mathbf{l}$$

with $\gamma = (-\omega^2\mu\epsilon + j\omega\mu\sigma)^{1/2}$.

Transmission Lines I

CHAPTER 20

Although physical fields are three-dimensional, in many practical engineering problems one, two, or three of the space coordinates can be eliminated from consideration. For example, in the study of electric circuit theory we found that none of the physical dimensions are important, provided the circuit dimensions are very small compared with the wavelength; the circuit equations do not involve the space coordinates. When problems deal with electrically long parallel cylinders, or transmission lines, the voltage and current are functions of distance as well as time. In this chapter the one-dimensional line equations are developed from the fundamental electromagnetic laws, and general solutions are examined. Special types of lines and their applications are discussed in Chapter 21.

20-1. UNIFORM TRANSMISSION LINES

A transmission line consists of two or more long parallel conductors that guide electromagnetic waves. The length is at least an appreciable fraction of a wavelength and may be many wavelengths. Otherwise, ordinary circuit theory applies. Lines are used mainly to transmit electrical energy from one point to another, this energy being for power or communication purposes. Some familiar examples are power distribution circuits, telephone wires, and lead-in conductors, which connect television and FM receivers to their antennas.

The physical length of a transmission system depends on the application. A telephone line may extend for many miles, whereas a pair of closely spaced wires only a few centimeters long becomes a transmission line at ultrahigh frequencies. In any event we shall assume that the length is at least an appreciable fraction of a wavelength. Such a line is *electrically long* regardless of its physical size. We shall consider only uniform lines, which have cross sections that do not change with distance. Two common types are the parallel-wire line and the coaxial cable.

A parallel-wire line connecting a source to a load is shown in Fig. 20-1. The z-coordinate is axial, extending in the direction of transmission from

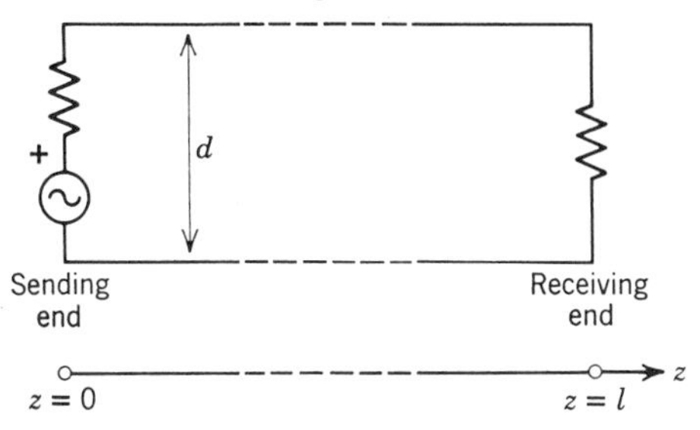

FIG. 20-1. Parallel-wire transmission line between source and load.

the sending end to the receiving end. As the system is electrically long, we expect the fields, the voltage, and the current to vary with z as well as with time.

The line of Fig. 20-1 can be viewed as a waveguide that guides the electromagnetic wave excited by the source to the load. There are ohmic losses in the imperfect conductors, and the insulation between the wires may permit *leakage currents* that heat the dielectric. In addition, there may be radiation losses. Clearly the wave is attenuated as it propagates. The energy reaching the receiving end may be considerably less than that supplied by the source. In fact, if the system is sufficiently long, the energy reaching the receiving end is negligible, and the line is then said to be *infinite*. As the wave is attenuated to zero before reaching the end, it is evident that the termination of such a line has no effect on the wave propagation. The infinite line is important in the development of transmission line theory.

Losses are undesirable but unavoidable. In power systems they reduce the efficiency of transmission, and in communication systems they weaken the signal. Along telephone lines amplifiers are placed at intervals to restore the energy of the wave. The transatlantic coaxial cables used for telephonic communication have underwater electronic amplifiers at frequent intervals. Without these, the signals fed into the cables would be almost completely attenuated due to ohmic losses, and normal communication would be impossible.

20-2. THE PRINCIPAL WAVE

We shall begin our investigation with a brief study of electromagnetic wave propagation along a uniform line with perfect conductors. Shown in Fig. 20-2 are parallel conductors with arbitrary cross sections, and the surface current densities are assumed to be axial.

In Sec. 13-4 we found that the magnetic vector potential **A** of a current element has the direction of the element. This is true even for a dielectric with losses, as shown in Prob. 19-40. Therefore, **A** has only the axial component A_z, and from the curl of **A** we deduce that the magnetic field

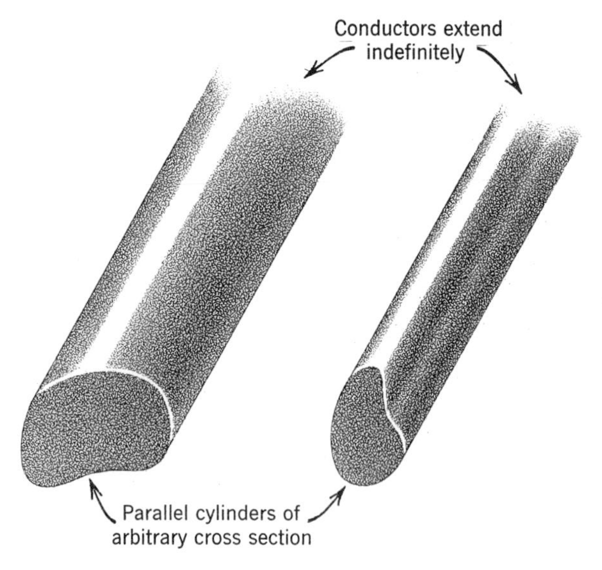

FIG. 20-2. Two-conductor transmission line.

H must be transverse, with $H_z = 0$. The lines of magnetic flux lie in planes transverse to the direction of propagation. At the surface of the perfect conductors these flux lines are, of course, tangential.

As H_z is zero, it is evident from the Maxwell-Faraday integral equation that the electric field **E** has zero circulation in any transverse plane. The voltage drop between any two points in the plane is the same for all paths of the plane. Furthermore, the field lines of **E** meet the perfect conductors at right angles. These requirements are satisfied by an electric field distribution that has the identical form of a *static distribution arising from the surface charges of the conductors.* The field lines leave the positive charges of one conductor, normal to the surface, and terminate on the negative charges of the other, with the lines entirely in transverse planes.

As E_z is zero, there are no axial displacement currents; therefore, each line of magnetic flux links a conduction current. The **H**-field has a distribution identical to that of a *static field arising from steady currents on the surfaces of the conductors.*

At all points of the dielectric we have the equations $\text{curl}_z\, \mathbf{E} = 0$ and $\text{div}\, \mathbf{E} = 0$, with $E_z = 0$. It is easily deduced that

$$\partial^2 E_x/\partial x^2 + \partial^2 E_x/\partial y^2 = 0 \tag{20-1}$$

and E_y satisfies a similar equation. From the equations $\text{curl}_z\, \mathbf{H} = 0$ and $\text{div}\, \mathbf{H} = 0$, we can likewise deduce that H_x and H_y satisfy Eq. (20-1). Thus each *rectangular* field component satisfies the *two-dimensional* Laplace equation (20-1). *Two-dimensional static fields also satisfy this same equation*, as is evident from Eq. (19-46) with $\omega = 0$. The field distribution in a transverse plane is governed by an equation identical to that for two-dimensional static fields. The boundary conditions at the surfaces of the perfect conductors correspond to the static boundary conditions, it being understood that the steady current is confined to the surface layer and that its surface distribution in the transverse plane is that of the actual current.

Along the uniform line with perfect conductors the propagating wave is a *transverse electromagnetic wave*, or *TEM wave*. The field lines of **E** and **H** lie entirely in transverse planes, with $E_z = H_z = 0$. In a transverse plane at z_1, with equal and opposite charges $\pm q_1$ per meter and with current i_1 at time t_1, the field configuration is due to the actual time- and space-varying charges and currents. However, *this is precisely that which would be produced by steady charges and currents equal to* $\pm q_1$ *and* i_1 *at all points along the line, provided these steady charges and currents are given the transverse distributions of the actual charges and currents.*

Shown in Fig. 20-3 are the field lines of a TEM wave in a coaxial cable. Note that **E** and **H** are respectively normal and tangential to the conductors. Each electric line begins and ends on electric charge, and each magnetic line encircles the current of the inner conductor. Also, **E** and **H** are normal to one another at each point, and the Poynting vector **S** is directed axially.

Actual transmission lines are not, of course, made of perfect conductors. The currents of such conductors are distributed over the cross sections in accordance with the skin-effect equation, and an axial electric field, though small, exists both inside and outside. In addition, the current densities in some types of conductors may not be entirely axial. Consequently, the propagating fields have small axial components, and the Poynting vector has a small transverse component that accounts for the heat supplied to the conductors. The losses in the conductors, as well as in the dielectric, cause the wave to be attenuated as it propagates. Also, the field configuration is changed, but *for practical lines it is still approximately transverse electromagnetic*, though not exactly so. The calculation of the line parameters from static field configurations in transverse planes gives reasonable results. Of course, dielectric and copper losses must be considered. The TEM wave is the *principal* wave of a transmission line; the transverse

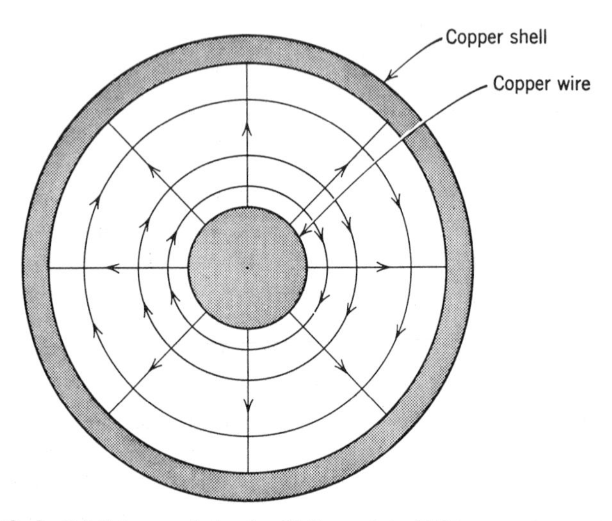

FIG. 20-3. Radial **E**-lines and circular **H**-lines of the TEM wave of a coaxial cable.

electric and the transverse magnetic waves, which have H_z and E_z respectively, are very much smaller on useful lines. TEM waves are discussed further in Sec. 22-8.

20-3. THE LINE EQUATIONS

There are four primary line parameters. These are the resistance R per unit length, the inductance L per unit length, the conductance G per unit length, and the capacitance C per unit length.

The parameter R, with the mks unit of ohm per meter, is used to account for the losses due to the line current i. R includes the resistances of *both* wires in one meter of axial length, and because of skin and proximity effects, it is a function of frequency. The voltage drop per unit length along the line, due to the series resistance R, is iR volts per meter.

The inductance L per unit length, with units of henrys per meter, is due to the magnetic field in the region in and around the conductors of the line. This magnetic field is produced by the axial, leakage, and displacement currents. There is, of course, energy stored in the magnetic field, and each conductor has magnetic flux linkages per unit length. Because of skin and proximity effects, L is a function of frequency. The voltage drop per unit length along the line, due to the inductance L, is $L\,\partial i/\partial t$ volts per meter.

Conductance G per unit length is the leakage conductance of the imperfect dielectric between the conductors. Its mks unit is the mho per meter. There is a flow of charge through this distributed conductance, resulting in a leakage current and ohmic losses. The leakage current per unit length is Gv amperes per meter, with v representing the voltage between the conductors. The line voltage v is, of course, a function of the axial coordinate z and time t.

The capacitance C per unit length, in farads per meter, is the ratio of the stored charge q per unit length to the line voltage v. At an arbitrary distance from one end of the line the charges on the two conductors are equal

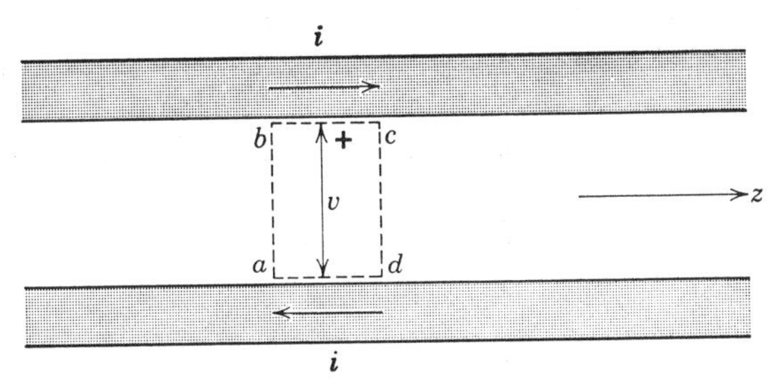

FIG. 20-4. A small section of a uniform line.

and opposite in sign; as shown in the preceding section, the electric field lines in the dielectric are essentially transverse, leaving the positive charges of one conductor and terminating on the negative charges of the other. This field stores energy and, as it is changing with time, it produces a displacement current between the conductors. This displacement current per unit length is $C\,\partial v/\partial t$ amperes per meter.

Shown in Fig. 20-4 is a small section of a line. It is not necessary that the two conductors be identical. As the electric field is essentially transverse, with zero circulation in a transverse plane, we can define a line voltage v at the axial coordinate z. This voltage is simply the line integral of **E** along any path in the plane, from one conductor to the other. It can be measured with a voltmeter, but the meter and its leads must be confined to the plane. The currents of the two conductors are equal and opposite, as indicated on the sketch. This follows from the fact that there are no axial displacement currents, and certainly the total current over an infinite plane normal to the z-axis is zero. Thus we have defined a line voltage and current, and these are functions of both z and t.

Let us now apply the Maxwell-Faraday law to the closed rectangular path *abcda* and its plane surface S. The paths *bc* and *da* along the surfaces of the conductors are assumed to be of differential length dz. The positive side of the surface S faces into the paper. Around the closed loop the sum of the voltage drops is

$$v_{ab} + v_{bc} + v_{cd} + v_{da} = -\partial(d\Phi)/\partial t$$

with $d\Phi$ denoting the differential magnetic flux out of the positive side of S. Rearranging terms gives

$$v_{cd} - v_{ba} = -(v_{bc} + v_{da}) - \partial(d\Phi)/\partial t$$

Clearly, $v_{cd} - v_{ba}$ is the differential increase dv in v as z increases by dz, and we obtain

$$dv = -(v_{bc} + v_{da}) - \partial(d\Phi)/\partial t \tag{20-2}$$

All terms of Eq. (20-2) are, of course, differentials.

For the moment let us suppose the conductors are lossless. This assumption requires that the voltages v_{bc} and v_{da} be zero, because the tangential component of **E** at the surface of a perfect conductor is zero. Equation (20-2) reduces to

$$dv = -\partial(d\Phi)/\partial t$$

As dv is the differential increase in the line voltage v corresponding to the increase dz in z, it is clear that *the increase in v per unit length at a fixed time is*

$$\frac{\partial v}{\partial z} = -\frac{\partial}{\partial t}\left(\frac{\partial \Phi}{\partial z}\right) \tag{20-3}$$

The term $\partial\Phi/\partial z$ represents the flux linkages per unit length at z; also, it is the space rate of increase, at the coordinate z, of the total flux linkages Φ of the line. Partial derivatives are used, for v and Φ are functions of both z and t. We note that there are no internal flux linkages.

It has been shown that the magnetic field lines are transverse; also, the field configuration in a transverse plane is identical to that of an infinite line with a current everywhere equal to that at the plane under consideration. Therefore, the instantaneous value of the magnetic flux linkages of an elemental section at the coordinate z is directly proportional to the instantaneous current *of the elemental section*, even though the current i is a function of z. Consequently, $\partial\Phi/\partial z = Li$, with L denoting a constant independent of both time and distance. Clearly L represents the flux linkages per ampere per unit length, and its unit is the henry per meter. In terms of the inductance parameter L, Eq. (20-3) becomes

$$\partial v/\partial z = -L\, \partial i/\partial t \tag{20-4}$$

Let us return to the more general case of imperfect conductors. The voltage drops v_{bc} and v_{da} in Eq. (20-2) are no longer zero, for a tangential field is required to produce the current. Because of skin effect the magnetic flux linkages of an elemental section are no longer precisely in time phase with the current of the section. Both R and L are functions of frequency, and *this requires that we consider a single-frequency excitation.* For sinusoidal time variations the sum of the voltages v_{bc} and v_{da} can be considered as consisting of two sinusoidal components; one of these is in time phase with i and the other is 90° out of time phase. Both components, however have amplitudes proportional to the amplitude of i. The fields along the paths bc and da depend on the value of the line current at the elemental section, *for the electromagnetic wave is still essentially a TEM wave.* Of course, the transverse field distribution is modified somewhat by skin effect, which is not always negligible. The component of $(v_{bc} + v_{da})$ that is in phase with i introduces into Eq. (20-4) a voltage iR, and the out-of-phase component can be combined into the term $L\,\partial i/\partial t$. The result can be written

$$-\frac{\partial v}{\partial z} = iR + L\frac{\partial i}{\partial t} \tag{20-5}$$

Equation (20-5) applies to nonsinusoidal time variations as well, provided R and L do not change appreciably throughout the range of the important frequency components of the excitation. This deduction relies on the principle of superposition and the Fourier series and integral. Precisely, the resistance R per unit length is the product of $1/i$ and that component of the sinusoidal line voltage drop per unit length, $-\partial v/\partial z$, that is in time phase with i. For sinusoidal time variations this definition clearly makes R a constant independent of time, regardless of skin effect, though R is a function of the frequency. Similiarly, we define the inductance L per unit length as the component of the line voltage drop per unit length that is 90° out of time phase with i, divided by $\partial i/\partial t$. Because of skin and proximity effects both R and L vary with frequency.

The second line equation will be derived with the aid of Fig. 20-5. Consider the closed surface S around the differential length dz of the top conductor. This surface consists of two cross sections and the outside surface between these sections. The current entering the left cross section is i, and that leaving the right cross section is $i + di$, with di denoting the increase in i as z increases by dz. Consequently, the net current *entering* S through the cross sections is $-di$. This, of course, must exactly equal the differential transverse current di_t leaving the length dz of the conductor. Therefore, $-di = di_t$, and on a per-unit-length basis this becomes

$$-\partial i/\partial z = \partial i_t/\partial z \tag{20-6}$$

The transverse current per unit length consists of two components. One is the leakage current per meter through the imperfect dielectric, and this is proportional to the line voltage v. The other component is the displacement current per meter through the capacitance of the conductors. As the displacement current density at a point is proportional to the time rate of change of the field **E**, it is evident that the displacement current per unit length is proportional to the time rate of change of the line voltage v. Thus the transverse leakage and displacement currents per

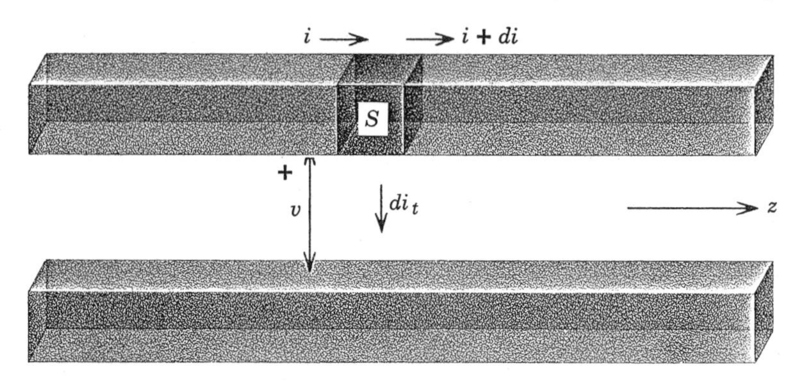

FIG. 20-5. A small section of a transmission line. The heavily shaded portion of the top conductor is of differential length dz and is surrounded by the closed surface S. The differential *transverse* current leaving S is di_t.

unit length are, respectively, vG and $C\,\partial v/\partial t$, with G and C representing constants independent of time. Equation (20-6) becomes

$$-\frac{\partial i}{\partial z} = vG + C\frac{\partial v}{\partial t} \tag{20-7}$$

Partial derivatives are used as i and v are functions of z and t. For sinusoidal time variations the term vG is the component of $-\partial i/\partial z$ that is in time phase with v, and the term $C\,\partial v/\partial t$ is the component that is 90° out of time phase with v. The justification for relating the transverse currents of an elemental section to the instantaneous line voltage of the section is based on our knowledge of the transverse field configuration of a TEM wave.

The resistance R, the inductance L, the conductance G, and the capacitance C correspond closely to equivalent circuit concepts. The distinction is that R, L, G, and C are, for the transmission line, always given on a per-unit-length basis. We can regard the line as a long circuit with parameters that are uniformly distributed along its length. Many of the principles of ordinary circuit theory can be utilized, but the equations contain the space coordinate z as well as the variable time. The distributed resistance, inductance, conductance, and capacitance cannot be lumped as is done in circuit theory, for the voltage and current vary with respect to the axial coordinate z. Each differential length dz has a resistance $R\,dz$, an inductance $L\,dz$, a conductance $G\,dz$, and a capacitance $C\,dz$. The distributed circuit that represents a small section of a line is shown in Fig. 20-6.

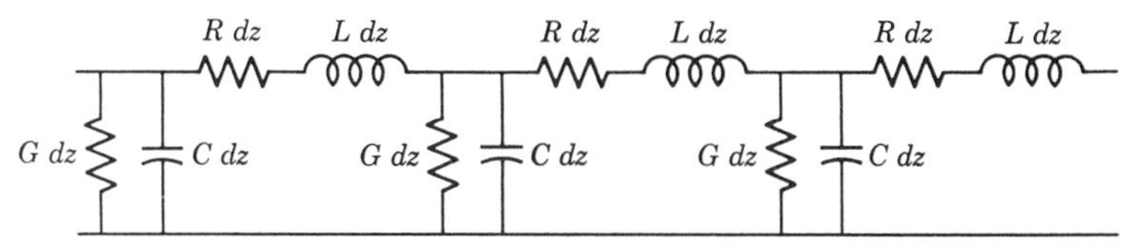

FIG. 20-6. A small section of a transmission line represented in terms of lumped elements of differential magnitudes.

For sinusoidal time variations Eqs. (20-5) and (20-7) can be written in complex-exponential form by replacing i with $\bar{I} \exp j\omega t$ and v with $\bar{V} \exp j\omega t$. As the exponentials of $j\omega t$ cancel, the equations become

$$d\bar{V}/dz = -(R + j\omega L)\bar{I} \tag{20-8}$$

$$d\bar{I}/dz = -(G + j\omega C)\bar{V} \tag{20-9}$$

The phasors are functions of the single variable z. Both sides of Eq. (20-8) have units of volts per meter, and the units of Eq. (20-9) are amperes per meter.

20-4. THE LINE PARAMETERS

The power supplied to a differential length dz of a line is the input power vi less the output power $(v + dv)(i + di)$. Neglecting the product $dv\,di$, this net power is $-i\,dv - v\,di$. From this we deduce that the net power per unit length supplied to the fields and charge carriers is

$$\frac{\partial p}{\partial z} = -i\frac{\partial v}{\partial z} - v\frac{\partial i}{\partial z} \tag{20-10}$$

The partial derivatives of v and i with respect to z can be eliminated by utilizing the line equations. The result is

$$\frac{\partial p}{\partial z} = i^2R + Li\frac{\partial i}{\partial t} + v^2G + Cv\frac{\partial v}{\partial t} \tag{20-11}$$

Suppose the current i of the differential section is $I_m \sin \omega t$. It is easily shown that the *time average* of the term $Li\,\partial i/\partial t$ is zero, and the same deduction applies to the term $Cv\,\partial v/\partial t$ for sinusoidal time variations. From Eq. (20-11) we find the time-average power per unit length to be

$$\frac{dP}{dz} = I_{rms}^2 R + V_{rms}^2 G \qquad (20\text{-}12)$$

This power is either dissipated as heat or it is radiated. Usually radiation is negligible. The Poynting vector of the principal wave is directed axially, and any radiation must be attributed to the much smaller wave components with axial fields. We note from Eq. (20-12) that R is the power loss per unit length, due to the line current, divided by I_{rms}^2; the conductance G is the average power loss per unit length, due to the leakage current, divided by V_{rms}^2.

The inductive term of Eq. (20-11) can be written $\partial(\frac{1}{2}Li^2)/\partial t$, and its average value is zero for sinusoidal time variations. Because of retardation associated with skin effect, the instantaneous energy $\frac{1}{2}Li^2$ of the inductance is not the instantaneous energy stored in the magnetic field. As time varies, however, the energy $\frac{1}{2}Li^2$ oscillates between zero and its maximum value, and over a complete period it contributes nothing to the average power dissipated. We deduce that the time-average energy $(W_H)_{\text{ave}}$ stored in the magnetic field per unit length equals $\frac{1}{2}LI_{rms}^2$, which is the average value of $\frac{1}{2}Li^2$. Accordingly, the inductance per unit length is

$$L = (2/I_{rms}^2)(W_H)_{\text{ave}} \qquad (20\text{-}13)$$

That part of L due to the energy stored within the conductors is the *internal inductance* per meter; that due to the energy of the external magnetic field is the *external inductance* per meter. At very high frequencies the currents are confined to thin surface layers, and the internal inductance is negligible. However, at low frequencies the internal inductance may be quite substantial. Equation (20-13) is similar to the expression for the inductance of an electric circuit. The difference is that Eq. (20-13) is on a per-unit-length basis, and hence L is a distributed parameter. Clearly *the expressions for inductance given in Chapters* 14 *and* 15 *also apply to the line parameter L*, provided the variables are understood to be for a unit length. If skin and proximity effects are negligible, or if the conductors are perfect, the instantaneous magnetic field at any point of a transverse plane is in phase with the current i at the location of the plane. For these cases $\frac{1}{2}Li^2$ is the instantaneous energy per unit length of the magnetic field of the line.

The capacitive term of Eq. (20-11) is similar in form to the inductive term, and the expression for C that corresponds to that deduced for L is

$$C = (2/V_{rms}^2)(W_E)_{\text{ave}} \qquad (20\text{-}14)$$

with $(W_E)_{\text{ave}}$ denoting the time-average energy per unit length stored in the electric field of the line. Also, we note from the line equation that the per-unit-length displacement current $\dot{\psi}$ between the conductors is $C\dot{v}$. As the electric flux ψ per meter equals the line charge q per meter, it is evident that $C\dot{v} = \dot{q}$. Integration gives

$$C = q/v \tag{20-15}$$

The constant of integration is zero, for in a transverse plane of a TEM wave, there is neither an electric field nor a voltage at the instant when the charge is zero.

For sinusoidal time variations the line constants R, L, G, and C are independent of time, and for uniform lines they are independent of z. However, they may be functions of frequency. Skin and proximity effects cause R and L to vary with frequency, and in practical lines other effects may cause all the parameters to depend on the frequency. For example, insulators used to support or space the conductors are likely to have frequency-dependent effects on the parameters. Also, radiation may be appreciable when discontinuities, including a mismatched load, produce waves that are not transverse electromagnetic. Of course, the parameters are approximately constant over a sufficiently limited frequency band, and at a single frequency they are truly constant. We note that the line equations are linear for constant R, L, G, and C. We shall now examine the transmission-line wave equations that govern the current and voltage distributions along the axial coordinate.

20-5. THE WAVE EQUATIONS

The line equations are

$$\frac{\partial v}{\partial z} = -iR - L\frac{\partial i}{\partial t} \tag{20-16}$$

$$\frac{\partial i}{\partial z} = -vG - C\frac{\partial v}{\partial t} \tag{20-17}$$

Taking the partial derivative of Eq. (20-16) with respect to z gives

$$\frac{\partial^2 v}{\partial z^2} = -R\frac{\partial i}{\partial z} - L\frac{\partial}{\partial t}\left(\frac{\partial i}{\partial z}\right)$$

Utilizing Eq. (20-17) to eliminate $\partial i/\partial z$ gives

$$\frac{\partial^2 v}{\partial z^2} = RGv + (LG + RC)\frac{\partial v}{\partial t} + LC\frac{\partial^2 v}{\partial t^2} \tag{20-18}$$

A similar equation in terms of the line current i can be obtained by differentiating Eq. (20-17) with respect to z and utilizing Eq. (20-16) to eliminate v. The result is

$$\frac{\partial^2 i}{\partial z^2} = RGi + (LG + RC)\frac{\partial i}{\partial t} + LC\frac{\partial^2 i}{\partial t^2} \tag{20-19}$$

Equations (20-18) and (20-19) are known as the *telegrapher's equations.* As we shall see, their mathematical solutions represent waves that propagate along the line. Transmission-line problems involve the application of these one-dimensional wave equations to lines with specified terminal conditions. It should be noted that the second partial time derivative drops out if either L or C is zero. The result resembles rather closely the diffusion equation, and the current and voltage are attenuated very rapidly. True wave propagation depends on the interchange of energy between the electric and magnetic fields. Consequently, both L and C are essential, for these are the energy-storage elements. The magnetic current density $\dot{\mathbf{B}}$ is associated with the inductance parameter, and the electric displacement current density $\dot{\mathbf{D}}$ is associated with the capacitance parameter. Both of these currents are present in electromagnetic waves.

For sinusoidal time variations we can eliminate the variable time by replacing v and i with $\bar{V}e^{j\omega t}$ and $\bar{I}e^{j\omega t}$, respectively. Of course, the amplitudes and angles of $\bar{V}$ and $\bar{I}$ are functions of the axial coordinate z. As $e^{j\omega t}$ cancels, the results are ordinary differential equations with the independent variable z. In complex-exponential form they are

$$\frac{d^2\bar{V}}{dz^2} = (R + j\omega L)(G + j\omega C)\bar{V} \tag{20-20}$$

$$\frac{d^2\bar{I}}{dz^2} = (R + j\omega L)(G + j\omega C)\bar{I} \tag{20-21}$$

Development of these from Eqs. (20-18) and (20-19) is suggested as an exercise.

The complex-exponential forms of the wave equations can be derived directly from Eqs. (20-8) and (20-9). Differentiation of Eq. (20-8) with respect to z gives

$$\frac{d^2\bar{V}}{dz^2} = -(R + j\omega L)\frac{d\bar{I}}{dz}$$

Replacing $d\bar{I}/dz$ with $-(G + j\omega C)\bar{V}$, from Eq. (20-9), gives Eq. (20-20). The corresponding equation for the current $\bar{I}$ is developed similarly.

Let

$$Z = R + j\omega L \text{ ohms/meter} \tag{20-22}$$

$$Y = G + j\omega C \text{ mhos/meter} \tag{20-23}$$

The parameters Z and Y are called the *loop impedance per unit length* and the *shunt admittance per unit length*, respectively. In terms of Z and Y the wave equations become

$$\frac{d^2\bar{V}}{dz^2} = ZY\bar{V} \tag{20-24}$$

$$\frac{d^2\bar{I}}{dz^2} = ZY\bar{I} \tag{20-25}$$

20-6. GENERAL SOLUTIONS OF THE WAVE EQUATIONS

Equations (20-24) and (20-25) are easily solved in terms of arbitrary constants. Each characteristic equation has the roots $\pm\sqrt{ZY}$ and, consequently, the general solutions are

$$\bar{V} = \bar{V}_1 e^{-\gamma z} + \bar{V}_2 e^{\gamma z} \tag{20-26}$$

$$\bar{I} = \bar{I}_1 e^{-\gamma z} + \bar{I}_2 e^{\gamma z} \tag{20-27}$$

with $\bar{V}_1$, $\bar{V}_2$, $\bar{I}_1$, and $\bar{I}_2$ representing complex constants and with γ representing $\sqrt{ZY}$. The constants $\bar{V}_1$ and $\bar{V}_2$ have units of volts, and the constants $\bar{I}_1$ and $\bar{I}_2$ have units of amperes. Of course, the product γz is dimensionless. The solutions are easily verified by direct substitution into the wave equations (20-24) and (20-25).

Let us consider the term $\bar{V}_1 e^{-\gamma z}$. The constant $\bar{V}_1$ is complex and can, therefore, be put in the form $V_1 e^{j\theta_1}$ with V_1 and θ_1 denoting real constants. As γ is complex, we can replace it with $\alpha + j\beta$ with α and β denoting the real and imaginary parts of γ. To obtain the instantaneous value as a function of time we multiply by $e^{j\omega t}$. The resulting voltage v_1 is

$$v_1 = V_1 e^{-\alpha z} e^{j(\omega t - \beta z + \theta_1)}$$

with either the real or imaginary part considered. Using Euler's identity and retaining only the imaginary part of the complex exponential give

$$v_1 = V_1 e^{-\alpha z} \sin(\omega t - \beta z + \theta_1) \tag{20-28}$$

This is a mathematical expression for a wave traveling in the positive z-direction. At any point z the maximum value of v_1 as time varies is $V_1 e^{-\alpha z}$. Thus the amplitude of the wave decreases exponentially with distance z.

The phase of the wave is $\omega t - \beta z + \theta_1$. Letting the phase equal a constant C gives $\omega t - \beta z + \theta_1 = C$, and the axial coordinate z of this point of constant phase is readily determined to be $z = (\omega/\beta)t + \theta_1/\beta - C/\beta$. The coordinate z is a function of time, and the rate at which it increases with respect to time is the velocity of the point of constant phase.

Therefore, the *phase* velocity, also called the *velocity of the wave*, is

$$v_p = \omega/\beta \text{ meters/second} \tag{20-29}$$

The voltage v_1 is a function of z and t. At a fixed point $z = z_1$, the voltage v_1 varies sinusoidally with time with a constant amplitude of $V_1 e^{-\alpha z_1}$. This is evident from Eq. (20-28) with $z = z_1$. At a fixed instant of time v_1 varies with z as indicated in Fig. 20-7. As time varies, this wave moves in the positive z-direction with a velocity ω/β meters per second. Each point of constant phase, such as a crest of the wave, decreases exponentially as it moves. This voltage wave, which propagates from the sending end of the line toward the receiving end, is called the *incident wave*.

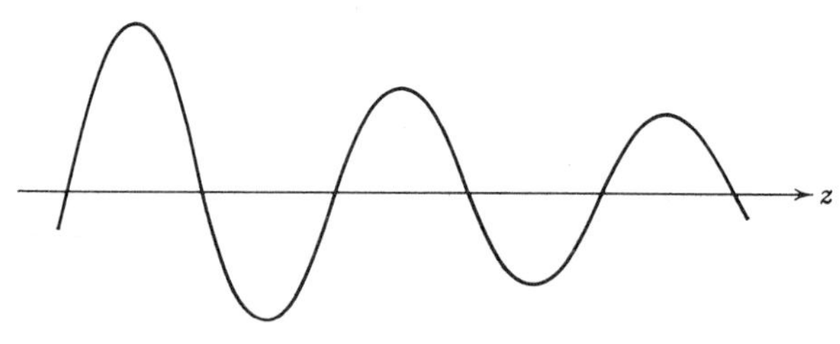

FIG. 20-7. The incident voltage wave along a portion of a line at a fixed instant of time.

Next, let us consider the term $\bar{V}_2 e^{\gamma z}$ in Eq. (20-26). A similar analysis reveals that this represents a wave traveling in the negative z-direction. Its phase velocity in the negative z-direction is also ω/β meters per second, and the amplitude $V_2 e^{\alpha z}$ decreases as z decreases. This wave, propagating from the receiving end toward the sending end, is called the *reflected wave*.

The terms of Eq. (20-27) represent traveling current waves. The expression $\bar{I}_1 e^{-\gamma z}$ is the incident wave that propagates in the positive z-direction; the expression $\bar{I}_2 e^{\gamma z}$ is the reflected wave that propagates in the direction of decreasing z. Both travel with a velocity ω/β meters per second, and both are attenuated as they propagate. The actual line current is, of course, the sum of the incident and reflected current waves; likewise, the voltage consists of both incident and reflected voltage waves. However, if the line is infinite, there is no reflected wave, and the reflected wave is also zero if the line is terminated at the receiving end in a manner such that all the energy of the incident wave is completely absorbed by the load.

In Eqs. (20-26) and (20-27), which are the general solutions of the line equations, the constant γ is

$$\gamma = \sqrt{ZY} \text{ meter}^{-1} \tag{20-30}$$

with $Z = R + j\omega L$ and $Y = G + j\omega C$. The constant γ is called the *complex propagation constant* of the line. The real part α of γ is the *attenuation constant*, and the imaginary part β is the *phase constant*. Thus

$$\gamma = \alpha + j\beta = \sqrt{ZY} \tag{20-31}$$

The attenuation constant α has dimensions of meter^{-1}, and its unit is the *neper per meter*, with *neper* being a dimensionless unit. The phase constant β also has dimensions of meter^{-1}, and its unit is the *radian per meter*. If R, L, G, C, and ω are known, α and β can be determined from Eq. (20-31). As an exercise, it is suggested that the student express each of the constants α and β directly in terms of the line parameters and the angular frequency.

For sinusoidal time variations the general solutions of the wave equations contain the four complex constants $\bar{V}_1$, $\bar{V}_2$, $\bar{I}_1$, and $\bar{I}_2$. However, the constants $\bar{V}_1$ and $\bar{I}_1$ are related, and the constants $\bar{V}_2$ and $\bar{I}_2$ are related. To show this let us write the line equations (20-8) and (20-9) in the form

$$\bar{I} = -\frac{1}{Z}\frac{d\bar{V}}{dz} \tag{20-32}$$

$$\bar{V} = -\frac{1}{Y}\frac{d\bar{I}}{dz} \tag{20-33}$$

We observe from Eq. (20-32) that $\bar{I}$ can be determined if $\bar{V}$ is known, and we likewise note from Eq. (20-33) that $\bar{V}$ can be determined if $\bar{I}$ is known. To obtain the relations between the constants let us substitute the expressions for $\bar{V}$ and $\bar{I}$ given in (20-26) and (20-27) into Eq. (20-33). The result is

$$\bar{V}_1 e^{-\gamma z} + \bar{V}_2 e^{\gamma z} = \frac{\gamma}{Y}\bar{I}_1 e^{-\gamma z} - \frac{\gamma}{Y}\bar{I}_2 e^{\gamma z}$$

Obviously, $\bar{V}_1 = (\gamma/Y)\bar{I}_1$ and $\bar{V}_2 = -(\gamma/Y)\bar{I}_2$. As $\gamma/Y = \sqrt{Z/Y}$, these relations can be written

$$\bar{V}_1 = Z_0\bar{I}_1 \tag{20-34}$$

$$\bar{V}_2 = -Z_0\bar{I}_2 \tag{20-35}$$

with Z_0 representing $\sqrt{Z/Y}$. The constant Z_0 is called the *characteristic impedance* of the line. Thus the general solutions of the line equations contain two arbitrary constants. These constants must be evaluated from the "boundary conditions" of a given problem.

20-7. THE INFINITE LINE

As stated previously, an infinite line is one whose length is so great that the energy of the guided electromagnetic wave is completely dissipated before the wave reaches the receiving end. Consequently, on an infinite line there can be no reflection and, therefore, the constants $\bar{V}_2$ and $\bar{I}_2$ in Eqs. (20-26) and (20-27) are zero. It follows that $\bar{V} = \bar{V}_1 e^{-\gamma z}$ and $\bar{I} = \bar{I}_1 e^{-\gamma z}$.

Let $\bar{V}_s$ and $\bar{I}_s$ denote the phasor line voltage and line current, respectively, at the sending end of the line, located at $z = 0$. Then $\bar{V}_1 = \bar{V}_s$ and $\bar{I}_1 = \bar{I}_s$. The voltage and current become

$$\bar{V} = \bar{V}_s e^{-\gamma z} \tag{20-36}$$

$$\bar{I} = \bar{I}_s e^{-\gamma z} \tag{20-37}$$

The ratio $\bar{V}/\bar{I}$ equals $\bar{V}_s/\bar{I}_s$, or $\bar{V}_1/\bar{I}_1$. By Eq. (20-34) this is Z_0, giving

$$\bar{V}/\bar{I} = Z_0 \tag{20-38}$$

The ratio $\bar{V}/\bar{I}$ at any point along the line is the impedance looking into the infinite length of the line from that point. It is clear that *the characteristic*

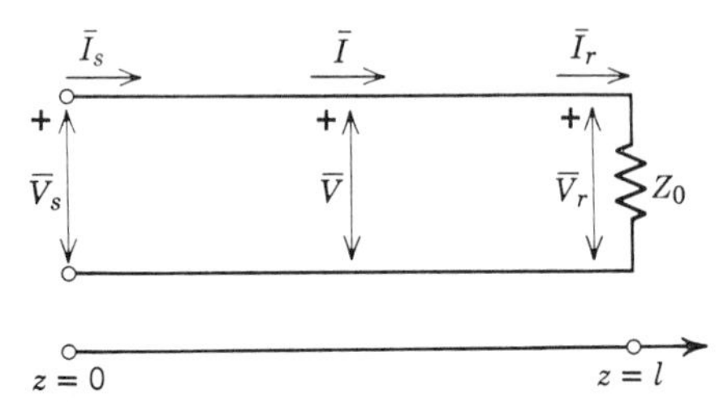

FIG. 20-8. A line terminated in its characteristic impedance.

impedance of a transmission line is the input impedance that would exist if the line were infinitely long. At each point along the infinite line the ratio of the phasor voltage to the phasor current equals this complex constant Z_0, which was defined as $\sqrt{Z/Y}$.

The voltage and the current of an infinite line are waves that propagate with velocity ω/β meters per second. The amplitudes of these waves decrease exponentially with respect to distance z from the sending end, and there is no reflection.

A line that is not infinite resembles an infinite line throughout its length l if it is terminated in its characteristic impedance Z_0. To verify this we shall consider the line illustrated in Fig. 20-8. The equations in terms of the arbitrary constants $\bar{I}_1$ and $\bar{I}_2$ are

$$\bar{V} = \bar{I}_1 Z_0 e^{-\gamma z} - \bar{I}_2 Z_0 e^{\gamma z} \tag{20-39}$$

$$\bar{I} = \bar{I}_1 e^{-\gamma z} + \bar{I}_2 e^{\gamma z} \tag{20-40}$$

The ratio $\bar{V}/\bar{I}$ at $z = l$ is $\bar{V}_r/\bar{I}_r$, which equals Z_0. Consequently, the right side of Eq. (20-39) divided by the right side of Eq. (20-40), with $z = l$, must equal Z_0. Thus

$$Z_0 = \frac{Z_0(\bar{I}_1 e^{-\gamma l} - \bar{I}_2 e^{\gamma l})}{\bar{I}_1 e^{-\gamma l} + \bar{I}_2 e^{\gamma l}}$$

It follows that $\bar{I}_2$ must be zero. Therefore, Eqs. (20-36) and (20-37) apply to a finite line terminated in its characteristic impedance Z_0.

The input impedance of a line terminated in Z_0 is equal to Z_0. In fact, the impedance at any point along the line, looking toward the load, is Z_0. All the energy of the incident wave that reaches the load impedance Z_0 is completely absorbed. If root-mean-square voltmeters and ammeters are placed at points along the line, their readings will decrease exponentially as their distance z from the sending end is increased. At each point the ratio of the voltage to the current is equal to Z_0.

EXAMPLE 1. At a frequency of 795.8 cps the parameters of a certain open-wire telephone line are

$$R = 4 \text{ ohms/mile} \qquad L = 3 \text{ mh/mile}$$

$$G = 1\ \mu\text{mho/mile} \qquad C = 0.015\ \mu\text{f/mile}$$

Determine the attenuation and phase constants, the phase velocity, and the characteristic impedance.

Solution. The angular frequency ω is 5000 radians/sec. Therefore,

$$Z = R + j\omega L = 4 + j15 = 15.53\underline{/75.1^\circ}$$

$$Y = G + j\omega C = (1 + j75)10^{-6} = 75 \times 10^{-6}\underline{/89.2^\circ}$$

$$\gamma = \sqrt{ZY} = \sqrt{0.001164\underline{/164.3^\circ}} = 0.03415\underline{/82.15^\circ}$$

The attenuation and phase constants are the real and imaginary parts of γ, respectively. Consequently,

$$\alpha = 0.00466 \text{ neper/mile} \qquad \beta = 0.0338 \text{ radian/mile}$$

The phase velocity v_p equals ω/β. This gives

$$v_p = \frac{5000}{0.0338} = 148{,}000 \text{ miles/sec}$$

The characteristic impedance Z_0 is obtained by evaluating $\sqrt{Z/Y}$, and the result is

$$Z_0 = 455\underline{/-7.1^\circ} = 452 - j56.1 \text{ ohms}$$

EXAMPLE 2. If the line of Example 1 is terminated in its characteristic impedance, find the voltage and current as functions of the length z from the sending end. Assume an input of one volt rms.

Solution. As the line is terminated in Z_0, its input impedance is Z_0, and $\bar{V}_s/\bar{I}_s$ equals Z_0. Therefore, using rms values,

$$\bar{I}_s = \bar{V}_s/Z_0 = (1\underline{/0^\circ})/(455\underline{/-7.1^\circ}) = 0.0022\underline{/7.1^\circ}$$

The phasor voltage and the phasor current are given by Eqs. (20-36) and (20-37) Replacing $\bar{V}_s$ with 1, $\bar{I}_s$ with 0.0022 exp $(j7.1^\circ)$, and the complex propagation constant γ with $0.00466 + j0.0338$, we obtain

$$\bar{V} = e^{-0.00466z}e^{-j0.0338z}$$

$$\bar{I} = 0.0022e^{-0.00466z}e^{j(-0.0338z+7.1^\circ)}$$

The voltage and current as instantaneous sinusoidal functions of time are

$$v = \sqrt{2}e^{-0.00466z} \sin (5000t - 0.0338z)$$

$$i = 0.0022\sqrt{2}e^{-0.00466z} \sin (5000t - 0.0338z + 7.1°)$$

At the sending end the rms phasor voltage is $1\underline{/0°}$. At a distance of 20 miles from this end the voltage is $0.911\underline{/-38.7°}$, and at a distance of 100 miles the voltage is $0.627\underline{/-194°}$.

20-8. REFLECTION

Let us now consider a line terminated in an arbitrary complex impedance Z_r. If some of the energy of the incident wave reaches the termination and

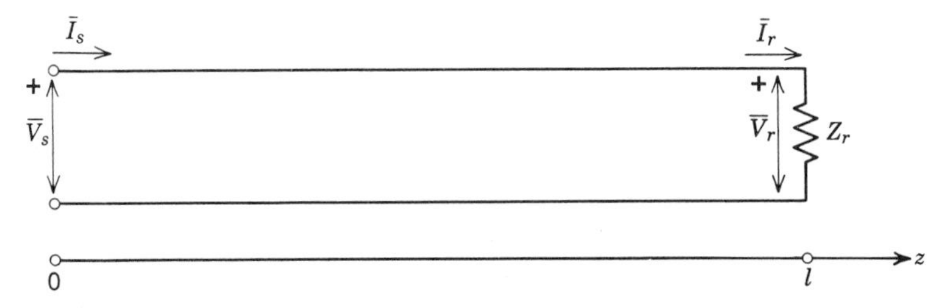

FIG. 20-9. Current and voltage designations.

if Z_r is not equal to Z_0, there will be a reflected wave. This component carries energy back to the source.

The general solutions of the line equations appear as Eqs. (20-26) and (20-27), which contain the complex constants $\bar{V}_1$, $\bar{V}_2$, $\bar{I}_1$, and $\bar{I}_2$. Two of these can be eliminated, for $\bar{V}_1 = \bar{I}_1 Z_0$ and $\bar{V}_2 = -\bar{I}_2 Z_0$ by Eqs. (20-34) and (20-35). In terms of $\bar{V}_1$ and $\bar{V}_2$, the general solutions are

$$\bar{V} = \bar{V}_1 e^{-\gamma z} + \bar{V}_2 e^{\gamma z} \tag{20-41}$$

$$\bar{I} = \frac{\bar{V}_1}{Z_0} e^{-\gamma z} - \frac{\bar{V}_2}{Z_0} e^{\gamma z} \tag{20-42}$$

The constants $\bar{V}_1$ and $\bar{V}_2$ depend on the conditions at the sending and receiving ends. Let the voltage and current at the sending end be designated $\bar{V}_s$ and $\bar{I}_s$, and let the corresponding quantities at the receiving end be $\bar{V}_r$ and $\bar{I}_r$. These are shown in Fig. 20-9.

At the sending end the axial coordinate z is zero, and the voltage and current are $\bar{V}_s$ and $\bar{I}_s$. Equations (20-41) and (20-42) become, at $z = 0$,

$$\bar{V}_s = \bar{V}_1 + \bar{V}_2 \tag{20-43}$$

$$\bar{I}_s = (\bar{V}_1/Z_0) - (\bar{V}_2/Z_0) \tag{20-44}$$

Solving for $\bar{V}_1$ and $\bar{V}_2$ gives

$$\bar{V}_1 = \tfrac{1}{2}(\bar{V}_s + \bar{I}_s Z_0) \tag{20-45}$$

$$\bar{V}_2 = \tfrac{1}{2}(\bar{V}_s - \bar{I}_s Z_0) \tag{20-46}$$

These express the constants $\bar{V}_1$ and $\bar{V}_2$ in terms of the sending-end conditions and Z_0.

At the receiving end the axial coordinate z equals the length l, and the voltage and current are $\bar{V}_r$ and $\bar{I}_r$. Equations (20-41) and (20-42) become

$$\bar{V}_r = \bar{V}_1 e^{-\gamma l} + \bar{V}_2 e^{\gamma l}$$

$$\bar{I}_r = \frac{\bar{V}_1}{Z_0} e^{-\gamma l} - \frac{\bar{V}_2}{Z_0} e^{\gamma l}$$

Solving for $\bar{V}_1$ and $\bar{V}_2$ gives

$$\bar{V}_1 = \tfrac{1}{2}(\bar{V}_r + \bar{I}_r Z_0) e^{\gamma l} \tag{20-47}$$

$$\bar{V}_2 = \tfrac{1}{2}(\bar{V}_r - \bar{I}_r Z_0) e^{-\gamma l} \tag{20-48}$$

These relations express the constants $\bar{V}_1$ and $\bar{V}_2$ in terms of the receiving-end conditions and the line constants.

The impedance looking into the line terminals from the sending end is the ratio $\bar{V}_s/\bar{I}_s$. This input impedance Z_i can be expressed in terms of the load impedance Z_r, which equals $\bar{V}_r/\bar{I}_r$. From Eqs. (20-43) and (20-44) we obtain

$$Z_i = Z_0 \frac{\bar{V}_1 + \bar{V}_2}{\bar{V}_1 - \bar{V}_2}$$

Utilizing (20-47) and (20-48) to replace $\bar{V}_1$ and $\bar{V}_2$, dividing both numerator and denominator by $\bar{I}_r$, and replacing $\bar{V}_r/\bar{I}_r$ with Z_r give

$$Z_i = Z_0 \frac{(Z_r + Z_0)e^{\gamma l} + (Z_r - Z_0)e^{-\gamma l}}{(Z_r + Z_0)e^{\gamma l} - (Z_r - Z_0)e^{-\gamma l}}$$

This can be put into the form

$$Z_i = Z_0 \frac{1 + \rho e^{-2\gamma l}}{1 - \rho e^{-2\gamma l}} \tag{20-49}$$

with the *reflection coefficient* ρ representing

$$\rho = \frac{Z_r - Z_0}{Z_r + Z_0} \tag{20-50}$$

To illustrate the use of the equations which have been developed, let us consider the line shown in Fig. 20-10. The known quantities are assumed to be the source voltage $\bar{V}_g$, the source impedance Z_g, the load impedance

Z_r, the length l, the parameters R, L, G, and C, and the frequency. The problem is to find the voltage and the current at points along the line. The main steps of the solution are:

1. *Calculate Z_0, γ, and the reflection coefficient ρ.* Recall that $Z_0 = \sqrt{Z/Y}$, $\gamma = \sqrt{ZY}$, and $\rho = (Z_r - Z_0)/(Z_r + Z_0)$.
2. *Determine the input impedance Z_i of the line.* This impedance is $Z_i = Z_0(1 + \rho e^{-2\gamma l})/(1 - \rho e^{-2\gamma l})$.
3. *Find the sending-end current $\bar{I}_s$ and voltage $\bar{V}_s$.* The current $\bar{I}_s$ is $\bar{V}_g/(Z_g + Z_i)$, and the voltage $\bar{V}_s$ equals $\bar{I}_s Z_i$.

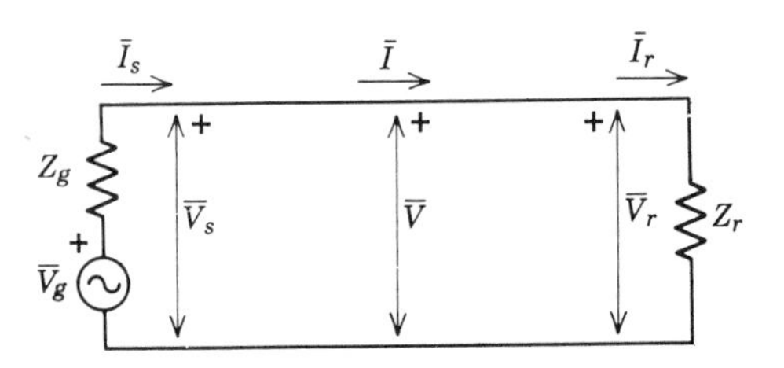

FIG. 20-10. Source, line, and load.

4. *Evaluate the coefficients $\bar{V}_1$ and $\bar{V}_2$.* Use $\bar{V}_1 = \frac{1}{2}(\bar{V}_s + \bar{I}_s Z_0)$ and $\bar{V}_2 = \frac{1}{2}(\bar{V}_s - \bar{I}_s Z_0)$.
5. *Determine $\bar{V}$ and $\bar{I}$*, using $\bar{V} = \bar{V}_1 e^{-\gamma z} + \bar{V}_2 e^{\gamma z}$ and $\bar{I} = (\bar{V}_1/Z_0)e^{-\gamma z} - (\bar{V}_2/Z_0)e^{\gamma z}$.

EXAMPLE. A 100-mile telephone line has a series resistance of 4 ohms/mile, an inductance of 3 mh/mile, a leakage conductance of 1 μmho/mile, and a shunt capacitance of 0.015 μf/mile, at an angular frequency $\omega = 5000$. At the sending end there is a generator supplying 100 volts peak, at 5000 radians per second, in series with a resistance of 300 ohms. The load at the receiving end consists of a 200-ohm resistor. Find the voltage and current as functions of z, and calculate their values at the midpoint of the line.

Solution. In Example 1 of the previous section the complex propagation constant γ and the characteristic impedance Z_0 were found to be

$$\gamma = 0.0342\underline{/82.15^\circ} = 0.00466 + j0.0338$$

$$Z_0 = 455\underline{/-7.1^\circ} = 452 - j56.1$$

The load impedance $Z_r = 200$. The reflection coefficient ρ is found to be $-0.396\underline{/-7.6^\circ}$.

Calculation of the input impedance Z_i requires evaluation of $e^{-2\gamma l}$. As $l = 100$ this exponential becomes

$$e^{-2\gamma l} = e^{-0.932}e^{-j6.76} = 0.394\underline{/-6.76} = 0.394\underline{/-27.3^\circ}$$

The product $\rho e^{-2\gamma l}$ becomes $-0.128 + j0.0890$. Calculation of Z_i yields $Z_i = 353\underline{/3.3^\circ} = 353 + j20.1$.

The sending-end current $\bar{I}_s$ is $\bar{V}_g/(Z_g + Z_i)$. The impedance Z_g is 300 ohms resistive, and $\bar{V}_g = 100\underline{/0°}$. Therefore, $\bar{I}_s = 100/(300 + 353 + j20.1) = 0.153\underline{/-1.8°}$. The sending-end voltage $\bar{V}_s$ is I_sZ_i, or $54\underline{/1.5°}$, or $54 + j1.41$.

The coefficients $\bar{V}_1$ and $\bar{V}_2$ are

$$\bar{V}_1 = \tfrac{1}{2}(\bar{V}_s + I_sZ_0) = 61.4\underline{/-4.35°}$$

$$\bar{V}_2 = \tfrac{1}{2}(\bar{V}_s - I_sZ_0) = -9.58\underline{/-39.35°}$$

Consequently, the line voltage $\bar{V}$ and the line current $\bar{I}$, as functions of z, are

$$\bar{V} = (61.4\underline{/-4.35°})e^{-\gamma z} - (9.58\underline{/-39.35°})e^{\gamma z}$$

$$\bar{I} = (0.135\underline{/2.75°})e^{-\gamma z} + (0.021\underline{/-32.3°})e^{\gamma z}$$

with $\gamma = 0.00466 + j0.0338$.

At the midpoint of the line, z is 50, and γz is $0.233 + j1.69$. The exponential of $-\gamma z$ becomes $e^{-0.233}e^{-j1.69}$, or $0.791\underline{/-96.8°}$. The exponential of γz becomes $1.262\underline{/96.8°}$. Therefore,

$$\bar{V} = (61.4\underline{/-4.35°})(0.791\underline{/-96.8°}) - (9.58\underline{/-39.35°})(1.262\underline{/96.8°})$$

Evaluation gives $\bar{V} = 60.0\underline{/-105.4°}$. This is the phasor voltage, maximum value, at $z = 50$ miles. Similarly, the current is found to be $\bar{I} = 0.0829\underline{/-87.4°}$. The instantaneous voltage and current at the midway point are

$$v = 60 \sin (5000t - 105.4°)$$

$$i = 0.0829 \sin (5000t - 87.4°)$$

The complex impedance at the midway point, looking toward the load, is the ratio of $\bar{V}$ to $\bar{I}$. This gives an impedance of $725\underline{/-18°}$. The same result can be obtained from Eq. (20-49), with $l = 50$.

The voltage and current are readily determined at any point z, although the calculations are tedious. The values of $\bar{V}$ and $\bar{I}$ at the sending end, at the 50-mile point, and at the receiving end are given below.

$$\bar{V}_s = 54\underline{/1.5°} \qquad \bar{I}_s = 0.153\underline{/-1.8°}$$

$$\bar{V}_{50} = 60\underline{/-105.4°} \qquad \bar{I}_{50} = 0.0829\underline{/-87.4°}$$

$$\bar{V}_r = 23.4\underline{/-193°} \qquad \bar{I}_r = 0.117\underline{/-193°}$$

If the line were terminated in its characteristic impedance, there would be no reflected wave, and the voltage and current would decrease exponentially with respect to the axial coordinate z. However, in this problem there is reflection, The voltage rises and then falls as z increases, and the current falls and then rises. The sum of the incident and reflected waves yields this standing-wave effect.

20-9. SOME USEFUL LINE EQUATIONS

By utilizing Eqs. (20-45) and (20-46) we can express the voltage and current in terms of the sending-end conditions and the line constants.

The results are

$$\bar{V} = \tfrac{1}{2}(\bar{V}_s + \bar{I}_s Z_0)e^{-\gamma z} + \tfrac{1}{2}(\bar{V}_s - \bar{I}_s Z_0)e^{\gamma z} \tag{20-51}$$

$$\bar{I} = \frac{1}{2Z_0}(\bar{V}_s + \bar{I}_s Z_0)e^{-\gamma z} - \frac{1}{2Z_0}(\bar{V}_s - \bar{I}_s Z_0)e^{\gamma z} \tag{20-52}$$

These are readily converted into the form

$$\bar{V} = \bar{V}_s \cosh \gamma z - \bar{I}_s Z_0 \sinh \gamma z \tag{20-53}$$

$$\bar{I} = \bar{I}_s \cosh \gamma z - \frac{\bar{V}_s}{Z_0} \sinh \gamma z \tag{20-54}$$

It is possible to eliminate either $\bar{V}_s$ or $\bar{I}_s$. From Eq. (20-49) we deduce that the current $\bar{I}_s = (\bar{V}_s/Z_0)(1 - \rho e^{-2\gamma l})/(1 + \rho e^{-2\gamma l})$. Eliminating $\bar{I}_s$ in Eqs. (20-51) and (20-52) yields

$$\bar{V} = \bar{V}_s \frac{e^{\gamma(l-z)} + \rho e^{-\gamma(l-z)}}{e^{\gamma l} + \rho e^{-\gamma l}} \tag{20-55}$$

$$\bar{I} = \frac{\bar{V}_s}{Z_0} \frac{e^{\gamma(l-z)} - \rho e^{-\gamma(l-z)}}{e^{\gamma l} + \rho e^{-\gamma l}} \tag{20-56}$$

The term $(l - z)$ represents the distance from the receiving end of the line. If Eq. (20-49) is employed to eliminate $\bar{V}_s$ in (20-51) and (20-52), expressions for $\bar{V}$ and $\bar{I}$ are obtained in terms of the sending-end current $\bar{I}_s$.

The voltage and current can also be expressed in terms of the receiving-end conditions. With the aid of Eqs. (20-47) and (20-48) we can write the voltage and current as

$$\bar{V} = \tfrac{1}{2}(\bar{V}_r + \bar{I}_r Z_0)e^{\gamma l}e^{-\gamma z} + \tfrac{1}{2}(\bar{V}_r - \bar{I}_r Z_0)e^{-\gamma l}e^{\gamma z} \tag{20-57}$$

$$\bar{I} = \frac{1}{2Z_0}(\bar{V}_r + \bar{I}_r Z_0)e^{\gamma l}e^{-\gamma z} - \frac{1}{2Z_0}(\bar{V}_r - \bar{I}_r Z_0)e^{-\gamma l}e^{\gamma z} \tag{20-58}$$

These are easily put into the form

$$\bar{V} = \bar{V}_r \cosh \gamma(l - z) + \bar{I}_r Z_0 \sinh \gamma(l - z) \tag{20-59}$$

$$\bar{I} = \bar{I}_r \cosh \gamma(l - z) + \frac{\bar{V}_r}{Z_0} \sinh \gamma(l - z) \tag{20-60}$$

By replacing $\bar{V}_r$ with $\bar{I}_r Z_r$ we obtain the voltage and current in terms of the receiving-end current. The results are readily converted to

$$\bar{V} = \tfrac{1}{2}\bar{I}_r[(Z_r + Z_0)e^{\gamma(l-z)} + (Z_r - Z_0)e^{-\gamma(l-z)}] \tag{20-61}$$

$$\bar{I} = \frac{\bar{I}_r}{2Z_0}[(Z_r + Z_0)e^{\gamma(l-z)} - (Z_r - Z_0)e^{-\gamma(l-z)}] \tag{20-62}$$

If the current is measured at the receiving end, Eqs. (20-61) and (20-62) can be used to calculate the voltage and current at any distance.

The input impedance of a line, given by Eq. (20-49), can be expressed in terms of hyperbolic functions, giving

$$Z_i = Z_0 \frac{Z_r \cosh \gamma l + Z_0 \sinh \gamma l}{Z_0 \cosh \gamma l + Z_r \sinh \gamma l} \tag{20-63}$$

The *transfer impedance* Z_t is defined as the ratio of $\bar{V}_s$ to $\bar{I}_r$. This ratio is obtained directly from Eq. (20-61) by letting z equal zero. The result is

$$Z_t = \frac{\bar{V}_s}{\bar{I}_r} = \tfrac{1}{2}[(Z_r + Z_0)e^{\gamma l} + (Z_r - Z_0)e^{-\gamma l}] \tag{20-64}$$

In hyperbolic form this becomes

$$Z_t = Z_0 \sinh \gamma l + Z_r \cosh \gamma l \tag{20-65}$$

The hyperbolic forms of the equations presented in this section are quite useful in the study of certain line phenomena. In most cases, however, they are not convenient for computational work.

The reflection coefficient ρ has been defined as the ratio $(Z_r - Z_0)/(Z_r + Z_0)$. From Eq. (20-61), noting the expressions for the incident and reflected waves, we observe that this is equal to the ratio of the reflected phasor voltage to the incident phasor voltage at the receiving end. Thus

$$\rho = \frac{Z_r - Z_0}{Z_r + Z_0} = \frac{\textit{reflected phasor voltage at } z = l}{\textit{incident phasor voltage at } z = l} \tag{20-66}$$

If $Z_r = Z_0$, the reflection coefficient is zero, and there is no reflected wave. If the receiving end is open, the reflection coefficient is unity, and the reflected voltage at the open equals the incident voltage. For a short circuit, $\rho = -1$. In this case the incident and reflected voltage waves at the short circuit are equal in magnitude and 180° out of time phase; their sum is, of course, zero. In general, ρ is a complex number, with a magnitude greater than or less than unity, depending upon the characteristic and load impedances.

20-10. THE EQUIVALENT TEE

The sending-end voltage and current of a line are expressed in terms of the receiving-end voltage and current by Eqs. (20-59) and (20-60) with $z = 0$. These equations are easily solved for $\bar{V}_s$ and $\bar{V}_r$ in terms of $\bar{I}_s$ and $\bar{I}_r$, and the results are

$$\bar{V}_s = z_{11}\bar{I}_s + z_{12}(-\bar{I}_r) \tag{20-67}$$

$$\bar{V}_r = z_{21}\bar{I}_s + z_{22}(-\bar{I}_r) \tag{20-68}$$

with

$$z_{11} = z_{22} = Z_0 \coth \gamma l \tag{20-69}$$

$$z_{12} = z_{21} = Z_0/\sinh \gamma l \tag{20-70}$$

The so-called *z-parameters* of the line are complex impedances.

The equivalent T-circuit of the line in terms of the z-parameters is shown in Fig. 20-11. This lumped circuit properly relates the input and output

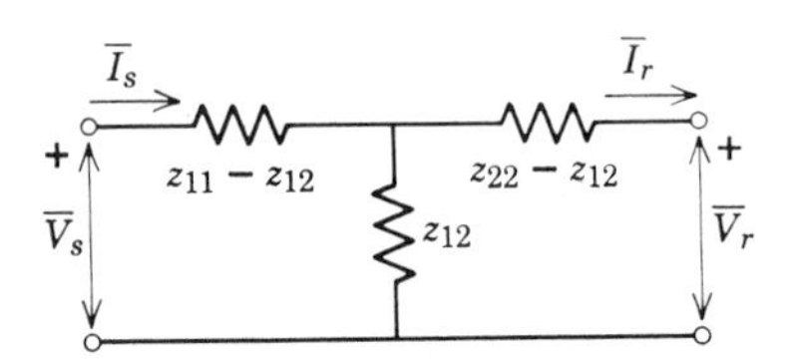

FIG. 20-11. Equivalent T-circuit.

voltages and currents, regardless of the external connections, for the application of Kirchhoff's voltage law to the two meshes yields Eqs. (20-67) and (20-68). Each of the series impedances equals $Z_0 \coth \gamma l - Z_0/\sinh \gamma l$, and it is easily shown that this expression equals $Z_0 \tanh \frac{1}{2}\gamma l$. Figure 20-12 gives the equivalent T in terms of the constants Z_0, γ, and l. As Z_0 and γ are functions of frequency, the impedances of the T are also functions of frequency.

The T-circuit is frequently helpful in analysis. For example, if we wish to investigate the effect of changing the load impedance, it may be desirable

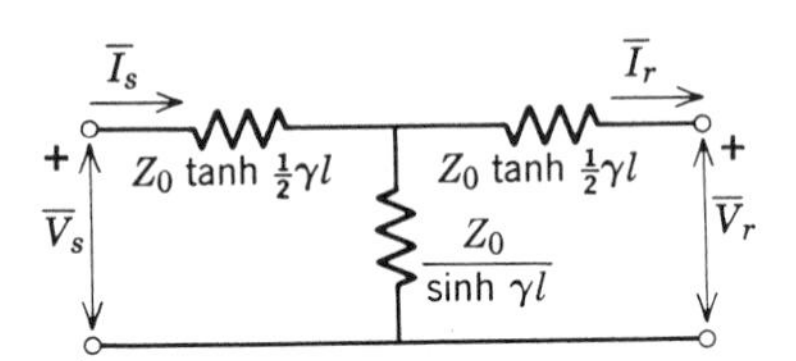

FIG. 20-12. Equivalent T-circuit.

to use the T-circuit; the same T is used for each load, provided the frequency is constant. The lumped circuit is valuable in the laboratory, for it can simulate an actual telephone or power line hundreds of miles long.

Suppose αl and βl are each very much less than unity. For this case it is easily shown that $\tanh \frac{1}{2}\gamma l \approx \frac{1}{2}\gamma l$, and $\sinh \gamma l \approx \gamma l$. The series and shunt impedances of the T become $\frac{1}{2}Z_0\gamma l$ and $Z_0/(\gamma l)$, respectively, and in terms of the loop impedance Z and shunt admittance Y these T-circuit impedances become $\frac{1}{2}Zl$ and $1/(Yl)$. Thus the circuit of Fig. 20-13 is a valid equivalent circuit, *provided* $\alpha l \ll 1$ and $\beta l \ll 1$. The advantage of this circuit is that it applies to all frequencies as long as αl and βl are small. As both α and β increase with frequency, it follows that the circuit of Fig. 20-13 applies to frequencies from zero to some maximum value. This maximum frequency is small if the length l is large, but the maximum frequency is large if the length l is small. A given line with a specified maximum frequency can be divided into a number of short lengths with each section having small values of αl and βl at the highest frequency. The circuit of Fig. 20-13 can then be used to simulate each section, and the cascade connection of

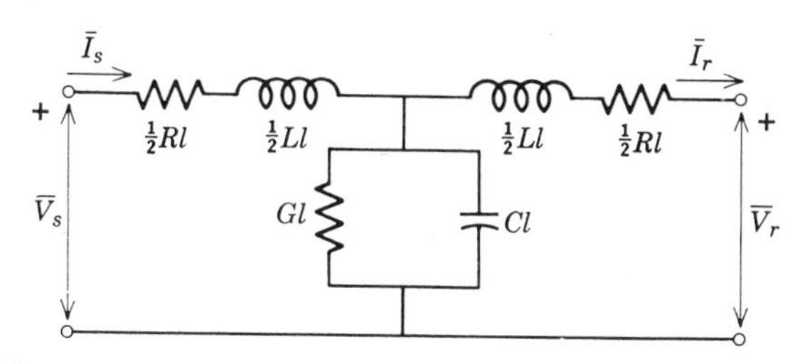

FIG. 20-13. Approximate T-circuit, provided αl and βl are small.

these circuits approximates the entire line over its frequency range. Such lumped-constant networks, which duplicate the behavior of actual lines, are called *artificial lines.*

Artificial lines can be constructed in the laboratory to simulate the performance of actual traveling waves. They also have other uses. For example, they are often used in high-power radar modulators to develop square pulses, with the duration of each pulse determined by the time of propagation along the simulated line. They are frequently used in oscilloscopes to delay the signal long enough for the sweep to begin. The following example illustrates the design of an artificial line.

EXAMPLE. Design an artificial line to duplicate the performance from zero to 2000 cycles of a 12-mile length of telephone line whose primary constants R, L, G, and C are 10 ohms/mile, 3 mh/mile, 10 μmhos/mile, and 0.012 μf/mile, respectively.

Solution. At 2000 cycles $Z = 39.0\underline{/75.1^\circ}$ and $Y = 0.000151\underline{/86.2^\circ}$. From these, the attenuation constant is determined to be 0.0124 neper/mile, and the phase constant is 0.0757 radian/mile. As β is greater than α, we must select the length l of each section so that βl is small compared with unity. A conservative design criterion is to select l so that $\beta l = 0.1$. This makes both αl and βl less than 0.1 for all frequencies up to the maximum of 2000 cycles. Thus $0.0757l = 0.1$, and $l = 1.32$ mile. For convenience, we select a length l of 1.2 miles, and the number of sections required to simulate the 12-mile line becomes 10. Each of the 10 cascaded circuits is the T of Fig. 20-13, with $\frac{1}{2}Rl = 6$ ohms, $\frac{1}{2}Ll = 1.8$ mh, $Gl = 12$ μmhos, and $Cl = 0.0144$ μf. The resulting network approximates the line for all frequencies up to about 2000 cycles.

REFERENCES

See References of Chapter 21.

PROBLEMS

Sections 20-1, 20-2, *and* 20-3

20-1. Calculate the ratio of the physical length l to the free-space wavelength λ of (*a*) a 200-mile 60-cycle power line; (*b*) a 5-mile telephone line at 4000 cycles; (*c*) a 10-foot TV lead-in line at 300 mc; and (*d*) a 2-inch 3000 mc line.

20-2. The current i is $0.02e^{-0.01z} \sin (10^4 t - 0.06z - 50°)$ along a certain telephone line, with z denoting the distance from the sending end in miles. The distributed resistance R and inductance L are 10 ohms/mile and 0.004 henry/mile, respectively. As sinusoidal functions of time, find the resistive and inductive voltage drops per mile at $z = 0$ and also at $z = 20$. Using complex exponentials, add these drops at $z = 20$, obtaining the total voltage drop per mile. This is the rate at which the voltage v between the conductors decreases with respect to the axial distance z at the specified point. Calculate this space rate of decrease at time $t = 0$.

20-3. The voltage v is $13.54e^{-0.01z} \sin (10^4 t - 0.06z - 54.6°)$ along a certain telephone line, with z denoting the distance from the sending end in miles. The distributed conductance G and capacitance C are 7.65 μmhos/mile and 0.00894 μf/mile, respectively. As sinusoidal functions of time, find the leakage and displacement currents per mile at $z = 0$ and also at $z = 20$. Using complex exponentials, add these currents at $z = 20$, obtaining the total shunt current per mile. This is the rate at which the current i along the line decreases with respect to the axial distance z at the specified point. Calculate this space rate of decrease at time $t = 0$.

20-4. The voltage v and the current i of the two preceding problems apply to the same line. Verify that these quantities satisfy the line equations, given as (20-5) and (20-7).

Section 20-4

20-5. For the line of Probs. 20-2 and 20-3, with the current and voltage as specified, calculate the time-average power loss per mile at $z = 0$ and at $z = 20$. In addition, at these same points find the time-average energy stored in the magnetic field per mile and also that stored in the electric field per mile.

20-6. If $i = 2e^{-0.016z} \sin (\omega t - 2.1z)$ at 100 mc along a certain coaxial line with negligible leakage, show that $d\bar{I}/dz = j\omega\bar{q}$, with $\bar{I}$ and $\bar{q}$ denoting the phasor current and phasor charge, respectively. Find the stored charge q per meter and the displacement current per meter between the conductors. Also, determine the line voltage v if C is 95 $\mu\mu$f/m.

20-7. The *dissipation factor* D of a medium is the ratio of the maximum value of the drift current density to the maximum value of the displacement current density. Show that $D = \sigma/(\omega\epsilon)$, with ω denoting the angular frequency. Also, show that the conductance G per unit length of a line equals ωCD, with C denoting the capacitance per unit length and D denoting the dissipation factor of the dielectric.

20-8. The inner conductor of a coaxial cable has a radius of 0.1 cm and the outer conductor has an inner radius of 0.4 cm and an outer radius of 0.5 cm. The conductors are copper with a conductivity of 5.8×10^7 mhos/m, and at one megacycle the dielectric has a dielectric constant of 2 and a dissipation factor (see Prob. 20-7) of 0.002. Calculate the line parameters at 1 mc. Do not neglect internal inductance.

(*Ans.:* $R = 0.0519$ ohm/m, $L = 0.286$ μh/m, $G = 1.01$ μmhos/m, $C = 80.3$ $\mu\mu$f/m.)

20-9. Calculate the line parameters of the coaxial line of Prob. 20-8 at a frequency of 60 cycles. Use the same dielectric constant and dissipation factor and neglect skin effect. Refer to Prob. 14-32.

(*Ans.:* $R = 0.00610$ ohm/m, $L = 0.344$ μh/m, $G = 60.5$ $\mu\mu$mhos/m, $C = 80.3$ $\mu\mu$f/m.)

20-10. The axes of two parallel wires, each of radius 0.25 cm, are 30 cm apart in free space. The wires are made of copper with a conductivity of 5.8×10^7 mhos/m. Find the line parameters per mile at 60 cycles. Skin effect is negligible.

Sections 20-6 and 20-7

20-11. The current i along a transmission line is the sum of the incident current wave i_1 and the reflected current wave i_2. Find the reading of an rms ammeter at $z = 20$, if the currents are

$$i_1 = 15e^{-0.05z} \cos(\omega t - 0.1z + 35°)$$

$$i_2 = 2e^{0.05z} \cos(\omega t + 0.1z - 40°)$$

20-12. A certain open-wire telephone line, with 104-mil copper wires spaced 12 inches apart, has a resistance R of 10.3 ohms/mile, an inductance L of 0.00366 henry/mile, a conductance G of 3.12 μmhos/mile, and a capacitance C of 0.00882 μf/mile, at 500 cycles. Calculate the attenuation and phase constants, the phase velocity, and the characteristic impedance.

(*Ans.:* $\gamma = 0.008485 + j0.01893$, $Z_0 = 744\underline{/-17.7°}$.)

20-13. If the line of the preceding problem is terminated in its characteristic impedance, find the line voltage and current as functions of the distance z from the sending end. The rms input voltage is $1\underline{/0°}$. For a length of 50 miles determine the voltage and current at the receiving end, and calculate the time-average power to the load.

20-14. A twisted pair of wires in a telephone cable has a resistance R of 440 ohms/mile, an inductance L of 0.000832 henry/mile, a conductance G of 47 μmhos/mile, and a capacitance C of 0.079 μf/mile, at 15,000 cycles. Calculate the attenuation and phase constants, the phase velocity, and the characteristic impedance.

(*Ans.:* $\gamma = 1.176 + j1.395$, $Z_0 = 245\underline{/-39.8°}$.)

20-15. If the line of the preceding problem is 2 miles long and terminated in its characteristic impedance, find the line voltage and current as functions of the distance z from the sending end. Also, calculate the efficiency of transmission, defined as the ratio of the power to the load to the power supplied to the input terminals of the line, multiplied by 100%. Assume an rms input voltage of $1\underline{/0°}$.

Section 20-8

20-16. A 50-mile telephone line with constants as given in Prob. 20-12 is fed at the sending end by a 500-cycle generator. The rms open-circuit voltage of the generator is 10 volts, and its internal impedance is 114 ohms resistive. The load at the receiving end is a 500-ohm resistor. Find the rms phasor voltages at the sending and receiving ends, and calculate the power supplied by the generator and the power to the load.

(*Ans.*: $\bar{V}_s = 8.89\underline{/-1.2^\circ}$, $\bar{V}_r = 4.33\underline{/-48.0^\circ}$, $P_g = 87.3$ mw, $P_L = 37.5$ mw.)

20-17. Repeat Prob. 20-16 with the 500-ohm load resistor replaced with a 300-ohm resistor.

20-18. A 1-mile telephone cable circuit with constants as given in Prob. 20-14 is fed at the sending end by a 15,000-cycle generator. The rms open-circuit voltage of the generator is 10 volts, and its internal impedance is 200 ohms resistive. The load at the receiving end is a 250-ohm resistor. Find the rms phasor currents at the sending and receiving ends, and calculate the power supplied by the generator and the power to the load.

Section 20-9

20-19. A transmission line has a propagation constant of $0.008 + j0.012$ per mile, a characteristic impedance of $850\underline{/-23^\circ}$ ohms, a length of 50 miles, and a resistive load of 600 ohms. Find the transfer impedance, and calculate the power to the load if the input voltage is 100 volts rms.

20-20. Calculate the current ratio $\bar{I}_r/\bar{I}_s$ of the line of the preceding problem. Use Eq. (20-62) with $z = 0$. For an rms input current of 10 ma, what is the power to the load?

20-21. The R, L, G, and C constants of a certain transmission system are 0.5 ohm/m, 0.4 μh/m, 50 μmhos/m, and 40 $\mu\mu$f/m, respectively. The angular frequency is 10^7 radians/sec, and the length of the line is 39.27 m. If the line is driven with an rms current of 0.1 ampere, find the input power and the power supplied to the load for load impedances of zero, Z_0, and infinity.

20-22. A 100-meter transmission line has R, L, G, and C constants of 0.5 ohm/m, 0.4 μh/m, 50 μmhos/m, and 40 $\mu\mu$f/m, respectively. If the voltage across the 50-ohm load resistor is $5 \cos 10^7 t$, find the instantaneous voltage and current at the sending end and also at the midpoint of the line.

Section 20-10

20-23. Find the 15,000-cycle equivalent T of a 1-mile length of the cable pair of Prob. 20-14. Also, design an artificial line that simulates this 1-mile length for frequencies from 0 to 15,000 cycles. Select the length l of each section so that αl and βl are less than 0.15 for all frequencies, and assume R, L, G, and C are constant.

20-24. Find the equivalent T of the transmission system of Prob. 20-21. Also, design an artificial line that simulates this system for angular frequencies from 0 to 10^7 radians/sec. Select the length l of each section so that αl and βl are less than 0.1 throughout the frequency band, and assume R, L, G, and C are constant.

Transmission Lines II

CHAPTER 21

Electric power generated in large central stations is transmitted to consumers over power transmission lines. Telephone lines guide communication signals from point to point. In the first part of this chapter special characteristics of these lines are briefly described.

Communication signals transmitted along lines are usually distorted. The different frequency components of a signal may propagate at different velocities and be attenuated unequally. Distortion along a line may be due to the characteristics of the line itself or to an improper termination, and both causes are investigated.

Attenuation of signals along a line depends on the losses and the physical length. If the losses per unit length are small and if the line is physically short, the attenuation may be negligible. In particular, lines at ultrahigh frequencies are usually short physically, though long electrically, and such lines are frequently treated as lossless. Both lossless and low-loss lines are considered in the latter part of this chapter.

21-1. POWER TRANSMISSION LINES

In the United States electric energy is transported by power lines that operate at a frequency of 60 cps. Under steady-state conditions most of these are electrically short, having lengths considerably less than 0.1 wavelength. Steady-state analysis is often accomplished by means of the T-circuit or the corresponding π-circuit. If the line is short, the shunt element is usually neglected, and the series impedance is simply the lumped resistance and inductance of the line.

A complex power transmission system involves numerous generators, loads, and lines that are interconnected. Practical solutions to power-system problems are frequently obtained with the aid of large digital computers. Also utilized are analogue computers known as *network analyzers*, which employ equivalent circuits to represent the lines, and contain sources and loads to simulate low-power models of complete systems. They are used in system studies to determine the proper dispatching of power from a number of generating stations to a number of loads, to determine the proper protective-breaker settings, and to solve the detailed stability problems.

Normally, the leakage conductance is negligible in power lines. The loss is almost entirely due to the series resistance of the conductors, and this loss is proportional to the square of the current. It follows that a given power is transmitted most efficiently by utilizing a large voltage and a small current. Line voltages of 115, 230, and 287 kv are common with substantially higher voltages in use. In order to obtain a large ratio of voltage to current, the impedance at any point along the line, looking toward the load, must be large. For electrically short lines this impedance is approximately equal to the load impedance. Consequently, a power line is terminated in an impedance that is usually greater than the characteristic impedance of the line. However, the source impedance is very small, for a voltage regulator is normally employed to maintain a fairly constant voltage at the sending end, regardless of the load. As power lines are designed for high efficiencies, the attenuation is only a small fraction of a decibel, whereas the attenuation between two repeater stations on a telephone system may be 30 decibels or more.

Under transient conditions power lines are no longer electrically short, because high frequencies are present. These transients are due primarily to switching operations, lightning, short circuits, and abrupt changes in the load. Transmission-line theory applies, and traveling-wave phenomena are present. Analysis is based on the line equations or the multiple-section artificial line, for the single-frequency T-circuit is obviously inapplicable.

If the voltage of a line is increased sufficiently, the dielectric will break down and lose its insulating properties. The air surrounding the wires becomes luminous and emits a hissing noise. This effect is known as *corona*. Because of the large voltages utilized on power lines, prevention of corona is a major problem.

There are always some ionized molecules in air, due largely to cosmic radiation. These ions are accelerated by the intense electric field near the wires of a power line. If the ions acquire sufficient energy between collisions with gas molecules, they may dislodge electrons from these molecules, creating new ions. The process is cumulative, and corona occurs. During the collision of ions and gas molecules, many electrons acquire energy but are not dislodged from their molecules. These electrons move momentarily to higher energy states in the molecules. Upon returning to lower energy levels, photons of light are emitted, and the air glows. This is the visual manifestation of corona. On small wires at moderate voltages corona may appear as a bluish white glow surrounding the wires rather uniformly. On larger conductors at higher voltages corona may appear as streamers extending several inches from the conductors, with the streamers terminating in a luminous glow that extends several more inches outward.

Corona occurs only when the electric field intensity is greater than the breakdown field, this being about 30,000 volts per centimeter for air at standard temperature, pressure, and humidity. For round wires the field is greatest at the surface, and this is the region where corona occurs. If the voltage is raised, the glow extends over a greater region, and eventually, complete breakdown occurs. An arc, or sparkover, results. The arc is a conducting region containing large numbers of positive ions and negative electrons. It is essentially a short circuit.

Because corona dissipates energy, causes radio interference, and may lead to sparkover, precautions must be taken to minimize it. Fields are intense around sharp points. Consequently, the surface of a transmission line should be smooth. For a given line voltage, increasing the radii of the wires reduces the maximum field intensity and, therefore, reduces corona. Care must be exercised in balancing conductor size against power loss and radio influence. Corona serves auseful purpose in that it helps to attenuate high-voltage traveling waves produced by lightning strokes.

Long-distance power lines are three-phase lines with three conductors. The three line voltages are 120° out of phase with one another. A three-phase system requires less copper than a single-phase system and has other advantages as well. Usually, a fourth conductor is suspended above the power conductors to intercept lightning strokes, and this wire is grounded at each tower. A double-circuit line contains six conductors in addition to the ground. Aluminum or copper conductors are normally used, and these may be solid, stranded, or hollow.

21-2. TELEPHONE LINES

The most familiar type of telephone line is the open-wire line attached to insulators on the crossarms of poles spaced about 40 to the mile. Usually, the conductors are bare copper wires with sizes specified by their diameters in mils. The parameters of open-wire telephone lines are considerably affected by the weather and the frequency of the signal. Their values are functions of both the temperature and the humidity. In wet weather the leakage conductance per unit length may be over 100 times greater than its dry-weather value. Skin effect causes R and L to vary with frequency, and the parameter G increases rapidly as the frequency increases. Proximity effect is usually negligible on open-wire lines.

Only a small per cent of the telephone wire mileage in the United States is on open-wire lines. The remainder is accounted for by the telephone cable, which contains many conductors surrounded by a lead or polyethylene sheath, often having an outside diameter of 2.6 inches. Inside the sheath are small insulated wires and perhaps several coaxial lines. The wire pairs have AWG wire gauges from number 10 to number 26. One common cable has 2121 pairs of 26-gauge wire.

A typical telephone cable has a number, oftentimes eight, of small coaxial lines, as well as many pairs of wires. The outer conductor of a common coaxial line has an inside diameter of 0.375 inch, and the diameter of the center conductor is 0.1 inch. The proper spacing between the coaxial conductors is maintained by means of polyethylene insulating disks about an inch apart. The telephone cable provides a large number of channels in a compact space. It may be suspended overhead on poles, or it may be underground or underwater.

By utilizing carrier transmission a single pair of conductors can be used to transmit many conversations simultaneously. The process of modulation shifts the voice frequencies to a new frequency band. A single-sideband telephone channel requires a bandwidth of about 4 kc and, consequently, in the frequency range from zero to 60 kc a pair of wires can provide 15 channels. Most intercity telephone mileage is on carrier systems. Common open-wire carrier systems provide 1, 3, or 15 additional circuits over a pair of wires, and a common cable system provides 12 circuits on each double pair of 19-gauge wires. Two coaxial lines may provide 1800 telephone circuits or a television channel and 600 telephone circuits.

Repeaters are placed at regular intervals along telephone lines, and are about 4 miles apart on carrier systems. A repeater consists of an amplifier, an equalizer, and a regulator. The amplifier, of course, amplifies the signal. The equalizer compensates for the phase and frequency distortion introduced by the line, and the regulator compensates for the variation in the line loss due to the variation in the temperature.

There are several telephone cables between North America and Europe and between California and Hawaii. Each system utilizes two underwater coaxial lines over 2000 miles long. Electronic amplifiers are on the ocean floor at about 40-mile intervals, and each amplifies the signal over a million times. One coaxial line transmits east to west while the other line of a system transmits west to east. Each of these cables can handle a number of conversations simultaneously.

A substantial amount of long-distance telephone mileage is on the microwave radio-relay system that operates at ultrahigh frequencies. The relay stations are placed within 25 miles of one another, and the signals are radiated in directed beams at a power level of less than a watt. The microwave antennas at each station are mounted on steel towers, with propagation from a transmitting to a receiving antenna being approximately line of sight. One microwave system can transmit simultaneously thousands of telephone conversations and many television programs as well.

21-3. DISTORTION

A signal at the output of a transmission system or network is said to be undistorted if it is identical to the input signal except for a change in amplitude and a delay in time. On the other hand, if the waveform of the output signal has a shape different from that of the input signal, then there is distortion.

A nonsinusoidal waveform can be regarded as consisting of the sum of an infinite number of sinusoidal components of different frequencies, amplitudes, and phase angles. In general, when such a signal is transmitted through a network, the different frequency components are each attenuated (or amplified) and shifted in phase. If the frequency components are attenuated different amounts, the waveform changes, and this type of distortion is *frequency distortion.* If the frequency components are shifted in phase in a manner that disturbs the relative phase relations of these components, again the waveform changes, and this type of distortion is known as *phase*, or *delay*, distortion. Both frequency and phase distortion are present on transmission lines.

Let the source voltage $v_g = V_g \sin \omega t$, and let the load voltage $v_r = V_r \sin (\omega t + \theta)$. Now suppose the frequency is varied. If the ratio V_r/V_g varies with frequency, there is frequency distortion. The voltage v_r can be expressed as $V_r \sin \omega(t + \theta/\omega)$, or $V_r \sin \omega t'$ with $t' = t + \theta/\omega$. If θ is directly proportional to ω, then t' represents the time t plus a constant. As the load voltage is $V_r \sin \omega t'$, it is evident that the phase relations at the load, as the frequency is varied, are identical to those at the input *provided θ is directly proportional to ω.* Consequently, the phase shift must be proportional to the frequency if phase distortion is to be avoided. Two sinusoidal waveforms with frequencies f and $2f$ are illustrated in Fig. 21-1. The dashed curves represent the lower-frequency waveform shifted 90° and the upper-frequency waveform shifted 180°. It should be noted that the relative phase relations are the same.

Let us consider a transmission line with both source and load impedances equal to Z_0. There is, of course, no reflection. For sinusoidal time variations the voltage in complex-exponential form is $\bar{V}_1 e^{-\gamma z}$. The instantaneous voltage can be written

$$v = V_1 e^{-\alpha z} \sin(\omega t - \beta z + \theta_1) \tag{21-1}$$

If frequency distortion is to be avoided when a nonsinusoidal waveform is applied, each frequency component must be attenuated the same amount.

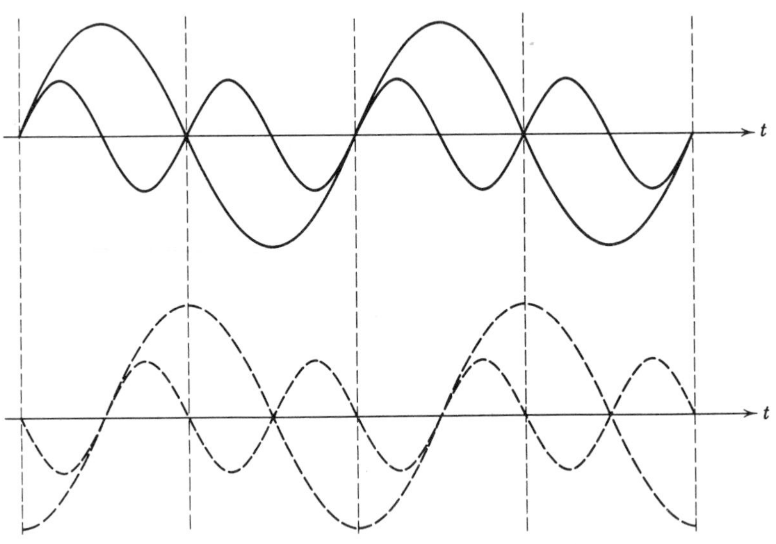

FIG. 21-1. Sinusoids with frequencies f and $2f$. The dashed curves represent the lower-frequency waveform shifted 90° and the upper-frequency waveform shifted 180°.

It follows from Eq. (21-1) that, for a line with $Z_g = Z_r = Z_0$, there is no frequency distortion if the attenuation constant α is independent of frequency.

The phase angle of v at the sending end is θ_1, and the phase angle at the receiving end is $-\beta l + \theta_1$. Thus a phase lag of βl radians is introduced. This phase shift and, therefore, β must be proportional to the frequency, if phase distortion is to be avoided. Recalling that the phase velocity is ω/β, we note that each frequency component propagates at the same velocity if β is proportional to the frequency. Summarizing, *for lines matched at both ends there is no distortion if α is independent of frequency and β is directly proportional to the frequency.*

The complex propagation constant is

$$\gamma = \alpha + j\beta = \sqrt{(R + j\omega L)(G + j\omega C)}$$

Suppose the line parameters are related at all frequencies by

$$R/G = L/C \tag{21-2}$$

We can then replace $G + j\omega C$ in the expression for γ by $k^2(R + j\omega L)$, with k^2 representing a constant independent of frequency, and the propagation constant γ becomes $k(R + j\omega L)$. Provided R and L are independent of frequency, α is constant, and β is directly proportional to the frequency. Consequently, a transmission line is distortionless if $R/G = L/C$, if R, L, G, and C are constants independent of frequency, and if the line is properly matched at both ends with its characteristic impedance.

Next, let us consider a lossless line terminated in its characteristic impedance. If R and G are zero, γ becomes $j\omega\sqrt{LC}$. Thus α is zero at all

FIG. 21-2. Transmission-line circuit.

frequencies, and β is proportional to the frequency. Therefore, lossless lines are distortionless. Of course, lossless lines do not exist, but many lines have losses that are very small.

Our discussion of distortion has thus far been limited to lines terminated in Z_0. Communication lines are usually terminated with impedances approximately equal to Z_0 in order to minimize reflection. However, the characteristic impedance is a function of frequency, and it is not practical, in the majority of cases, to match impedances at all frequencies. If the load impedance is not equal to Z_0, there is reflection which produces traveling waves propagating back toward the source. The phenomenon of reflection, in general, depends on the frequency. Consequently, reflection may introduce both frequency and phase distortion.

In order to investigate the effect of reflection on distortion let us consider the circuit of Fig. 21-2. The source voltage and the source impedance are $\bar{V}_g$ and Z_g, respectively. The receiving-end voltage can be expressed in terms of the sending-end voltage by letting $z = l$ in Eq. (20-55), giving

$$\bar{V}_r = \bar{V}_s \frac{1 + \rho}{e^{\gamma l} + \rho e^{-\gamma l}} = \bar{V}_s e^{-\gamma l} \frac{1 + \rho}{1 + \rho e^{-2\gamma l}}$$

In terms of $\bar{V}_g$ the sending-end voltage $\bar{V}_s$ is $\bar{V}_g Z_i/(Z_g + Z_i)$, with Z_i denoting the input impedance of the line. Making this substitution for $\bar{V}_s$ gives

$$\frac{\bar{V}_r}{\bar{V}_g} = e^{-\gamma l} \frac{Z_i}{Z_g + Z_i} \frac{1 + \rho}{1 + \rho e^{-2\gamma l}}$$

Utilizing Eq. (20-49) to eliminate Z_i yields

$$\frac{\bar{V}_r}{\bar{V}_g} = e^{-\gamma l} \left[\frac{Z_0(1 + \rho)}{Z_g(1 - \rho e^{-2\gamma l}) + Z_0(1 + \rho e^{-2\gamma l})} \right] \tag{21-3}$$

If there is to be no distortion, the ratio $\bar{V}_r/\bar{V}_g$ must have a magnitude that is independent of frequency and an angle that is directly proportional to the frequency. Let us suppose the line itself is distortionless. Then the expression in brackets in Eq. (21-3) must have a magnitude independent of frequency and an angle proportional to frequency if distortion is to be avoided. As it is evident that these requirements are not, in general, satisfied, we conclude that impedance mismatches at the source and at the load usually produce both frequency and phase distortion.

Now suppose that $Z_g = Z_0$. Equation (21-3) becomes

$$\frac{\bar{V}_r}{\bar{V}_g} = e^{-\gamma l}[\tfrac{1}{2}(1 + \rho)] = e^{-\gamma l} \left[\frac{1}{1 + Z_0/Z_r} \right]$$

If the ratio Z_0/Z_r has constant magnitude and zero angle at all frequencies, clearly there is no distortion introduced by reflection. For example, Z_0 and Z_r may be constant resistances of different magnitudes. Thus reflection does not always produce distortion, although it usually does.

If both Z_g and Z_r are equal to Z_0, Eq. (21-3) gives the voltage ratio $\bar{V}_r/\bar{V}_g$ to be $\frac{1}{2}e^{-\gamma l}$. For an ideal line α is independent of frequency, and β is proportional to the frequency. Therefore, there is no distortion on an ideal line, provided both Z_g and Z_r are equal to the characteristic impedance.

On communication lines reflection is undesirable for several reasons. We have seen that reflection is a source of frequency and phase distortion. It also causes standing waves of current and voltage, which are due to the phase relations of the incident and reflected waves. In certain regions these waves are in phase and add, and in other regions they are out of phase and subtract. Figure 21-3 illustrates a voltage standing wave due to reflection compared with the voltage along a properly terminated line, shown as the smooth curve. Standing waves are objectionable for several reasons. They subject the insulation to greater peak voltages, possibly causing dielectric breakdown, and they increase the ohmic line losses I^2R and V^2G. In addition, there is more radiation as a consequence of the larger wave components with axial fields.

As reflection is a source of distortion and undesirable standing waves, a communications line should be terminated in its characteristic impedance. Frequently, the characteristic impedance is nearly a pure resistance. For such cases the load impedance that will absorb the maximum power is equal to Z_0. Therefore, reflection usually indicates that the load is not

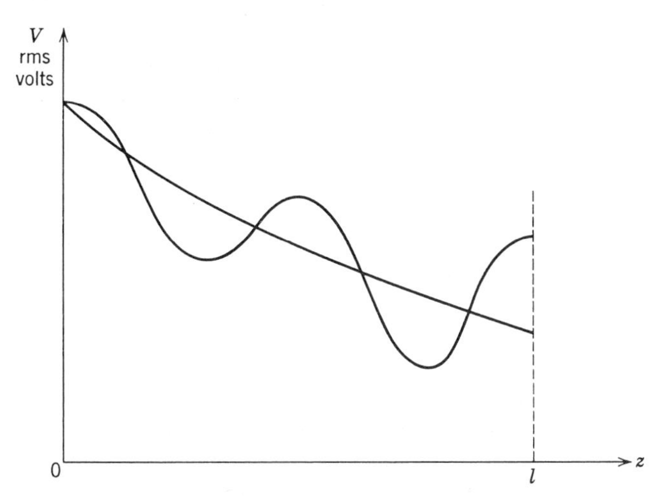

FIG. 21-3. Comparison of the standing wave along a line with reflection with the smooth curve of a properly terminated line.

receiving the available power. On transmission systems the impedances should be matched at every junction if distortion and standing waves are to be avoided.

21-4. WAVE VELOCITY

It is easily shown that the velocity along a lossless line is that of light. For R and G equal to zero, the electromagnetic wave is a TEM wave, and the wave equation for $\bar{E}_x$ is determined from Eq. (19-46) to be $\nabla^2\bar{E}_x = -\omega^2\mu\epsilon\bar{E}_x$. Also, we know that $\bar{E}_x$ satisfies the two-dimensional Laplace equation, given as Eq. (20-1). We deduce that $\partial^2\bar{E}_x/\partial z^2 = -\omega^2\mu\epsilon\bar{E}_x$, and a solution of this is

$$\bar{E}_x = F(x, y)e^{-j\omega\sqrt{\mu\epsilon}z}$$

Similar expressions apply, of course, to the other rectangular components of the TEM wave. We note that the phase constant β is $\omega\sqrt{\mu\epsilon}$, and the phase velocity $\omega/\beta = c$, with c denoting the velocity of light $1/\sqrt{\mu\epsilon}$. With $R = G = 0$, the phase constant β is $\omega\sqrt{LC}$. It is evident that *the product*

LC of the line equals the product $\mu\epsilon$ of the dielectric, provided the line is lossless.

The inductance per unit length of a nondissipative coaxial cable is $(\mu/2\pi)\ln(b/a)$, from Example 4 of Sec. 16-8. The capacitance per unit length is $2\pi\epsilon/\ln(b/a)$ by Eq. (18-21). The product LC equals $\mu\epsilon$. For any uniform lossless line the product LC equals $\mu\epsilon$, and the wave velocity along the line equals the velocity of light in the dielectric.

If either L or C of a lossless line is known, the other parameter can be found from the relation $LC = \mu\epsilon$. For example, the capacitance C per unit length of a parallel-wire line in free space is

$$\pi\epsilon_0/\ln\left(D/2a + \sqrt{(D/2a)^2 - 1}\right)$$

from Eq. (18-29) and Prob. 19-15. Therefore, the inductance L per unit length is

$$L = \frac{\mu_0}{\pi}\ln\left[\frac{D}{2a} + \sqrt{\left(\frac{D}{2a}\right)^2 - 1}\right] \tag{21-4}$$

This expression applies to a nondissipative parallel-wire line with no limitation on the ratio of D to a. Thus proximity effect is included.

Let us now consider the effect of line losses on the velocity of propagation. The complex propagation constant $\gamma = (R + j\omega L)^{1/2}(G + j\omega C)^{1/2}$. This can be put in the form

$$\gamma = j\omega\sqrt{LC}\left(1 - j\frac{R}{\omega L}\right)^{1/2}\left(1 - j\frac{G}{\omega C}\right)^{1/2}$$

If R is very small compared with ωL and if G is very small compared with ωC, γ is approximately

$$\gamma \approx j\omega\sqrt{LC}\left[1 - \frac{j}{2}\left(\frac{R}{\omega L} + \frac{G}{\omega C}\right) + \frac{1}{8}\left(\frac{R}{\omega L} - \frac{G}{\omega C}\right)^2\right] \tag{21-5}$$

Equation (21-5) was derived from the previous expression by applying the binomial expansion to the terms with the exponent $\frac{1}{2}$, rejecting higher order terms as negligible for small R and G. It is evident that, for small losses, β is

$$\beta \approx \omega\sqrt{LC}\left[1 + \frac{1}{8}\left(\frac{R}{\omega L} - \frac{G}{\omega C}\right)^2\right] \tag{21-6}$$

The phase velocity ω/β is approximately

$$v_p \approx \frac{1}{\sqrt{LC}}\left[1 - \frac{1}{8}\left(\frac{R}{\omega L} - \frac{G}{\omega C}\right)^2\right] \tag{21-7}$$

We note from Eq. (21-7) that the effect of dissipation on the wave velocity is to decrease this velocity. On lines with substantial losses the wave velocity may be considerably less than that of light.

The equation of a wave component traveling along a line in the positive z-direction is $e^{-\alpha z} \sin(\omega t - \beta z + \theta_1)$. The phase velocity is, of course, the velocity with which a point of constant phase moves. The distance traversed in one cycle is the wavelength λ_g along the waveguide. Therefore, the phase velocity v_p equals the product $f\lambda_g$. As this also equals ω/β, we define λ_g by

$$\lambda_g = 2\pi/\beta \tag{21-8}$$

The frequency f equals v_p/λ_g. Also, the frequency equals c/λ, with c denoting the velocity of light and λ denoting the free-space wavelength. It follows that

$$v_p/\lambda_g = c/\lambda \tag{21-9}$$

For a dissipative line v_p is less than c. Consequently, the wavelength along the line is less than the free-space wavelength.

EXAMPLE 1. A voltage wave traveling along a line is

$$v = 10e^{-0.05z} \sin(2 \times 10^8 t - 0.7z + 0.5)$$

volts, with z in meters. Determine the wave velocity and the wavelength, and compare these with the free-space values.

Solution. The wave velocity v_p is ω/β, or 2.86×10^8 meters/second. This is 0.953 of the velocity of light in free space. The wavelength λ_g along the line is $2\pi/\beta$, or 8.99 meters, which is 0.953 of the free-space wavelength.

In amplitude modulation the amplitude of a high-frequency sinusoid, referred to as the *carrier*, is made to vary in accordance with the time variations of a low-frequency signal. Such a wave contains a small frequency band centered on the carrier frequency. The time-varying amplitude of the carrier, called the *envelope*, contains the intelligence to be transmitted. Therefore, the signal velocity of an AM wave is the *phase velocity of the envelope*, and this velocity is called the *group velocity* v_g of the wave.

Suppose two waves with frequencies that differ slightly are propagating in the positive z-direction. If the waves have unit amplitudes, they can be expressed mathematically as

$$\sin[(\omega + \Delta\omega)t - (\beta + \Delta\beta)z] \quad \text{and} \quad \sin[(\omega - \Delta\omega)t - (\beta - \Delta\beta)z]$$

with ω representing the angular midfrequency and with β denoting the corresponding phase constant. Assuming $\Delta\omega$ is very small, the phase velocity of each wave is ω/β. By application of a well-known trigonometric identity the sum of the waves can be expressed as

$$2\cos[(\Delta\omega)t - (\Delta\beta)z]\sin(\omega t - \beta z)$$

The phase velocity of this resultant wave is ω/β. The equation of the slowly varying amplitude is $2 \cos [(\Delta\omega)t - (\Delta\beta)z]$; the phase velocity of the envelope, which is the group velocity v_g of the wave, is $\Delta\omega/\Delta\beta$. Actually group velocity is defined as the limit of this ratio as the elemental quantities approach zero and, therefore, group velocity is

$$v_g = d\omega/d\beta \tag{21-10}$$

The phase constant β equals ω/v_p. Differentiating β with respect to ω gives $1/v_p - (\omega/v_p^2)\, dv_p/d\omega$. The reciprocal of this is the group velocity v_g, which becomes

$$v_g = \frac{v_p}{1 - (\omega/v_p)(dv_p/d\omega)} \tag{21-11}$$

This result can be used to find the group velocity as a function of frequency, provided the phase velocity is known.

A signal consisting of many sinusoidal components propagates without distortion along an ideal line, which has $R/L = G/C$. Each frequency component travels at the same phase velocity, and $dv_p/d\omega$ in Eq. (21-11) is zero. Clearly the phase, group, and signal velocities are equal. This phenomenon is said to be *nondispersive*.

Along nonideal lines the different frequency components have different phase velocities, and there is *dispersion*. If $dv_p/d\omega$ is negative, it is clear from Eq. (21-11) that v_g is less than v_p; this dispersion is called *normal*. On the other hand, if $dv_p/d\omega$ is positive, v_g exceeds v_p, and the dispersion is *anomalous*. From Eq. (21-7) we note that the phase velocity along a low-loss line increases as ω increases. Consequently, for this case v_g is greater than v_p.

The frequencies of a signal propagating along a dispersive line can be divided into a number of very narrow bands, and *each of these bands has its own group velocity*. The signal is deformed in the course of its journey, and it is difficult to define a *signal velocity* precisely. The group and signal velocities are equal only if the bandwidth is very small. In general, the signal velocity can never exceed the *wave-front velocity*, which is that of light, but the group velocity may be infinite, or even negative.

EXAMPLE 2. A twisted pair of wires in a telephone cable has a loop resistance of 50 ohms per mile and a distributed capacitance of 0.06 μf/mile, at a frequency of 1000 cps. Assume the inductance and conductance per unit length are negligible. Determine the phase and group velocities at 1000 cycles.

Solution. As L and G are negligible, the propagation constant γ is $\sqrt{(R)(j\omega C)}$. Therefore, the phase constant β is $\sqrt{\omega RC/2}$. The phase velocity v_p is ω/β, or $\sqrt{2\omega/(RC)}$. Substituting for ω, R, and C gives $v_p = 64{,}700$ miles per second.

The group velocity can be found by using either $d\omega/d\beta$ or Eq. (21-11). Choosing the latter, we find $dv_p/d\omega$ to be $1/\sqrt{2\omega RC}$. Multiplying by ω/v_p yields $\frac{1}{2}$, and Eq.

(21-11) gives $v_g = 2v_p$. Therefore, the group velocity at 1000 cycles is 129,400 miles per second.

21-5. LOSSLESS LINES

Frequently transmission lines used at very high and ultrahigh frequencies are physically quite short in length. At these frequencies a line that is physically short may be electrically long. For example, a line only 25 centimeters in length is a quarter of a wavelength long at a frequency of 300 megacycles. If a line is sufficiently short, the exponential of αl is practically unity, and attenuation is negligible. Neglecting attenuation is equivalent to assuming that the parameters R and G are zero. Such a line is lossless.

For a lossless line $Z = j\omega L$ and $Y = j\omega C$, and the characteristic impedance $Z_0 = \sqrt{L/C}$, a pure resistance. The propagation constant $\gamma = j\omega\sqrt{LC}$. Thus α is zero, and β is $\omega\sqrt{LC}$. The phase and group velocities both equal $1/\sqrt{LC}$, which is the velocity of light for a non-dissipative line. Because there is no attenuation and all frequencies propagate with the same phase velocity, the line itself is distortionless; because Z_0 is a pure resistance, reflection from resistive loads does not produce distortion. We conclude that there is no distortion on a lossless line terminated in a pure resistance.

The wave equation for the voltage of a lossless line is

$$\partial^2 v/\partial z^2 = LC\ddot{v} \tag{21-12}$$

In complex-exponential form this becomes

$$d^2\bar{V}/dz^2 = -\omega^2 LC\bar{V} \tag{21-13}$$

The general solution of (21-13) is

$$\bar{V} = \bar{V}_1 e^{-j\beta z} + \bar{V}_2 e^{j\beta z} \tag{21-14}$$

with $\beta = \omega\sqrt{LC}$. Equations (21-12), (21-13), and (21-14) should be compared with Eqs. (20-18), (20-20), and (20-26), respectively. Similar equations apply to the line current.

It follows from Eq. (21-14) that the instantaneous voltage is

$$v = V_1 \sin(\omega t - \beta z + \theta_1) + V_2 \sin(\omega t + \beta z + \theta_2) \tag{21-15}$$

The voltage is the sum of the incident and reflected waves, and neither of these is attenuated on a lossless line. The constants V_1, V_2, θ_1, and θ_2 are determined by the conditions at the sending and receiving ends.

Equations (20-59) and (20-60) express the phasor voltage and current in terms of the line parameters and the conditions at the receiving end.

For lossless lines γ becomes $j\beta$. Recalling that $\sinh jx = j \sin x$ and that $\cosh jx = \cos x$, we deduce from Eqs. (20-59) and (20-60) that

$$\bar{V} = \bar{V}_r \cos \beta(l - z) + j\bar{I}_r Z_0 \sin \beta(l - z) \tag{21-16}$$

$$\bar{I} = \bar{I}_r \cos \beta(l - z) + j(\bar{V}_r/Z_0) \sin \beta(l - z) \tag{21-17}$$

The input impedance of a line is given by Eq. (20-49) and also by Eq. (20-63). For lossless lines these become

$$Z_i = Z_0 \frac{1 + \rho e^{-j2\beta l}}{1 - \rho e^{-j2\beta l}} \tag{21-18}$$

$$Z_i = Z_0 \frac{Z_r \cos \beta l + jZ_0 \sin \beta l}{Z_0 \cos \beta l + jZ_r \sin \beta l} \tag{21-19}$$

Let us consider a lossless line terminated in its characteristic impedance. In Eq. (21-14) the constant $\bar{V}_2$ is zero, for there is no reflection. The constant $\bar{V}_1$ is evidently the sending-end voltage $\bar{V}_s$. Therefore,

$$\bar{V} = \bar{V}_s e^{-j\beta z} = \bar{V}_s \underline{/-\beta z} \tag{21-20}$$

The line current $\bar{I}$ is

$$\bar{I} = \bar{I}_s e^{-j\beta z} = \bar{I}_s \underline{/-\beta z} \tag{21-21}$$

The input impedance is Z_0, which equals $\sqrt{L/C}$. The sending-end voltage and current are in time phase and, in fact, the voltage and current at any point along the line are in time phase. The magnitudes of the voltage and current do not vary with respect to the axial coordinate z. This is explained by the fact that there is no attenuation and no reflection. The phase angle of the voltage or current at the axial coordinate z lags the phase angle of the sending-end voltage by βz radians. Standing waves do not exist.

Next, let us consider a lossless line that is open at the receiving end. As Z_r is infinite, the current $\bar{I}_r$ is zero. From Eqs. (20-57) and (20-58) it is clear that

$$\bar{V} = \tfrac{1}{2}\bar{V}_r e^{j\beta(l-z)} + \tfrac{1}{2}\bar{V}_r e^{-j\beta(l-z)}$$

$$\bar{I} = \tfrac{1}{2}(\bar{V}_r/Z_0)e^{j\beta(l-z)} - \tfrac{1}{2}(\bar{V}_r/Z_0)e^{-j\beta(l-z)}$$

We note that the incident and reflected waves have the same amplitudes, and these amplitudes are independent of the axial coordinate z. At the open the reflected voltage wave is in time phase with the incident voltage wave. The reflected current wave is, however, 180° out of time phase with the incident current wave at the open, and their sum is zero at every instant of time.

The equations for the voltage and current can be written

$$\bar{V} = \bar{V}_r \cos \beta z' \tag{21-22}$$

$$\bar{I} = j(\bar{V}_r/Z_0) \sin \beta z' \tag{21-23}$$

with $z' = l - z$, which is the distance from the receiving end. The constant β equals $2\pi/\lambda_g$. As the line is lossless, the wavelength λ_g is equal to the free-space wavelength λ. If the amplitude and phase angle of $\bar{V}_r$ are denoted by V_r and θ_r, respectively, the instantaneous voltage v and the instantaneous current i are

$$v = V_r \cos \left(2\pi \frac{z'}{\lambda}\right) \sin (\omega t + \theta_r) \tag{21-24}$$

$$i = V_r \sqrt{C/L} \sin \left(2\pi \frac{z'}{\lambda}\right) \sin (\omega t + 90^\circ + \theta_r) \tag{21-25}$$

We note that the voltage and current are 90° out of time phase and, consequently, the time-average power is everywhere zero. This agrees

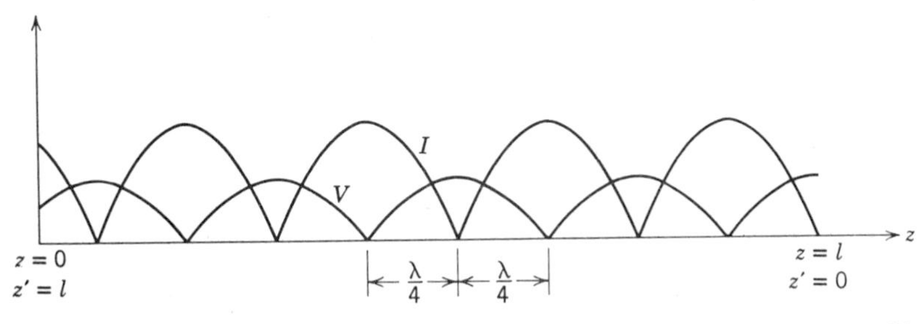

FIG. 21-4. Voltage and current amplitudes along an open-circuited lossless line excited by a single-frequency source.

with our assumptions of a lossless line terminated in an open circuit. The amplitude of the line voltage is $V_r \cos (2\pi z'/\lambda)$. It is evident that voltage maxima exist at the open and at distances from the open equal to $\frac{1}{2}\lambda$ and multiples of $\frac{1}{2}\lambda$. At these voltage maxima the incident and reflected waves are in time phase. Halfway between two voltage maxima the amplitude is zero, and a node exists. At these nodal points the voltage is zero at every instant, the incident and reflected waves being 180° out of phase and canceling. The amplitude of the line current is obviously a maximum at the locations of the voltage nodes, and current nodes exist at the locations of voltage maxima. These relations are indicated in the plots of Fig. 21-4.

Suppose a lossless line is terminated in a short circuit. In this case the voltage $\bar{V}_r$ is zero. The reflected voltage wave is 180° out of phase with the incident wave at the receiving end. The reflected current wave is not

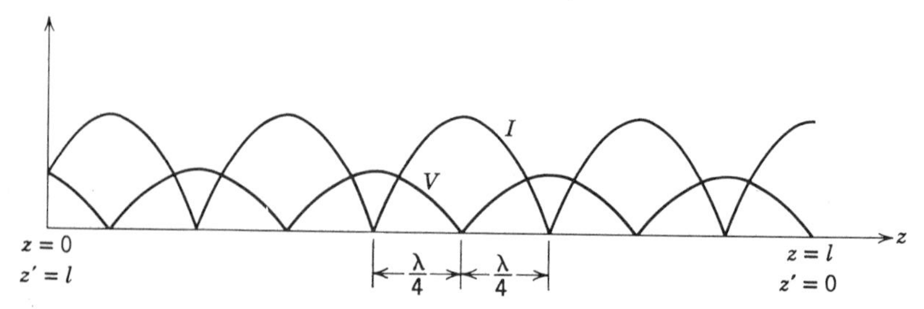

FIG. 21-5. Voltage and current amplitudes along a shorted lossless line excited by a single-frequency source.

reversed in time phase but is in time phase with the incident current wave. Therefore, a current maximum exists at the short. As $\bar{V}_r$ is zero, Eqs. (21-16) and (21-17) become

$$\bar{V} = j\bar{I}_r Z_0 \sin \beta z' \tag{21-26}$$

$$\bar{I} = \bar{I}_r \cos \beta z' \tag{21-27}$$

with z' again denoting the distance from the receiving end. The voltage and current amplitudes are plotted in Fig. 21-5.

21-6. STANDING-WAVE RATIO

There is reflection on a line not terminated in its characteristic impedance, and the reflected wave combines with the incident wave to produce standing waves. The *amplitudes* of the sinusoidal time functions vary with distance. A point of minimum voltage is referred to as a voltage node, and a point of maximum voltage is a voltage antinode. Current nodes and antinodes are defined similarly. On a lossless line the incident and reflected waves are not attenuated, and consequently, the voltage amplitudes at the various nodes are the same. A similar statement applies to the voltage antinodes, the current nodes, and the current antinodes.

On a lossless line the *standing-wave ratio* of voltage or current is defined as the ratio of the amplitude at an antinode to the amplitude at a node. If a lossless line is terminated in an open or short, it is evident that the standing-wave ratio is infinite. On the other hand, if the line is terminated in its characteristic impedance, there is no reflection, and the ratio is unity. For other terminations the ratio is between unity and infinity.

The standing-wave ratio is easily expressed in terms of the reflection coefficient ρ. The line voltage $\bar{V}$ is the sum of the incident wave $\bar{V}_1 e^{-j\beta z}$ and the reflected wave $\bar{V}_2 e^{j\beta z}$. The ratio of the reflected phasor voltage to the incident phasor voltage, at the receiving end, equals the reflection coefficient ρ, by Eq. (20-66). Therefore,

$$\rho = \frac{\bar{V}_2 e^{j\beta l}}{\bar{V}_1 e^{-j\beta l}}$$

We note that $\bar{V}_2 = \bar{V}_1 \rho e^{-j2\beta l}$, and the voltage $\bar{V}$ can be expressed as

$$\bar{V} = \bar{V}_1 e^{-j\beta z} + \bar{V}_1 \rho e^{-j2\beta l} e^{j\beta z}$$

This can be written in the form

$$\bar{V} = \bar{V}_1 e^{-j\beta z}(1 + \rho \underline{/-2\beta z'})$$

with z' representing the distance from the receiving end.

The reflection coefficient ρ is complex. Let $\rho = |\rho| \underline{/\theta}$. Then the voltage $\bar{V}$ is

$$\bar{V} = \bar{V}_1 e^{-j\beta z}(1 + |\rho| \underline{/\theta - 2\beta z'})$$

The amplitude V of $\bar{V}$ is

$$V = V_1 \left|(1 + |\rho| \underline{/\theta - 2\beta z'})\right|$$

It is evident that the maximum amplitude V_{max} equals $V_1(1 + |\rho|)$. The voltage maxima occur at points at which the angle $\theta - 2\beta z'$ equals $\pm 2\pi n$ with n representing any integer from zero to infinity. This requirement locates the voltage maxima at distances from the receiving end equal to

$$z'_{max} = \frac{\theta}{2\beta} \pm n\frac{\lambda}{2} \tag{21-28}$$

Adjacent maxima are separated by a distance equal to $\frac{1}{2}\lambda$.

The minimum amplitude V_{min} is obviously $V_1(1 - |\rho|)$, with voltage minima occurring at points at which the angle $\theta - 2\beta z'$ equals $\pi \pm 2\pi n$. It follows that voltage nodes are located at

$$z'_{min} = \frac{\theta}{2\beta} \pm n\frac{\lambda}{2} + \frac{\lambda}{4} \tag{21-29}$$

Adjacent nodes are separated by a distance equal to $\frac{1}{2}\lambda$. Comparison of Eqs. (21-28) and (21-29) shows that the spacing between a node and an adjacent antinode is $\lambda/4$.

The standing-wave ratio S of voltage is the ratio of V_{max} to V_{min}. In terms of the reflection coefficient ρ this is

$$S = \frac{V_{max}}{V_{min}} = \frac{1 + |\rho|}{1 - |\rho|} \tag{21-30}$$

A similar analysis in terms of the current reveals that the standing-wave ratio of current is equal to the standing-wave ratio of voltage. The current nodes and the voltage antinodes appear at the same points along the line, and the current antinodes and the voltage nodes also coincide.

The characteristic impedance Z_0 of a lossless line is a pure resistance, and Z_0 is frequently designated by the symbol R_0. Suppose the load impedance Z_r is a pure resistance R_r. Then the reflection coefficient ρ is

$$\rho = \frac{R_r - R_0}{R_r + R_0} = \frac{r_r - 1}{r_r + 1} \tag{21-31}$$

with r_r representing the normalized load impedance R_r/R_0. We note that the angle θ of the reflection coefficient ρ is either zero or π radians, depending on whether r_r is greater than or less than unity. If R_r is greater than R_0, the angle θ is zero, and from Eq. (21-28) it is evident that a voltage maximum occurs at the load. On the other hand, if R_r is less than R_0, θ is π radians, and Eq. (21-29) requires a voltage minimum to exist at the load. For complex terminations the load voltage is neither a maximum nor a minimum.

A complex load impedance can be calculated from voltage measurements made along the line. The first voltage minimum from the load is located by sliding a voltmeter along the line, and $z'_{\min}$ is measured. From Eq. (21-29) we calculate the angle θ of ρ. The magnitude of ρ is found by measuring the standing-wave ratio S, noting from Eq. (21-30) that this magnitude is

$$|\rho| = \frac{S - 1}{S + 1} \tag{21-32}$$

In terms of ρ the load impedance is found from Eq. (20-50) to be

$$Z_r = R_0 \frac{1 + \rho}{1 - \rho} \tag{21-33}$$

EXAMPLE. A 100-megacycle voltage is supplied to a lossless line 5 meters long in free space. The line is terminated in a load impedance Z_r, and the first voltage minimum is found to be located 0.5 m from the load. The standing-wave ratio is measured as 1.5. Assuming a characteristic impedance of 100 ohms, calculate Z_r.

Solution. From Eq. (21-29) the angle θ is $2\beta(z'_{\min} - \lambda/4 \pm n\lambda/2)$. As $\beta = 2\pi/\lambda$, this becomes $4\pi z'_{\min}/\lambda - \pi \pm 2\pi n$. The wavelength at 100 mc is 3 m, and the ratio of $z'_{\min}/\lambda$ is 1/6. Therefore, θ becomes $2\pi/3 - \pi \pm 2\pi n$, or $-\pi/3$. The magnitude of ρ is $(1.5 - 1)/(1.5 + 1)$, or 0.2, and $\rho = 0.2\underline{/-60^\circ}$. From Eq. (21-33) the load impedance is

$$Z_r = 100\left[\frac{1 + 0.2\underline{/-60^\circ}}{1 - 0.2\underline{/-60^\circ}}\right] = 114 - j41 \text{ ohms}$$

21-7. THE HALF-WAVELENGTH LOSSLESS LINE

The product βl of a half-wavelength line is $(2\pi/\lambda)(\lambda/2)$, or π radians. It follows from Eqs. (21-16) and (21-17) that $\bar{V}_s = -\bar{V}_r$ and $\bar{I}_s = -\bar{I}_r$. Thus the input voltage and current are equal in magnitude to the corresponding load quantities, but reversed in time phase. The input impedance of the line is obviously equal to the load impedance Z_r.

A half-wavelength line is similar to a 1 : 1 transformer with respect to impedance transformation. The phase reversal can, if desired, be eliminated by transposing, or crossing, the conductors in a manner that does not change the spacing between them. Half-wavelength lines are frequently used to supply the voltages to antenna arrays having elements spaced not more than a half-wavelength apart. Either in-phase or out-of-phase voltages of equal magnitudes are readily obtained at the inputs of the various elements.

21-8. THE QUARTER-WAVELENGTH LOSSLESS LINE

For a quarter-wavelength line the product βl is $\frac{1}{2}\pi$, and the input impedance is found from Eq. (21-19) to be R_0^2/Z_r, with R_0 denoting the characteristic impedance of the lossless line. We note that the input impedance is increased as Z_r is decreased, and vice versa. If Z_r is resistive, the input impedance is resistive. If Z_r is reactive, the input impedance is reactive with opposite sign.

The quarter-wavelength line is useful in transforming impedance levels, and it is frequently referred to as a *quarter-wave transformer*. For example, suppose we wish to match resistances of 100 and 400 ohms. This could be accomplished with a quarter-wavelength line having a characteristic impedance of 200 ohms.

If the load impedance Z_r is infinite, the input impedance is zero. An open-circuited quarter-wavelength stub is somewhat similar to a series resonant circuit as far as input impedances are concerned. Because open stubs radiate appreciably and because the physical length is not readily varied, they are seldom used.

The input impedance of a shorted stub of length l is

$$Z_i = jR_0 \tan \beta l \tag{21-34}$$

If the stub is $\lambda/4$ in length, the input impedance is theoretically infinite, but because of small losses, the impedance is actually finite, though large. The shorted quarter-wave stub is equivalent to an antiresonant circuit with very small losses. Such stubs are used in high-frequency oscillators to control the frequency, and they are used in high-frequency amplifiers as antiresonant circuits. Also, because of the very large input impedance, shorted quarter-wave stubs make excellent insulating supports. In addition, they can be connected across lines to suppress second harmonics, because a quarter-wave stub at the fundamental frequency becomes a half-wave stub at the second harmonic. The half-wave shorted line is, of course, a short circuit.

At high radio frequencies the physical size of ordinary inductors and capacitors becomes very small. Consequently, it is frequently advantageous at these high frequencies to use shorted stubs as reactors. We note from Eq. (21-34) that a shorted stub has an inductive reactance if it is slightly less than a quarter wavelength and a capacitive reactance if slightly greater than a quarter wavelength. The shorting bar is normally movable, with sliding taps, thus providing for easy adjustment of the physical length.

21-9. LINES WITH SMALL LOSSES

A transmission line with absolutely no losses does not exist. All lines have some resistance and conductance, although these quantities may be negligibly small in certain cases. However, in other cases the line losses, though small, may be of considerable importance.

The characteristic impedance of a line is

$$Z_0 = \sqrt{\frac{R + j\omega L}{G + j\omega C}} = \sqrt{\frac{L}{C}}\left[\frac{1 + R/j\omega L}{1 + G/j\omega C}\right]^{1/2}$$

By the binomial expansion $(1 + a)^{1/2}$ is approximately equal to $1 + \frac{1}{2}a$ provided $a \ll 1$. For small R and G the impedance becomes

$$Z_0 \approx \sqrt{\frac{L}{C}}\left[\frac{1 - jR/2\omega L}{1 - jG/2\omega C}\right]$$

Or

$$Z_0 \approx \sqrt{\frac{L}{C}}\left[1 + \frac{j}{2\omega}\left(\frac{G}{C} - \frac{R}{L}\right)\right] \tag{21-35}$$

The characteristic impedance of a line with small losses contains a small reactive term.

From Eqs. (21-6) and (21-7) we note that the parameters R and G increase the phase constant β and decrease the phase velocity v_p. As the phase velocity v_p is less than the free space velocity c, the wavelength along the line is less than the free space wavelength. These differences are small for low-loss lines.

The attenuation constant α for a line with small losses is found from Eq. (21-5) to be

$$\alpha = \tfrac{1}{2}(R\sqrt{C/L} + G\sqrt{L/C}) \tag{21-36}$$

There is always some attenuation, although it is small if the losses are small. The input impedance of a quarter-wave shorted stub is infinite for a lossless line. However, the finite attenuation always present on physical lines causes the reflected wave to have an amplitude slightly less than the incident wave, and the input impedance is finite though large.

Frequently, the power loss on a low-loss line is desired. The approximate current distribution is obtained rather easily by considering the line to be lossless. The power loss in a differential length dz is $I^2R\,dz$, with I denoting the root-mean-square current in the length dz. The total power loss in the length l is found by integration.

EXAMPLE. At a frequency of 4000 kilocycles a parallel-wire transmission line has the following parameters: $R = 0.025$ ohm/m, $L = 2\ \mu$h/m, $G = 0$, $C = 5.56$ $\mu\mu$f/m. The line is 100 meters long, terminated in a resistance of 300 ohms. Find the efficiency of transmission, defined as the ratio of the power delivered to the load to the power supplied to the input terminals.

Solution. The angular frequency ω is $8\pi \times 10^6$, and ωL is 50.3 ohms. The ratio $R/\omega L$ equals 0.0005. From Eq. (21-35) we note that the characteristic impedance is approximately equal to $\sqrt{L/C}$, or 600 ohms. By Eq. (21-36) the attenuation constant α is approximately 0.000021. The exponential of $-\alpha l$, with l equal to 100 meters, is 0.998. Thus the attenuation is very small, and the line is nearly lossless.

If I denotes the rms line current, the power lost in the differential length dz is $I^2R\,dz$, and the power delivered to the load R_r is $I_r^2R_r$, with I_r denoting the rms load current. In order to determine the efficiency of transmission we need to find the line losses in terms of the load current I_r.

As $V_r = I_rR_r$, it follows from Eq. (21-17) that

$$I^2 = I_r^2[\cos^2 \beta y + (R_r/R_0)^2 \sin^2 \beta y]$$

with y denoting the distance from the receiving end. The line loss can be expressed as $\int_0^l I^2R\,dy$. Substitution for I^2, with R_r/R_0 replaced by $\frac{1}{2}$, gives

$$P_{\text{lost}} = I_r^2R \int_0^{100} (\cos^2 \beta y + \tfrac{1}{4}\sin^2 \beta y)\,dy$$

The constant R is 0.025, and the constant β is $\omega\sqrt{LC}$, or 0.0838. Making these substitutions and evaluating the integral, we find the power loss to be $1.51I_r^2$.

The power to the load is $300I_r^2$. Therefore, the efficiency of transmission is

$$\frac{P_{\text{load}}}{P_{\text{load}} + P_{\text{loss}}} = \frac{300I_r^2}{300I_r^2 + 1.51I_r^2} = 99.5\%$$

REFERENCES

Adler, R. B., L. J. Chu, and R. M. Fano, *Electromagnetic Energy Transmission and Radiation,* John Wiley and Sons, New York, 1960, Chaps. 2, 3, 4, 5.

Bewley, L. V., *Traveling Waves on Transmission Systems*, John Wiley and Sons, New York, 2nd ed., 1951.
Breazeale, W. M., and L. R. Quarles, *Lines, Networks, and Filters*, International Textbook Co., Scranton, Pa., 1951, Chaps. 1 to 9.
Brown, R. G., R. A. Sharpe, and W. L. Hughes, *Lines, Waves, and Antennas*, The Ronald Press Co., New York, 1961, Chaps. 1 to 7.
Everitt, W. L., and G. E. Anner, *Communication Engineering*, McGraw-Hill Book Co., New York, 3rd ed., 1956, Chaps. 8, 9, 10.
Johnson, W. C., *Transmission Lines and Networks*, McGraw-Hill Book Co., New York, 1950, Chaps. 1 to 10.
Jordan, E. C., *Electromagnetic Waves and Radiating Systems*, Prentice-Hall, Englewood Cliffs, N.J., 1950, Chap. 8.
Karakash, J. J., *Transmission Lines and Filter Networks*, The Macmillan Co., New York, 1950, Chap. 1.
King, R. W. P., H. R. Mimno, and A. H. Wing, *Transmission Lines, Antennas, and Wave Guides*, McGraw-Hill Book Co., New York, 1945, Chap. 1.
Kraus, J. D., *Electromagnetics*, McGraw-Hill Book Co., New York, 1953, Chap. 11.
Moore, R. K., *Traveling-wave Engineering*, McGraw-Hill Book Co., New York, 1960, Chaps. 2 to 9.
Ramo, S., and J. R. Whinnery, *Fields and Waves in Modern Radio*, John Wiley and Sons, New York, 2nd ed., 1953, Chap. 1.
Ryder, J. D., *Networks, Lines and Fields*, Prentice-Hall, Englewood Cliffs, N.J., 2nd ed., 1955, Chaps. 6, 7, 8.
Skilling, H. H., *Electric Transmission Lines*, McGraw-Hill Book Co., New York, 1951.
Slater, J. C., *Microwave Transmission*, McGraw-Hill Book Co., New York, 1942, Chap. 1.
Stewart, J. L., *Circuit Analysis of Transmission Lines*, John Wiley and Sons, New York, 1958.
Walsh, J. B., *Electromagnetic Theory and Engineering Applications*, The Ronald Press Co., New York, 1960, Chap. 9.
Ware, L. A., and H. R. Reed, *Communication Circuits*, John Wiley and Sons, New York, 3rd ed., 1949, Chaps. 5, 6, 7, 8, 11.

PROBLEMS

Section 21-1

21-1. A 60-mile transmission system supplies one phase of a Y-connected load with an rms voltage of $66{,}400\underline{/0^\circ}$ and an rms current of $250\underline{/-20^\circ}$ at 60 cycles. The R, L, G, and C parameters that apply to this phase are 0.22 ohm/mile, 2 mh/mile, zero, and 0.0149 μf/mile, respectively. Find the equivalent T, and from this T-circuit calculate the sending-end voltage and current. Also, calculate the power loss of this phase and the efficiency of transmission, defined as $(P_{\text{out}}/P_{\text{in}}) \times 100\%$.

(*Ans.:* $\bar{V}_s = 73{,}400\underline{/7.4^\circ}$, $\bar{I}_s = 242\underline{/-14.9^\circ}$, 800 kw, 95.1%).

21-2. A 150-mile transmission system supplies one phase of a Y-connected load with an rms voltage of $127{,}000\underline{/0^\circ}$ and an rms current of $278\underline{/-30^\circ}$ at 60 cycles. The $R, L, G,$ and C parameters that apply to this phase are 0.133 ohm/mile, 2.2 mh/mile, zero, and 0.0135 μf/mile, respectively. Find the equivalent T, and calculate the sending-end voltage and current and the efficiency of transmission.

21-3. The sending-end voltage V_s on an open-circuited 60-cycle power line is 120,000 volts. The line is 0.1 wavelength long with negligible losses. Calculate the receiving-end voltage and compare with V_s.

Section 21-2

21-4. A pair of wires in a telephone cable has a propagation constant of $0.169 + j0.169$ per mile at 300 cycles and a propagation constant of $0.525 + j0.545$ at 3000 cycles. Calculate the distance in which the time delays of the two frequencies differ by one-fifth of the period of the higher frequency.

21-5. If $v = \sin 3000t + \sin 10{,}000t$ at the input of an open-wire telephone line, with per-mile propagation constants of $0.0085 + j0.02$ and $0.0095 + j0.07$ at the lower and higher frequencies, respectively, find the voltage at a distance of 50 miles. Also, compare the amplitudes of the two components and their phase retardations (θ/ω). Assume the line is terminated in its characteristic impedance at both frequencies.

21-6. From 50 to 2000 cycles a 26-gauge cable circuit has a resistance of 440 ohms/mile, an inductance of 0.952 mh/mile, a capacitance of 0.069 μf/mile, and a conductance of $0.001f$ μmhos/mile, with f denoting the frequency. Compute and plot curves of α, v_p, and $|Z_0|$ versus frequency, with data determined at 50, 200, 500, and 2000 cycles.

Sections 21-3 and 21-4

21-7. The source voltage $v_g = \sin \omega_1 t + \sin \omega_2 t$, with $\omega_1 = 6\pi \times 10^8$ and $\omega_2 = 12\pi \times 10^8$, on a 1-meter length of lossless line with $\gamma = j\omega/(3 \times 10^8)$ and $Z_g = Z_0 = 100\underline{/0^\circ}$. Find the instantaneous load voltage v_r for load impedances of (*a*) $50\underline{/30^\circ}$ ohms at both frequencies and (*b*) $50\underline{/0^\circ}$ ohms. For each load compare the phase retardations (θ/ω) of the two components, and determine whether there is distortion due to reflection.

21-8. Each conductor of a nonferromagnetic parallel-wire line in free space has a radius of 0.4 cm, and the separation between the axes is 1.0 cm. Calculate the d-c inductance per meter, using Eq. (16-42). Also, calculate the inductance assuming the line is lossless.

21-9. A lossless transmission line consists of two parallel cylinders, one inside the other. The radius of the smaller cylinder is 0.5 cm, the inner radius of the larger cylinder is 2.0 cm, and the axes are 1.0 cm apart. The dielectric between the cylinders has a dielectric constant of 2.5. Calculate the line constants L and C, referring to Eq. (18-28).

21-10. An open-wire telephone line has a resistance of 10.4 ohms/mile, an inductance of 3.66 mh/mile, a conductance of 3.50 μmhos/mile, and a capacitance of 0.00876 μf/mile, at 1000 cycles. (*a*) Find the phase velocity. (*b*) Calculate the wavelength along the line and compare with the free-space wavelength. (*c*) Express the propagation constant γ as a function of ω and show that $d\gamma/d\omega \approx 5.58 \times 10^{-6}\underline{/89.5^\circ}$ at 1000 cycles. Use this result to find the group velocity.

21-11. At 1 megacycle, calculate the wavelength and the phase and group velocities of a radio wave propagating in fresh water having a conductivity of 0.005 mho/m and a dielectric constant of 81. To find the group velocity, first evaluate $d\gamma/d\omega$. Use Eq. (22-82).

21-12. Repeat Prob. 21-11 for sea water with a conductivity of 4 mhos/m and a dielectric constant of 81.

21-13. For a line with small losses find the group velocity, using Eq. (21-6), and show that $v_p + v_g = 2/\sqrt{LC}$. Also, deduce that the group velocity on the low-loss line of Prob. 20-8 exceeds the phase velocity by 37,700 meters/sec.

Section 21-5

21-14. A lossless line in free space has a characteristic impedance of 100 ohms. Determine L and C.

21-15. The radius of the inner conductor of a lossless coaxial line is a, and the inner radius of the outer conductor is b. For a dielectric constant of 2 calculate the ratio b/a that gives a characteristic impedance of 50 ohms.

21-16. If $v = \sin(\omega t - \beta z) + \sin(\omega t + \beta z)$ along a certain lossless line, with $\beta = 2\pi/\lambda$, calculate the rms voltages for values of z equal to 0, $\lambda/8$, $\lambda/4$, $3\lambda/8$, and $\lambda/2$.

21-17. If $i = \sin(\omega t - \beta z) - \sin(\omega t + \beta z)$ along a certain lossless line, with $\beta = 2\pi/\lambda$, calculate the rms currents for values of z equal to 0, $\lambda/8$, $\lambda/4$, $3\lambda/8$, and $\lambda/2$.

21-18. Deduce Eq. (21-19), which gives the input impedance of a lossless line, from the equivalent T.

21-19. A lossless line of length $\lambda/8$ has a characteristic impedance of 100 ohms and is terminated in a resistance of 150 ohms. Find the equivalent T of the line, and utilize this circuit to determine the input impedance. Also, calculate the input impedance, using Eq. (21-19).

21-20. A 2.3-wavelength 70-ohm lossless line is terminated with a 0.4-wavelength 200-ohm lossless line having a resistive load of 60 ohms. Find the power to the 60-ohm load for an rms input voltage of 100.

21-21. An 85-cm 50-ohm lossless line in free space is terminated in a resistance of 90 ohms. At the input is a 600-mc generator with an open-circuit voltage of 1 volt and an internal impedance of $10 + j30$ ohms. Find the phasor voltage and current at the load.

21-22. A 0.7-wavelength 100-ohm lossless line has its receiving end shorted. The line is fed with a generator whose open-circuit voltage is 100 volts and whose internal impedance is $40 + j30$ ohms. Find the receiving-end current.

Section 21-6

21-23. A 50-ohm 300-mc lossless line in free space is terminated in an impedance of $50 + j50$ ohms. Find the standing-wave ratio S and determine the distances from the load to the first and second voltage minimums.

21-24. Calculate the standing-wave ratios of a 100-ohm lossless line with load resistances of 0, 50, 100, 500, and infinity.

21-25. A 50-ohm lossless line feeding an antenna has a standing-wave ratio of 2 with a voltage minimum 0.08λ from the antenna. Calculate the antenna impedance.

21-26. A 50-ohm lossless line has a standing-wave ratio of 1.47. If the first and second voltage minimums are located 6 cm and 31 cm from the load, find the load impedance.

21-27. A 100-ohm lossless line with a standing-wave ratio of 4 has its first and second voltage minimums located 0.5 m and 2 m from the load. Calculate the load impedance and the frequency. The medium is free space.

21-28. A 70-ohm lossless line with a standing-wave ratio of 1.25 has successive voltage minimums 25 and 50 centimeters from the load. Calculate the load impedance and the frequency. The medium is free space.

Section 21-7

21-29. A generator supplies a current of $0.01\underline{/0^\circ}$ ampere to the sending end of a 100-ohm half-wavelength lossless line shorted at the receiving end. Find the phasor voltages and currents at distances of 0, $\lambda/8$, $\lambda/4$, $3\lambda/8$, and $\frac{1}{2}\lambda$ from the sending end.

21-30. A generator supplies a voltage of $1\underline{/0^\circ}$ volt to the sending end of a 100-ohm half-wavelength lossless line open at the receiving end. Find the phasor voltages and currents at distances of 0, $\lambda/8$, $\lambda/4$, $3\lambda/8$, and $\frac{1}{2}\lambda$ from the sending end.

21-31. Show that the approximate input impedance of a lossless shorted stub that is approximately one-half wavelength long is $-j2\pi R_0(0.5 - l/\lambda)$. Calculate this impedance for a 100-ohm shorted stub with a length of 0.5005λ.

Section 21-8

21-32. Show that the approximate input impedance of a lossless shorted stub that is approximately one-quarter wavelength long is $jR_0/[2\pi(0.25 - l/\lambda)]$. Calculate this impedance for a 100-ohm shorted stub with a length of 0.251λ.

21-33. Sketch the equivalent T for a quarter-wavelength lossless line and, using this T, show that the input impedance is R_0^2/Z_r.

21-34. From Eq. (20-64) or from the equivalent T show that the transfer impedance of a quarter-wavelength lossless line is independent of the load impedance. Using the T for a 100-ohm quarter-wavelength lossless line with a sending-end voltage of $1\underline{/0^\circ}$, find the phasor current $\bar{I}_r$. Note that this current does not depend on the load impedance.

21-35. A generator with an open-circuit rms voltage of 10 volts and an internal resistance of 100 ohms is connected to a 900-ohm resistance load. Calculate the power to the load. Also, calculate the power to the load if a quarter-wave matching transformer is connected between the generator and the load.

Section 21-9

21-36. By integrating I^2R over the length of a quarter-wavelength shorted low-loss line, with the rms current I approximately equal to $I_r \cos \beta z'$ by Eq. (21-27), show that the power dissipated is $\frac{1}{2}I_r^2Rl$. As the input voltage is approximately I_rR_0 from Eq. (21-26), show that the input resistance is $2R_0^2/(Rl)$. Calculate the input resistance of a 300-mc 100-ohm quarter-wave insulator with a series resistance R of 0.025 ohm/m. The distributed conductance G is negligible, and the medium is free space.

Waveguides

CHAPTER 22

A waveguide is a system of conductors and dielectrics utilized to guide electromagnetic energy from one point to another. In this chapter we shall investigate the hollow-pipe waveguides commonly used at microwave frequencies, in order to illustrate the application of classical field theory to an important dynamic problem. We shall analyze mathematically the rectangular waveguide, working with Maxwell's curl equations, the wave equations, and the Poynting vector. Boundary conditions are applied to evaluate constants appearing in solutions of differential equations, and complex exponentials are employed to eliminate from the equations a space variable, as well as the time variable. The copper losses of imperfect conductors, along with dielectric losses, are used to find the attenuation constant of the propagating wave.

The student who diligently studies the material of this chapter will undoubtedly be rewarded with a greater understanding of Maxwell's equations and the phenomenon of wave propagation. Also, he will acquire a suitable background for more advanced studies of waveguide systems.

22-1. THE WAVE EQUATIONS

In a region devoid of charge accumulations and convection current densities other than drift current densities, the wave equation for the electric field $\mathbf{E}$ is

$$\nabla^2\mathbf{E} = \mu\sigma\dot{\mathbf{E}} + \mu\epsilon\ddot{\mathbf{E}} \tag{22-1}$$

This was first presented as Eq. (11-22). A similar equation applies to the magnetic field **H**. Solutions of Eq. (22-1) are, of course, traveling waves.

Suppose the z-coordinate of a rectangular system is oriented in the direction of wave propagation. For sinusoidal time variations we can anticipate the manner in which the field components vary with respect to z. Along a transmission line we know that sinusoidal voltage and current waves propagating in the positive z-direction are attenuated exponentially. A transmission line is one type of waveguide. Consequently, we might expect the amplitudes of the field components to decrease exponentially with respect to z. It should be recalled that the derivative of the exponential of $-\alpha z$ is proportional to the original exponential function. Therefore, an exponential attenuation implies that the fields decrease at a rate proportional to their magnitudes, clearly a reasonable assumption considering the linearity of the wave equations.

Let us next consider retardation. Retardation is the result of the finite velocity of propagation of the electromagnetic wave. Along transmisson lines the phase of a wave is retarded by an amount proportional to the distance from the source. This phase retardation resulted in the term $-\beta z$ appearing in the angle of the sine function. A similar retardation term appeared in the expressions for the fields of a current element. Accordingly, it seems logical to assume that $\mathbf{E} = \mathscr{E}_x\mathbf{i} + \mathscr{E}_y\mathbf{j} + \mathscr{E}_z\mathbf{k}$ with

$$\mathscr{E}_x = E_x e^{-\alpha z} \sin(\omega t - \beta z + \theta_x) \tag{22-2}$$

$$\mathscr{E}_y = E_y e^{-\alpha z} \sin(\omega t - \beta z + \theta_y) \tag{22-3}$$

$$\mathscr{E}_z = E_z e^{-\alpha z} \sin(\omega t - \beta z + \theta_z) \tag{22-4}$$

The quantities E_x, E_y, E_z, θ_x, θ_y, and θ_z are functions of x and y only. Similar expressions can be written for the magnetic field components. Our assumptions regarding the variation with respect to z are correct for any specific waveguide, *provided solutions of the wave equations can be made to satisfy the boundary conditions.*

It is convenient to utilize the mathematics of complex exponentials. Let the complex propagation constant γ represent $\alpha + j\beta$, with α and β being the attenuation and phase constants, respectively. Define $\bar{E}_x$ as $E_x e^{j\theta_x}$, and define $\bar{E}_y$ and $\bar{E}_z$ similarly. We note that $\bar{E}_x$, $\bar{E}_y$, and $\bar{E}_z$ are complex, having magnitudes and angles, and are functions of the variables x and y only. In complex-exponential form the field components become

$$\mathscr{E}_x = \bar{E}_x e^{j\omega t - \gamma z} \tag{22-5}$$

$$\mathscr{E}_y = \bar{E}_y e^{j\omega t - \gamma z} \tag{22-6}$$

$$\mathscr{E}_z = \bar{E}_z e^{j\omega t - \gamma z} \tag{22-7}$$

with the imaginary part understood. Similar expressions can be written for the magnetic field components.

If we let $\bar{\mathbf{E}} = \bar{E}_x\mathbf{i} + \bar{E}_y\mathbf{j} + \bar{E}_z\mathbf{k}$, Eqs. (22-5), (22-6), and (22-7) can be combined into the vector equation

$$\mathbf{E} = \bar{\mathbf{E}}e^{j\omega t - \gamma z} \tag{22-8}$$

The corresponding equation for $\mathbf{H}$ is

$$\mathbf{H} = \bar{\mathbf{H}}e^{j\omega t - \gamma z} \tag{22-9}$$

Of course, we understand that only the imaginary (or real) part is understood. Each component of the vectors $\bar{\mathbf{E}}$ and $\bar{\mathbf{H}}$ is a complex function of the variables x and y, and $\bar{\mathbf{E}}$ and $\bar{\mathbf{H}}$ are independent of z and t.

We shall now substitute the complex-exponential form of $\mathbf{E}$ into the wave equation. From Eq. (22-8) we note that $\partial\mathbf{E}/\partial z = -\gamma\mathbf{E}$ and $\partial\mathbf{E}/\partial t = j\omega\mathbf{E}$. Thus Eq. (22-1) becomes

$$\frac{\partial^2\mathbf{E}}{\partial x^2} + \frac{\partial^2\mathbf{E}}{\partial y^2} + \gamma^2\mathbf{E} = j\omega\mu\sigma\mathbf{E} - \omega^2\mu\epsilon\mathbf{E} \tag{22-10}$$

Let us substitute for $\mathbf{E}$, using Eq. (22-8). The exponential of $j\omega t - \gamma z$, being common to all terms, cancels. Thus $\bar{\mathbf{E}}$ replaces $\mathbf{E}$. Rearranging terms, we obtain

$$\frac{\partial^2\bar{\mathbf{E}}}{\partial x^2} + \frac{\partial^2\bar{\mathbf{E}}}{\partial y^2} = -(\gamma^2 + \omega^2\mu\epsilon - j\omega\mu\sigma)\bar{\mathbf{E}} \tag{22-11}$$

The expression in parentheses will appear frequently in our equations and, therefore, it is convenient to represent this expression by the symbol k_c^2. Then

$$k_c^2 = \gamma^2 + \omega^2\mu\epsilon - j\omega\mu\sigma \tag{22-12}$$

In terms of k_c the equation for $\bar{\mathbf{E}}$ and the corresponding equation for $\bar{\mathbf{H}}$ are

$$\frac{\partial^2\bar{\mathbf{E}}}{\partial x^2} + \frac{\partial^2\bar{\mathbf{E}}}{\partial y^2} = -k_c^2\bar{\mathbf{E}} \tag{22-13}$$

$$\frac{\partial^2\bar{\mathbf{H}}}{\partial x^2} + \frac{\partial^2\bar{\mathbf{H}}}{\partial y^2} = -k_c^2\bar{\mathbf{H}} \tag{22-14}$$

Equations (22-13) and (22-14) are functions of the variables x and y only. *The variables z and t have been eliminated with the aid of complex exponentials.* Of course, to obtain the actual fields from $\bar{\mathbf{E}}$ and $\bar{\mathbf{H}}$ we must multiply by the exponential of $j\omega t - \gamma z$ and take the real or imaginary part of the result. The equations are partial differential equations which can be converted into ordinary differential equations by the separation-of-variables method discussed in Sec. 12-3.

From Eq. (22-13) we obtain

$$\nabla^2 \bar{E}_z = -k_c^2 \bar{E}_z \tag{22-15}$$

$\bar{E}_z$ is a complex function of x and y. Let $\bar{E}_z = XY$ with X denoting a function of x only and Y denoting a function of y only. Using primes to denote derivatives, Eq. (22-15) becomes

$$X''Y + XY'' = -k_c^2 XY$$

Or

$$X''/X + Y''/Y = -k_c^2$$

Since X''/X is independent of y and Y''/Y is independent of x, it is evident that each of the ratios are independent of both x and y. Let

$$X''/X = -k_x^2 \qquad Y''/Y = -k_y^2 \tag{22-16}$$

with k_x and k_y denoting constants. These constants must satisfy the relation

$$k_x^2 + k_y^2 = k_c^2 \tag{22-17}$$

Equations (22-16) are ordinary differential equations. Their solutions are readily found to be

$$X = A_1 \sin k_x x + A_2 \cos k_x x$$

$$Y = A_3 \sin k_y y + A_4 \cos k_y y$$

with the A coefficients representing complex constants. It follows that $\bar{E}_z$ is

$$\bar{E}_z = (A_1 \sin k_x x + A_2 \cos k_x x)(A_3 \sin k_y y + A_4 \cos k_y y) \tag{22-18}$$

Similarly,

$$\bar{H}_z = (B_1 \sin K_x x + B_2 \cos K_x x)(B_3 \sin K_y y + B_4 \cos K_y y) \tag{22-19}$$

The A and B constants and also the constants k_x, k_y, K_x, and K_y must be evaluated from the boundary conditions of the particular problem, with

$$k_x^2 + k_y^2 = K_x^2 + K_y^2 = k_c^2 \tag{22-20}$$

Similar expressions for the other field components can be derived from the wave equations for $\bar{\mathbf{E}}$ and $\bar{\mathbf{H}}$. However, it is usually more convenient to find $\bar{E}_z$ and $\bar{H}_z$ from Eqs. (22-18) and (22-19) and then to utilize Maxwell's equations to determine the other components directly from $\bar{E}_z$ and $\bar{H}_z$. In the next section the transverse fields $\bar{E}_x$, $\bar{E}_y$, $\bar{H}_x$, and $\bar{H}_y$ are found in terms of $\bar{E}_z$ and $\bar{H}_z$.

22-2. THE TRANSVERSE FIELDS

Maxwell's curl equations applied to the dielectric region of a waveguide are

$$\nabla \times \mathbf{E} = -\mu\dot{\mathbf{H}} \tag{22-21}$$

$$\nabla \times \mathbf{H} = \sigma\mathbf{E} + \epsilon\dot{\mathbf{E}} \tag{22-22}$$

Let us substitute the complex-exponential expressions for **E** and **H**, given as Eqs. (22-8) and (22-9). We note that the operator $\partial/\partial z$ can be replaced with $-\gamma$ and the operator $\partial/\partial t$ can be replaced with $j\omega$. After performing these operations, we observe that each term of Eqs. (22-21) and (22-22) contains the factor $\exp(j\omega t - \gamma z)$, which can be canceled. The results are

$$\partial\bar{E}_z/\partial y + \gamma\bar{E}_y = -j\omega\mu\bar{H}_x \tag{22-23}$$

$$-\gamma\bar{E}_x - \partial\bar{E}_z/\partial x = -j\omega\mu\bar{H}_y \tag{22-24}$$

$$\partial\bar{E}_y/\partial x - \partial\bar{E}_x/\partial y = -j\omega\mu\bar{H}_z \tag{22-25}$$

$$\partial\bar{H}_z/\partial y + \gamma\bar{H}_y = (\sigma + j\omega\epsilon)\bar{E}_x \tag{22-26}$$

$$-\gamma\bar{H}_x - \partial\bar{H}_z/\partial x = (\sigma + j\omega\epsilon)\bar{E}_y \tag{22-27}$$

$$\partial\bar{H}_y/\partial x - \partial\bar{H}_x/\partial y = (\sigma + j\omega\epsilon)\bar{E}_z \tag{22-28}$$

These equations are independent of the variables z and t.

We wish to express $\bar{E}_x$, $\bar{E}_y$, $\bar{H}_x$, and $\bar{H}_y$ in terms of $\bar{E}_z$ and $\bar{H}_z$. This is readily accomplished. For example, Eq. (22-26) relates $\bar{E}_x$ to $\bar{H}_y$ and $\bar{H}_z$. If $\bar{H}_y$ is eliminated by utilizing Eq. (22-24), we obtain an equation involving $\bar{E}_x$, $\bar{E}_z$, and $\bar{H}_z$. Solving for $\bar{E}_x$ gives the desired relation. The other transverse components can be expressed in terms of $\bar{E}_z$ and $\bar{H}_z$ by a similar procedure. The results are

$$\bar{E}_x = -\frac{\gamma}{k_c^2}\frac{\partial\bar{E}_z}{\partial x} - \frac{j\omega\mu}{k_c^2}\frac{\partial\bar{H}_z}{\partial y} \tag{22-29}$$

$$\bar{E}_y = -\frac{\gamma}{k_c^2}\frac{\partial\bar{E}_z}{\partial y} + \frac{j\omega\mu}{k_c^2}\frac{\partial\bar{H}_z}{\partial x} \tag{22-30}$$

$$\bar{H}_x = \frac{\sigma + j\omega\epsilon}{k_c^2}\frac{\partial\bar{E}_z}{\partial y} - \frac{\gamma}{k_c^2}\frac{\partial\bar{H}_z}{\partial x} \tag{22-31}$$

$$\bar{H}_y = -\frac{\sigma + j\omega\epsilon}{k_c^2}\frac{\partial\bar{E}_z}{\partial x} - \frac{\gamma}{k_c^2}\frac{\partial\bar{H}_z}{\partial y} \tag{22-32}$$

If $\bar{E}_z$ and $\bar{H}_z$ are known, Eqs. (22-29), (22-30), (22-31), and (22-32) can be used to find the transverse fields. As these fields are obtained from $\bar{E}_z$

and $\bar{H}_z$ by processes of differentiation, we observe that $\bar{E}_z$ and $\bar{H}_z$ *are utilized as potential functions.*

EXAMPLE. In the free-space dielectric of a rectangular waveguide the axial magnetic field H_z is zero, and the axial electric field E_z is

$$E_z = 10{,}000 \sin 20\pi x \sin 40\pi y\, e^{-0.02z} \cos (18\pi \times 10^9 t - 40\pi z + 30^\circ)$$

Find H_x as a function of the space coordinates and time, and evaluate H_x at $(x, y, z, t) = (0.01, 0.01, 2, 0)$.

Solution. Letting $\gamma = 0.02 + j40\pi$ and $\omega = 18\pi \times 10^9$, E_z in complex-exponential form is

$$E_z = 10{,}000 \sin 20\pi x \sin 40\pi y\, e^{j30^\circ}\, e^{j\omega t - \gamma z}$$

with the real part understood. Thus $\bar{E}_z$ is

$$\bar{E}_z = 10{,}000 \sin 20\pi x \sin 40\pi y\, e^{j30^\circ}$$

Differentiating with respect to y gives

$$\partial \bar{E}_z / \partial y = 400{,}000\pi \sin 20\pi x \cos 40\pi y\, e^{j30^\circ}$$

Equation (22-31) will be used, with σ and $\bar{H}_z$ set equal to zero. The partial derivative of $\bar{E}_z$ with respect to y has been determined. This must be multiplied by $j\omega\epsilon_0/k_c^2$. As $\gamma^2 = -1600\pi^2$ and $\omega^2\mu_0\epsilon_0 = 3600\pi^2$, the sum $\gamma^2 + \omega^2\mu_0\epsilon_0$ gives $k_c^2 = 2000\pi^2$. Multiplying $\partial\bar{E}_z/\partial y$ by $j\omega\epsilon_0/k_c^2$ gives

$$\bar{H}_x = j31.8 \sin 20\pi x \cos 40\pi y\, e^{j30^\circ}$$

or

$$\bar{H}_x = 31.8 \sin 20\pi x \cos 40\pi y \,\underline{/120^\circ}$$

Inserting the exponential of $j\omega t - \gamma z$ and dropping the imaginary part of the result, we obtain

$$H_x = 31.8 \sin 20\pi x \cos 40\pi y\, e^{-0.02z} \cos (\omega t - 40\pi z + 120^\circ)$$

At $(x, y, z, t) = (0.01, 0.01, 2, 0)$ the expression for H_x becomes

$$H_x = 31.8 \sin 0.2\pi \cos 0.4\pi\, e^{-0.04} \cos (-80\pi + 120^\circ)$$

Evaluation gives $H_x = -2.77$ amperes per meter.

22-3. THE RECTANGULAR WAVEGUIDE

This type of waveguide consists of a hollow conducting pipe with a rectangular cross section. The pipe is most often made of copper, and the enclosed dielectric is usually air. A small probe, or antenna, is frequently employed to excite electromagnetic waves, which propagate through the dielectric, carrying electromagnetic energy along the axial length of the guide. The conducting pipe effectively confines the fields to the interior region. The transverse dimensions of hollow-pipe waveguides must be appreciable compared with the wavelength of the exciting source. Therefore, such waveguides are of practical size only for frequencies in the microwave region, and they are extensively used to transmit energy at these frequencies. The rectangular waveguide is the most common of the hollow-pipe guides.

The electric and magnetic fields inside a waveguide excite currents on the inner surface of the conducting pipe. Because of skin effect these currents are confined mostly to a very thin layer. However, the conducting material is not perfect, and there are some copper losses. In addition, there

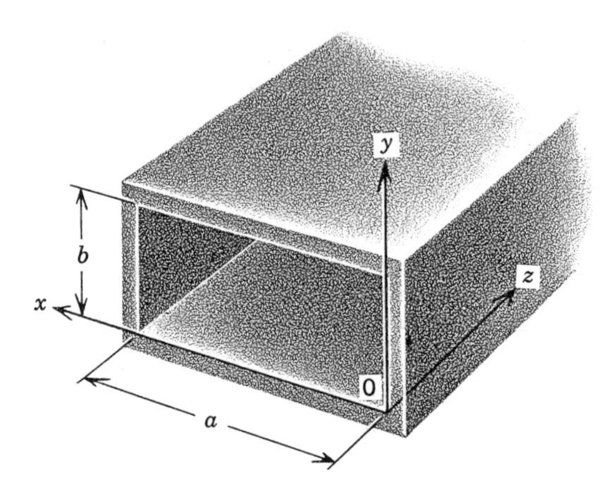

FIG. 22-1. A rectangular waveguide.

are dielectric losses for an imperfect dielectric. These copper and dielectric losses withdraw energy from the fields and, consequently, the electromagnetic waves are attenuated as they propagate.

Figure 22-1 shows a rectangular waveguide and a rectangular coordinate system oriented so that the z-axis is along the axial length. The transverse dimensions are a and b, with $a \geq b$. The dielectric has conductivity σ, permittivity ϵ, and permeability μ, and the conductors are assumed to be perfect. The practical effect of the copper losses, which we are neglecting by assuming perfect conductors, is to increase the attenuation constant α.

The field components $\bar{E}_z$ and $\bar{H}_z$ are given by Eqs. (22-18) and (22-19), and the constants in these equations must be evaluated from the boundary conditions. At the surface of a perfect conductor the tangential component of **E** must be zero. Also, the normal component of **H** must be zero; as we shall see, this condition is automatically satisfied by making the tangential electric field zero.

With reference to Fig. 22-1, let us consider the right and left conductor surfaces, located at $x = 0$ and $x = a$. At these surfaces $\bar{E}_y$ and $\bar{E}_z$ must be zero. We note from Eq. (22-30) that $\partial \bar{H}_z/\partial x$ must also be zero, because

$\partial \bar{E}_z / \partial y$ is certainly zero. Equation (22-27) assures us that $\bar{H}_x$ will be zero, as required. Therefore,

$$\text{at } x = 0 \qquad \bar{E}_z = \partial \bar{H}_z / \partial x = 0 \tag{22-33}$$

$$\text{at } x = a \qquad \bar{E}_z = \partial \bar{H}_z / \partial x = 0 \tag{22-34}$$

Consideration of the bottom and top surfaces shows that

$$\text{at } y = 0 \qquad \bar{E}_z = \partial \bar{H}_z / \partial y = 0 \tag{22-35}$$

$$\text{at } y = b \qquad \bar{E}_z = \partial \bar{H}_z / \partial y = 0 \tag{22-36}$$

Let us now apply these boundary conditions to the expressions for $\bar{E}_z$ and $\bar{H}_z$. At $x = 0$, $\bar{E}_z = 0$ by Eq. (22-33), and examination of Eq. (22-18) reveals that the coefficient A_2 of the term $\cos k_x x$ must be zero. At $y = 0$, $\bar{E}_z = 0$ by Eq. (22-35), and examination of Eq. (22-18) reveals that the coefficient A_4 of the term $\cos k_y y$ must be zero. The result is

$$\bar{E}_z = A \sin k_x x \sin k_y y \tag{22-37}$$

with $A = A_1 A_3$. Similarly, application of Eqs. (22-33) and (22-35) to Eq. (22-19) for $\bar{H}_z$ shows that the coefficients B_1 and B_3 of the sine terms are zero, giving

$$\bar{H}_z = B \cos K_x x \cos K_y y \tag{22-38}$$

with $B = B_2 B_4$.

We have not yet considered the requirements of Eqs. (22-34) and (22-36). By Eq. (22-34) we note that $\bar{E}_z = 0$ at $x = a$ for all values of y. It follows from Eq. (22-37) that $\sin k_x a = 0$, and this requires that $k_x a$ equal zero or some multiple of π. Therefore,

$$k_x = m\pi/a \quad \text{with } m = 0, 1, 2, 3 \text{ etc.}$$

Boundary condition (22-36) states that $\bar{E}_z = 0$ at $y = b$ for all values of x. From Eq. (22-37) it follows that $k_y b$ must be zero or a multiple of π. Consequently,

$$k_y = n\pi/b \qquad \text{with } n = 0, 1, 2, 3 \text{ etc.}$$

Similarly, application of Eqs. (22-34) and (22-36) to Eq. (22-38) for $\bar{H}_z$ shows that $K_x = m\pi/a$ and $K_y = n\pi/b$, with m and n representing integers as before. The expressions for $\bar{E}_z$ and $\bar{H}_z$ become

$$\bar{E}_z = A \sin m\pi x/a \sin n\pi y/b \tag{22-39}$$

$$\bar{H}_z = B \cos m\pi x/a \cos n\pi y/b \tag{22-40}$$

The propagation constant γ can now be determined. From Eq. (22-20) it is clear that

$$k_c = \sqrt{(m\pi/a)^2 + (n\pi/b)^2} \tag{22-41}$$

We note that *only certain discrete values of k_c are allowed*, for m and n are integers. These allowed values are often called *characteristic values* or *eigenvalues*. By utilizing Eq. (22-12) we find γ to be

$$\gamma = \sqrt{-\omega^2\mu\epsilon + (m\pi/a)^2 + (n\pi/b)^2 + j\omega\mu\sigma} \qquad (22\text{-}42)$$

This gives γ in terms of the angular frequency, the dielectric properties σ, ϵ, and μ, and the integers m and n.

We have determined $\bar{E}_z$ and $\bar{H}_z$ as functions of x and y. The expressions contain the dimensions a and b of the waveguide, the integers m and n, and the constants A and B. Each of the integers m and n can have values from zero to infinity, and *the boundary conditions at the surfaces of the conductors are satisfied for any mn combination.* The constants A and B depend on the exciting signal, and these have both magnitude and phase. The transverse field components can be derived from the expressions for $\bar{E}_z$ and $\bar{H}_z$ by means of Eqs. (22-29), (22-30), (22-31), and (22-32). This is done in the next section.

EXAMPLE. If $\bar{E}_z = 1000 \sin 20\pi x \sin 25\pi y$ and $\bar{H}_z = j5 \cos 20\pi x \cos 25\pi y$, determine E_x as a function of the space coordinates and time. The frequency is 5000 megacycles, and the dielectric has a dielectric constant of 4 and a conductivity of 0.0001. Assume perfect conductors and cosinusoidal time variations.

Solution. It is evident that $m\pi/a = 20\pi$ and $n\pi/b = 25\pi$. Therefore, k_c^2 is $(20\pi)^2 + (25\pi)^2$, or 10,120. As $\omega = \pi 10^{10}$, $\mu = \mu_0$, $\epsilon = 4\epsilon_0$, and $\sigma = 0.0001$, Eq. (22-42) becomes

$$\gamma = \sqrt{-33{,}880 + j3.96} = 0.011 + j184$$

Equation (22-29) shows that $\bar{E}_x$ has one component due to $\bar{E}_z$ and a second component due to $\bar{H}_z$. These components are

$$\bar{E}_x' = -\frac{\gamma}{k_c^2}\frac{\partial \bar{E}_z}{\partial x} \qquad \bar{E}_x'' = -\frac{j\omega\mu}{k_c^2}\frac{\partial \bar{H}_z}{\partial y}$$

with $\bar{E}_x = \bar{E}_x' + \bar{E}_x''$. The constant $-\gamma/k_c^2 = -j0.0182$. Multiplying $\partial\bar{E}_z/\partial x$ by this constant gives

$$\bar{E}_x' = -j1140 \cos 20\pi x \sin 25\pi y$$

The constant $-j\omega\mu/k_c^2 = -j3.90$. Multiplying $\partial\bar{H}_z/\partial y$ by this gives

$$\bar{E}_x'' = -1530 \cos 20\pi x \sin 25\pi y$$

The sum of $\bar{E}_x'$ and $\bar{E}_x''$ is

$$\bar{E}_x = -(1530 + j1140) \cos 20\pi x \sin 25\pi y$$

Multiplying $\bar{E}_x$ by $\exp(j\omega t - \gamma z)$, with $\gamma = 0.011 + j184$, and selecting the real part of the resulting expression, we obtain

$$E_x = 1910 \cos 20\pi x \sin 25\pi y\, e^{-0.011z} \cos(\omega t - 184z - 143.3°)$$

The amplitude of E_x is $1910 \cos 20\pi x \sin 25\pi y\, e^{-0.011z}$, and the phase is $(\omega t - 184z - 143.3°)$. The amplitude decreases exponentially with z. The wave velocity ω/β is 1.71×10^8 m/sec. This is greater than the normal velocity of light in this dielectric, this velocity being 1.5×10^8 m/sec.

22-4. TE AND TM WAVES

It is clear from Eqs. (22-29), (22-30), (22-31), and (22-32) that each transverse field component has a component that depends on $\bar{E}_z$ and a component that depends on $\bar{H}_z$. The expression for $\bar{E}_z$ contains the constant A, and the expression for $\bar{H}_z$ contains the constant B. These constants depend on the excitation. The excitation may be such that, for a particular *mn mode*, one of these constants is small or even zero. Frequently, waveguides are excited so that either $\bar{E}_z$ or $\bar{H}_z$ is zero.

As $\bar{E}_z$ can be excited independently of $\bar{H}_z$, it is desirable to group together $\bar{E}_z$ and the transverse components *that are derived directly from* $\bar{E}_z$. The resulting wave has no $\bar{H}_z$. Because the magnetic field is transverse to the direction of propagation, this type of wave is called a *transverse magnetic, or TM, wave.*

Also, $\bar{H}_z$ and the transverse components derived directly from $\bar{H}_z$ are grouped together. This wave has no $\bar{E}_z$. Because the electric field is transverse to the direction of propagation, this type of wave is called a *transverse electric, or TE, wave.* Both TM and TE waves may propagate along the same waveguide, but usually only one type will be excited.

The equations for the transverse fields of TM waves are found by substituting the expression for $\bar{E}_z$ into Eqs. (22-29), (22-30), (22-31), and (22-32) with $\bar{H}_z = 0$. The equations for the transverse fields of TE waves are obtained by using the expression for $\bar{H}_z$ with $\bar{E}_z = 0$. The total transverse fields, for a given mn mode, are found by adding the corresponding TM and TE components together.

The TM wave components are

$$\bar{E}_z = A \sin \frac{m\pi x}{a} \sin \frac{n\pi y}{b} \tag{22-43}$$

$$\bar{E}_x = -\frac{m\pi\gamma}{ak_c^2} A \cos \frac{m\pi x}{a} \sin \frac{n\pi y}{b} \tag{22-44}$$

$$\bar{E}_y = -\frac{n\pi\gamma}{bk_c^2} A \sin \frac{m\pi x}{a} \cos \frac{n\pi y}{b} \tag{22-45}$$

$$\bar{H}_x = \frac{n\pi(\sigma + j\omega\epsilon)}{bk_c^2} A \sin \frac{m\pi x}{a} \cos \frac{n\pi y}{b} \tag{22-46}$$

$$\bar{H}_y = -\frac{m\pi(\sigma + j\omega\epsilon)}{ak_c^2} A \cos \frac{m\pi x}{a} \sin \frac{n\pi y}{b} \tag{22-47}$$

The TE wave components are

$$\bar{H}_z = B \cos \frac{m\pi x}{a} \cos \frac{n\pi y}{b} \tag{22-48}$$

$$\bar{E}_x = \frac{n\pi j\omega\mu}{bk_c^2} B \cos \frac{m\pi x}{a} \sin \frac{n\pi y}{b} \tag{22-49}$$

$$\bar{E}_y = -\frac{m\pi j\omega\mu}{ak_c^2} B \sin \frac{m\pi x}{a} \cos \frac{n\pi y}{b} \tag{22-50}$$

$$\bar{H}_x = \frac{m\pi\gamma}{ak_c^2} B \sin \frac{m\pi x}{a} \cos \frac{n\pi y}{b} \tag{22-51}$$

$$\bar{H}_y = \frac{n\pi\gamma}{bk_c^2} B \cos \frac{m\pi x}{a} \sin \frac{n\pi y}{b} \tag{22-52}$$

To express the fields as functions of x, y, z and t we must multiply the preceding expressions by the exponential of $(j\omega t - \gamma z)$, accepting only the real or imaginary part of the result. For a given m and n the total value of a transverse component is found by combining the TM and TE components. For example, the total $\bar{E}_x$ is

$$\bar{E}_x = -\frac{\pi}{k_c^2}\left(\frac{m\gamma A}{a} - j\,\frac{n\omega\mu B}{b}\right) \cos \frac{m\pi x}{a} \sin \frac{n\pi y}{b} \tag{22-53}$$

For each value of m, the integer n can have values from zero to infinity; for each value of n, the integer m can have values from zero to infinity. *Thus there are an infinite number of allowed modes.* The different modes have, in general, different A and B constants, different propagation constants, different wave velocities, and different values of k_c. Each wave component can be expressed as a double summation, with m and n individually taking values from zero to infinity. For example, H_z is

$$H_z = \sum_{m=0}^{\infty} \sum_{n=0}^{\infty} B_{mn} \cos \frac{m\pi x}{a} \cos \frac{n\pi y}{b} \exp\,(j\omega t - \gamma_{mn}z)$$

with the real or imaginary part understood. Of course, many of the B_{mn} coefficients may be zero or be very small.

For specified values of m and n the TM and TE waves are commonly designated as TM_{mn} and TE_{mn}. For example, a TM mode with $m = 2$ and $n = 1$ is designated a TM_{21} wave. The most important mode in the rectangular waveguide is the TE_{10} wave, having $m = 1$ and $n = 0$. Examination of the equations for the TM wave components reveals that, if either m or n is zero, all the field components are zero; therefore *TM_{10} and*

TM_{01} waves do not exist. Although the lowest-order TM mode is the TM_{11} mode, both TE_{10} and TE_{01} waves are possible.

22-5. CUT-OFF FREQUENCIES

A hollow-pipe waveguide acts somewhat like a high-pass filter. Frequencies greater than a certain cut-off frequency are rather freely propagated, while those less than this cut-off frequency are rapidly attenuated. Each mode has its own cut-off frequency. Let us begin our investigation of this phenomenon by examining the propagation constant of the rectangular waveguide, assuming perfect conductors around a lossless dielectric.

From Eqs. (22-41) and (22-42), with $\sigma = 0$, we obtain

$$\gamma = \sqrt{-\omega^2\mu\epsilon + k_c^{\,2}} = \sqrt{-\omega^2\mu\epsilon(1 - k_c^{\,2}/\omega^2\mu\epsilon)}$$

If we let

$$\omega_c = 2\pi f_c = k_c/\sqrt{\mu\epsilon} \tag{22-54}$$

then $k_c^{\,2}/(\omega^2\mu\epsilon) = (\omega_c/\omega)^2 = (f_c/f)^2$, and γ becomes

$$\gamma = j\omega\sqrt{\mu\epsilon}\,\sqrt{1 - (f_c/f)^2} \tag{22-55}$$

For given values of m and n, f_c is a constant. It is evident that γ is a pure imaginary if the frequency f is greater than the constant f_c. On the other hand, if the frequency f is less than the constant f_c, the propagation constant γ is a real number. The constant f_c is the *cut-off frequency*.

At frequencies greater than the cut-off frequency, γ is a pure imaginary and the attenuation constant α is zero. Thus there is no attenuation, provided the conductors and the dielectric are perfect. The main effect of copper and dielectric losses is to introduce a small amount of attenuation.

At frequencies less than the cut-off frequency, γ is real, and attenuation is present. The attenuation constant is quite large at frequencies appreciably below cut-off. Furthermore, *the phase constant β is zero, there is no wave propagation, and the time-average power flow along the guide is zero.* The waveguide presents a reactive load to the excitation, with the power that is supplied to the guide in half a cycle being returned to the source in the next half cycle. Actually, there will be a very small phase constant because of copper and dielectric losses, which have been neglected in this analysis. It should be noted that the large attenuation below cut-off is not due to these losses.

The angular cut-off frequency ω_c is $k_c/\sqrt{\mu\epsilon}$. Substitution for k_c gives

$$\omega_c = (1/\sqrt{\mu\epsilon})\,\sqrt{(m\pi/a)^2 + (n\pi/b)^2} \tag{22-56}$$

The cut-off frequency f_c is

$$f_c = (\tfrac{1}{2}/\sqrt{\mu\epsilon})\sqrt{(m/a)^2 + (n/b)^2} \tag{22-57}$$

The higher-order waves, with large m and n, have high cut-off frequencies. Those modes with cut-off frequencies higher than the excitation frequency are not propagated. If m and n are both zero, the fields are zero and, therefore, the lowest cut-off frequency exists for the mode with $m = 1$ and $n = 0$, recalling that $a \geq b$. Thus *the TE_{10} mode has the lowest cut-off frequency, and this frequency is* $1/(2a\sqrt{\mu\epsilon})$. If the excitation frequency is slightly greater than this, only the TE_{10} mode will propagate, for the frequency is below the cut-off frequencies of all the other modes.

Frequency multiplied by the wavelength λ of the excitation yields the velocity of light $1/\sqrt{\mu\epsilon}$ in the dielectric. If the frequency is the cut-off frequency f_c, the wavelength is the cut-off wavelength λ_c. Therefore, $f_c\lambda_c = 1/\sqrt{\mu\epsilon}$, with μ and ϵ being the permeability and permittivity of the dielectric of the waveguide. Utilizing Eq. (22-57) gives the cut-off wavelength to be

$$\lambda_c = 2/\sqrt{(m/a)^2 + (n/b)^2} \tag{22-58}$$

It is evident that $k_c = 2\pi/\lambda_c$.

For an mn mode to propagate, the wavelength λ of the exciting source must be less than the cut-off wavelength λ_c. The cut-off wavelength of the TE_{10} mode is equal to $2a$. The larger dimension a must be greater than one-half the wavelength of the exciting source, or there will be no energy flow. Obviously, the required dimensions are impractical at the lower radio frequencies with longer wavelengths.

EXAMPLE. A rectangular waveguide, 5 cm by 2.5 cm, has an air dielectric. At an excitation frequency of 4000 megacycles, determine the propagation constants of the 10, 01, 20, 11, 02, and 55 modes. Assume perfect conductors.

Solution. From Eq. (22-55) the propagation constant γ is determined to be

$$\gamma = j83.8\sqrt{1 - (f_c/4000)^2}$$

with f_c in megacycles. From Eq. (22-57) we find that

$$f_c = 3000\sqrt{m^2 + 4n^2} \text{ megacycles}$$

The cut-off frequencies of the 10, 01, 20, 11, 02, and 55 modes are found to be 3000, 6000, 6000, 6720, 12,000, and 33,500 megacycles, respectively. As the excitation frequency is 4000 megacycles, only the 10 mode will propagate without attenuation.

Using the calculated cut-off frequencies, the propagation constants are determined to be $j55.4$ for the 10 mode, 93.8 for the 01 and 20 modes, 113 for the 11 mode, 237 for the 02 mode, and 697 for the 55 mode. The propagation constants for all modes except the 10 mode are positive real numbers. When a wave propagates through a distance z_1 such that $\alpha z_1 = 1$, the amplitude decreases to $1/e$, or 36.8%, of its original value. For the 01 and 20 modes this distance z_1 is 1.07 cm, and for the 55 mode the distance is 0.14 cm. All modes except the TE_{10} wave are very rapidly attenuated.

22-6. THE TE_{10} WAVE

The most important type of wave that can propagate along a rectangular waveguide is the TE_{10} wave. It is also the simplest. Because its cut-off frequency, which equals $1/(2a\sqrt{\mu\epsilon})$, is the lowest, this wave can be excited without interference from higher-order waves. The cut-off wavelength equals $2a$.

Let us first determine the propagation and phase constants and the phase and group velocities. We shall several times utilize the relation

$$\omega\sqrt{\mu\epsilon} = 2\pi/\lambda \tag{22-59}$$

which follows directly from the fact that the velocity of light $1/\sqrt{\mu\epsilon}$ equals the product of frequency and wavelength. From Eqs. (22-55) and (22-59) we deduce that γ and β are

$$\gamma = (j2\pi/\lambda)\sqrt{1 - (\lambda/2a)^2} = j\beta \tag{22-60}$$

The phase velocity ω/β is

$$v_p = \frac{1/\sqrt{\mu\epsilon}}{\sqrt{1 - (\lambda/2a)^2}} \tag{22-61}$$

To obtain the expression for the group velocity $d\omega/d\beta$ we can replace λ in Eq. (22-60) with $2\pi/(\omega\sqrt{\mu\epsilon})$ and then find $d\beta/d\omega$. The reciprocal of this result gives

$$v_g = (1/\sqrt{\mu\epsilon})\sqrt{1 - (\lambda/2a)^2} \tag{22-62}$$

We note that the phase velocity is greater than the velocity of light, the group velocity is less, and the product of the two equals the velocity of light squared.

The field components for the TE_{10} wave are found from Eqs. (22-48) through (22-52) by replacing m with 1 and n with 0. Utilizing Eq. (22-60) to eliminate γ and noting that $k_c = \pi/a$, we obtain

$$\bar{H}_z = B\cos \pi x/a \tag{22-63}$$

$$\bar{E}_y = -jB_1 \sin \pi x/a \tag{22-64}$$

$$\bar{H}_x = jB_2 \sin \pi x/a \tag{22-65}$$

with $B_1 = 2f\mu a B$ and $B_2 = (2a/\lambda)\sqrt{1 - (\lambda/2a)^2}B$. If the zero of time is selected so that the phase of B is zero, then the constants B, B_1, and B_2 are positive real numbers. The components $\bar{E}_x$, $\bar{E}_z$, and $\bar{H}_y$ are zero.

To find the fields as functions of x, y, z, and t, we multiply by $\exp(j\omega t - \gamma z)$ and take the imaginary part of the result. Assuming the B coefficients are real, we obtain

$$H_z = B \cos \pi x/a \sin (\omega t - \beta z) \tag{22-66}$$

$$E_y = -B_1 \sin \pi x/a \cos (\omega t - \beta z) \tag{22-67}$$

$$H_x = B_2 \sin \pi x/a \cos (\omega t - \beta z) \tag{22-68}$$

Plots of the **E** and **H** field lines enable us to visualize the propagating wave. We can make the plots at any instant of time, understanding that the waves are moving in the positive z-direction with velocity ω/β. It is convenient to select time zero, and at this instant the fields are

$$H_z = -B \cos \pi x/a \sin \beta z \tag{22-69}$$

$$E_y = -B_1 \sin \pi x/a \cos \beta z \tag{22-70}$$

$$H_x = B_2 \sin \pi x/a \cos \beta z \tag{22-71}$$

Let us refer to the expression for E_y at time zero and also to Fig. 22-2, which depicts the electric field lines. The lines are drawn for values of βz from 0 to 2π at intervals of $\pi/4$ radians. In accordance with the equation for E_y, the sketch shows that E_y is a negative maximum at $\beta z = 0$ and 2π, and a positive maximum at $\beta z = \pi$. The field is zero at $\beta z = \pi/2$ and $3\pi/2$. For any given x the field varies sinusoidally with respect to z. It should be noted that the electric field is polarized with the field lines directed across the narrow dimension of the guide. For a given z the electric field varies sinusoidally with distance x. The field is zero at the sides and a maximum at the center, with zero tangential component at all conductor surfaces. The arrow labeled v_p denotes that the field lines are moving in the indicated direction with velocity v_p.

Next, let us refer to the expressions for H_x and H_z at time zero and also to Fig. 22-3, which depicts the magnetic field lines shown as solid lines. From the equations we note that the **H** field does not vary with distance y. *Thus the* **H**-*lines of Fig. 22-3 apply to each plane section normal to the y-axis.* The student can easily verify that the sketch is in agreement with the equations. It should be noted that the **H**-lines are everywhere tangential to the conductor surfaces as required by the boundary conditions. The field lines move in the z-direction with velocity v_p. Each line encircles an electric displacement current resulting from the sinusoidally time-varying electric field at each point of the dielectric.

The dashed lines of Fig. 22-3 indicate the surface current densities, which are on the inner surfaces, of course. At any point on the surface the current density is equal to $\mathbf{n} \times \mathbf{H}$ amperes per meter, with $\mathbf{n}$ representing a unit normal vector directed into the dielectric. Thus the surface current

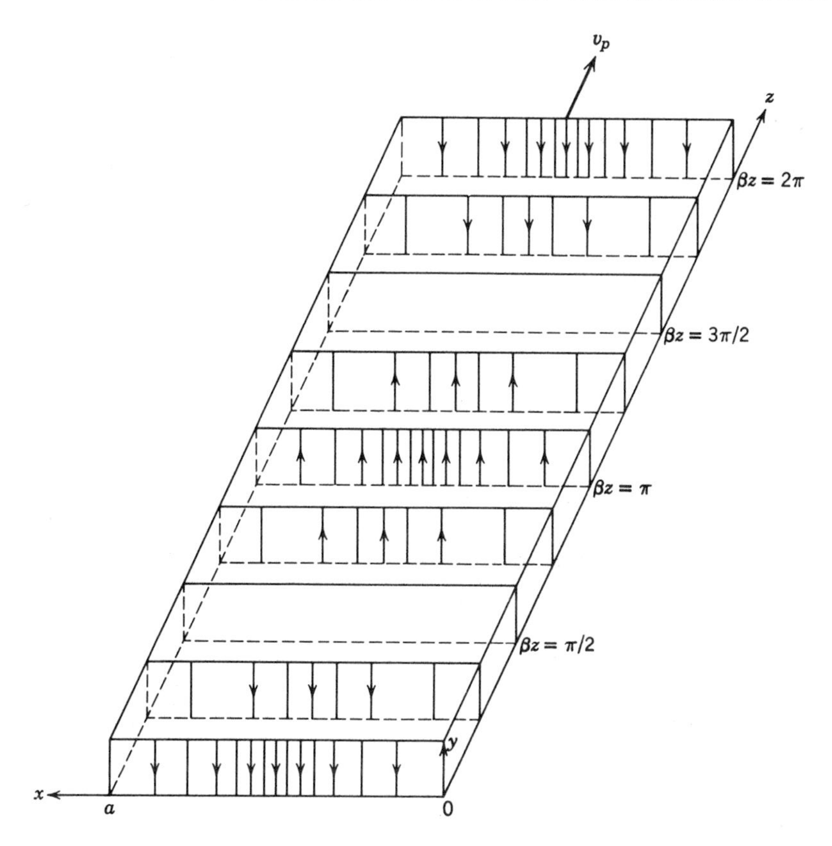

FIG. 22-2. **E**-lines of a TE_{10} wave.

density at a point is normal to the **H** field at that point and equal to the magnitude of **H**. It should be noted that the lines representing the current densities are normal to the **H**-lines. At points on the sides of the waveguide the current densities are entirely transverse, for the **H** field here is axial. On the bottom they are directed opposite to those on the top. These current densities produce copper losses in actual waveguides, resulting in attenuation.

The time-average power flow along the guide is of interest. In terms of the instantaneous field components the Poynting vector **S** is

$$\mathbf{S} = E_y H_z \mathbf{i} - E_y H_x \mathbf{k} \qquad \text{watts/meter}^2$$

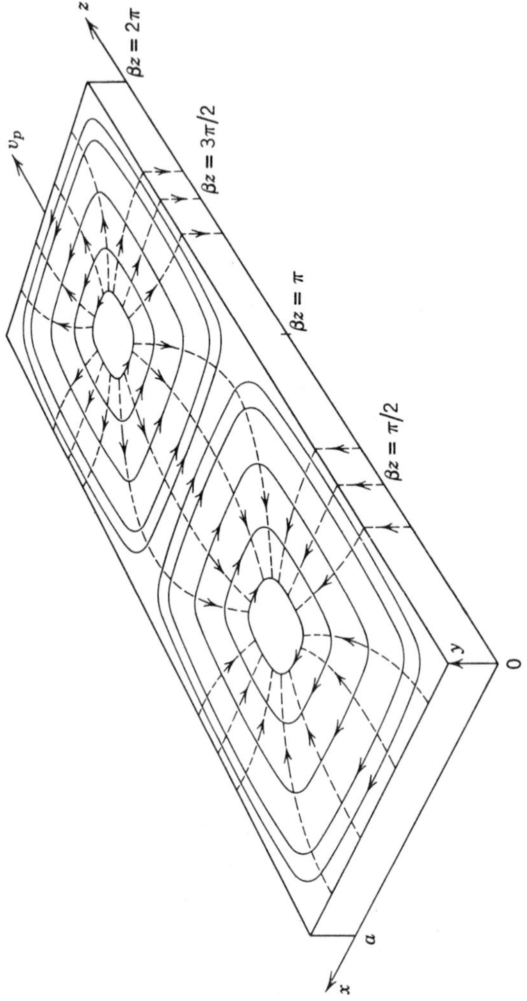

FIG. 22-3. **H**-lines (solid) and current densities (dashed) of a TE_{10} wave. The **H**-field does not vary with respect to y.

The instantaneous fields are given by Eqs. (22-66), (22-67), and (22-68). The product $E_y H_z$ contains the product of a sine and a cosine function of time, and the time average is zero. The product E_y and H_x contains the product of two cosine functions of time, and the time average of the cosine squared function is $\frac{1}{2}$. Therefore, the time-average Poynting vector at frequencies above cut off is

$$\mathbf{S}_{\text{ave}} = \tfrac{1}{2} B_1 B_2 \sin^2 \frac{\pi x}{a} \, \mathbf{k}$$

The total time-average power P over the cross-sectional area is

$$P = \tfrac{1}{2} B_1 B_2 \int_0^b \int_0^a \sin^2 \frac{\pi x}{a} \, dx \, dy = \frac{abB_1 B_2}{4}$$

Substitution for B_1 and B_2, with some manipulation of the terms, gives

$$P = \frac{ab}{4} \sqrt{\frac{\mu}{\epsilon}} \left(\frac{f}{f_c}\right)^2 \sqrt{1 - \left(\frac{f_c}{f}\right)^2} \; B^2 \text{ watts} \tag{22-72}$$

The power is zero at the cut-off frequency.

22-7. ATTENUATION

We have conveniently assumed ideal conditions in much of the previous discussion of waveguides. We shall now consider attenuation due to copper and dielectric losses, examining copper losses first.

Because of considerable skin effect, it is certainly permissible to treat the conductors of the waveguide as though they occupy all space outside the dielectric region of wave propagation. Therefore, each surface becomes the surface of a semi-infinite conductor of the type considered in Secs. 14-1 and 14-8. The resistance R_s of a semi-infinite conductor whose surface is a meter wide and a meter long is, by Eq. (14-39),

$$R_s = \sqrt{\pi f \mu / \sigma} \text{ ohms} \tag{22-73}$$

The resistance R_s is the surface resistivity of the material.

Let the instantaneous surface current density be

$$\mathbf{J}_s = J_x \mathbf{i} + J_y \mathbf{j} + J_z \mathbf{k} = J_s \mathbf{a} \text{ amperes/meter}$$

with **a** denoting a unit vector. The components of the current density are sinusoidal time functions. J_s is always positive, and the orientation of **a** varies with time.

Let dl_1 denote a differential surface length normal to $\mathbf{J}_s$, and let dl_2 represent a differential length in the direction of $\mathbf{J}_s$. The current i in the elemental section of width dl_1, of length dl_2, and with infinite depth is

$J_s\,dl_1$. From the discussion in Sec. 14-8 it is evident that the resistance R of the section is $R_s\,dl_2/dl_1$. Therefore, the instantaneous power i^2R becomes $J_s^2R_s\,dl_1\,dl_2$. As the product $dl_1\,dl_2$ is the differential surface area of the section, the instantaneous dissipated power per unit surface area is

$$p = J_s^2R_s = (J_x^2 + J_y^2 + J_z^2)R_s \text{ watts/m}^2$$

The rectangular components of $\mathbf{J}_s$ are sinusoidal time functions. The time average of $\sin^2(\omega t + \theta)$ is $\frac{1}{2}$; therefore, in terms of the *amplitudes* of these sinusoidal components, the time-average power P per unit area is

$$P = \tfrac{1}{2}(|J_x|^2 + |J_y|^2 + |J_z|^2)R_s \tag{22-74}$$

At points on the surface, J_s equals the instantaneous magnitude H of the magnetic field intensity, and the instantaneous power p that is dissipated per unit area is H^2R_s. In terms of the amplitudes of the sinusoidally time-varying components of $\mathbf{H}$, the time-average power per unit area becomes

$$P = \tfrac{1}{2}(|H_x|^2 + |H_y|^2 + |H_z|^2)R_s \text{ watts/m}^2 \tag{22-75}$$

This result can be used to determine the copper losses of a waveguide from the fields and the surface resistivity of the conducting material. The copper loss *per unit length* of waveguide is found by integrating Eq. (22-75) around the perimeter C of a cross section. This gives

$$P_c = \tfrac{1}{2}R_s \oint_C (|H_x|^2 + |H_y|^2 + |H_z|^2)\,dl \text{ watts/m} \tag{22-76}$$

The electromagnetic fields of a waveguide are usually determined by assuming that the dielectric and the conductors are perfect. If actual losses are small, *the field distribution in the dielectric is approximately the same as though the losses are zero.* In most practical waveguides the power losses per unit length are very small compared with the power transmitted along the guide, and the fields can be found with losses neglected. Then Eq. (22-76) can be used to obtain the copper loss per unit length.

To illustrate the procedure we shall employ Eq. (22-76) to find the copper loss per unit length for a TE_{10} wave in a rectangular guide. The magnetic field components for a lossless guide are given by Eqs. (22-66) and (22-68). Substituting the amplitudes of these components into Eq. (22-76) gives

$$P_c = \tfrac{1}{2}R_s \oint_C \left(B_2^2 \sin^2\frac{\pi x}{a} + B^2\cos^2\frac{\pi x}{a}\right) dl$$

Figure 22-4 shows the closed path C divided into four sections. Recalling that dl is always a positive differential, we can let dl equal dx along paths C_1 and C_3, provided we integrate from 0 to a along each path. Clearly, the integral along C_1 is equal to the integral along C_3, and the sum of these two integrals is $a(B^2 + B_2^2)$. Along paths C_2 and C_4 the differential length dl equals dy, provided we integrate from 0 to b. The integrand is simply B^2 along each path, and the sum of these two integrals is $2bB^2$. It follows that the integral evaluated around the entire path C equals $a(B^2 + B_2^2) + 2bB^2$. Replacing B_2 with $(2a/\lambda)\sqrt{1 - (\lambda/2a)^2}\,B$ and multiplying by $\frac{1}{2}R_s$ yield P_c. Thus the copper loss per unit length for the TE_{10} wave is

$$P_c = R_s[b + \tfrac{1}{2}a(f/f_c)^2]B^2 \text{ watts/m} \tag{22-77}$$

Copper and dielectric losses result in attenuation. The field components contain the factor $e^{-\alpha z}$, as shown in Eq. (22-2), and the attenuation constant α at frequencies above cut-off is due to these losses. Because the

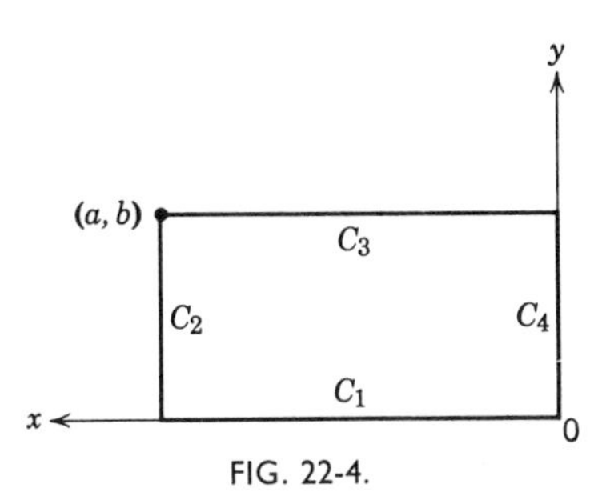

FIG. 22-4.

Poynting vector involves the *product* of electric and magnetic field components, the time-average power flow decreases exponentially with z by the factor $e^{-2\alpha z}$. The rate at which the power P decreases with respect to z is $-\partial P/\partial z = 2\alpha P$. This power decrease per unit length is equal to the copper and dielectric loss per unit length. Therefore, $2\alpha P$ *equals the total power loss* P_l *per unit length*, and the attenuation constant α is

$$\alpha = \tfrac{1}{2}P_l/P \tag{22-78}$$

Let α_c denote the attenuation constant due to the copper losses and let α_d denote the attenuation constant due to the dielectric losses. Then the attenuation constant α is the sum of α_c and α_d. Clearly, α_c is

$$\alpha_c = \tfrac{1}{2}P_c/P \tag{22-79}$$

The copper loss per unit length can be determined from the fields by means of Eq. (22-76), and the power flow P is found by integrating the Poynting vector over the cross-sectional area.

For the TE_{10} wave α_c can be found from Eq. (22-79) by utilizing Eqs. (22-72) and (22-77). The result is

$$\alpha_c = \frac{R_s}{\sqrt{\mu/\epsilon}}\left[\frac{1}{b} + \frac{2}{a}\left(\frac{f_c}{f}\right)^2\right] \Big/ \sqrt{1 - \left(\frac{f_c}{f}\right)^2} \tag{22-80}$$

We note from Eq. (22-80) that apparently α_c approaches infinity as f approaches f_c. This is quite erroneous, for α_c is normally much less than a neper per meter at the cut-off frequency. It should be understood that Eq. (22-80) is a reasonable approximation only if the power losses per unit length are very small compared with the power flow. Near cut-off the energy flow per unit time is small.

The attenuation constant α_d is rather easily found. The propagation constant γ of a rectangular waveguide is given in Eq. (22-42) in terms of the conductivity σ of the dielectric, and the real part of γ is α_d. Equation (22-42) can be written

$$\gamma = \sqrt{-\omega^2\mu\epsilon + k_c^2 + j\omega\mu\sigma} = \alpha_d + j\beta$$

Squaring and equating the reals and imaginaries yield

$$\alpha_d^2 - \beta^2 = -\omega^2\mu\epsilon + k_c^2 \qquad 2\alpha_d\beta = \omega\mu\sigma$$

These are readily solved for α_d and β. If $\alpha_d^2 \ll \beta^2$, which is normally true, it is easily shown that

$$\alpha_d = \frac{\sigma\sqrt{\mu/\epsilon}}{2\sqrt{1 - (f_c/f)^2}} \tag{22-81}$$

This result applies to all wave types as long as the attenuation constant α_d is small compared with the phase constant β.

Copper and dielectric losses cause undesirable attenuation. Usually, an air dielectric with negligible losses is utilized. The copper losses are minimized by using a good conducting material, such as copper, and by keeping the inner surfaces clean. It is evident from Eq. (22-80) that the smaller dimension b of a waveguide propagating a TE_{10} wave should not be unduly small, because the attenuation constant increases as b is decreased. In addition, if b is too small, the dielectric may break down, for the **E**-lines of a TE_{10} wave are directed across the smaller dimension.

EXAMPLE. A TE_{10} wave is excited at 4000 megacycles at $z = 0$ in a rectangular waveguide with transverse dimensions 5 by 2.5 centimeters. The dielectric has a conductivity of 2×10^{-6} mho/m, the copper has a conductivity of 5.8×10^7, and the permittivity and permeability are everywhere the same as for free space. Assume that the excitation is such that B_1 in Eq. (22-64) equals $j1000$. Calculate the phase and group velocities, the power flow, and the copper and dielectric losses per unit length. Also, determine the fields as functions of the space coordinates and time.

Solution. As the cut-off frequency is $1/(2a\sqrt{\mu\epsilon})$, or 3000 mc, the excitation frequency is above cut-off. The wavelength is 7.5 cm, and the cut-off wavelength is 10 cm.

The phase and group velocities, calculated from Eqs. (22-61) and (22-62), are 4.54×10^8 m/sec and 1.99×10^8 m/sec, respectively. The phase constant β is determined from Eq. (22-60) to be 55.4 radians per meter.

In order to calculate the attenuation constant we must find the surface resistivity of copper. From Eq. (22-73) we obtain $R_s = 0.0165$ ohm. Utilizing Eqs. (22-80) and (22-81), we find $\alpha_c = 0.00413$ and $\alpha_d = 0.00057$. Therefore, $\alpha = 0.0047$ neper/m.

From $B_1 = 2f\mu aB = j1000$, we find that $B = j1.99$. Equation (22-72) can now be employed to determine the power flow. The calculated power P is 548 milliwatts, and because of attenuation, this must be multiplied by the exponential of $-2\alpha z$. Therefore

$$P = 548e^{-0.0094z} \text{ milliwatts}$$

At $z = 0$, the power is 548 mw, and at $z = 10$ meters the power is 498 mw. The difference is due to copper and dielectric losses.

The copper loss P_c per unit length equals $2\alpha_c P$, or $4.53e^{-0.0094z}$ mw/m. This could also have been determined from Eq. (22-77). The dielectric loss P_d per unit length is $2\alpha_d P$, or $0.62e^{-0.0094z}$ mw/m. At $z = 0$ the copper loss is 4.53 mw/m, the dielectric loss is 0.62 mw/m, and the total loss is 5.15 mw/m. At $z = 10$ the total loss is 4.7 mw/m.

The constant $B_2 = (2a/\lambda)\sqrt{1 - (\lambda/2a)^2}\, B = j1.75$. Equations (22-63), (22-64), and (22-65) become

$$\bar{H}_z = j1.99 \cos 20\pi x$$

$$\bar{E}_y = 1000 \sin 20\pi x$$

$$\bar{H}_x = -1.75 \sin 20\pi x$$

If we multiply by $\exp(j\omega t - \gamma z)$, with $\gamma = 0.0047 + j55.4$, and accept the real part only, we obtain

$$H_z = 1.99 \cos 20\pi x\, e^{-0.0047z} \cos(\omega t - 55.4z + 90^\circ)$$

$$E_y = 1000 \sin 20\pi x\, e^{-0.0047z} \cos(\omega t - 55.4z)$$

$$H_x = 1.75 \sin 20\pi x\, e^{-0.0047z} \cos(\omega t - 55.4z + 180^\circ)$$

22-8. TEM WAVES

We learned in Sec. 20-2 that transverse electromagnetic waves propagate along two-conductor waveguides referred to as transmission lines. Suppose a TEM wave is presumed to exist in a hollow-pipe guide with perfect conductors. We know from the Maxwell-Ampère law that every line of magnetic flux must link either a convection or displacement current. As the fields are transverse, the magnetic field lines of the TEM wave must link axial currents. However, there are no axial currents in the dielectric, for E_z is everywhere zero. Furthermore, the magnetic field lines cannot penetrate into the perfect conductors to link those axial currents, and we conclude that *TEM waves cannot exist in hollow-pipe waveguides with perfect conductors.*

In Sec. 11-6 we studied some of the properties of uniform plane waves. As a uniform plane wave has its electric and magnetic field vectors in planes transverse to the axis of propagation, it is a TEM wave. It is a special case, however, because it is uniform and planar, and these are not necessary conditions. TEM waves along transmission lines are nonuniform. The radiation wave of an electric current element is a spherical TEM wave, with the field vectors at each point being perpendicular to the radial direction of radiation. In fact, all electromagnetic waves far away from radiating structures are essentially TEM waves.

Let us consider a TEM wave, with sinusoidal time variations, propagating in the positive z-direction with a complex propagation constant γ. Then $\mathbf{E} = \bar{\mathbf{E}} \exp(j\omega t - \gamma z)$ and $\mathbf{H} = \bar{\mathbf{H}} \exp(j\omega t - \gamma z)$, with the real or imaginary part understood. $\bar{\mathbf{E}}$ and $\bar{\mathbf{H}}$ are functions of x and y only, and $\bar{E}_z$ and $\bar{H}_z$ are zero. By substituting the complex expressions for $\mathbf{E}$ and $\mathbf{H}$ into Maxwell's curl equations and canceling the exponentials, we obtain

$$\gamma \bar{E}_y = -j\omega\mu \bar{H}_x \qquad \gamma \bar{H}_y = (\sigma + j\omega\epsilon)\bar{E}_x$$

$$\gamma \bar{E}_x = j\omega\mu \bar{H}_y \qquad -\gamma \bar{H}_x = (\sigma + j\omega\epsilon)\bar{E}_y$$

$$\partial \bar{E}_y/\partial_x = \partial \bar{E}_x/\partial y \qquad \partial \bar{H}_y/\partial x = \partial \bar{H}_x/\partial y$$

These are Eqs. (22-23) through (22-28), with $\bar{E}_z$ and $\bar{H}_z$ equal to zero.

The ratio $\bar{E}_x/\bar{H}_y$ is the *wave impedance*. It is easily shown from the equations that

$$\bar{E}_x/\bar{H}_y = -\bar{E}_y/\bar{H}_x = j\omega\mu/\gamma = \gamma/(\sigma + j\omega\epsilon)$$

From this we deduce that the complex propagation constant is

$$\gamma = \sqrt{j\omega\mu(\sigma + j\omega\epsilon)} = \alpha + j\beta \tag{22-82}$$

with α and β denoting the attenuation and phase constants. Clearly, the constant k_c of Eq. (22-12) is zero. In terms of the frequency and the constants of the medium, the wave impedance is

$$\bar{E}_x/\bar{H}_y = \sqrt{j\omega\mu/(\sigma + j\omega\epsilon)} \tag{22-83}$$

For free space α is zero, β becomes $\omega\sqrt{\mu_0\epsilon_0}$, the wave velocity is 3×10^8 m/sec, and the wave impedance is 377 ohms. The propagation constant of Eq. (22-82) and the wave impedance of Eq. (22-83) are known as the *intrinsic propagation constant* and the *intrinsic impedance* of the medium. The wave equations for $\bar{\mathbf{E}}$ and $\bar{\mathbf{H}}$ are given as Eqs. (22-13) and (22-14). As k_c is zero, these become

$$\frac{\partial^2 \bar{\mathbf{E}}}{\partial x^2} + \frac{\partial^2 \bar{\mathbf{E}}}{\partial y^2} = \frac{\partial^2 \bar{\mathbf{H}}}{\partial x^2} + \frac{\partial^2 \bar{\mathbf{H}}}{\partial y^2} = 0$$

It should be recalled that $\bar{\mathbf{E}}$ and $\bar{\mathbf{H}}$ are transverse fields which are functions of the variables x and y. Each rectangular component of $\bar{\mathbf{E}}$ and $\bar{\mathbf{H}}$ satisfies the scalar Laplace equation. This is a two-dimensional equation, because both $\bar{\mathbf{E}}$ and $\bar{\mathbf{H}}$ are independent of z. Of course, the fields have a static-type distribution as discussed in Sec. 20-2. They are attenuated and retarded in phase as they propagate, and at any fixed point they vary with time. However, the configuration in any transverse plane at any instant is precisely that which would exist if the instantaneous charges and currents of the plane were steady with time and infinite in extent in both directions normal to the plane. As the electric field has zero circulation in a transverse plane, the **E**-lines begin on positive charges and end on negative charges. In so far as variations in the transverse plane are concerned, **E** can be expressed as the gradient of a scalar potential.

We know that the electric current over any closed surface is zero. As an infinite transverse plane can be closed by a surface at infinity, it is evident that the current over such a plane is zero. There are no axial dielectric currents because E_z is everywhere zero. Consequently, the net conduction current through any infinite transverse plane is zero. Clearly, *there must be at least two conductors present.* Furthermore, *these conductors must be perfect*, for otherwise the axial field E_z would not be exactly zero. Let us now consider briefly the circular waveguide.

22-9. THE CIRCULAR WAVEGUIDE

Although hollow-pipe waveguides with circular cross sections are frequently used in engineering applications, we shall omit the mathematical details. Let us note, however, that the results are generally quite similar to those obtained for the rectangular guide. The procedure is identical. We eliminate the variables z and t from the field equations by assuming variations of the form $\exp(j\omega t - \gamma z)$. The resulting wave equations for the axial field components, in cylindrical coordinates, can be separated into ordinary differential equations by the separation-of-variables method. The equation with the variable r is *Bessel's equation*, with solutions in terms of *Bessel functions.*

The boundary conditions at the inner surface of the conductor must be satisfied. In addition, the fields must be finite everywhere, in particular at the origin. Also, each field component must not change when the coordinate φ is increased by 2π radians. These boundary conditions restrict the constant k_c to certain discrete values, and these eigenvalues of k_c lead to infinite sets of allowed TM and TE waves. The details of the analysis are suggested as an exercise for the student familiar with the Bessel equation.

Figure 22-5 shows a TM_{02} wave of a circular waveguide. The cross-sectional view illustrates the circular **H**-lines. The side view applies to any plane containing the axis of the cylinder, and the **H**-lines in this view are represented by crosses and dots, with a dot indicating a line coming out of the paper. Note that some **E**-lines form closed loops while others begin

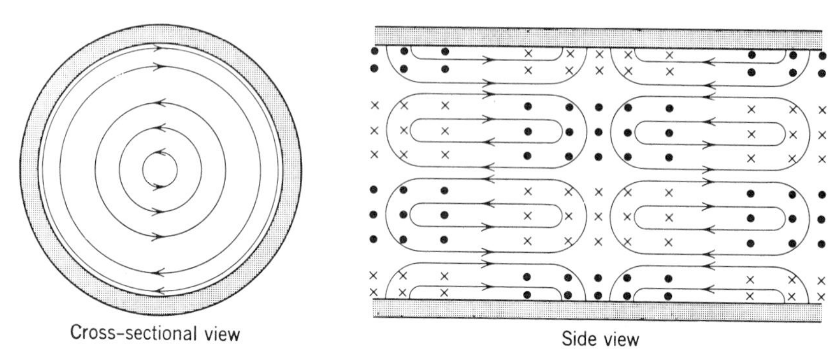

FIG. 22-5. TM_{02} wave of the circular waveguide. The cross-sectional view shows the circular **H**-lines. The side view, applying to any plane containing the axis, shows the **E**-lines. The crosses and the dots indicate the transverse **H**-lines.

and end on surface charges. This wave is not of particular importance, but is presented to illustrate a typical TM wave in a circular guide.

REFERENCES

Adler, R. B., L. J. Chu, and R. M. Fano, *Electromagnetic Energy Transmission and Radiation*, John Wiley and Sons, New York, 1960.

Brown, R. G., R. A. Sharpe, and W. L. Hughes, *Lines, Waves, and Antennas*, The Ronald Press Co., New York, 1961, Chaps. 9, 10, 11.

Harrington, R. F., *Time-Harmonic Electromagnetic Fields*, McGraw-Hill Book Co., New York, 1961.

Jordan, E. C., *Electromagnetic Waves and Radiating Systems*, Prentice-Hall, Englewood Cliffs, N.J., 1950, Chap. 9.

King, R. W. P., H. R. Mimno, and A. H. Wing, *Transmission Lines, Antennas, and Wave Guides*, McGraw-Hill Book Co., New York, 1945, Chap. 3.

Kraus, J. D., *Electromagnetics*, McGraw-Hill Book Co., New York, 1953, Chap. 12.

Langmuir, R. V., *Electromagnetic Fields and Waves*, McGraw-Hill Book Co., New York, 1961, Chaps. 8, 9, 12.

Moon, P., and D. E. Spencer, *Foundations of Electrodynamics*, D. Van Nostrand Co., Princeton, N.J., 1960, Chaps. 8, 9.

Moore, R. K., *Traveling-wave Engineering*, McGraw-Hill Book Co., New York, 1960, Chap. 9.

Plonsey, R., and R. E. Collin, *Principles and Applications of Electromagnetic Fields*, McGraw-Hill Book Co., New York, 1961, Chap. 10.

Ramo, S., and J. R. Whinnery, *Fields and Waves in Modern Radio*, John Wiley and Sons, New York, 2nd ed., 1953, Chaps. 7 to 12.

Reich, H. J., J. G. Skalnik, P. F. Ordung, H. L. Krauss, *Microwave Principles*, D. Van Nostrand Co., Princeton, N.J., 1957, Chaps. 2 to 6.

Ryder, J. D., *Networks, Lines and Fields*, Prentice-Hall, Englewood Cliffs, N.J., 2nd ed., 1955, Chaps. 11, 12.

Skilling, H. H., *Electric Transmission Lines*, McGraw-Hill Book Co., New York, 1951, Chap. 13.

Slater, J. C., *Microwave Transmission*, McGraw-Hill Book Co., New York, 1942, Chaps. 3, 4.

Southworth, G. C., *Principles and Applications of Waveguide Transmission*, D. Van Nostrand Co., Princeton, N.J., 1950.

Ware, L. A., and H. R. Reed, *Communication Circuits*, John Wiley and Sons, New York, 3rd ed., 1949, Chaps. 12, 13, 14.

PROBLEMS

Section 22-1

22-1. If $k_c = 150$ in a waveguide whose conductors are perfect and whose dielectric is free space, find the complex propagation constants at frequencies of 10,000 mc, 7200 mc, and 5000 mc.

(*Ans.*: $j146$, $j15.5$, 107.)

22-2. Repeat the preceding problem, except let the dielectric have a conductivity of 3 μmhos/m. The dielectric constant is unity.

(*Ans.*: $0.00081 + j146$, $0.0055 + j15.5$, $107 + j0.000552$.)

22-3. At the given frequencies, calculate the phase velocities of the waveguide of Prob. 22-1.

22-4. At the given frequencies calculate the phase velocities of the waveguide of Prob. 22-2.

Section 22-2

22-5. Derive Eqs. (22-29), (22-30), (22-31), and (22-32).

22-6. Verify that the axial electric field E_z of the Example of Sec. 22-2 approximately satisfies the wave equation.

22-7. For the waveguide of the Example of Sec. 22-2, find E_x, E_y, and H_y as functions of the space coordinates and time, and evaluate each at $(x, y, z, t) = (0.01, 0.01, 2, 0)$.

22-8. In the free-space dielectric of a rectangular waveguide the axial electric field E_z is zero, and the axial magnetic field H_z is $\cos 4\pi x \sin (\omega t - 3\pi z)$, with $\omega = 15\pi \times 10^8$. Find the transverse electric and magnetic fields E_x, E_y, H_x, and H_y.

Section 22-3

22-9. For the waveguide of the Example of Sec. 22-3, find E_y, H_x, and H_y as functions of the space coordinates and time.

22-10. If $\bar{H}_z = 100 \cos 20\pi x$ and $\bar{E}_z = 0$ in a rectangular waveguide, determine the attenuation constant, the phase constant, and the phase velocity of the electromagnetic wave. The frequency is 3000 mc, and the dielectric has a dielectric constant of 4 and a conductivity of 0.0001. Assume perfect conductors.

(*Ans.*: $\alpha = 0.0109$, $\beta = 109$, $v = 1.73 \times 10^8$.)

22-11. For the waveguide of the preceding problem, determine the rectangular components of **E** and **H** as functions of the space coordinates and time. Assume cosinusoidal time variations.

Section 22-4

22-12. If $\bar{H}_z = \cos 20\pi x \cos 20\pi y$ at 5000 megacycles in a rectangular waveguide, 10 cm by 5 cm, having perfect conductors and a dielectric of free space, what TE mode is being propagated? Using Eqs. (22-48) through (22-52), find the transverse field components. Also, find each field component, as a function of time, at the point (0.01, 0.01, 0.01).

22-13. A lossless rectangular waveguide, 10 cm by 10 cm with a dielectric of free space, has TE_{11} and TM_{11} waves excited at 3000 mc. If E_x is everywhere zero, find the ratio E_z/H_z.

Section 22-5

22-14. A rectangular waveguide, 10 cm by 5 cm with a dielectric of free space, is excited at 5000 megacycles by means of a small probe. Determine the eight modes that are freely propagated at this frequency.

22-15. For the waveguide of the preceding problem, calculate the propagation constant of the TE_{44} wave, and determine the distance this wave propagates with an amplitude greater than 36.8% of its original value.

22-16. A rectangular waveguide, with $a/b = 1.1$ and a dielectric of free space, is designed to propagate the TE_{10} wave at a frequency of 2000 mc. If the attenuation constants of all other modes are 15 or greater, determine the dimensions of the waveguide.

22-17. Required is a rectangular waveguide that will propagate the TE_{10} wave at 2000 megacycles in a dielectric of free space. The TE_{01} mode must be attenuated with an attentuation constant of at least 25. Investigate the suitability of a guide with $a/b = 1.1$.

22-18. From Eq. (22-55) deduce that the phase velocity v_p in a lossless rectangular waveguide is $c/\sqrt{1 - f_c^2/f^2}$, with $c = 1/\sqrt{\mu\epsilon}$, and that the group velocity v_g equals c^2/v_p, provided the frequency is greater than the cut-off frequency.

Section 22-6

22-19. A rectangular waveguide, 6 cm by 4 cm with a dielectric of free space, has a TE_{10} wave excited by means of a small probe carrying a 3000-mc current. If the excitation is such that the constant B in Eq. (22-63) is 100, find the field components as functions of the space coordinates and time. Also, determine the phase and group velocities, the time-average Poynting vector, and the time-average power flow in watts, and show that no other modes are freely propagated. Assume perfect conductors.

22-20. Design a rectangular waveguide with air dielectric for a 2500-mc TE_{10} wave. The cut-off frequency for this wave is to be 2000 mc, and the cut-off frequency of the wave type with the next higher cut-off is to be 3000 mc.

Section 22-7

22-21. Verify Eq. (22-81).

22-22. A rectangular waveguide, 5 cm by 2.5 cm, has a dielectric of free space and copper conductors of conductivity 5.8×10^7 mhos/m. Find the frequency at which the attenuation of the TE_{10} wave is a minimum, and calculate the attenuation constant at this frequency.

(*Ans.*: 7230 mc, 0.00303 neper/m.)

22-23. Repeat Prob. 22-22 for a waveguide 5 cm by 0.5 cm, and compare results.

22-24. A TE_{10} wave is excited at 5000 mc in a rectangular waveguide 5 cm by 2.5 cm. The dielectric has a conductivity of 2×10^{-6} mho/m, the copper has a conductivity of 5.8×10^7, and the dielectric constant is unity. Assume that the excitation is such that B_1 in Eq. (22-64) equals $j1000$. Calculate the phase and group velocities, the power flow, and the copper and dielectric losses per unit length. Also, determine the fields as functions of the space coordinates and time.

Section 22-8

22-25. A 500-kilocycle TEM wave is propagating in fresh water with a conductivity of 0.005 mho/m and a dielectric constant of 81. Calculate the attenuation constant, the wave velocity, and the wave impedance.

22-26. Using the scalar product, show that the electric and magnetic fields of a plane TEM wave are everywhere orthogonal.

Section 22-9

22-27. Deduce that Eq. (22-15) applies also to a circular waveguide. Write the partial differential equation for $\bar{E}_z$ in terms of the cylindrical coordinates r and φ. Apply the method of separation of variables, and obtain the general solution for $\bar{E}_z$ in terms of trigonometric and Bessel functions. Also, express the transverse field components $\bar{E}_r$, $\bar{E}_\varphi$, $\bar{H}_r$, and $\bar{H}_\varphi$ in terms of $\bar{E}_z$ and $\bar{H}_z$.

Antennas

CHAPTER 23

In radio communication, signals are propagated great distances without the use of connecting wires. The transmission medium is free space. At the sending end an antenna system is employed as a coupling device that transfers the energy from the transmitter to free space. The receiving antenna transfers energy from free space to the receiver. In this chapter we shall investigate some of the basic aspects of antenna theory and practice.

23-1. RADIATION CONCEPTS

Electric charges exert forces on other charges. A transmitting antenna with variable currents has time-changing charges at points along the antenna. These charges exert forces on the free electrons present in the conductors of a receiving antenna, thereby inducing signal currents and voltages. Retardation is present, of course, for the fields propagate at a finite velocity.

Let us consider a small electric dipole with charges $+q$ and $-q$. The electrostatic field decreases quite rapidly as the distance from the dipole increases, and at large distances the fields of the equal and opposite charges cancel completely. Now suppose the charges $+q$ and $-q$ vary sinusoidally with time at a frequency such that the distance between them is comparable with the wavelength. The fields of the equal and opposite charges no longer tend to cancel in all directions. In some directions retardation causes the individual fields of the two charges to arrive in phase, thus strengthening one another, and in other directions the fields cancel. The result is directive radiation.

It is often helpful to view the antenna as a matching device. Consider a horn antenna at the end of a hollow-pipe waveguide. The purpose of the horn is to match wave impedances in order to avoid reflecting energy back to the transmitter. The taper of the horn provides a gradual transition from the waveguide to free space. This viewpoint can also be applied to many other types of antennas.

We have learned that an alternating current radiates energy. A low-frequency electric circuit will not radiate an appreciable amount of energy, because the fields from equal and opposite current elements nearly cancel. In the design of antennas current elements are arranged so that the fields of the various elements reinforce each other in the desired directions. This requires antenna dimensions that are substantial in comparison with the wavelength. Consequently, efficient transmitting antennas designed for low frequencies are large, and those designed for high frequencies are small.

Three factors especially important in the design of an antenna system are the directivity, the input impedance, and the efficiency. The antenna should radiate in the desired directions or receive from the desired directions. Sometimes the proper directivity is obtained from a single radiator, but at other times an array of elements is required. The input impedance is the ratio of the phasor voltage to the phasor current at the input terminals. This impedance determines an antenna's ability to transfer power. Usually, one desires the input impedance to be resistive and to match the resistance of the network connected to the antenna. This impedance match should be approximately maintained over the frequency band utilized. Matching networks can be employed, but these networks introduce ohmic losses. The efficiency of an antenna is a measure of the power radiated compared with the ohmic losses in the antenna. If a matching network is used, its losses should also be considered.

23-2. FUNDAMENTAL EQUATIONS

In Sec. 13-4 the fields of a current element were obtained. A radiating system can be regarded as composed of a large number of differential current elements and, if the current distribution is known, the superposition principle can be applied to the fields of the current elements to find the total electric and magnetic fields. Consequently, *the equations giving the fields of a current element are the most important equations in antenna theory*. For a nondissipative medium the fields are given as Eqs. (13-52), (13-53), and (13-54).

In studying the reactions between antennas that are close together, it may be necessary to consider all the field terms of the fundamental equations. Some antenna methods utilize the near fields in the determination of antenna impedance and current distribution. However, usually the radiation fields are the ones of greatest importance to the antenna engineer. These radiation fields of a current element are given as Eqs. (13-55) and (13-56), and in complex-exponential form at a point $P(r, \theta, \varphi)$ they are

$$d\bar{H}_\varphi = \frac{j\beta \bar{I}\, dz}{4\pi r} \sin\theta\, e^{-j\beta r} \tag{23-1}$$

$$d\bar{E}_\theta = \frac{j\beta \bar{I}\, dz}{4\pi r} \sqrt{\frac{\mu}{\epsilon}} \sin\theta\, e^{-j\beta r} \tag{23-2}$$

FIG. 23-1. A dipole antenna.

The current $\bar{I}$ includes the amplitude and phase angle, with the positive direction taken in the direction of increasing z, and dz is the differential length of the element. The constant β represents $\omega\sqrt{\mu\epsilon}$, or $2\pi/\lambda$. To determine the instantaneous fields, we must multiply by exp $j\omega t$ and select the real or imaginary part.

It is evident that the electric and magnetic radiation fields of a current element are normal to each other and in time phase at each point in the medium. The ratio $\bar{E}_\theta/\bar{H}_\varphi$ equals $\sqrt{\mu/\epsilon}$. This is the intrinsic impedance η of the dielectric and, for free space, has a value of 377 ohms. The Poynting vector, applied to the distant fields of a current element, is directed radially away from the element at every instant of time. In Sec. 13-5 we found, by integration of the Poynting vector over a spherical surface, the power radiated by a current element in free space. This power is $395 I_m{}^2\, (dz/\lambda)^2$ watts. The current element is often referred to as an infinitesimal dipole, or *Hertzian dipole.*

23-3. THE DIPOLE ANTENNA

One of the simplest and most widely used of all antennas is simply a straight wire broken at some point where it is fed with a signal. Such an antenna is called a *dipole.* Usually a dipole is center-fed, as illustrated in Fig. 23-1. The energy may be supplied directly from a generator, or it may be delivered to the antenna from a transmission line or waveguide. The most common dipole is the *half-wave dipole*, which has a total length equal to approximately half a wavelength.

Determination of the fields of an antenna requires knowledge of the current distribution. Finding the precise current distribution is normally a very difficult problem, and approximate methods are resorted to. The boundaries of even the simpler antennas are too complicated for an exact solution of Maxwell's equations. Our analysis of the dipole antenna will assume a sinusoidal current distribution along the length of the antenna. We shall now investigate briefly the justification for this assumption.

The principal wave along a transmission line is a TEM wave. If the line is open at the receiving end, this wave is reflected, and standing waves of voltage and current result. The amplitude of the sinusoidally time-changing current varies sinusoidally with distance. At the open the current

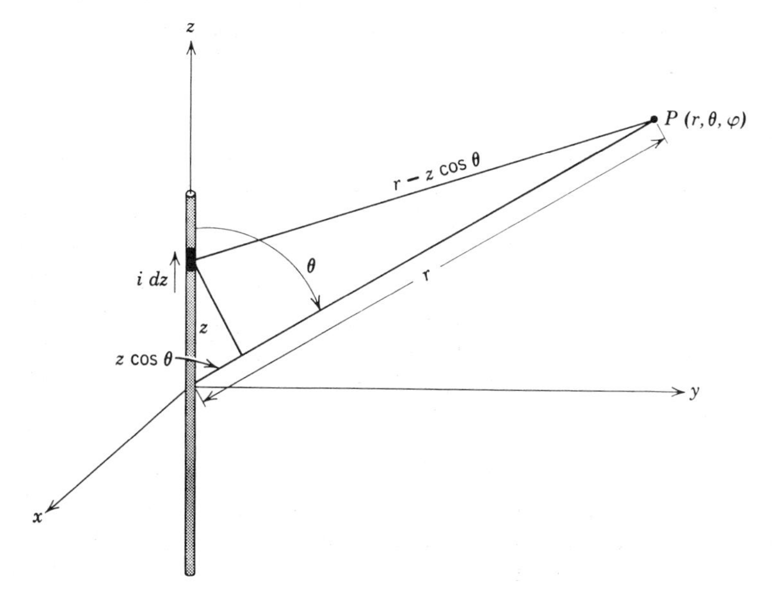

FIG. 23-2. A dipole antenna and a distant point P.

must be zero, and a current node exists. Suppose the two conductors of a parallel-wire transmission line are pulled apart so as to form a dipole antenna. We might reasonably expect the principal wave along the straight wire to be a TEM wave. At the ends of the antenna there will be considerable reflection of this wave, resulting in a standing wave of current. If the TEM wave were totally reflected and if no other waves were present, we would expect a sinusoidal standing wave. However, reflection is not complete, and higher order waves are present. Therefore, the current only approximates a sinusoidal distribution. If the wires are very thin, the approximation is excellent, and the error involved in the determination of the radiation fields is slight.

A dipole antenna and a distant point $P(r, \theta, \varphi)$ are shown in Fig. 23-2. The current varies sinusoidally with time with angular frequency ω. The amplitude of the current is assumed to vary sinusoidally with distance, being zero at the open ends of the antenna. Thus for positive z

$$i = I_m \sin \beta(h - z) \sin \omega t$$

and for negative z

$$i = I_m \sin \beta(h + z) \sin \omega t$$

with h equal to one-half the total length l of the antenna. The current I_m is the amplitude of the current at a distance z that makes $\sin \beta(h - |z|)$ equal to unity. As $\beta = \omega\sqrt{\mu\epsilon} = 2\pi/\lambda$, this distance is $\lambda/4$ meters from either end of the antenna. Using complex exponentials, the current i equals the imaginary part of $\bar{I} \exp (j\omega t)$, with

$$\bar{I} = I_m \sin \beta(h - |z|) \tag{23-3}$$

To determine the magnetic field at the distant point P we shall substitute the expression for $\bar{I}$ into Eq. (23-1) and integrate over the length of the antenna. In Eq. (23-1) the symbol r denotes the distance from the current element to the point P. With reference to Fig. 23-2, we observe that this distance is approximately equal to $r - z \cos \theta$, with r and θ representing the spherical coordinates of P and with z denoting the location of the current element. Replacing r in Eq. (23-1) with $r - z \cos \theta$ and substituting for $\bar{I}$ give the differential magnetic field at P due to a current element at z. Thus

$$d\bar{H}_\varphi = \frac{j\beta I_m \sin \theta}{4\pi(r - z \cos \theta)} e^{-j\beta(r - z \cos \theta)} \sin \beta(h - |z|)\, dz$$

The distance $z \cos \theta$ is very, very small compared with r. Therefore, this term does not appreciably affect the magnitude of the field. It does, however, have an appreciable effect on the phase. Consequently, the differential magnetic field becomes

$$d\bar{H}_\varphi = A e^{j\beta z \cos \theta} \sin \beta(h - |z|)\, dz \tag{23-4}$$

with

$$A = \frac{j\beta I_m \sin \theta}{4\pi r} e^{-j\beta r} \tag{23-5}$$

The total magnetic field is found by integrating over the length of the antenna. We obtain

$$\bar{H}_\varphi = A\left[\int_{-h}^{0} e^{j\beta z \cos \theta} \sin \beta(h + z)\, dz + \int_{0}^{h} e^{j\beta z \cos \theta} \sin \beta(h - z)\, dz\right]$$

With reference to a table of integrals [Pierce (936)], the integrals are readily evaluated, giving

$$\bar{H}_\varphi = A\left[\frac{2 \cos (\beta h \cos \theta) - 2 \cos \beta h}{\beta \sin^2 \theta}\right]$$

Upon substitution for A, utilizing Eq. (23-5), the expression becomes

$$\bar{H}_\varphi = \frac{jI_m}{2\pi r} e^{-j\beta r} \left[\frac{\cos(\beta h \cos\theta) - \cos\beta h}{\sin\theta}\right] \tag{23-6}$$

This is the magnetic field in complex-exponential form.

The instantaneous magnetic field is found by multiplying Eq. (23-6) by $\exp(j\omega t)$ and taking the imaginary part of the result. This gives

$$H_\varphi = \frac{I_m}{2\pi r}\left[\frac{\cos(\beta h \cos\theta) - \cos\beta h}{\sin\theta}\right]\cos(\omega t - \beta r) \tag{23-7}$$

The electric field E_θ equals ηH_φ, with $\eta = \sqrt{\mu/\epsilon}$.

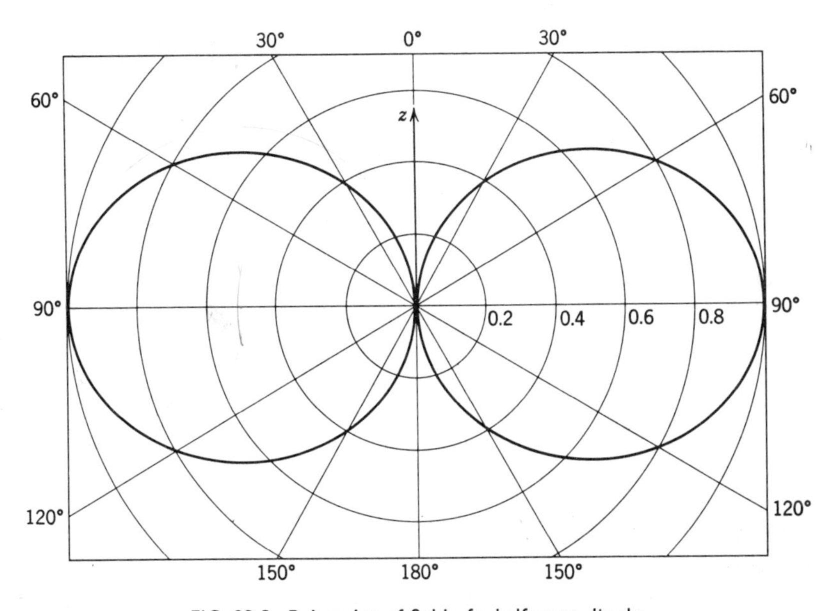

FIG. 23-3. Polar plot of field of a half-wave dipole.

EXAMPLE. The current I_m of a half-wave dipole is 2π amperes. In a plane containing the antenna, make a polar plot of the amplitude of the radiation field H_φ, as a function of θ, with $r = 1$. The dipole is aligned with the z-axis and located at the origin of the coordinate system.

Solution. As h represents half the length, $h = \lambda/4$. The product βh equals $\pi/2$ radians, or 90°. With $I_m = 2\pi$, the amplitude of H_φ at a distance of 1 meter is found from Eq. (23-7) to be

$$|H_\varphi| = \frac{\cos(90^\circ \cos\theta)}{|\sin\theta|}$$

Obviously, the field is independent of the quadrant. Therefore, we need to calculate the amplitude for values of θ from 0 to 90° only. The resulting polar plot is shown in Fig. 23-3. Note that the amplitude at any angle θ, at a distance of 1 meter, is determined by the length of the radius vector drawn from the origin to the curve. For example, H_φ is zero at $\theta = 0$, and H_φ is unity at $\theta = 90°$. The corresponding directivity pattern in a plane normal to the antenna is a polar plot of H_φ as a function of φ. From symmetry it is evident that this plot is circular. The dipole fields are strongest in the plane normal to the antenna at its midpoint, and the fields are zero off the ends of the antenna.

23-4. RADIATION INTENSITY AND GAIN

Of considerable interest to the antenna engineer is the directive pattern of the radiated power. The Poynting vector $\mathbf{S}$ gives the energy flow per unit area at a point, in watts per square meter. In the region about an antenna the Poynting vector is a function of the spherical coordinates r, θ, and φ. We know that the amplitude of each radiation-field component varies inversely with distance r. Consequently, the Poynting vector $\mathbf{S}$, which equals $\mathbf{E} \times \mathbf{H}$, has a time-average value that is inversely proportional to the distance r squared.

Let $|\mathbf{S}_{ave}|$ denote the positive magnitude of the time-average Poynting vector. Then the product $r^2 |\mathbf{S}_{ave}|$ is independent of distance r, and this product can be used to obtain a directive pattern of the radiated power. The product is called the *radiation intensity* K. Thus

$$K = r^2 |\mathbf{S}_{ave}| \text{ watts} \tag{23-8}$$

At a distance r of one meter the radiation intensity K is equal to the magnitude of the time-average Poynting vector. Consequently, *the radiation intensity K, in watts, equals the radiated power density, in watts per square meter, at points on the surface of a sphere of unit radius.*

The radiation intensity in a given direction is often described as the power radiated per unit solid angle. The *solid angle* Ω of a closed curve in a region is the space enclosed by a conical surface generated by a radius vector from the origin and sliding around the closed curve; if S is the area intercepted by the solid angle Ω on a sphere of radius r, then the ratio S/r^2 is used to measure Ω. As the area of a sphere is $4\pi r^2$, obviously the total solid angle at a point is 4π *steradians.*

We deduced that the radiation intensity K equals the radiated power per unit area at points on the surface of a sphere of unit radius. The differential solid angle $d\Omega$ of a differential surface area dS of such a sphere is equal to dS. It follows that K can be expressed as the radiated power per unit solid angle. The total power radiated by an antenna can be found by integration of the time-average Poynting vector over a spherical surface of radius r. An equivalent method is the integration of K over the entire solid angle of the origin. Thus the time-average radiated power P is

$$P = \oint_S |\mathbf{S}_{\text{ave}}| \, dS = \oint K \, d\Omega \tag{23-9}$$

In spherical coordinates $dS = r^2 \sin\theta \, d\theta \, d\varphi$, and $d\Omega = dS/r^2$.

Let us determine the radiation intensity K of a dipole antenna. The Poynting vector $\mathbf{S}$ is $E_\theta H_\varphi \mathbf{a}_r$, or $\eta H_\varphi{}^2 \mathbf{a}_r$. The magnitude of the time-average

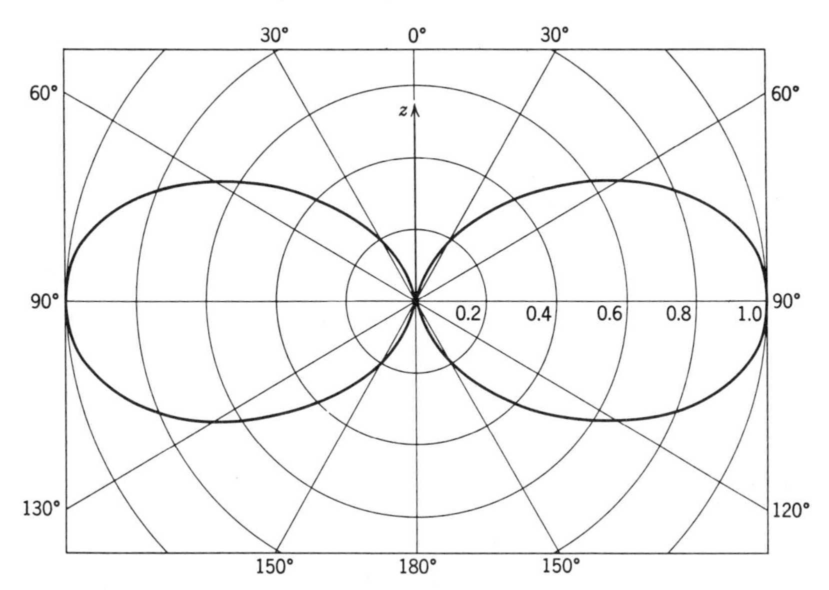

FIG. 23-4. Radiation pattern of a half-wave dipole. The sketch is a polar plot of the radiation intensity K in a plane containing the antenna.

Poynting vector is $\frac{1}{2}\eta \, |H_\varphi|^2$, and K is $\frac{1}{2}r^2\eta \, |H_\varphi|^2$. Employing Eq. (23-7) gives

$$K = \frac{\eta I_m{}^2}{8\pi^2} \left[\frac{\cos(\beta h \cos\theta) - \cos\beta h}{\sin\theta} \right]^2 \tag{23-10}$$

Antenna radiation patterns are graphical representations of the radiation intensity K. Sometimes graphs of $\sqrt{K}$ are used. As the purpose of a radiation pattern is to show the relative power radiated in different directions, the scale is often omitted or arbitrarily selected. Frequently, the scale is selected so that the maximum of K is unity. Figure 23-4 shows the radiation pattern of a half-wave dipole, in a plane containing the antenna, and Fig. 23-5 shows the corresponding pattern of a full-wave dipole. Both patterns are plots of Eq. (23-10), with βh equal to 90° for the half-wave dipole and 180° for the full-wave dipole. Radiation patterns in planes normal to the antennas are circular. When the orientation of an antenna is normally fixed with respect to ground, the radiation patterns in horizontal and vertical planes are referred to as *horizontal* and *vertical* radiation patterns, respectively.

The ratio of the radiation intensity K in a certain direction to the average radiation intensity K_{ave} is called the *gain* g of the antenna in the given direction. In the direction of maximum radiation intensity K_{max}

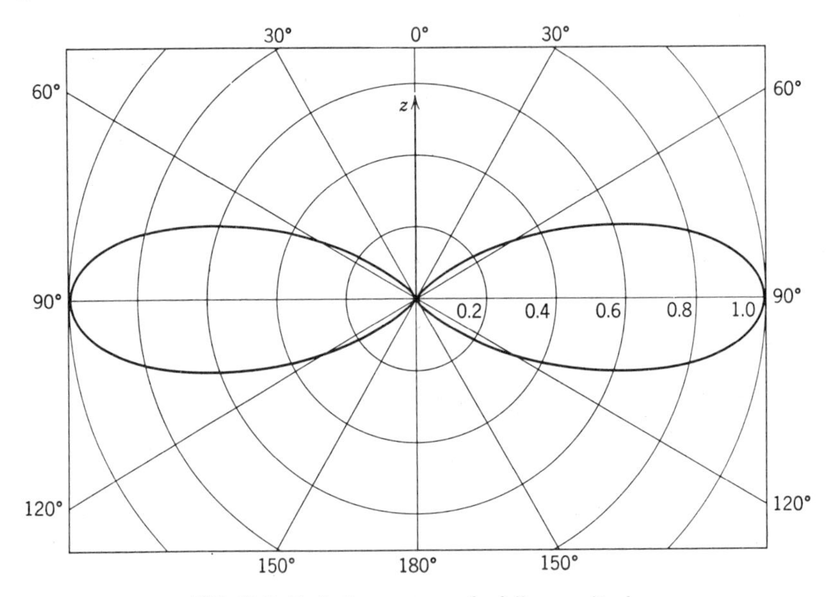

FIG. 23-5. Radiation pattern of a full-wave dipole.

the gain is a maximum. Unless the direction is specified, the gain is understood to be the maximum gain. Thus

$$g = K_{\text{max}}/K_{\text{ave}} \tag{23-11}$$

The average radiation intensity K_{ave} is the average radiated power density over the surface of a sphere of unit radius. As the area of this spherical surface is 4π, it follows that $4\pi K_{\text{ave}}$ equals the total time-average radiated power P. From another viewpoint K_{ave} is the average radiated power per unit solid angle, and multiplication by the total solid angle of 4π steradians gives the time-average radiated power. Consequently, Eq. (23-11) can be written

$$g = 4\pi K_{\text{max}}/P \tag{23-12}$$

The power P can be determined from the time-average Poynting vector, or from the radiation intensity, by means of Eq. (23-9).

23-5. THE HALF-WAVE DIPOLE

The total length of this dipole is $\frac{1}{2}\lambda$ meters. Therefore, $h = \lambda/4$ and $\beta h = \frac{1}{2}\pi$. Noting that the intrinsic impedance η of free space is approximately 120π ohms, we obtain the radiation intensity K from Eq. (23-10) and the result is

$$K = \frac{15I_m{}^2 \cos^2(\frac{1}{2}\pi \cos\theta)}{\pi \sin^2\theta} \text{ watts} \tag{23-13}$$

K is the radiated power density at a distance of 1 meter.

We shall use Eq. (23-9) to find the total radiated power. A differential solid angle $d\Omega$ is $\sin\theta\, d\theta\, d\varphi$. The entire solid angle at a point is included by letting θ vary from 0 to π and letting φ vary from 0 to 2π. As K is independent of φ, the integral with respect to φ introduces the factor 2π. Equation (23-9) becomes

$$P = 2\pi \int_0^{\pi} K \sin\theta\, d\theta$$

As the value of $K \sin\theta$ does not change when the angle θ is replaced with $(\pi - \theta)$, we may integrate from 0 to $\frac{1}{2}\pi$ provided we multiply by 2. Making this change and substituting for K, we obtain

$$P = 60I_m{}^2 \int_0^{\frac{1}{2}\pi} \frac{\cos^2(\frac{1}{2}\pi \cos\theta)}{\sin\theta}\, d\theta \tag{23-14}$$

We must now evaluate the integral. Let us introduce a new variable of integration by substituting u for $\cos\theta$. Equation (23-14) becomes

$$P = 60I_m{}^2 \int_0^1 \frac{\cos^2 \frac{1}{2}\pi u}{1 - u^2}\, du$$

By the method of partial fractions we find that $1/(1 - u^2)$ equals the sum of $\frac{1}{2}/(1 - u)$ and $\frac{1}{2}/(1 + u)$. Therefore,

$$P = 30I_m{}^2 \left[\int_0^1 \frac{\cos^2 \frac{1}{2}\pi u}{1 - u}\, du + \int_0^1 \frac{\cos^2 \frac{1}{2}\pi u}{1 + u}\, du\right]$$

If we replace $1 - u$ in the first integral with the new variable v and if we replace $1 + u$ in the second integral with v, we obtain

$$P = 30I_m{}^2 \left[\int_0^1 \frac{\sin^2 \frac{1}{2}\pi v}{v}\, dv + \int_1^2 \frac{\sin^2 \frac{1}{2}\pi v}{v}\, dv\right]$$

The two integrals can be combined into a single integral with limits 0 and 2. Substitution of w for πv gives

$$P = 30I_m{}^2 \int_0^{2\pi} \frac{\sin^2 \frac{1}{2}w}{w}\, dw$$

This can be written in the form

$$P = 15I_m^2 \int_0^{2\pi} \frac{1 - \cos w}{w}\, dw \tag{23-15}$$

To evaluate the integral of Eq. (23-15), let us replace $\cos w$ with its infinite series, given as Eq. (19-15). The expression for the radiated power becomes

$$P = 15I_m^2 \int_0^{2\pi} \left(\frac{w}{2!} - \frac{w^3}{4!} + \frac{w^5}{6!} - \cdots\right) dw$$

This can be integrated term by term. Integration and substitution of the limits give

$$P = 15I_m^2 \left[\frac{(2\pi)^2}{(2)(2!)} - \frac{(2\pi)^4}{(4)(4!)} + \frac{(2\pi)^6}{(6)(6!)} - \cdots\right]$$

The series does not converge rapidly. Evaluation of about eight terms yields four significant figures, and the result is

$$P = 36.56 I_m^2 \text{ watts} \tag{23-16}$$

We can now find the maximum gain of a half-wave dipole. The maximum radiation, as Fig. 23-4 indicates, is in the plane with $\theta = 90°$. From Eq. (23-13) we find the maximum radiation intensity to be $(15/\pi)I_m^2$. It follows from Eqs. (23-12) and (23-16) that the gain is

$$g = \frac{(4\pi)(15/\pi)I_m^2}{36.56 I_m^2} = 1.64$$

The amplitude of the input current of a half-wave dipole is I_m. This is evident from Eq. (23-3), with $z = 0$, and also from physical reasoning. The input power is $\frac{1}{2}I_m^2 R$, with R representing the real part of the input impedance. If ohmic losses are negligible, this power equals the radiated power P, and the input resistance becomes $2P/I_m^2$. Substitution for P, using Eq. (23-16), gives a resistance of 73.12 ohms. This resistance, determined from the radiated power and the current I_m, is called the *radiation resistance* of the antenna. Because of ohmic losses, there will be an additional ohmic resistance, which should be small compared with the radiation resistance in order to obtain high efficiency. The input reactance of a half-wave dipole is negligible if the length is properly adjusted. Actually, the impedance may be a few ohms greater than or less than 73 ohms, for this impedance is somewhat dependent on the radius of the wire and the input conditions.

The radiation pattern of a quarter-wave vertical antenna above a perfect ground is the same as that of the half-wave dipole in free space. There is, in effect, an *image antenna* in the ground. Considering the antenna and its image, we note that the voltage is actually applied to one-half the center gap, for half of the gap is the image gap behind the ground plane. Consequently, the radiation resistance is only one-half the radiation resistance of the half-wave dipole in free space, which gives a resistance of 36.5 ohms for the quarter-wave vertical antenna above ground.

23-6. DIRECTIVE ARRAYS

Antenna arrays, which are systems of similar antennas similarly oriented, are often employed when directive radiation patterns are desired. Variables in the design of arrays are the number of elements to be used, their

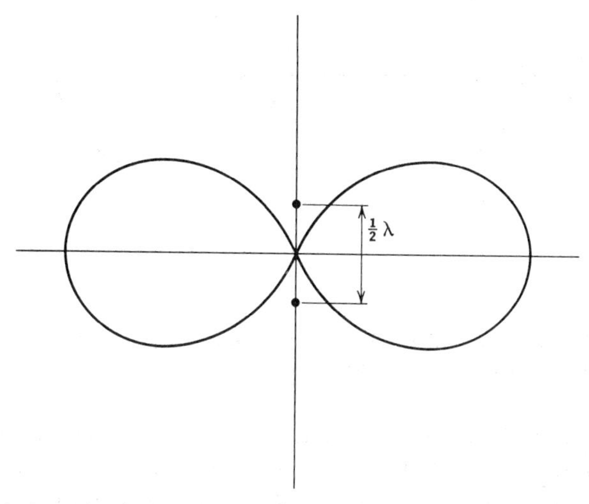

FIG. 23-6. Horizontal radiation pattern of two vertical dipoles a half-wavelength apart and fed with equal in-phase currents.

spacing, and the magnitudes and phase angles of the exciting currents. Proper adjustment of these variables enables us to obtain almost any desired directive pattern.

Let us consider the horizontal radiation patterns of two vertical dipole antennas spaced half a wavelength apart in free space. If the exciting currents are equal in magnitude and in time phase, the radiation pattern is as illustrated in Fig. 23-6. Note that the radiation is most intense in the direction normal to the line of the antennas, for the fields of the dipoles reinforce one another in this direction. On the other hand, due to the half-wavelength spacing of the elements, the fields of the two dipoles cancel along the line of the antennas. Figure 23-7 shows the radiation pattern of the dipole array when the exciting currents are 180° out of phase. In this case the fields of the two dipoles reinforce each other along the line of the antennas.

Commercial AM broadcast stations commonly use a number of quarter-wave vertical elements spaced and excited in a manner that gives the desired directivity. As the wavelengths of the broadcast frequency band are rather

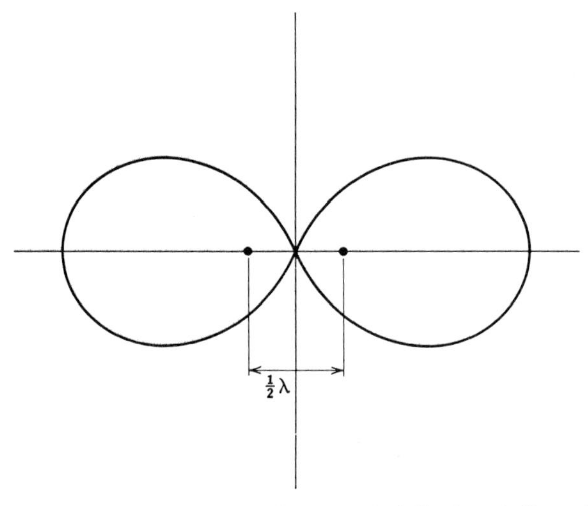

FIG. 23-7. Horizontal radiation pattern of two vertical dipoles a half-wavelength apart and fed with currents 180° out of phase.

long, the vertical elements are quite tall. A quarter-wavelength element at 1000 kilocycles is 75 meters long. Often, a large network of copper wires is embedded in the ground around the towers to increase the effective conductivity of the ground.

23-7. OTHER ANTENNA TYPES

A directional antenna commonly used at high radio frequencies is the rhombic antenna, illustrated in Fig. 23-8. This antenna is essentially a transmission line with the conductors spaced so as to radiate energy in the forward direction. Each of the four straight wires are usually several wavelengths long, and the entire antenna is mounted horizontally over level ground. The terminating impedance is selected to eliminate reflection. Consequently, the current waves in the wires are traveling waves. The rhombic antenna is simple in construction and has high directivity. However, it is physically large, and its terminating impedance consumes considerable power.

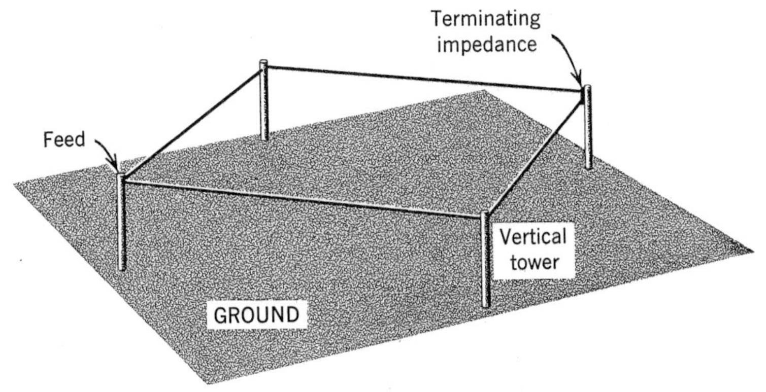

FIG. 23-8. Rhombic antenna.

A simple and inexpensive directional antenna frequently used in the meter-wavelength range is the *Yagi array*. This antenna consists of a half-wave dipole, a reflector, and one or more directors. A Yagi array with one director is shown in Fig. 23-9. If the dipole is energized, the fields excite currents in the "parasitic" elements. The phases of these currents are determined by the lengths of the conductors and the spacing between them. The fields of the three antennas interfere, and with proper design, the radiation will be directed along the line from reflector to director. Yagi arrays are often used as television receiving antennas in fringe areas.

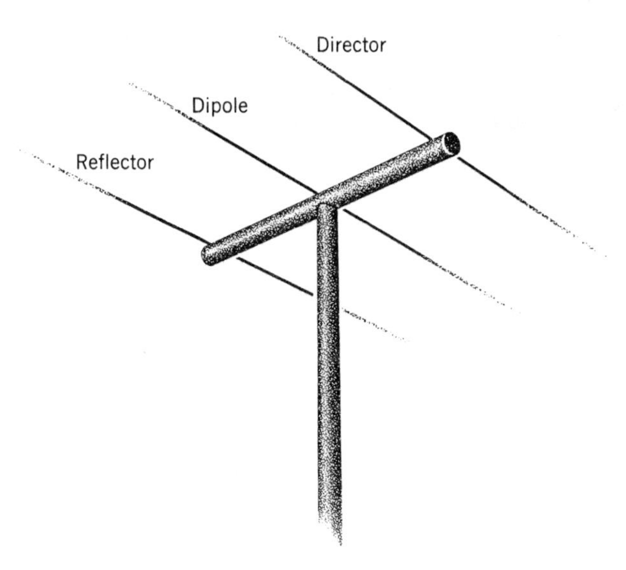

FIG. 23-9. A Yagi array.

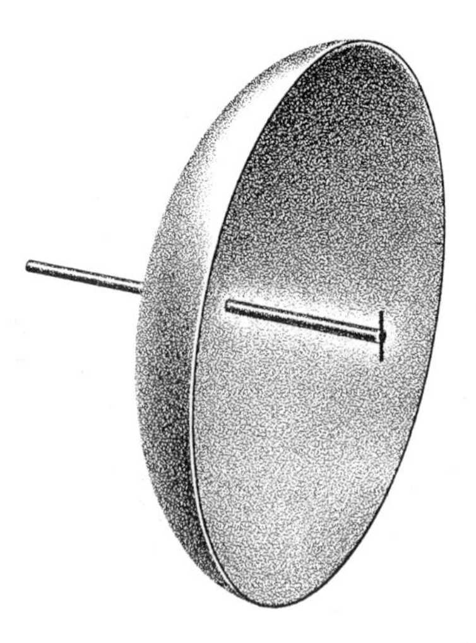

FIG. 23-10. Half-wave dipole at focus of parabolic reflector.

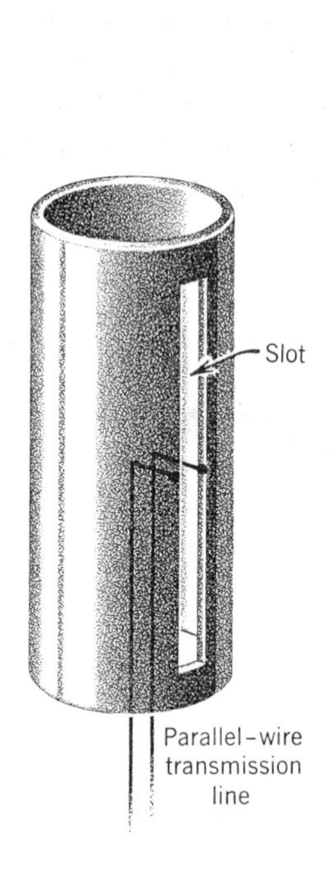

FIG. 23-11. A slotted-cylinder antenna, consisting of a copper pipe with an axial slot.

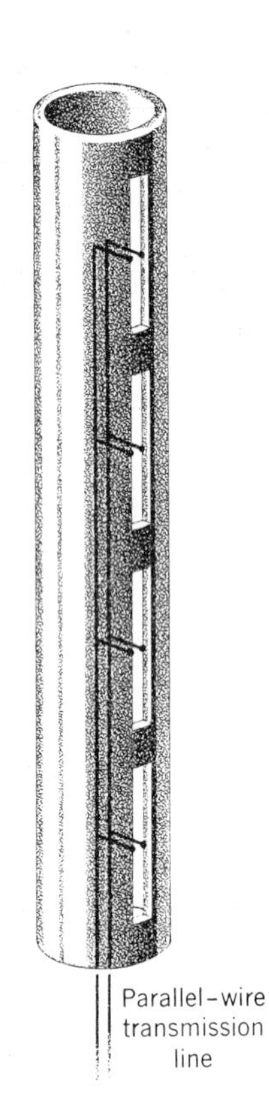

FIG. 23-12. A slotted-cylinder array, consisting of a copper pipe with four axial slots.

Many types of antennas utilize reflectors made of wire screens or conducting sheets. A familiar example is a radar antenna containing a half-wave dipole located at the focus of a parabolic reflector, shown in Fig. 23-10. The field of the dipole and the fields of the current elements of the reflector interfere to produce a sharp beam of radiation.

Figure 23-11 shows a slotted-cylinder antenna. The axial slot, usually about half a wavelength long, is cut in the side of a hollow-pipe cylinder, and the slot is fed at its midpoint by means of a parallel-wire transmission line inside the cylinder. The current elements of the metallic conductor radiate electromagnetic waves. A slotted-cylinder array is illustrated in Fig. 23-12. In such an array the phases of the exciting currents are determined by the axial spacing of the slots. A slot cut in the side of a high-speed aircraft, and filled with a dielectric material, provides a dragless antenna, and such antennas are used by many modern aircraft.

There are a great many other important antenna types—far too numerous to mention here.

REFERENCES

Adler, R. B., L. J. Chu, and R. M. Fano, *Electromagnetic Energy Transmission and Radiation*, John Wiley and Sons, New York, 1960, Chap. 10.

Aharoni, J., *Antennae*, Oxford University Press, London, 1946.

A. R. R. L. Antenna Book (Am. Radio Relay League), West Hartford, Conn.

Brown, R. G., R. A. Sharpe, and W. L. Hughes, *Lines, Waves, and Antennas*, The Ronald Press Co., New York, 1961, Chaps. 9, 10, 11.

Harnwell, G. P., *Principles of Electricity and Magnetism*, McGraw-Hill Book Co., New York, 2nd ed., 1949, Chap. 16.

Harrington, R. F., *Time-Harmonic Electromagnetic Fields*, McGraw-Hill Book Co., New York, 1961.

Jordan, E. C., *Electromagnetic Waves and Radiating Systems*, Prentice-Hall, Englewood Cliffs, N. J. 1950, Chaps. 10 to 16.

King, R. W. P., *The Theory of Linear Antennas*, Harvard University Press, Cambridge, Mass., 1956.

King, R. W. P., H. R. Mimno, and A. H. Wing, *Transmission Lines, Antennas, and Wave Guides*, McGraw-Hill Book Co., New York, 1945, Chap. 2.

Kraus, J. D., *Antennas*, McGraw-Hill Book Co., New York, 1950.

Kraus, J. D., *Electromagnetics*, McGraw-Hill Book Co., New York, 1953, Chap. 13.

Moon, P., and D. E. Spencer, *Foundations of Electrodynamics*, D. Van Nostrand Co., Princeton, N.J., 1960, Chap. 10.

Plonsey, R., and R. E. Collin, *Principles and Applications of Electromagnetic Fields*, McGraw-Hill Book Co., New York, 1961, Chap. 11.

Ramo, S., and J. R. Whinnery, *Fields and Waves in Modern Radio*, John Wiley and Sons, New York, 2nd ed., 1953, Chap. 12.

Reich, H. J., J. G. Skalnik, P. F. Ordung, H. L. Krauss, *Microwave Principles*, D. Van Nostrand Co., Princeton, N.J., 1957, Chaps. 6, 7.

Schelkunoff, S. A., and H. T. Friis, *Antennas: Theory and Practice*, John Wiley and Sons, New York, 1952.

Silver, S., *Microwave Antenna Theory and Design*, McGraw-Hill Book Co., New York, 1949.

Skilling, H. H., *Fundamentals of Electric Waves*, John Wiley and Sons, New York, 2nd ed., 1948, Chaps. 11, 12.

Slater, J. C., *Microwave Transmission*, McGraw-Hill Book Co., New York, 1942, Chaps. 5, 6.

Watson, W. H., *The Physical Principles of Wave Guide Transmission and Antenna Systems*, Oxford University Press, London, 1947.

PROBLEMS

Section 23-3

23-1. Show in detail the derivation of Eq. (23-7), which gives the magnetic field of a dipole antenna, and write the expression for the instantaneous current at the input terminals.

23-2. Suppose the dipole antenna of Fig. 23-2 has a total length of $\lambda/3$ and is driven with a current of $0.1 \sin 10^9 t$ at its input. Assuming a sinusoidal current distribution, find the radiation electric field in air as a function of the space coordinates and time. Evaluate E_θ at $\theta = \frac{1}{2}$ at a distance of 300λ at time zero. (*Ans.*: $E_\theta = 2.72$ mv/m.)

Section 23-4

23-3. Find the maximum value of the radiation intensity K of the dipole antenna of the preceding problem. Also, find the angle θ less than 90° at which K is one-half the maximum radiation intensity, with θ defined in Fig. 23-2.

23-4. If the current I_m of a full-wave dipole antenna in air is 1 ampere, determine the maximum radiation intensity and find within 1 degree the angle θ less than 90° at which K is one-half the maximum radiation intensity. θ is defined in Fig. 23-2. Assume the current distribution is sinusoidal.

23-5. In a plane containing the antenna plot on polar-coordinate paper the radiation pattern of a dipole antenna of length 1.5λ. Assume the current distribution is sinusoidal.

23-6. Repeat Prob. 23-5 for a dipole of length 2λ.

23-7. Repeat Prob. 23-5 for a dipole of length 3λ.

Section 23-5

23-8. Find the gain of a half-wave dipole at an angle θ of 72°, with θ measured from the axis. Also, find the gain at $\theta = 33°$.

23-9. Determine the rms input current required to radiate 100 watts from a half-wave dipole, and calculate the maximum value of the radiation intensity. If the ohmic losses and the input reactance are negligible, what is the rms input voltage?

Bibliography on Electromagnetic Theory

INTRODUCTORY LEVEL

Attwood, S. S., *Electric and Magnetic Fields*, John Wiley and Sons, New York, 3rd ed., 1949.

Boast, W. B., *Principles of Electric and Magnetic Fields*, Harper and Brothers, New York, 2nd ed., 1956.

Booker, H. G., *An Approach to Electrical Science*, McGraw-Hill Book Co., New York, 1959.

Carter, G. W., *The Electromagnetic Field in Its Engineering Aspects*, Longmans, Green and Co., London, 1954.

Coulson, C. A., *Electricity*, Oliver and Boyd Ltd., Edinburgh, Great Britain, 4th ed., 1956.

Cullwick, E. G., *The Fundamentals of Electro-magnetism*, Cambridge University Press, London, 2nd ed., 1949.

Frank, N. H., *Introduction to Electricity and Optics*, McGraw-Hill Book Co., New York, 2nd ed., 1950.

Ham, J. M., and G. R. Slemon, *Scientific Basis of Electrical Engineering*, John Wiley and Sons, New York, 1961.

Harrington, R. F., *Introduction to Electromagnetic Engineering*, McGraw-Hill Book Co., New York, 1958.

Hayt, W. H. Jr., *Engineering Electromagnetics*, McGraw-Hill Book Co., New York, 1958.

Kraus, J. D., *Electromagnetics*, McGraw-Hill Book Co., New York, 1953.

Langmuir, R. V., *Electromagnetic Fields and Waves*, McGraw-Hill Book Co., New York, 1961.

Moullin, E. B., *The Principles of Electromagnetism*, Oxford University Press, London, 2nd ed., 1950.

Neal, J. P., *Electrical Engineering Fundamentals*, McGraw-Hill Book Co., New York, 1960.

Peck, E. R., *Electricity and Magnetism*, McGraw-Hill Book Co., New York, 1953.

Plonsey, R., and R. E. Collin, *Principles and Applications of Electromagnetic Fields*, McGraw-Hill Book Co., New York, 1961.

Rogers, W. E., *Introduction to Electric Fields*, McGraw-Hill Book Co., New York, 1954.

Seeley, S., *Introduction to Electromagnetic Fields*, McGraw-Hill Book Co., New York, 1958.

Skilling, H. H., *Fundamentals of Electric Waves*, John Wiley and Sons, New York, 2nd ed., 1948.

Walsh, J. B., *Electromagnetic Theory and Engineering Applications*, The Ronald Press Co., New York, 1960.

INTERMEDIATE LEVEL

Abraham, M., and R. Becker, *The Classical Theory of Electricity and Magnetism*, Hafner Publishing Co., New York, 2nd ed., 1949.

Adler, R. B., L. J. Chu, and R. M. Fano, *Electromagnetic Energy Transmission and Radiation*, John Wiley and Sons, New York, 1960.

Fano, R. M., L. J. Chu, and R. B. Adler, *Electromagnetic Fields, Energy, and Forces*, John Wiley and Sons, New York, 1960.

Harnwell, G. P., *Principles of Electricity and Magnetism*, McGraw-Hill Book Co., New York, 2nd ed., 1949.

Jordan, E. C., *Electromagnetic Fields and Radiating Systems*, Prentice-Hall, Englewood Cliffs, N. J., 1950.

Moon, P., and D. E. Spencer, *Foundations of Electrodynamics*, D. Van Nostrand Co., Princeton, N.J., 1960.

Ramo, S., and J. R. Whinnery, *Fields and Waves in Modern Radio*, John Wiley and Sons, New York, 2nd ed., 1953.

Reitz, J. R., and F. J. Milford, *Foundations of Electromagnetic Theory*, Addison-Wesley Publishing Co., Reading, Mass., 1960.

Weber, E., *Electromagnetic Fields: Theory and Application*, John Wiley and Sons, New York, 1950.

ADVANCED LEVEL

Collin, R. E., *Field Theory of Guided Waves*, McGraw-Hill Book Co., New York, 1960.

Cullwick, E. G., *Electromagnetism and Relativity*, Longmans, Green and Co., New York, 1957.

Harrington, R. F., *Time-Harmonic Electromagnetic Fields*, McGraw-Hill Book Co., New York, 1961.

Mason, M., and W. Weaver, *The Electromagnetic Field*, Dover Publications, New York, 1929.

Maxwell, J. C., *A Treatise on Electricity and Magnetism*, Vol. 1 and 2, Dover Publications, New York, 3rd ed., 1954.

Panofsky, W. K. H., and M. Phillips, *Classical Electricity and Magnetism*, Addison-Wesley Publishing Co., Reading, Mass., 1955.

Schelkunoff, S. A., *Electromagnetic Waves*, D. Van Nostrand Co., Princeton, N.J., 1943.

Slater, J. C., and N. H. Frank, *Electromagnetism*, McGraw-Hill Book Co., New York, 1947.

Smythe, W. R., *Static and Dynamic Electricity*, McGraw-Hill Book Co., New York, 2nd ed., 1950.

Sommerfeld, A., *Electrodynamics*, Academic Press, New York, 1952.

Stratton, J. A. *Electromagnetic Theory*, McGraw-Hill Book Co., New York, 1941.

Index

(Boldface figures in parentheses are problem numbers.)

Some Differential Operations of Vector Analysis

Rectangular Coordinates (x, y, z)

$$\nabla\phi = \frac{\partial\phi}{\partial x}\mathbf{i} + \frac{\partial\phi}{\partial y}\mathbf{j} + \frac{\partial\phi}{\partial z}\mathbf{k}$$

$$\nabla\cdot\mathbf{A} = \frac{\partial A_x}{\partial x} + \frac{\partial A_y}{\partial y} + \frac{\partial A_z}{\partial z}$$

$$\nabla\times\mathbf{A} = \left(\frac{\partial A_z}{\partial y} - \frac{\partial A_y}{\partial z}\right)\mathbf{i} + \left(\frac{\partial A_x}{\partial z} - \frac{\partial A_z}{\partial x}\right)\mathbf{j} + \left(\frac{\partial A_y}{\partial x} - \frac{\partial A_x}{\partial y}\right)\mathbf{k}$$

$$\nabla^2\phi = \frac{\partial^2\phi}{\partial x^2} + \frac{\partial^2\phi}{\partial y^2} + \frac{\partial^2\phi}{\partial z^2}$$

Cylindrical Coordinates (r, φ, z)

$$\nabla\phi = \frac{\partial\phi}{\partial r}\mathbf{a}_r + \frac{1}{r}\frac{\partial\phi}{\partial\varphi}\mathbf{a}_\varphi + \frac{\partial\phi}{\partial z}\mathbf{a}_z$$

$$\nabla\cdot\mathbf{A} = \frac{1}{r}\frac{\partial}{\partial r}(rA_r) + \frac{1}{r}\frac{\partial A_\varphi}{\partial\varphi} + \frac{\partial A_z}{\partial z}$$

$$\nabla\times\mathbf{A} = \left[\frac{1}{r}\frac{\partial A_z}{\partial\varphi} - \frac{\partial A_\varphi}{\partial z}\right]\mathbf{a}_r + \left[\frac{\partial A_r}{\partial z} - \frac{\partial A_z}{\partial r}\right]\mathbf{a}_\varphi + \frac{1}{r}\left[\frac{\partial}{\partial r}(rA_\varphi) - \frac{\partial A_r}{\partial\varphi}\right]\mathbf{a}_z$$

$$\nabla^2\phi = \frac{1}{r}\frac{\partial}{\partial r}\left(r\frac{\partial\phi}{\partial r}\right) + \frac{1}{r^2}\frac{\partial^2\phi}{\partial\varphi^2} + \frac{\partial^2\phi}{\partial z^2}$$

Spherical Coordinates (r, θ, φ)

$$\nabla\phi = \frac{\partial\phi}{\partial r}\mathbf{a}_r + \frac{1}{r}\frac{\partial\phi}{\partial\theta}\mathbf{a}_\theta + \frac{1}{r\sin\theta}\frac{\partial\phi}{\partial\varphi}\mathbf{a}_\varphi$$

$$\nabla\cdot\mathbf{A} = \frac{1}{r^2}\frac{\partial}{\partial r}(r^2A_r) + \frac{1}{r\sin\theta}\frac{\partial}{\partial\theta}(\sin\theta\, A_\theta) + \frac{1}{r\sin\theta}\frac{\partial A_\varphi}{\partial\varphi}$$

$$\nabla\times\mathbf{A} = \frac{1}{r\sin\theta}\left[\frac{\partial}{\partial\theta}(A_\varphi\sin\theta) - \frac{\partial A_\theta}{\partial\varphi}\right]\mathbf{a}_r + \frac{1}{r}\left[\frac{1}{\sin\theta}\frac{\partial A_r}{\partial\varphi} - \frac{\partial}{\partial r}(rA_\varphi)\right]\mathbf{a}_\theta + \frac{1}{r}\left[\frac{\partial}{\partial r}(rA_\theta) - \frac{\partial A_r}{\partial\theta}\right]\mathbf{a}_\varphi$$

$$\nabla^2\phi = \frac{1}{r^2}\frac{\partial}{\partial r}\left(r^2\frac{\partial\phi}{\partial r}\right) + \frac{1}{r^2\sin\theta}\frac{\partial}{\partial\theta}\left(\sin\theta\frac{\partial\phi}{\partial\theta}\right) + \frac{1}{r^2\sin^2\theta}\frac{\partial^2\phi}{\partial\varphi^2}$$